MW00389115

STP 1419

Bearing Steel Technology

John M. Beswick, editor

ASTM Stock Number: STP1419

ASTM
100 Barr Harbor Drive
PO Box C700
West Conshohocken, PA 19428-2959

Printed in the U.S.A.

Library of Congress Cataloging-in-Publication Data

Bearing steel technology / John M. Beswick, editor.
   p. cm.
"ASTM Stock Number: STP1419."
Includes bibliographical reference and index.
ISBN 0-8031-2894-0
   1. Steel, Bearing–Congresses. I. Beswick, John M., 1945-

TA472 .B33 2002
672–dc21   2002071729

Photocopy Rights

Peer Review Policy

Each paper published in this volume was evaluated by two peer reviewers and, at least one editor.
The authors addressed all of the reviewers' comments to the satisfaction of both the technical
editor(s) and the ASTM International Committee on Publications.
   To make technical information available as quickly as possible, the peer-reviewed papers in this
publication were prepared "camera-ready" as submitted by the authors.
   The quality of the papers in this publication reflects not only the obvious efforts of the authors and
the technical editor(s), but also the work of the peer reviewers. In keeping with long-standing
publication practices, ASTM International maintains the anonymity of the peer reviewers. The ASTM
International Committee on Publications acknowledges with appreciation their dedication and
contribution of time and effort on behalf of ASTM International.

Printed in Philadelphia, PA
July 2002

Foreword

This publication, *Bearing Steel Technology,* contains papers presented at the symposium of the same name held in Phoenix, AZ., on 8–10 May 2001. The symposium was sponsored by ASTM International Committee A1 on Steel, Stainless Steel, and Related Alloys and its Subcommittee A1.28 on Bearing Steels. The symposium chairman was John M. Beswick, SKF Group Purchasing, Engineering and Research Centre, B. V., Nieuwegein, The Netherlands.

Contents

Overview

This ASTM International Special Technical Publication represents the work of numerous rolling bearing experts who presented papers at the 6th International Symposium on Bearing Steels, held in Phoenix, 8–10 May, 2001. The almost traditional five-yearly cycle for the ASTM International bearing steel symposia resulted in the Phoenix location being selected for the third time in association with the ASTM International A1 committee week and the A1.28 subcommittee for bearing steel meetings. The remit for the subcommittee A1.28 on bearing steels is to have jurisdiction over the standards for steels commonly used for ball and roller bearings. This subcommittee is responsible for preparing, reviewing and maintaining these standards and assuring that they reflect current technology. Currently the A1.28 subcommittee is faced with many challenges, not the least of which is to keep the ASTM International specifications aligned with steel making processes changes. In addition, vindication of the current specifications in light of the economic pressure within the industry is an increasing requirement. It is generally recognized that many of the steel quality assessment methods and related specification limits, used within the industry, were developed for steel making methods, either obsolete or inappropriate to current methods or product functional requirements. Resistance to change is always present and product liability considerations, together with the related risk of litigation, place a high burden material, on engineers responsible for major specification changes. However the preparation and application of state-of-the-art, ASTM International bearing steel assessment methods and related acceptance limits (specifications) provides a professional forum for the introduction of progressive changes. Cross border joint-ventures or mergers are becoming increasingly common, within the rolling bearing industry, which adds to the requirement for up to date, state of the art bearing steel specifications.

The rolling bearing industry is truly global and bearing steels and rolling bearings are manufactured, and, or assembled in all industrialized countries. Some of the largest bearing steel producers have manufacturing facilities in more than one country and all of the largest rolling bearing producers have manufacturing plants located world-wide. The rolling bearing industry statistics are:

- Rolling bearings are a 20 billion U.S. dollar global business and rolling bearings are produced in 17 countries
- Approximately 500 rolling bearings are produced, per second, by about 30 manufactures
- More than 55 steel producers manufacture bearing steels
- In the Year 2000, 2.6 million tons of 1C-1.5Cr bearing steel was produced which represents about 0.5% of current global steel production
- Currently 37 different bearing steels are specified by ASTM International

The rolling bearing industry is characterized as investment intensive with a relatively low return on capital employed. In addition, the industry is highly competitive with, as previously shown, in excess of 55 bearing steel producers, about the same number of component producers and about 30 rolling bearing manufactures.

The economic use of materials and heat treatments can be identified as a key success factor for profitable rolling bearing manufacture. It therefore is appropriate to pursue an ASTM International symposium in which the state-of-the-art in bearing steel technology is reviewed. Such a review can provide a platform for the bearing steel purchasers and bearing users to analyze bearing industry trends and develop economic acquisition strategies.

A committee comprising representatives from bearing steel makers, "commercial" bearing manufacturers, aerospace bearing manufacturers, and the ASTM International symposium operations staff organized the 6th International Symposium on Bearing Steels, and the members of organization committee were as follows:

John Beswick,	SKF Group Purchasing, Nieuwegein, The Netherlands
Dorothy Fitzpatrick	ASTM, Conshohocken, PA
James Carosiello	The Timken Company, Canton, OH
Jeff Fuller,	Brenco, Petersburg, VA
Ronald Spitzer	MRC Bearings, Jamestown, NY
Paul Dimitry	Macsteel, Jacksson, MI

This symposium, being the 6th in the series, was significant in that it enjoyed the best ever attendance and attracted 190 attendees from eleven nations. In addition, the event enjoyed a significant level of sponsorship from the following companies:

Aichi Steel Company	MRC Bearings	Saarstahl
Ascometal-Lucchini Group	Nedstaal B. V.	SKF AB
Aubert & Duval	Nippon Steel Corporation	SNR Roulements
Brenco	NSK Ltd	The Timken Company
Crucible Compaction	NTN Corporation	Timken Latrobe
FAG	Ovako Steel	The Torrington Company
Macsteel	Sanyo Special Steel	VSG

The global nature of the industry attracted 42 presentations at the symposium and the symposium program was divided into the nine technical sessions over three days. The presenters had the following affiliations:

- Rolling bearing producers   17
- Bearing steel producers   15
- University and R&D institutes   8
- Rolling bearing ulcers   2

The broad goal of the symposium, and this book, was, and is to bring clarity into what is important in respect of rolling bearing steel technologies and the relevant disciplines are described in nine sections in this book. The 34 papers that were accepted for publication have been peer reviewed by 46 rolling bearing technology practitioners from 8 nationalities.

Bearing Steel Process Developments

In this section the global bearing steel making technologies were reviewed, at the symposium, and bearing steel purchasers find the potential price reduction due to the use of billet casting, of rolling bearing steels, very attractive. The reduced cost in billet casting and/or "hot charging" is primary due to the elimination of the rolling operations and/or reduction of the post casting thermal treatments such as the ingot or blooms "soak". In support of the technical information on this subject a paper was given describing a billet casting friendly steel grade. Another paper provided hitherto never published data on the relative segregation levels for ingot and continuously cast 1C-1.5Cr, bearing steel and the effect of steel making processing parameters and soaking practice on the bearing steel segregation properties.

Steel Technology and Bearing Component Manufacture

For the first time at the ASTM International bearing steel symposia, a session was included on the rolling bearing component manufacturing aspects of bearing steel technologies. In one paper, the machinability parameters in bearing steels were reviewed and relevant testing methodologies described. In another paper, a modernistic steel technologies related to improved environmental aspects of the hardening heat treatment process was described. It was generally agreed that future ASTM International bearing steel symposia would benefit from having more papers on the bearing manufacturing aspects of bearing steel technologies.

Developments in Bearing Steel Quality Assessment and Correlation's with Bearing Life

The bearing steel industry is highly dependent upon the availability of clean steel making methods and the related techniques to assess steel cleanliness were reviewed. The use of statistics of extreme values (SEV) and a new method based on generalized Pareto distribution (GPD), when using optical microscopy, were presented. These technologies are being accepted as relevant methods for the new generation of rolling bearing steel specifications and the methods will be seriously considered in future ASTM International bearing steel specifications.

The attractiveness in the use of ultrasonic techniques, for internal cleanliness assessment, was covered in some papers. The use of an ultrasonic method was advocated at the first ASTM International bearing steel symposium in 1974, and it is significant that currently, all the top level bearing steel technologists are now applying advanced ultrasonic testing competencies in support of their product integrity guarantees.

Developments in Bearing Service Life Testing

Rolling bearing service life, as opposed to "pure" rolling contact fatigue life testing, was covered in some papers. Rolling bearing life tests for improved service life under hard particle contaminant in the lubricant, water ingress and dented raceways due to artificial indentations, were described. The challenges and opportunities in effective integration of bearing metallurgy, tribology and mechanical testing to perform meaningful service life tests were adequately demonstrated in these papers.

Bearing Metallurgy Developments for Improved Service Life

The technologies pertaining to new alloys, heat treatments and microstructure control for improved served life and extreme conditions were described in a number of presentations at the symposium. The use of steels alloyed with silicon to improve the service life, particularly for elevated temperature demanding applications, was a reoccurring theme in new rolling bearing steel developments.

Developments in High Alloy Steel for Improved High Temperature and Enhanced Corrosion Resistance Properties

The rolling bearing industry, particularly aerospace, demands for high temperature and corrosion resistance was addressed in some papers. The advantages of powder metallurgy for the creation of microstructures, not possible by conventional melting, to give elevated wear and corrosion resistant rolling bearing properties were presented. In addition, the relative properties of contemporary and new alloys for aerospace, as well as carburized and nitrogen alloyed steels were covered.

Microstructural Changes and its Relationships with Bearing Life and Life Time Predictions

The material physics aspects associated with the Hertzian contact cycle process in rolling bearing contacts were presented in some papers at the symposium. The well known aspects of microstructure change in the Herzian contact zones of rolling bearing was treated in one paper, presented at the symposium, using a thermo-mechanical response model for the prediction bearing rolling contact fatigue life.

Material Factors in Bearing Life Calculations

Material factoring of rolling bearing life is known to be difficult, and at times emotive, when comparing different bearing steel and rolling bearing producer manufacturing philosophies. Eminent North American and Western European workers in the field of rolling bearing life modeling presented papers on the subject. The development of rolling bearing life endurance models were reviewed and new physically based endurance limit model, for life estimates on surface and through hardened rolling bearings were presented, as well as advanced testing and a modeling information on steel quality, life factors.

Bearing User Future Requirements

The future user requirements in respect of rolling bearing steel technologies were presented by representatives from prime user segments. The aerospace—aircraft engine rolling bearing steel requirements were reiterated as being improved service life for the rolling elements and cages in conditions of corrosion and lubricant contaminate, as well as "slow and graceful spall propagation rates when the bearing starts to fail."

The high demands in the earthmoving industrial equipment, manufacturing segment were presented and the steel and rolling bearing technologist were challenged with an industry wish list of requirements for society and industry standards for basic parameters tests, and the ability to determine value of the enhancement in specific applications, and the ability to quantitatively rate suppliers enhanced product against other suppliers' products.

In the relatively short time, which has elapsed between the symposium, and the publication of this book, quite significant changes have occurred within the bearing steel and the rolling bearing manufacturing industries. The global economic down turn has necessitated cutbacks in the rolling bearing steel technology budgets resulting in some producer R&D facilities being downsized. These changes require increased diligence within the bearing steel technology fraternity in order to retain a competitive posture within the context of an ever increasingly price sensitive steel supply and bearing sales markets.

The ASTM International standardization committees, together with the ASTM International symposium and publications staff, have an important role to play to sustain growth within the rolling bearing industry. The ASTM International symposia are a neutral forum to address the "added value" relationship in rolling bearing steel technologies. Bearing steel technologies and purchasing managers, interested in utilizing the global bearing steel supply market opportunities, will benefit from a closer look at the information and wisdom contained in this publication.

John M. Beswick
SKF Engineering & Research Centre B. V.
3430DT Nieuwegein, The Netherlands
Symposium Chairman and STP Editor

Bearing Steel Process Developments

P. V. Dimitry,[1] P. J. McDonough,[1] G. Beck,[2] R. Eberhard,[2] and H-W. Zock[3]

Development of 5280 Rolling Bearing Steel for Improved Performance and Productivity

Reference: Dimitry, P. V., McDonough, P. J., Beck, G., Eberhard, R., and H-W. Zock, "Development of 5280 Rolling Bearing Steel for Improved Performance and Productivity," Bearing Steel Technology, ASTM STP 1419, J. M. Beswick, Ed., American Society for Testing and Materials International, West Conshohocken, PA, 2002.

Abstract: A new optimized steel analysis has been developed in which the carbon and chromium are reduced and the manganese increased to improve the solidification during continuous casting. The aim of this new grade is a steel far more suitable for continuous casting than 52100 (100Cr6).

The bearing steel 52100 (100Cr6) has a proven track record throughout the world as the high carbon material of choice. With the increased production from the continuous casting process and the efficiencies of direct rolling, in combination with higher stress conditions for bearings, certain weaknesses have been recognized with the grade 52100 (100Cr6). Due to the high productivity rates of modern continuous casters, the long homogenizing cycles to minimize carbide segregation in 52100 are no longer practical. Without these long homogenizing cycles the result is more pronounced forms of segregation and adverse carbide distributions. These disadvantages can result in restricted mechanical and thermo-mechanical physical properties leading to difficulties in conventional and induction heat treatments.

The new grade under development can be classified 5280 (80CrMn4) and has been evaluated from both the steel production aspects as well as metallurgical behavior. With regard to the decisive properties of microstructure, life and processing the 5280 (80CrMn4) was equivalent to or better than the 52100 (100Cr6) steel. Continuous casting improved significantly; porosity, cracks or cavities were not present. The carbon segregation index was reduced. Carbide distributions measured according to SEP 1520 were at a minimum level, without excessive soaking prior to direct rolling. Heat treatment response was slightly modified to lower quenching temperatures, tempering at 220°C and 240°C resulted in the same values for hardness and retained austenite as in the case of 52100 (100Cr6). After martensitic heat treatment the hardness stabilization in 5280 (80CrMn4) required no process change from 52100 (100Cr6) to achieve the same degree of stabilization.

Mechanical properties of tensile strength, impact bending and notch impact strength; wear resistance and rotating bending strength were evaluated with direct comparisons to 52100 (100Cr6). Rolling contact fatigue tests were carried out on angular contact ball bearings of type 7205B where the inner rings were the test specimens. Test conditions were selected in such a way that it would be possible to make comparisons with 52100 (100Cr6) under diverse types of stress. The fatigue life of the 5280 (80CrMn4) was equivalent to the 52100 (100Cr6) base data.

Keywords: through-hardening bearing steel, rolling contact fatigue, mechanical properties

[1] Mgr. Technical Service and Product Development and Mgr. Quality Assurance and Metallurgy, MACSTEEL®, One Jackson Sq. #500, Jackson, MI 49201
[2] Mgr. Laboratory and Research Engineer, FAG OEM und Handel AG, D-97419 Schweinfurt, Germany
[3] Director Research, New Materials Bayreuth Inc.

Introduction

The use of 52100 for high carbon bearing applications is the standard material by which all other steel compositions are judged. In the production of high carbon steel with modern continuous casting machines the main difficulties are low productivity, heavy segregation and difficult processing. The aim of this project was to develop new rolling bearing steel with equivalent or better properties than possible with 52100. The introduction of 5280 is a significant steel composition to meet the bearing industry needs while reducing the difficulty in continuous casting 52100.

Steel Production Efficiency

Improved Chemical Analysis

The basis for the new chemistry was to reduce carbon, increase the Mn:Si ratio and lower the chromium content. The new chemistry must develop equivalent hardness and hardenability, less carbide segregation, and rolling bearing performance characteristics similar to 52100. The steel analysis to improve, among other factors, the segregation susceptibility during solidification and therefore the properties is presented below.

Chemical composition:

Carbon	Manganese	Silicon	Chromium
0.78%	0.78%	0.24%	0.82%

Steelmaking/Manufacturing Properties

The new grade 5280 was evaluated for steelmaking and manufacturing properties. Electric furnace melting and secondary refining operations improved with better control of lower carbon and chromium. The 4:1 Mn/Si ratio for 5280 (vs. <2:1 for 52100) was considered an improvement for continuous casting and slag control. Steel cleanliness evaluations for microscopic and macroscopic were equivalent with 52100.

Continuous Casting Properties

This experimental material was rotary cast into a 205mm billet. The casting rate for 5280 was increased by +15% compared to 52100, due to lower %C and %Cr contents. Carbon segregation index was 1.13 max. and no porosity was observed.

Rolling Mill Properties

The experimental billets were direct charged from the rotary continuous caster at 950θC into a gas fired furnace, held 45 minutes and direct rolled into 55mm bars having a reduction ratio of about 14:1. Steel grade 52100 is rarely direct rolled. Generally a long heating cycle is required to allow soaking time at temperature for carbon diffusion. Thus primary carbides can breakdown into diffused carbides that slowly begin to fade into a homogenous structure. Soaking times can be as long as 24 hours and higher soaking temperatures, to reduce diffusion time, can lead to melting of primary carbides resulting in porosity. Decarburization is a further negative from this practice of long heating time prior to rolling. The experience with 5280 was to direct charge and roll within one hour to final dimension with 0.47mm decarburization.

Comparative Study 5280 to 52100

Metallurgical Test Results

The following material inspections were performed on 12 bars randomly selected from a 50 ton heat of 5280, produced by EAF melting, ladle refining, vacuum degassing, rotary continuous casting, and directly charged and rolled to 55   mm by 6400 mm long bar. The microscopic cleanliness of the heat was (acc. to DIN 50602) K1 = 1.6 and there were no internal defects such as cavities, pores or cracks.

The blue fracture test on 12 coupons revealed 2 defects of 0.7mm and 0.1mm length by 20 µm in width. The limiting value of 2.5 mm/dm^2 was observed.

The carbide formation (acc. To SEP 1520) is 5.1, 6.0 and 7.1 at a maximum value.

Figure 1 shows comparative photomicrographs of 5280 and 52100 at surface, mid-radius and core locations at 100x and 500x.

Heat Treatment

Soft Annealing

The standard 52100 (100Cr6) annealing program for rolling bearing steel when applied to the 5280 material resulted in a hardness of 198 HB and a structure of lamellar pearlite (>80%) with small amounts of spheroidized carbide. This microstructure was optimized by means of decreasing the annealing temperature in the high temperature range from 800°C to 760°C then cooling down to 700°C for 7 hours. The result was a hardness of 180-190HB and a general spheroidization according to CG 2.0-2.2 with a slight lamellar share in the core area.

Hardness-austenitizing-response / microstructure, retained austenite

To develop suitable heat treatments, a hardness austenitizing response was prepared and the microstructure and retained austenite were analyzed. Figure 2 provides the results as compared with 52100. The hardness required is reached at lower quenching temperatures in the case of 5280 than with 52100. This is due to the reduction of chromium content. Hardness is the same though, after tempering at 180°C.

The metallographic evaluation of the martensite structure shows that austenitising at about 820°C-870°C is possible with a retained austenite content 9-15%. Figure 3 illustrates the martensite structure.

Tempering behavior

Hardness and retained austenite reaction to tempering was tested. In order to maintain the S0 or S1 dimensional stabilization 52100 is tempered at 220°C or at 240°C resulting in a mean value of hardness 60.5 HRC and 60 HRC for the SO and S1 respectively. The corresponding retained austenite measured was δ 5% and δ 2% respectively.

Figure 4 provides the tempering diagram of 5280 in which hardness and retained austenite are indicated. With tempering temperatures of 220°C and 240°C the same values for hardness and retained austenite are achieved as in the case of 52100. It is therefore assured that after martensitic hardening of 5280, stabilization does not require a change in procedure.

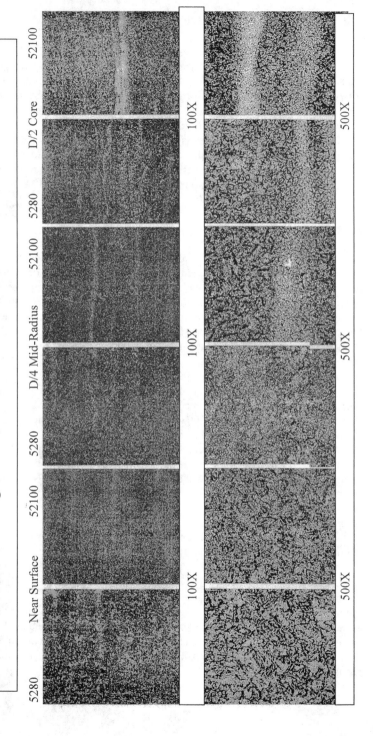

Fig 1: Micro-structure comparison of 5280 vs 52100 Near surface, Mid-radius, Core. The 5280 exhibits far less carbide streaking than 52100. No carbides are exhibited and the acc. to SEP 1520 the 5280 ratings are 5.1, 6.0 and 7.1 at a maximum.

Figure 2: Hardness - Austenitising - Response of 100Cr6 and 5280

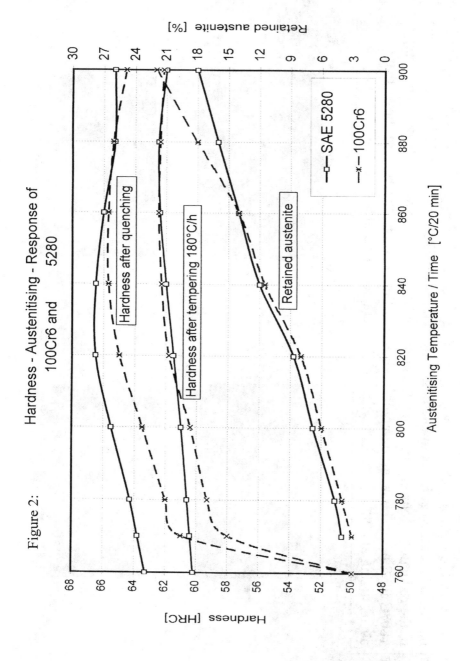

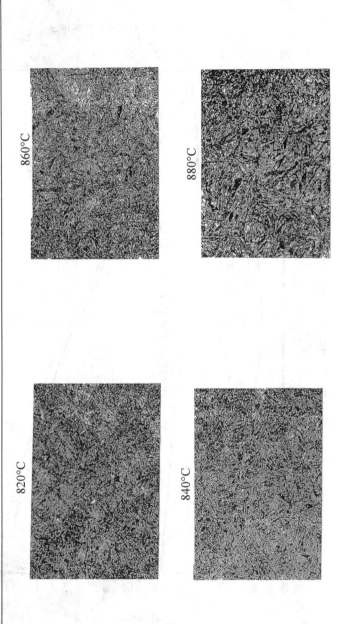

Fig. 3: Micro-structure after quenching from 820°C, 840°C, 860°C, 880°C . The required hardness is reached at lower quenching temperatures for 5280 than with 52100. This is due to the reduction in chromium content. Hardness is the same as 52100 after tempering at 180°C for 2 hrs. The metallographic evaluation of the martensite structure shows that austenitizing at 820°-870°C is possible with a retained austenite content of 9-15%.

Fig 4: Relationship of hardness and retained austenite to tempering temperature. The S0 and S1 dimensional stabilization aim hardness is 60.5 and 60 HRC, while retained austenite of δ 5% and δ 2% for 52100. As can be seen when tempering at 220C and 240C the same values are achieved in 5280. Therefore, no change in procedure from 52100 is necessary.

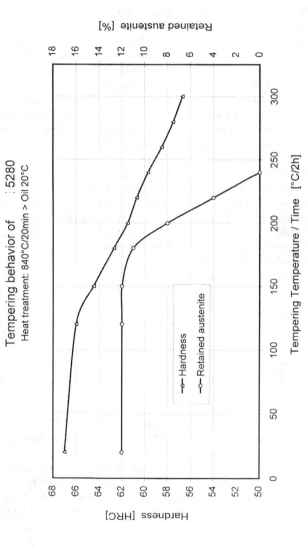

Tempering behavior of   : 5280
Heat treatment: 840°C/20min > Oil 20°C

Hardenability

A complete substitute of 52100 by 5280 is only possible when the current limiting cross section can be through hardened. The surface layer at the edge of the part must be free of pearlite. The hardenability was calculated from an FAG program based on the chemical analysis, austenitizing temperature and quenching medium and compared with 52100. The through-hardening QM value (QM= reference cross section) in relation to the hardening temperature and the quenching intensity is indicated in Figure 5. Considering a maximum hardening temperature of 860°C-870°C about 26-29 mm could be through hardened with 5280. This is about the same as for 52100. It can be assumed therefore, that the hardenability of 5280 and 52100 is roughly the same. In general the 52100 has to be austenitized 25-30°C higher than 5280.

Considering the sensitivity to pearlite dispersion during hardening from a theoretical viewpoint the 5280 would be less sensitive then 52100 due to the lower carbon content and fewer segregation zones. Further processing and development of TTT diagram will lead to a more accurate determination.

Inductive heat treatment

Future testing is planned to gain experience with induction raceway hardening using medium frequency. Theoretically induction hardening of 5280 is expected to be easier than 52100, since the hardness was reached more quickly and the tendency to form pearlite is probably less. This is expected from the low carbon content and substitution of chrome by manganese as the element to increase hardenability. The effect of Mn in short cycle induction hardening is less dependent on the austenitizing temperature and time since it substitutional in the matrix and immediately available. In contrast the extremely carbide forming Cr requires time to dissolve, so that the heating time (cycle time) during hardening could be 30-50% longer. Thus the hardening zone can be defined more closely with 5280 and the danger of through hardening in the case of thin walls is not nearly as great.

Austempering

The bainitic transformation is bound to residual stresses for bearing steels. In some part designs this a most important item, because it helps to prevent cracks during hardening.

The aim of this test protocol was to examine if a bainitic hardening was possible and if the results in a surface hardness of 60 ρ2 HRC and compressive residual stress of approximately -200 MPa at the edge could be achieved with 5280.

Figure 6 shows the hardness and retained austenite contents reached. Figure 7 shows the residual stresses' resulting from the austempering heat treatment.

It has been concluded that the hardness and residual stresses were not reached; therefore a bainitic heat treatment to the properties of 52100 is not possible with 5280.

Mechanical properties

Fig. 5: The Hardenability was calculated from the chemical analysis. Assuming a maximum hardness temperature of 860-870°C about 26-29 mm could be through hardened with 5280. This is about the same range which is reached for 52100 at the temperature of 880°C. Therefore the hardenability of 5280 and 52100 is roughly the same. The sensitivity to pearlite dispersion during hardening would theoretically be less, due to the lower carbon content and fewer segregation zones.

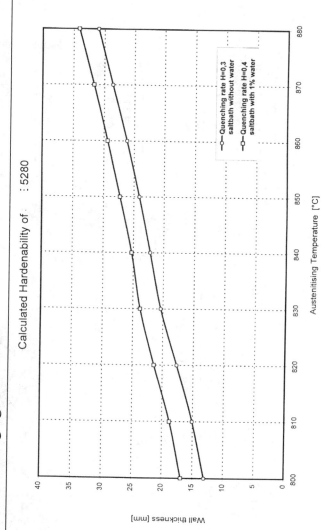

Calculated Hardenability of : 5280

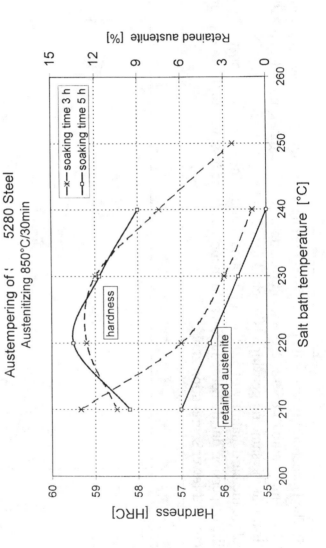

Fig. 6: The objective was to prove if a bainitic hardening (60 ±2 HRc) and compressive residual stress of -200 MPa at the edge of 52x25x30 mm test rings could be obtained. The exact M_S for 5280 is not known. The hardness can only be obtained in the 220° to 230°C range. A bainitic heat treatment to properties of 52100 is not possible with 5280.

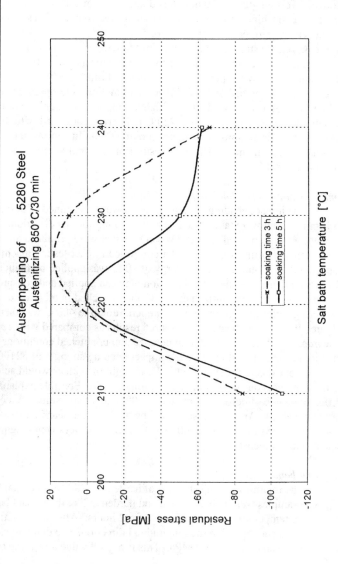

Fig. 7: Stresses measured by X-Ray diffraction at a depth of 0.2 mm at the outer diameter in a circumferential direction did not meet the -200 MPa desired value. Therefore, a bainitic heat treatment to the properties of 52100 is not possible with 5280.

Tensile strength

Specimens were taken in the longitudinal direction of the bars. They were heat treated, ground and lapped in the longitudinal direction within the test length to avoid grooves. Test length was 30 mm, test diameter 6 mm. Tensile testing was conducted on a hydraulic machine with a torsional moment free adapter. 4 tests per point were conducted and plotted against values of 52100.

Figure 8: Tensile strength and elastic limit to tempering temperature. The profiles are very similar with a slight advantage to the 5280 for the strength maximum and a slight disadvantage at low temperature for the elastic limit.

Fracture elongation of 5280 and 52100 as a function of tempering temperature are given in Figure 9. Starting from 180°C to higher temperatures significant differences is visible. A slight decrease of elongation at 220°C tempering combined with the end of retained austenite transformations is characteristic of 52100. In contrast the 5280 demonstrates a constant high elongation. This may result from the more homogenous microstructure found in the 5280 steel.

Impact bending test, Notch impact strength

The impact bending strength of 5280 was determined with flat bending samples 5x10mm, which were taken from a bar in the longitudinal direction. The notch impact strength was determined with DVM samples that were produced analogously.

Tests were performed on a computer controlled impact-testing machine that has a capacity of 300 joules. Impact energy of 100 J was applied by reducing the drop height. As a result there was an optimal relation between applied and consumed energy.

The samples were austenitized at 830°C and quenched in oil (Isomax 166E). A tempering series by a graduation in temperature up to 400°C was then prepared.

Figures 10 and 11 indicate the measured results as compared with 52100 values available. The impact energy AV of 5280 in notched and unnotched conditions is somewhat lower than in the case of 52100. Also the impact bending strength of 52100 was higher.

We had not expected such a result. We thought the values would actually be higher due to the homogeneous structural constitution of 5280. Possible explanations could lie in the different degree of deformations (the 52100 comparison values had come from ingot tested material). Another reason could be the lamellar pearlite that was present in the initial structure prior to hardening which is why a lower quenching temperature was selected to compensate.

Rotating bending strength

The rotating bending strength of hardened 5280 samples can be taken from Figure 12. The samples were manufactured and hardened like the impact bending samples. The tempering temperature was 180°C, held for 2 hours. After the heat treatment the samples were ground and lapped in the longitudinal direction. The diagram shows that the endurance strength is at 1050 MPa. This is a good value and comparable to 52100 (900-1000 MPa).

Wear resistance (pin on disc)

Comparative tests were conducted on a pin-on-disc wear measuring instrument in a dry condition, with a constant path and increasing leads. The hardness of the pins made

Fig,.8 : The tensile strength and elastic limit of 5280 is compared to 52100. The profiles are very similar. The 6 I mm x 30 mm test pieces were heat treated, ground and lapped in a longitudinal direction to avoid cross grooves. Testing was conducted on a hydraulic machine with a torsional moment free adapter.

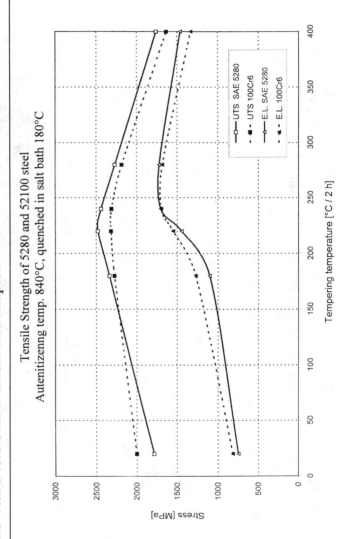

Tensile Strength of 5280 and 52100 steel
Autenitizenng temp. 840°C, quenched in salt bath 180°C

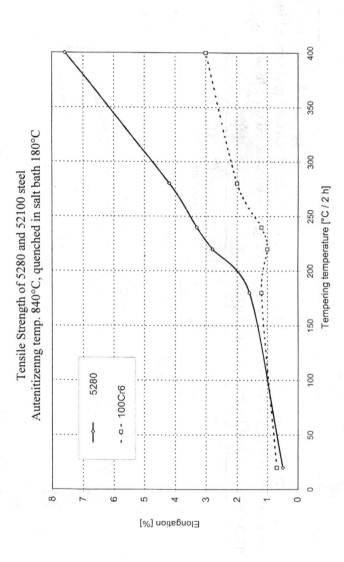

Fig. 9: The fracture elongation differences are evident with tempering temperatures 180°F and above. The slight decrease of elongation at 220°C coincides with the end of retained austenite for 52100. The 5280 demonstrates a very high elongation; this very positive attribute may result for the more homogenous microstructure.

Fig. 10: The notch impact stength test were determined with DVM samples. An impact energy of 100 J was applied. The impact energy of 5280 is lower than 52100, which was unexpected. We thought the homogeneous micro-structure of 5280 would be better.

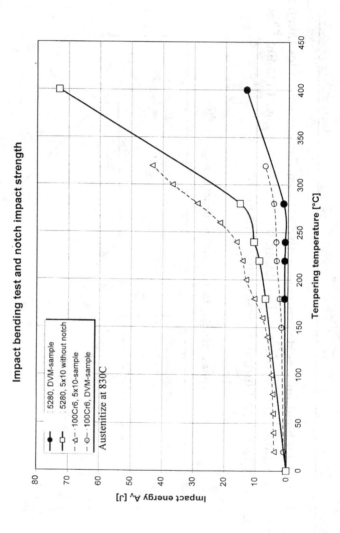

Impact bending test and notch impact strength

Fig. 11: The impact bending was determined with 5x10mm flat bend samples taken in a longitudinal direction. The impact bending strength of 52100 is higher than the 5280. This result was not expected and further investigation is required.

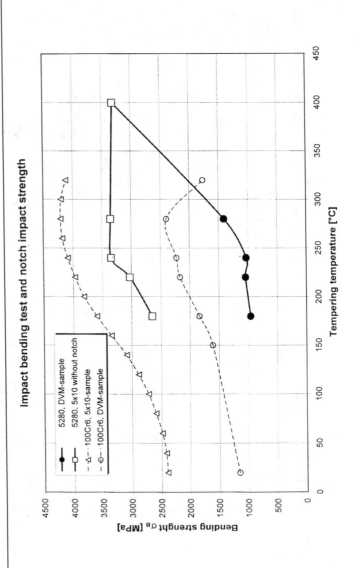

Impact bending test and notch impact strength

Fig 12: The samples were prepared similar to the impact bending and tempered at 180°C then ground and lapped in the longitudinal direction. The endurance strength of 1050 MPa is a good value, comparable to 52100 (900-1000 MPa)

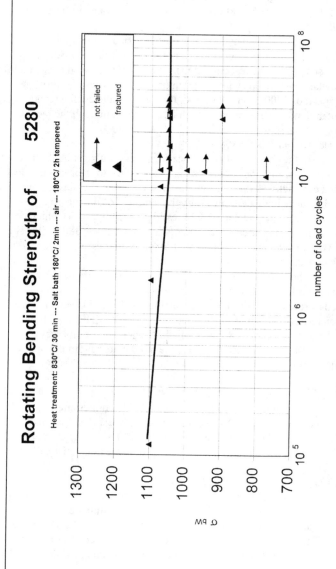

Rotating Bending Strength of   5280

Heat treatment: 830°C/ 30 min --- Salt bath 180°C/ 2min -- air --- 180°C/ 2h tempered

of 5280 was 704 HV, the hardness of the pins made of 52100 was 680 and 836 HV. In Figure 13 the mean values of 3 measured values each are shown. It is apparent that up to a load of 25 N the wear rates are nearly identical. With higher loads, however, the wear rate of 5280 is greater. This is probably due to the different carbide volumes. The carbide content of 52100 is higher due to the higher carbon content.

Rolling contact fatigue life ˈ

The following cycling tests were carried out on angular contact bearings of type 7205B whereby the inner rings were the test specimens. All other bearing components were standard. The test conditions were selected in such a way that it would be possible to make comparisons with 52100 under diverse types of stress.

At speed of 10000 and 12000 rpm the load and the cycling conditions were varied and contamination was simulated with HRC-indentations in the raceway.

Mixed friction (po = 3800 MPa)

In the field of car wheel bearings, very high test loads are used in comparative tests in order to obtain short testing cycles. Due to their magnitude, experts dispute these loads especially as the loads are always located in the plastic zone, which means that the result is decisively determined by the hardness of the material.

The tests were conducted on L38 test rigs (see Figure 14) which permit the application of high contact pressures. The test conditions were po= 3800 MPa, speed 10000 rpm and a thin oil, under mixed friction conditions. With these conditions a service life of 7 hr. was calculated.

The results of the cycling test are shown in Figure 15. As these test rigs are so new, no reference values are yet available for the mixed friction condition. Therefore we used as reference values, results obtained with 52100, M50 and Cronidur 30 which had been tested only with full fluid lubrication under EHD conditions.

In the test result for 5280, with mixed friction conditions prevailing, the L10 life is twice the L10 life of SAE 52100. Thus, the 5280 material did not only pass the high-load test but far surpassed the requirements.

Mixed friction (po = 2500 MPa)

Tests under mixed friction and a Hertzian pressure of po = 2500 MPa are presented in Figure 16. The comparison with 52100 shows that the 5280 is somewhat better. While there were 2 failures within 100 hr. in the case of 52100, the first failure with 5280 occurred after 110 hr. The results are not statistically different.

Mixed friction (po = 3800 MPa and HRC indentations)

The conditions: mixed friction and pre-damage by Rockwell C indentations (160-μm diameter) in the inner ring raceway should simulate a contaminated lubricant. It is important for this cycling test that the material is quite tough so the edges raised by the HRC indentations are flattened back again and no cracks or fatigue damage occurs. Figure 17: shows the comparison between 5280 and 52100, with 5280 reporting a slight advantage.

In summary, the results of all three life tests revealed an advantage in 5280. We expect to achieve this cycling behavior when suing sample bearings in the field. False

Fig. 13: A pin of 5280 (hardness 704 HV) were compared to 52100 (hardness 680 & 836HV) in the dry condition. For loads up to 25N the wear rates are nearly identical, with higher loads the 5280 wear rate is greater. This is probably due to the higher carbide volume in 52100, resulting from the higher carbon content.

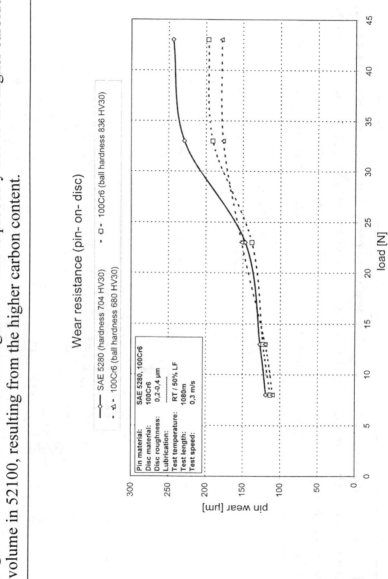

Wear resistance (pin- on- disc)

Fig 14: Rolling contact fatigue cycling test were carried out on angular contact bearings of type 7205B, whereby the inner rings were the test specimens. The test conditions were selected in ways to make comparisions with 52100 under diverse types of stress. This schematic shows the test rig which was operated at speeds of 10000 to 12000 rpm.

fatigue life
test rig FAG-L38B

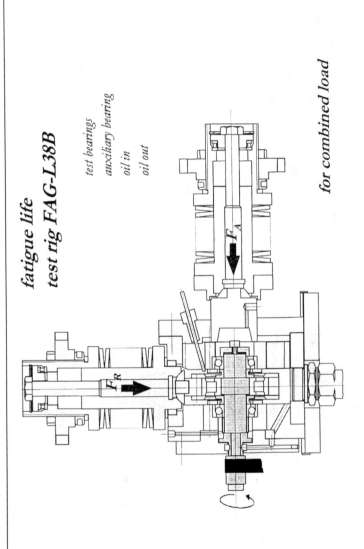

test bearings
auxiliary bearing
oil in
oil out

F_A

F_R

for combined load

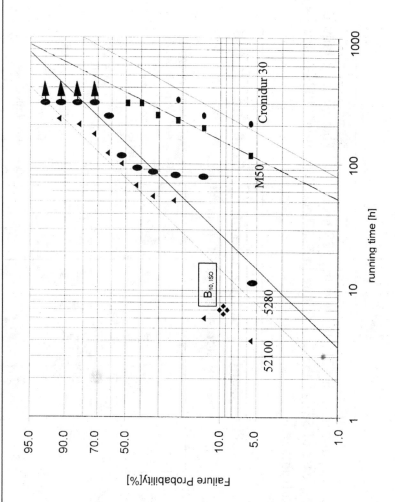

Fig 15: Test of 5280 (Mixed friction) to 52100, M50 and Cronidur 30 with full fluid film lubrication under EHD conditions. Test rig L38B, Axil Load: 8.5 and Radial Load: 9.5 kN/Bearing, po = 3800 MPa, Oil: Shell Morlina 46, Speed: 10000, Bearing o.d. temp.:70°C, 12 inner rings / material

Fig 16: The comparison with 52100 shows the 5280 is better. There were 2 failures within 100 hrs in the case of 52100, the first failure in 5280 occurred after 110 hrs. This is not a significant advantage.

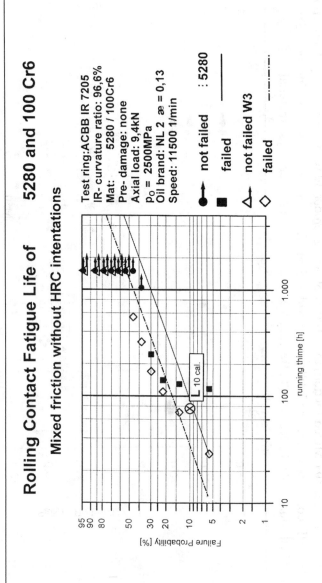

Rolling Contact Fatigue Life of   5280 and 100 Cr6

Mixed friction without HRC intentations

Test ring:ACBB IR 7205
IR- curvature ratio: 96,6%
Mat: 5280 / 100Cr6
Pre- damage: none
Axial load: 9,4kN
$p_o = 2500MPa$
Oil brand: NL 2 æ = 0,13
Speed: 11500 1/min

not failed   : 5280

failed

not failed W3

failed

running thime [h]

Failure Probability [%]

$L_{10 cal.}$

Fig. 17: Mixed friction and damage by HRc (160 μm indentations) was designed to simulate a contaminated lubricant. A material must be quite tough so the edges of the HRc marks are flattened back and no cracks or fatigue damage occurs. The 5280 again showed a slight advantage compared to 52100.

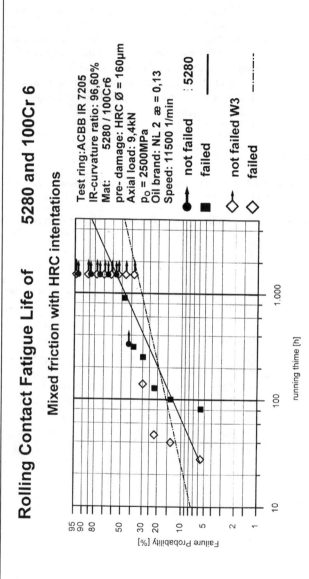

Rolling Contact Fatigue Life of   5280 and 100Cr 6

Mixed friction with HRC intentations

Test ring: ACBB IR 7205
IR-curvature ratio: 96,60%
Mat: 5280 / 100Cr6
pre- damage: HRC Ø = 160μm
Axial load: 9,4kN
P_0 = 2500MPa
Oil brand: NL 2 æ = 0,13
Speed: 11500 1/min

● not failed   : 5280
■ failed   ——————
◇ not failed W3
◇ failed   ——·——··——

Failure Probability [%]

running thime [h]

brinelling tests are also planned for field trials when original flange bearing units are tested.

Manufacturing behavior of 5280

Changes in forging, rolling, distortion and decarburization during heat treatment, soft and hard machining and corrosion during bearing manufacturing are not expected, with 5280, to deviate much from 52100. Any tendency to decarburize, due to the lower absolute %C content, can be determined with further experience.

What is significant with the introduction of 5280, is the formulation of a "continuous caster friendly" steel analysis that offers to reduce susceptibility to chemical segregation, improve production efficiencies at lower costs and with comparable or improve performance characteristics compared to 52100.

References

(1) Eberhard R., Internal Report Development and testing of a new bearing steel SAE 5280, FAG , Schweinfurt, Germany.

(2) MACSTEEL Certified Material Test Report 3M23110, Fort Smith, AR, March 28, 1998.

P. K. Adishesha

Effect of Steel Making and Processing Parameters on Carbide Banding in
Commercially Produced ASTM A-295 52100 Bearing Steel.

Reference: Adishesha. P. K, "**Effect of Steel Making and Processing Parameters on
Carbide Banding in Commercially Produced ASTM A-295 52100 Bearing Steel**",
Bearing Steel Technology, ASTM STP 1419, J. M. Beswick, Ed., American Society for
Testing and Materials International, West Conshohocken, PA, 2002.

Abstract: Carbides are an essential phase in high carbon alloy steels used for bearing
applications. Carbides provide wear resistance, inhibit grain growth and are the reservoirs
of alloys, which enable the steel to develop the desired properties during heat treatment.
High carbide heterogeneity and large carbides are known to affect adversely the wear
resistance of bearing steels. Heterogeneity originates from the solidification process of
ingots and cast blooms. An attempt has been made to study the effect of various steel
making and processing parameters such as teeming/casting temperature, ingot size,
reduction ratio, soaking time at the rolling temperature and heat treatment on the carbide
banding in the commercially produced ASTM A 295 - 52100 type bearing steel.
Carbide banding was found to decrease with the decrease in super heat and increase in
the reduction ratio. Increasing soaking time at the rolling temperature also decreased the
degree of banding. Increasing the austenetizing temperature or increasing the soaking
time at the same austenitizing temperature also reduced the degree of banding; the effect
of temperature is being more significant. High temperature soaking prior to hot rolling
significantly decreased the degree of banding in continuously cast products. Carbide
banding reduced with reduction in carbon content and sulphur content. Other alloying
elements had very little or no significant influence on carbide banding.

Key Words: High carbon bearing steel, carbides, carbide banding, solidification, steel
making.

Introduction

Bearings are perhaps the most wide spread type of mechanical engineering
components used in all types of machinery. The load applied on a bearing determines its

---

1 Vice President (Metallurgical Services and Development), Mahindra Ugine Steel Co.
Ltd., Khopoli, India. 410216.

dimensions and, in turn, the size of associated mechanical components such as housings, shafts and others. In order to build smaller, more efficient and cheaper assemblies there has been a steady trend to increase the allowable load on bearings.

Bearing steels must possess high strength, toughness, wear resistance, dimensional stability, annealability, machinability, manufacturing reliability, mechanical and rolling contact fatigue resistance and freedom from internal defects. A steel containing 1.0%C and 1.5% Cr (ASTM A 295-52100) is the most widely used steel for the manufacture of bearings because of its good wear resistance and rolling contact resistance. It is generally supplied by mills in the spherodised-annealed condition for ease of fabrication. Post fabrication heat treatment generally consists of partial austenitization at a temperature just below the Ac_m followed by quenching to a hardness of 60-63 HRC C and tempering.

Deleterious effect of Carbide Banding.

High carbide heterogeneity and large carbides are known to adversely affect the wear resistance of bearing steels [1]. Segregated carbides are significantly more difficult to take into solution during austenitization and can lead to 'hard spots' after quenching. Cracking is also sometimes observed along the carbide bands. Large carbides and banded carbides have been found [2] to lead to early spalling failures on inner ring raceways of bearings running at high speed. Rolling element fatigue resistance is expected to be reduced by a factor of four, by large banded carbides. Sometimes a carbide network causes premature failure of bearings. [3]. For all these reasons carbide segregation is considered undesirable in bearing steels.

Micro-segregation in killed steel ingots

Solidification of any alloy, which possesses a finite freezing range, produces a non-homogeneous solid. The solidification of an alloy begins with the appearance of small solid particles (nucleii), which contain more of higher melting point constituents than any subsequently formed solid. Thus, as successive layers of the solid phases are deposited, each layer will be richer than its predecessor in the low melting point constituents. The final solid is composed, then, of a 'cored' structure, in which each unit has a high melting point central portion surrounded by lower melting point material. This process is called coring or dendritic- or micro-segregation. Since solidification generally, does not occur under equilibrium conditions, concentration differences will also appear in the liquid phase. This will further increase the concentration difference between the first and last solidified parts of the solid phase. In solid steel, the rate of diffusion of most of the alloying elements is so low that micro-segregation during solidification will be equalized only to a small extent. Segregation causes structural differences that might lead to banded structures and also differences in the properties of the material. For this reason it is important to know how different factors affect segregation during solidification.

Factors affecting segregation

The final extent of inter-dendritic segregation that is observed at any point in a steel ingot is the product of three main influences:

- The cooling rate
- The type of crystal growth
- The composition of the steel.

Increasing the cooling rate decreases the segregation, whereas with alloying additions, particularly carbon, segregation increases. The work of Doherty and Melford [4] has shown that segregation is characteristically higher for equiaxed crystal growth rather than for columnar growth in the same region of the ingot. Most alloying elements in steel have distribution coefficients between the solid and liquid phases of less than one. Consequently, when liquid alloy freezes, according to theory of differential or selective solidification, metal of high purity solidifies first.

The solute enriched liquid, i.e. segregate (principally carbon, phosphorus and sulphur), diffuses inwards at finite rates, but solidification also progresses at a finite rate that decreases with distance from the surface. Hence, segregation does not extend far into the liquid, but is restricted by a narrow layer of liquid metal immediately adjacent to the solid/liquid interface in the "mushy" zone. If liquid solidifies at this point, micro-segregation will result.

Micro-segregation of chromium is found to be decreased by both silicon and manganese additions [5]. In the case of silicon this is due to a smaller solidification interval, whereas manganese increases the partition coefficient for chromium between austenite and liquid. Therefore, in high carbon alloy steels in addition to segregation of alloying elements, various types of carbides will be present.

Origin of banded structure
A banded structure can be described as a segregated structure of approximately parallel bands of two different phases, e.g. ferrite and pearlite, aligned in the direction of working. With the advent of modern Metallographic techniques it is now well established that banded microstructure in wrought steels are manifestations of the heterogeneous distribution of alloying elements that result from dendritic or small scale segregation during solidification of an ingot or a bloom. These include, elements like nickel, chromium, molybdenum, titanium, manganese, etc., used as alloying additions and phosphorus, sulphur, arsenic, tin, copper, etc., present as residuals.

The essential steps through which a banded structure in steel develops are: -
- Micro-segregation of alloying elements during ingot solidification and subsequent alignment by mechanical working.
- Carbon re-distribution into banded layers on cooling from austenitizing temperature.

Some elements in steel segregate more readily than others. [6]. Carbon diffuses very rapidly whereas elements such as manganese, nickel, chromium, molybdenum, tin, copper, etc., diffuse very slowly at temperatures normally used for rolling or forging, so the alloy segregation persists throughout processing. During mechanical working, the cast structure is broken down and after a large reduction in cross section, the network of the segregated pattern is formed into distinct bands. The alloy rich and alloy-depleted bands have different transformation characteristics and, thus, on cooling a laminated microstructure are produced. The alloy-depleted bands transforming at a relatively high temperature will have lower carbon, whereas, alloy rich bands enriched with carbon will transform into a carbon-rich phase.

Mechanism to reduce segregation and structural banding
Some of the proposed mechanisms for reducing the severity of carbide segregation in ball bearing steels are:
- Faster cooling of ingots

- Prolonged heating prior to rolling
- Reduced finish rolling temperature
- Intensive cooling after rolling including quenching prior to annealing
- More prolonged annealing (spheroidization)
- Thermo-mechanical treatment.

An increase in the rate of cooling ingots during solidification increase the rate of crystallization [7] and the zone of directional columnar dendrite is reduced and carbides are expected to be refined and uniformly distributed. Prolonged soaking of the cast ingots or blooms before rolling is supposed to homogenize the ingot [8]. Stepped heating at high temperature 1160 ° C, 1200° C, 1280° C and 1180°C is expected to reduce structural banding significantly and improve bearing life [9]. Similarly reduced finish rolling temperature and intensive cooling after rolling are also reported to reduce severity of carbide banding [10].

An attempt has been made to study the effects of these factors on carbide banding in commercially produced ingots/products of ASTM A 295- 52100 bearing steel, with the objective of arriving at optimum process parameters to reduce degree of carbide banding.

Experimental Procedure

Melts of ASTM A295-52100 steel were made in a commercial 45 ton Electric Arc Furnace at Mahindra Ugine Steel Company Limited (MUSCO), aluminum killed, ladle refined and vacuum degassed. Molten steel was homogenized by purging inert gas and then cast into ingots of 3ton weight having an average cross section of 450x450mm, by up-hill teeming. Continuous casting was done in a three strand, 9/16m radius, closed pouring caster having facilities for electro-magnetic stirring and auto mould level control and mould size 250X200 mm. Solidified ingots/blooms were subsequently rolled in a 2-high, 860mm reversible blooming mill, and cooled under controlled conditions, surface conditioned and subsequently rolled to different sizes in a 550mm 3-high, 4-stand bar mill. Samples were selected from the rolled products for evaluation of banding.

To study the effects of super heat on banding, teeming temperatures were varied from 1500°C to 1560°C (liquidus temperature 1435°C) and other parameters were kept the same. Similarly, for studying the effect of reduction ratio ingots from the same heat were rolled into different sizes. For studying the effects of soaking time ingots and blooms were soaked at high temperature for a prolonged period prior to hot rolling and samples were selected from the rolled products.

For studying the effect of ingot size on banding, ingots of average cross section 370X370mm, 395X395mm, 450X450mm and 500X500mm were cast in the same heat and were rolled to different sizes so that super heat and reduction ratio were constant.

The effect of heat treatment on the carbide banding was studied on this steel. The heat treatment was conducted in a muffle furnace on samples selected from spheroidized annealed bars. Approximately, 15-mm thick slices were austenitized at different temperatures by soaking for 20 min and then quenched in oil. The quenched samples were polished and etched and examined for carbide banding. Similarly, samples were austenitized at 850° C and soaked for different periods at the same temperature and then quenched in oil.

For the examination of banding, samples with full cross section of approximately 15mm thickness were cut from the rolled products on an abrasive cut-off machine and oil quenched from 850° C (soaking time 25 min). Quenched samples were polished on series of micro-polishing papers, finished with 1 micron and 0.5 micron alumina powders and etched with 10% nital. Etched samples were examined using an optical microscope. Stahl Eisen Prufblatt 1520-78 chart was used for rating the banding. Series 7 was used as reference.

Since there was a high degree of scatter in the data for the banding index over the cross section of a sample and also from sample to sample, in a particular melt, each melt was assigned an average Carbide Banding Index (CBI). This was assessed by examining several fields across the sample for about 10 samples per melt, instead of evaluating by the conventional worst field rating. Whenever, several heats were examined graphs have been plotted showing them as separate series and a typical trend line has been drawn to show the correlation.

Results and Discussions.

Effect of SuperHeat.

Figure 1 shows the effect of super heat on the carbide banding in square ingots having an average cross section of 450x450mm. And Figure 2 shows the effect of super heat on the carbide-banding index on continuously cast products. As can be seen there seems to be an optimum super heat, which gives the lowest degree of banding. This was about 35 °C for continuous casting and about 65°C for ingot casting for the type of caster and ingots used at MUSCO. At higher super heats, as expected, the carbide banding is high. This correlates with the accepted theory that larger the solidification range higher the segregation. In general continuous cast products exhibit higher degree of banding than ingot cast products for the same reduction ratio.

Effect of Reduction Ratio

Figure 3 shows the effect of reduction ratio on the carbide banding in ingots. As can be seen from the results, the higher the percentage reduction, the lower is the degree of banding. During rolling/forging the network is broken down mechanically. As the reduction ratio increases, the working also increases, which increases the degree of break down of the network to give a more homogenous carbide distribution.

Effect of Ingot Size

The effect of the size of ingot on the CBI is shown in Figure 4. As the ingot size increases the CBI also increases. Though the reduction increases as the ingot size increases, it is well known that the segregation also increases with size. Hence, as expected the CBI has shown a good correlation with respect to ingot size.

Effect of Soaking Time.

Figure 5 shows the effect of soaking time on the carbide banding in ball bearing steel ingots. Diffusion treatment are governed by $(Dt)^{1/2}$, where D is the diffusion coefficient and t the time of treatment. It is expected that as the soaking time at rolling temperature increases, the homogenization will be better because of the dissolution of Cr and diffusion of carbon in the solid state and hence banding will be lesser. The experimental results also show a similar trend though the difference is not very significant in Ingot products for the time periods for which they were soaked. However, soaking at higher temperature (1260°C) prior to rolling and bringing down the temperature down to 1220°C for rolling has very significant effect in lowering the degree of carbide banding in concast blooms. Figure 6 shows these results for 250x200mm concast blooms.

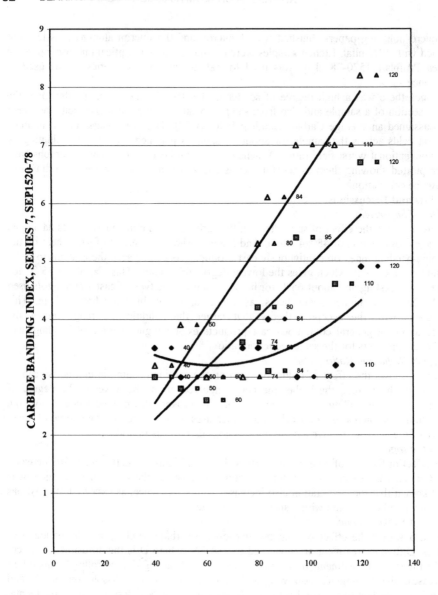

SUPER HEAT IN °C

Figure-1 Effect of super heat on carbide banding index in commercially produced ASTM A295-52100 ingots

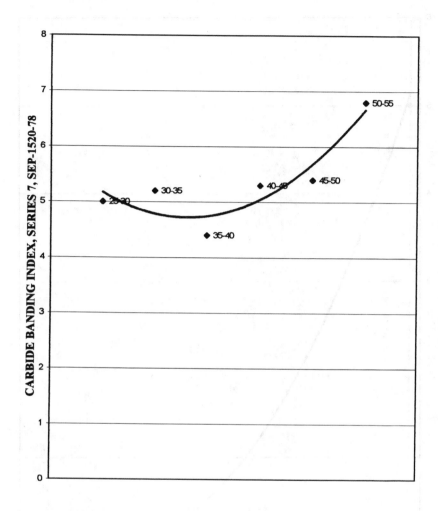

SUPER HEAT IN °C

Figure 2-Effect of super heat on carbide banding index in ASTM A295-52100 concast blooms of size 250X200mm.

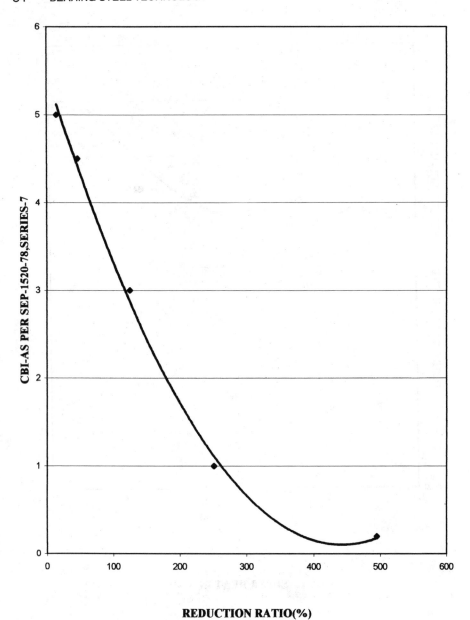

Figure 3-Effect of reduction ratio on carbide banding index in commercially produced ASTM A295-52100 ingot of size 45X450mm(3 tons)

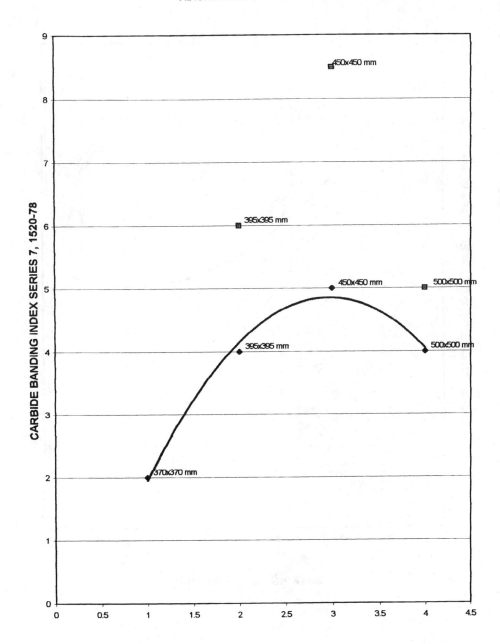

INGOT SIZE IN TONS(AVERAGE SIZE IN mmSHOWN AT EACH VALUE)

Figure 4-Effect of ingot size on carbide banding index in ASTM A295-52100.

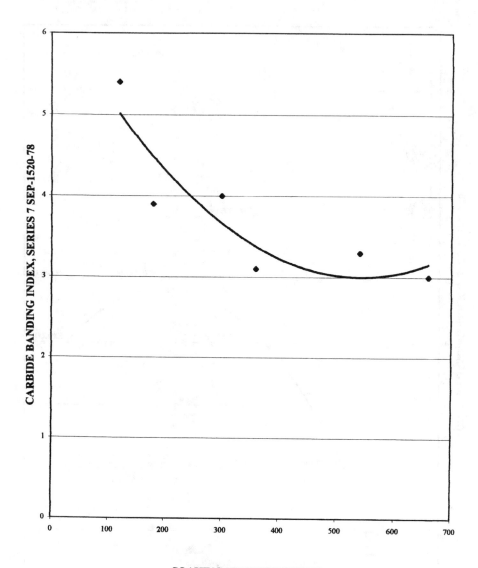

SOAKING TIME IN MINUTES

Figure 5-Effect of soaking time at rolling temperature on carbide banding index in commercially produced ASTM A295-52100 ingots of 3 tons(450X450mm)

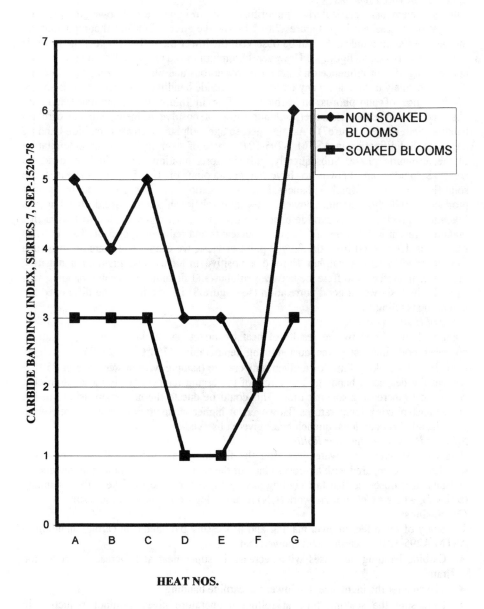

HEAT NOS.

Figure 6-Effect of high temperature soaking on carbide banding index in ASTM A 295-52100,250X200mm, concast blooms.

Effect of Alloying Elements.
Alloying elements, particularly, impurities and residuals are known to promote segregation in steel castings. Figures 7 to 10 show the effect of chemical composition on the carbide-banding index. As can be observed, the lower the carbon content the lower is the degree of banding (figure 9). However, chromium in the range of 1.40 to 1.60% does not have significant influence on banding. Phosphorous and tin in the ranges of .012 and .015 respectively do not show any trend on the carbide banding. A typical trend is shown for influence of phosphorus on carbide banding in figure 10. A similar trend was observed for tin also. However, sulphur shows a positive influence on the carbide-banding index (see figure7). As the percentage sulphur increases carbide-banding increases. Solidification in ASTM A295-52100 type of steel begins by the precipitation of the austenitic phase. Subsequently, sulphide precipitation occurs in inter-dendritic areas. Sulphides are known to have larger amount of Cr. Sulphur increases the solidification range, which enhances axial segregation and V-segregation in as cast products. Similarly, titanium showed a negative relationship with carbide banding. As titanium content increases carbide-banding decreases. This could be due to reason that titanium present in the form of TiN act as nucleants and reduce segregation. However, as titanium is detrimental from the fatigue point of view, we cannot add titanium to reduce carbide banding. Since sulphur showed a positive influence and titanium a negative influence, the effect of difference between sulphur and titanium on carbide banding was studied which showed a good correlation (see figure 8) i.e. the higher the difference the higher the banding.

Effect of Heat Treatment
Figures11 and 12 show the results of heat treatment on carbide banding. As can be observed both increasing the austenitizing temperature (750°C - 925°C) as well as increasing the soaking time for a given temperature (sample were austenitized at 850°C) reduces the degree of banding. The effect of increasing temperature is more significant compared to increasing soaking time. This could be due to the higher diffusion rates at higher austenitizing temperatures. However, at higher austenitizing temperatures, grain growth and also occasional quench cracks were observed.

Effect of Rapid Cooling after Rolling.
Bars were sprayed with water jets after the finishing pass in the rolling process and samples were compared with air-cooled bars of the same heat so that other parameters are constant. It is observed that fast cooling has no significant effect on the carbide banding (series 7), where as, carbide network (CN) reduces. Figure 13 shows these results.

Conclusions:
The study of the effect of steel making and processing parameter on carbide banding in ASTM A295-52100 bearing steel showed that:

- Carbide banding decreases with decrease in super heat and increase in reduction ratio.
- The smaller the ingot size, the lower the carbide banding.
- Increasing the soaking time at rolling temperature gives a minor reduction in banding. However, soaking at a high temperature prior to rolling significantly reduces the degree of banding.

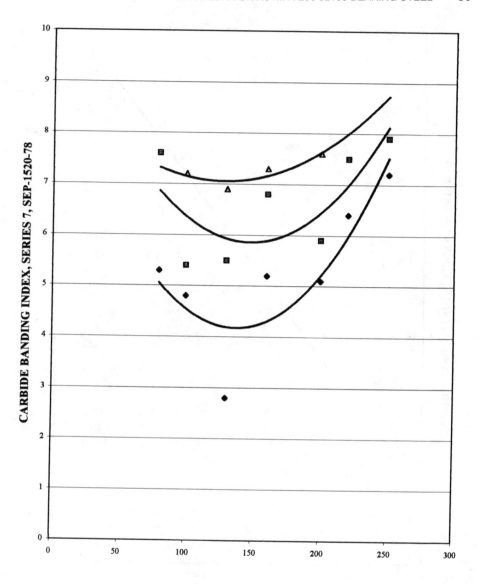

SULPHUR CONTENT IN PPM

*Figure 7-Effect of residual sulphur content on the carbide index in commercially
produced ASTM A295-52100 ingots of 3 tons(450X450mm)*

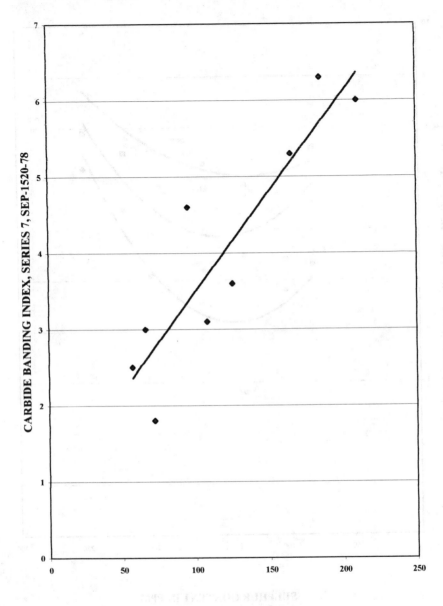

S minus Ti content in ppm

Figure 8-Effect of residuals-sulphur minus titanium on carbide banding index in ASTM A295-52100 ingots of 3 ton(450X450mm)

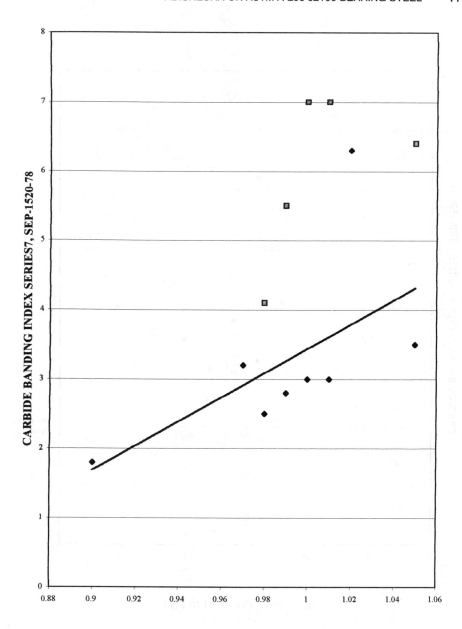

CARBON CONTENT IN PERCENTAGE POINT

*Figure 9-Effect of carbon content on the carbide banding index in commercially
produced ASTM A295-52100 ingots*

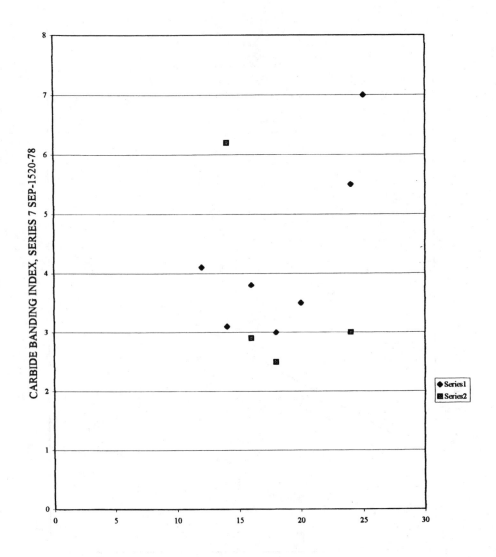

PHOSPHORUS CONTENT IN PPM

Figure 10-Effect of phosporus content on carbide banding index in commercially produced ASTM A295-52100 ingots

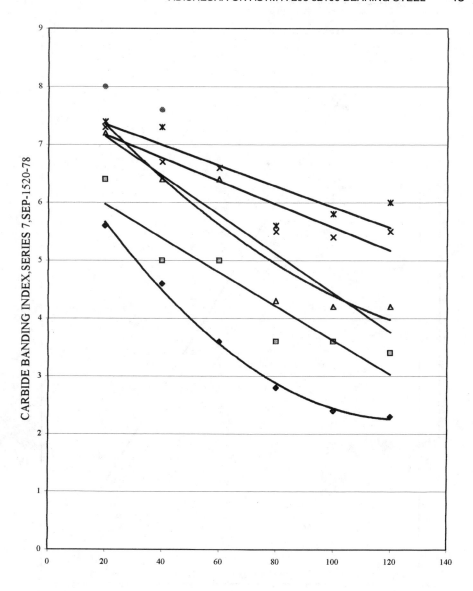

SOAKING TIME IN MINUTES

Figure 11-Effect of soaking time at austenitizing temperature on carbide banding index in commercially produced ASTM A295-52100

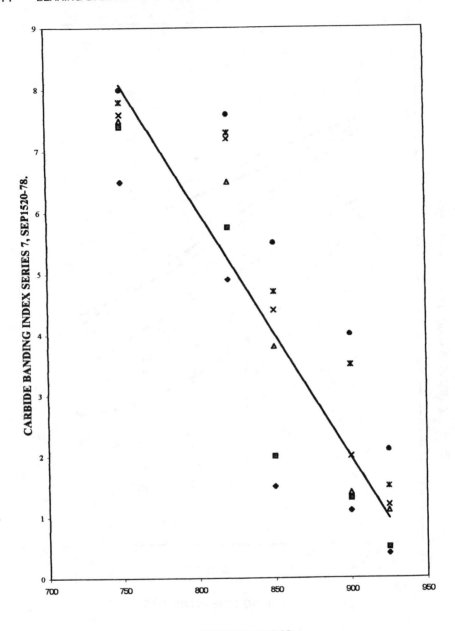

Figure 12-Effect of austenitizing temperature on carbide banding index in ASTM A295-52100

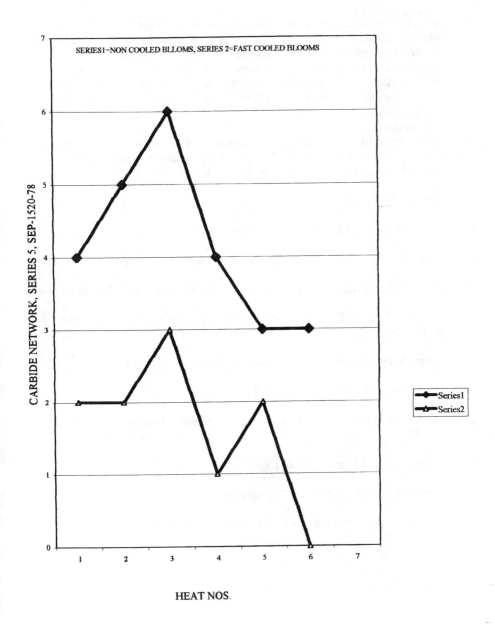

Figure 13-Effect of fast cooling during rolling on carbide banding index in commercially produced ASTM A295-52100.

- The higher the austenitizing temperature lower is the degree of banding and the longer the soaking time at austenitizing temperature the lower the degree of banding. The effect of temperature is more significant compared to the soaking time.
- Sulphur and carbon have positive influence and titanium has negative influence on carbide banding in ASTM A 295-52100. Phosphorus and tin in the levels normally present in commercially produced ASTM A 295-52100 does not have any influence on carbide banding

Acknowledgements.

The author would like to express sincere gratitude to the management of Mahindra Ugine Steel Co. Ltd., Khopoli, for their kind permission to carryout this work and publish this paper and would also like to thank all those colleagues who helped in carrying out experiments.

References:

[1]   Levitin V.S. et al, *Metaalloved Term Obrab*, Met Oct.1981, 20-23(Russian Metal Abstracts)

[2]   Parkar R.J. and Banhagor E.N., *NASA Tech Paper* No.2189, pp14

[3]   Barui K.L. & Bhattacharya B, *Journal of Material Science* 4, (1985), pp 685-687

[4]   Doherty R.D. & .Melford D.A, *Journal of Iron and Steel Institute*, Nov.1966, pp1131

[5]   Staffan Malm, *Scandinavian Journal of Metallurgy* 5, 1976, pp137-144

[6]   Mukherjee G, *Tool and Alloy Steels*, Feb.1977, pp55

[7]   Fredrickson H and Hellner H, *Scandinavian Journal of Metallurgy* 3, 1974, pp61-68

[8]   Malinovskaya J.J. et al, *Steel in USSR (Translation)*

[9]   Petrov A.K. et al., *Stal*, Nov.1975, pp1034-1036.

[10]   Lyashenko V.P. et al., *Steel in USSR*, Feb.1985, pp92-94

S. Ganguly,[1] I. Chakrabarti,[2] M. D. Maheshwari,[3] and T. Mukherjee[4]

Ultra Clean Steel For Anti-Friction Bearing Applications

Reference: Ganguly, S., Chakrabarti, I., Maheshwari, M. D., and Mukherjee, T., **"Ultra Clean Steel For Anti-Friction Bearing Applications,"** *Bearing Steel Technology, ASTM STP 1419*, J. M. Beswick, Ed., American Society for testing and Materials International, West Conshohocken, PA, 2002.

Abstract: Bearing manufacturing technology of today enables relatively small sized bearings to have high duty ratings. Such bearings are highly stressed and more vulnerable to onset of rolling contact fatigue. Since contact fatigue is initiated at hard non-metallic inclusions, modern day bearings call for exceptional levels of cleanliness. Onset of rolling contact fatigue occurs in a statistical mode that depends on the probability of finding a hard phase of adequate size in the zone of maximum Hertzian stress. Therefore, an objective prediction of bearing life is possible only by counting the number of inclusions present per unit volume of steel with the help of ultrasound based assessment and not by the conventional chart based method.

    Considerable work has been done to respond to the emerging needs of the bearing industry. The steel plant has been successfully producing both through hardening and case hardening steels satisfying the requirements of some of the leading bearing manufacturers. The present paper discusses the manufacturing process for bearing steel through Basic Oxygen Furnace-Vacuum Arc Degassing route. This paper also brings out the strategy to control oxygen and titanium. Test results obtained from some leading customers and collaborators are presented.

Keywords: Antifriction bearings, ultrasonic testing, steel-making, titanium, oxygen

[1]Deputy Manager, [2]Divisional Manager, [3]Chief of Scientific Services, and [4]Executive Director of Operations respectively, Tata Iron and Steel Company Ltd., Jamshedpur, Jharkhand-831001, India.

Introduction: Antifriction bearings are among the most critical engineering components used in a wide variety of machinery. The bearing dimension determines its load rating. The size of the bearing in turn governs the sizes of other components such as shafts and housings. In the recent past there has been increased demands to raise the rated load on a given size of bearing in order to enable building smaller, more energy efficient and cheaper assemblies. Some authors have coined the expression "Power Density" to describe the effort of transmitting more power through reduced sizes of components [1,2]. Hence, bearings are now stressed at increasingly higher levels making them all the more vulnerable to failure by onset of rolling contact fatigue. Rolling contact fatigue is known to be initiated at hard non-metallic inclusions [3-7]. Therefore, modern day bearings call for exceptional high levels of cleanliness, not only for oxide inclusions, but also for other hard non-metallic inclusions like titanium nitrides/carboritrides [8-11].

The first part of this paper attempts to review the various techniques used for the evaluation of cleanliness of bearing steel and their effectiveness in predicting the fatigue life of bearings. The second part describes the work carried out at the authors' plant to respond to the emerging needs of ultra clean steel for the bearing industry. The steel plant has been producing both low carbon(case carburising grades)and high carbon(through hardening grades) of antifriction bearing steel satisfying the needs of some leading bearing manufactures. The process comprises oxygen blowing in BOF vessel followed by refining under vacuum. The refined steel is then uphill teemed into ingots. Special precautions taken to control oxygen and titanium have been also brought out in the paper. Finally, the paper also presents the test result observed by the author and, also, by and some of the leading bearing manufacturers.

Cleanliness Measurement Techniques and Their Co-Relation with Fatigue Properties

The cleanliness measurement technique of bearing steel plays a major role in assessing the quality of the steel. Because non-metallic inclusions are always present in steel, it is important to identify and classify the size and nature of inclusions [12].

The ASTM method of inclusion rating [13] is a useful technique in categorizing the size and type of inclusion where the worst field from top and bottom of an ingot rolled product from first, middle and last usable ingot is rated against standard comparison charts. This method was particularly useful when steel used to be less clean and there was a greater probability of detection of inclusions. With higher levels of cleanliness achieved by most steel makers nowadays, the very low volume of material inspected using the ASTM method gives a reduced chance of detection of inclusion stringers that could have adversely impact the life of bearings in service. Therefore, any direct corelation between inclusion rating and fatigue life can hardly be established [12].

Realizing the shortcomings of the ASTM technique the bearing manufacturers have adopted the Aerospace Material Specification (AMS), which is more quantitative and involves deposition of magnetic particles at sites where inclusions are present on or below the surface of a cylindrical sample. In this method the frequency based on number of streaks per unit area and severity based on total length of inclusion stringers over the entire surface of the specimen is reported. The limitation of this method with respect to the performance of a bearing lies in that the method does not distinguish between hard inclusions (extremely harmful) and relatively softer inclusions (less harmful). Therefore, it remains impossible to co-relate the AMS test ratings with the fatigue life performance [12].

The total oxygen content in a steel is an excellent indicator of steel cleanliness because the entire amount of oxygen reported is present in the steel as hard oxide inclusions [14] (Mostly alumina for aluminium killed steel).It has now become customary to specify oxygen content as apart of specification of bearing steel. However, it needs to be borne in mind that it is the length and distribution of oxide inclusions that determine the fatigue life of bearings in use. The distribution and length of oxide inclusions primarily depends upon the type of steel making and teeming practices deployed . Hence, neither the oxygen content nor the ASTM microscopic nor even the AMS magnetic evaluation of ingots can reliably predict the fatigue life performance of finished bearings.

The ultrasound based evaluation method, on the other hand, provides the most effective technique for determining the cleanliness of steel in a qualitative as well as quantitative way. In this method bearing races/cones or test pieces are submerged in a large water filled tank in which pulses of ultrasonic energy are transmitted by a transducer through the water and through the part being inspected [15]. Each component being inspected is subjected to thorough scanning by rotation of the transducer. Ultra sound waves reflected from interfaces between bearing surfaces and inclusions stringers are detected by transducers.

The ultrasound evaluation based technique is the only bulk scanning method that gives the best available correlation between the observed level of cleanliness and the fatigue life of bearings for the ultra clean steel of today [12].

Customers Requirement

With the advancement of bearing manufacturing technology, enhancement of "Power Density" and the consequent reduction of safety margin, steel cleanliness of a very high order is demanded from bearing steel manufacturers. Apart from oxygen content, inclusion size and composition, restricted Ti content and ultrasound based cleanliness assessment are some of the notable features in the specifications desired by bearing manufacturers. An excerpt of specifications from some leading bearing manufacturers is shown below (Tables 1 and 2).

Table 1 - *Cleanliness requirement of high carbon through hardening bearing steel*

Features	Specification		
Macro inclusion test	In Blue fracture test macro inclusions should not exceed 2.5 mm/dm².		
Micro inclusions	Sulphide	2 T	1.5 H
	Alumina	1.5 T	0.5 H
	Silicate	-	-
	Oxide	0.5 T	0.5 H
Crack, Flakes, Pipes and Porosity	No indications are acceptable which are corresponding to defects visible at 2X magnifications on the fracture surface of hardened and cracked test samples.		
Oxygen content	The average oxygen content of six samples should not exceed 15 ppm and that of any individual sample should not exceed 20 ppm		
Titanium content	Ti content should not exceed 30 ppm in finished steel.		

Table 2- *Cleanliness requirement of low carbon, case carburising bearing steel*

Features	Specification		
Microscopic inclusion rating	Sulphide	2 T	2 H
	Alumina	1.5 T	0.5 H
	Silicate	1.0 T	0.5 H
	Globular Oxide	1.0 T	0.5 H
Magnetic particle inspection	Acceptance rating as per AMS 2304 specification is: Frequency - 0.25 max. & Severity – 0.50 max.		
Ultrasonic Testing	A special ultrasonic audit for macro inclusions will be conducted 2 times a year to evaluate the process capability for producing clean steel.		
Oxygen content	The average oxygen content should not exceed 20 ppm.		

All leading bearing makers also specify macroscopic evaluation, which shows the breakdown of dendrites formed during solidification and also reflects the cleanliness of steel. The centre, surface and random areas of the rolled cross sections are checked and evaluated in accordance with ASTM E 112 to evaluate the soundness of the structure. Apart from specifying the product features for high life in applications, bearing manufacturers also make demands on the process routes used by bearing steel producers, so that the cleanliness of steel results from a robust process.

Production Route For Bearing Steel

The basic process route for bearing steel as practiced in authors' works is shown in Figure 1.

Figure 1 - *Process route for production of antifriction Bearing Steel through 6 tonne ingot route at Tata Steel (melt size – 130 ton)*

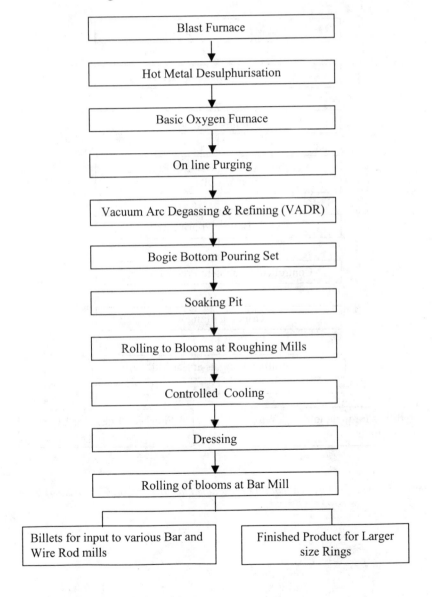

The basic process route is further being modified, to enable production of bars through single conversion of ingots. The modified process route is depicted in Figure 2.

Figure 2 - *Process route for production of Ball Bearing Steel through 2tonne(ton) /3.35 tonne (ton) ingot route at Tata Steel. (melt size – 130 ton)*

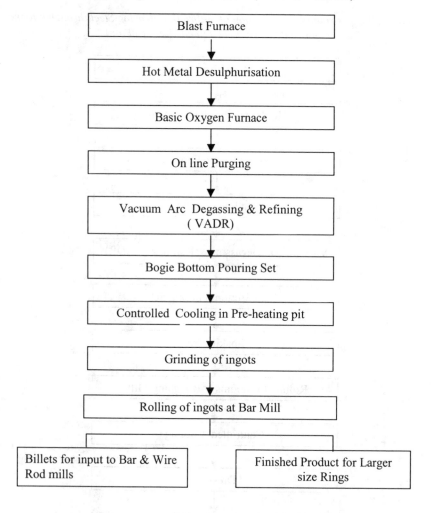

Note: *Pre warming/controlled cooling is excluded for low carbon (carburising) bearing steel.*

Steelmaking As shown in Figure1 and Figure2, bearing steel at the authors' works is produced by oxygen blowing blast furnace hot metal in the BOF vessel. Online purging for homogenization after tapping and then refining under vacuum follows the process of blowing. Figure3 represents the schematic process flow for ball bearing steel (through hardened grade) in the BOF shop.

The succeeding paragraphs of this paper elaborate the individual stages of steel making practices for bearing steel as followed at the authors' works.

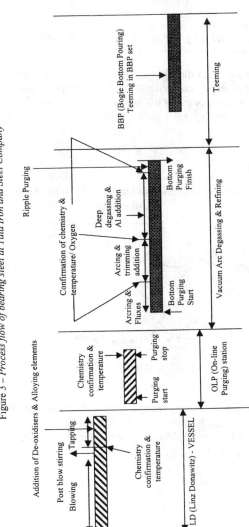

Figure 3 – Process flow of bearing steel at Tata Iron and Steel Company

BOF Since the oxygen content of the crude steel has a direct bearing on the cleanliness of the final product, selective hot metal composition is used to produce bearing quality steel. A typical hot metal composition used for production of bearing steel is shown below (Table 3).

Table 3: *Typical hot metal composition for producing bearing grade of steel at Tata Steel.*

Chemical composition (%)					
C	Mn	Si	P	S	Ti
3.9/4.1	0.07/0.15	0.70/0.90	0.20/0.25	0.06/0.08	0.06

The virgin hot metal from the blast furnace is externally desulphurised by a calcium carbide based proprietary compound, and slag produced in the process of desulphurisation is completely raked off before charging the BOF vessel. Figure 4 shows the sulphur level before and after desulphurisation.

Figure 4 - *Variation of sulphur before and after desulphurisation*

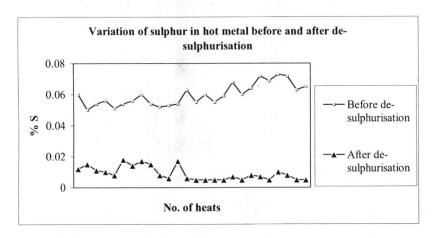

The charge mix used for bearing steel also contains minimum amount of iron ore to reduce the titanium content. Return scraps (which, for an integrated steel plant, has low residual elements like Ni, Cr, Cu, Mo etc.) are used in the charge. A typical charge make up is shown below (Table 4).

Table 4 -*Typical metallic input for bearing steel.*

Input	% Charge Mix
Hot Metal	90%
Scrap	8.5%
Iron ore	1.5%

The hot metal is blown in the vessel, which is equipped with six tuyers at the bottom to introduce inert gas (argon) for bath agitation, while oxygen is blown through the top lance. The bottom stirring prevents formation of dead zones inside the bath and also helps in reducing build up of dissolved oxygen in the liquid steel much in excess of the equilibrium level [16]. The profile of the blow is adjusted so that most of the heats can be tapped directly without any reblow or at the most with a short reblow, if necessary. Reblow at very low levels of carbon is not permitted as at each temperature the product of (% oxygen) and (% carbon) is constant, i.e. %$\underline{O}$ x %$\underline{C}$ = C (constant). Reblow at very low levels of carbon is not allowed because it result in higher oxygen content in the steel (which is detrimental to bearing grade steel) than that which is equivalent to the carbon content. The equilibrium between carbon and oxygen is put out of play. More iron is fluxed than wished. The iron recovery also becomes poor for making bearing quality steels. Before tapping, the steel in the vessel is subjected to post blow stirring with argon to scavenge out most of the oxygen in the bath.

A typical chemical composition before tapping is shown below (Table 5).

Table 5- *Typical chemical analysis at turn down.*

CHEMICAL COMPOSITION						
% C	% Mn	% S	% P	%Si	N$_2$ (ppm)	Ti (ppm)
0.03	0.03	0.023	0.020	Trace	35	4

The temperature of tapping is kept to minimum to avoid reversal of phosphorus as at the end of blowing, the phophorus content in the steel can increase despite favourable conditions (at the end of blow the slag contains a relatively large amount of oxygen and lime (CaO), which are both required to bind up the phosphorus) because the temperature has become relatively high. The stability of the formed phosphorus pentaoxide decreases with rising temperature, resulting in part of the phosphorus returning to the bath, resulting in "the phosphorus bump". So, tap temperature is kept to the minimum, at around 1700°C t to avoid reversal of phosphorous. Before tapping, dissolved oxygen content of the bath is measured by celox probe. BOF slag formed during primary steel making is rich in oxygen and contains a large amount of impurities including titanium and phosphorus which are known to be taken back into the metal during subsequent refining. Therefore, carryover of BOF slag into the refining stage must be avoided. The geometry of the tap hole is maintained in order to ensure streamline flow of metal, which helps in restricting carryover of slag. An electromagnetic system of early detection of slag and a pneumatic stopper to block the tap hole as soon as slag is seen are in place. De-oxidizing agents, primarily ferro-manganese and ferro-silicon, are added during tapping based on celox reading of dissolved oxygen in the hot metal. For high carbon (through hardening) ball bearing steel grades, the required quantity of calcined petroleum coke is also added during tapping to recarburise the steel. A small quantity of aluminium is also added during tapping of high carbon bearing steel grades. The aluminium addition is restricted for high carbon bearing grades to prevent reversal of titanium from slag to metal phase during refining. For case carburising bearing steel sufficient aluminium is added during tapping only to meet the requirement of grain refinement. This gives enough time for alumina to float out in the slag phase during refining.

On Line Purging

After tapping the ladle is taken to the Online Purging Station (OLP) where argon gas is blown for a few minute through a top lance for complete homogenization of the steel bath. The steel chemistry, temperature and dissolved oxygen are measured after completion of homogenization, which gives the guideline to the vacuum Arc Degassing & Refining (VADR) operator for further processing.

VADR (Vacuum Arc Degassing & Refining)

The refining treatment in VADR is carried out with the following objectives.
* Removal of dissolved gases.
* Floatation of inclusion formed due to de-oxidizing process into the slag phase.
* Trimming addition to obtain the target chemistry.
* Attainment of target temperature for teeming.

Fluxes are added after placement of ladle in the VADR unit, in order to ensure a proper reducing, basic slag. Arcing commenced after addition of fluxes for proper melting. During arcing the entire system is kept under vacuum and ripple purging continues so that inclusions float up into the slag phase. Vacuum and inert gas purging ensures a proper slag metal reaction and hence refining of the steel. The steel chemistry along with temperature is checked to determine the trimming addition after completion of arcing. Second phase of arcing coupled with vacuum is started after trimming addition. The purging rate in this stage is increased to ensure complete homogenization of the bath. The bath is subjected to strong degassing (below 2 torr) under increased purging rate after a calculated period of arcing. During degassing an extensive slag metal interaction ensures refining and removal of inclusions into the slag phase. Before degassing aluminium is added to fix all free oxygen, which later joins in the slag phase. A difference of less than 0.003% between total Al and dissolved Al proves that alumina inclusions are mostly out of the liquid steel. Lowering of the ambient pressure results in an effective removal of entrapped gases from the liquid steel. For effective removal of sulphur, the following factors is considered in addition to the type of desulphurisation agent used.
a) Oxygen in Steel, as O2 is deterrent in S removal. Steel is deoxidised to lowest possible limit preferably by Al
b) Oxides in Slag, as FeO and Mn in slag are deterrents. Slag carryover from LD is kept

minimum.

c) Oxides in Desulpurisation reaction.

$CaO + FeS \longrightarrow CaS + FeO$. Additional Al should is added to take care of FeO generated.

d)Degree of mixing of reagent and steel.

Gas stirring is carried out by blowing an inert gas , argon into the bath and at the same time steel surface is exposed to vacuum which makes degassing more efficient . A greater turbulence at the bath surface increases the risk for exposure of the steel to the atmosphere, i.e. risk for oxidation with gas stirring.

The bath is kept under ripple purging for about 15 to 20 minutes after degassing. This ensures the maximum floatation of inclusions without a significant temperature drop. It is well documented that an increased duration of purging results in improved cleanliness of steel [17]. Figure 5 shows a typical variation of dissolved oxygen at different stages of processing. A dissolved oxygen content of less than 2.5 ppm ensures adequate cleanliness of the bath. Although the total amount of oxygen reflects the general cleanliness of a steel, it does not completely characterize its internal state. Oxygen have a very low, if any, solubility in solid steel. What is dissolved in *liquid* steel at the moment of solidification will therefore form oxides in the *solid* state, then being present as inclusions. These oxides have detrimental influence on the steel properties. whereas the free oxygen results in the formation of pipes,.secondary pipes and effects internal soundness of steel.

Figure 5 - *Variation of dissolved oxygen at various stages of processing steel through hardening Grade.*

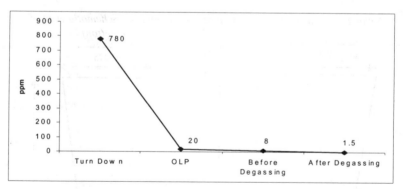

Teeming

Bearing steel is uphill teemed through a bogie bottom pouring set. The use of bottom teeming technology ensures the production of high quality ingots and gives superior yield as compared to top pouring route which is well documented [18]. Figure 6 shows the schematic plan of the BBP set used at the authors' works.

Figure 6 – *Schematic plan view of bottom bogie pouring set.*

Moldset   Trumphet   Runner

During the last year ingot size and shape has undergone a major modification to enable single conversion in place of double conversion as shown earlier in Figure – 1 and 2. Figures 7, 8, and 9 describes the ingot geometry for the basic 6tonne ingot, 2tonne ingot used for high carbon bearing steel grades, and 3.35tonne ingot for low carbon case carburising bearing steel grades, respectively. A large ingot size is essential to cater to the requirement of customers for sections above 125mm square as the minimum reduction ratio of 8:1 cannot be fulfilled with smaller size ingots.

Figure 7 – *Schematic view of 6tonne(ton) ingot.*   Figure 8 – *Schematic view of 2tonne(ton) ingot.*

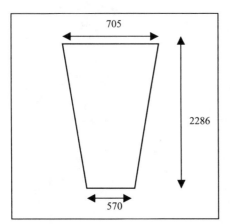

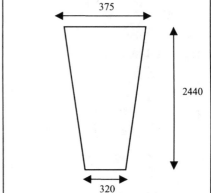

Figure 9- *Schematic view of 3.35tonne(ton) ingot.*

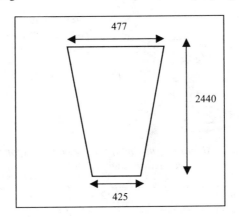

After completion of vacuum arc degassing operation the steel is uphill teemed into five sets of the bogies in the teeming station. Teeming rate is such that there is 300-400mm/min rise of metal in the mould. Teeming is carried out into the trumpet located centrally in each bogie as shown in Figure 6. Shrouding of the stream by inert nitrogen gas using a shroud designed and developed in-house, protects the metal stream between the ladle and the trumpet. The effect of shrouding on the formation of re-oxidized product is well documented [12]. Hot top and antipiping compound also plays a vital role in achieving higher cleanliness level of steel. To decrease the depth of the pipe (also called "sink head"), the top of the mould is equipped with a so-called "hot top". This "hot top" consists of heat-insulating plates that are wedged into place in the form of a box on the inside of the mould. By keeping the steel liquidified in this "box" at the top of the mould after casting, a refilling of the "funnel" will take place along with the shrinkage. The result is a shallow "bowl" instead of a pointed funnel. The volume is naturally the same in both cases, but the difference is that a considerably larger part of the ingot can now be used. To further decrease heat losses from the top and reduce piping defects further, an insulating and often exothermic (heat-releasing) material, commonly known as antipiping compound is used to cover the top surface of the ingot.

Customized hot tops have been developed with the help of vendors for each type of ingot geometry with varying combination of insulating and exothermic characteristics. Major modifications for hot top and anti-piping compounds carried out for the proper solidification characteristics of small size ingots is shown below (Table 6).

Figure 10 - *Schematic three dimensional view of nitrogen shroud*

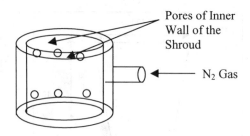

Pores of Inner
Wall of the
Shroud

N_2 Gas

Table 6 - *Characteristics of hot top and anti piping compounds for 6tonne(ton) and 2tonne(ton) ingot route*

	6T ingot route	2 T ingot route
Hot Top	Duplex type, facing exothermic backing insulating. Tile thickness more	Insulating Tile thickness less
APC	APC is exothermic and insulating nature	APC more exothermic as solidification time is less.

Bottom pouring compounds also play a major role in ensuring cleanliness of steel [19] and also in controlling solidification characteristics. The characteristics of the bottom pouring flux used for bearing steel are presented below (Table 7).

Table7-*Nominal composition Range and Characteristics of BBP flux.*

Chemical Composition	SiO_2	20.5 – 23.5%
	Al_2O_3	9.0 – 11.0%
	Fe_2O_3	4.0% maximum
	CaO	24.0 – 27.0%
	Na_2O	4.0 – 6.0%
	F	6.0 – 7.0%
	Fixed Carbon	17.0 – 19.0%
Basicity		1.16 - 0.06
Density		0.50 – 0.70 kg/m3
Moisture		0.80% maximum
Softening temperature		1130 - 30
Melting temperature		1170 - 20
Fluidity temperature		1200 - 20

Fluxes used for both high carbon and low carbon bearing steel are insulating in nature. A moderate amount of alumina in these fluxes induce the insulating property to prevent heat loss from the steel meniscus inside the mould. The bottom pouring flux used in bearing steel is also required to have a basic composition to enable absorption of non-metallic inclusions floating up during teeming and solidification. A high carbon content is needed to prevent sintering and entrapment of flux in the solidifying liquid. In addition, a high carbon content in flux reduces its melting rate and thus preventing the flux from being depleted too fast. The retarded rate of melting and non-sintering characteristics of the powder layers helps in maintaining a uniform protective cover throughout the teeming operation.

Results And Discussion

The results of various tests for evaluation of cleanliness at the authors' works are presented below.

Micro inclusion content

Micro inclusion rating is carried out as per ASTM E45-97 worst field rating method A to be compared to images on Plate I-r. Figure-10 and 11 shows the Type B alumina and Type D oxide inclusion variation in through hardening and case carburising bearing grades respectively. It can be observed that ratings of alumina and globular oxide inclusions, major initiators of contact fatigue, meet the requirement of most customers.

Figure 11- *Alumina Inclusion (thin series) variation in through hardening and case carburising grade.*

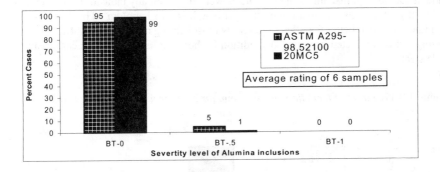

Figure 12 – *Oxide inclusion (thin series)* variation in through hardening and case carburising grade*

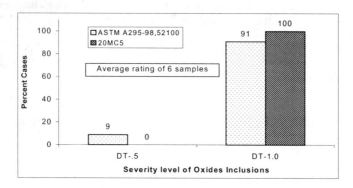

(*No thick series inclusion (alumina and oxide) observed in through hardening as well as case carburising bearing steel.)

Blue Fracture Test

The blue fracture test is an effective method of exposing alumina inclusions. Figure 13 shows the distribution of alumina stringers in 30 heats of ASTM A295-98, 52100 grade. It can be seen that almost half the heats were free from any indications and up to a total 94% of the heats had an alumina stringer length within 1mm/dm^2. This level of cleanliness is much better than that required by most bearing manufacturers. Blue fracture test is conducted in annealed condition for both hardening and core carburising grade steel.

Figure 13- *Variation of inclusion stringer (mm/dm2)in through hardening bearing steel grade*

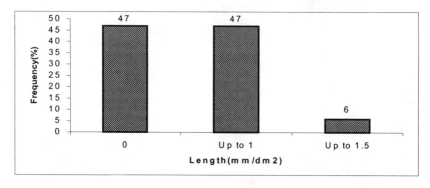

Titanium Content

With the oxide inclusion level perpetually coming down other non-oxide type particles (notable titanium nitrides and carbonitrides) are assuming increasing importance in determining the contact fatigue life of bearings. As such an emerging trend is to demand a titanium content in steel below 30ppm, because it is believed that below this level of titanium, titanium bearing intermetallic phases do not have large enough particle size to initiate spalling [3]. Figure 14 presents the distribution of titanium content ASTM A295-98, 52100 grade of steel produced at the authors' works. It can be seen that it has been possible to restrict titanium below 25ppm in over 60% of cases, notwithstanding the high level of titanium in the indigenous raw material.

Figure14- *Variation of titanium in through hardening bearing steel grade.*

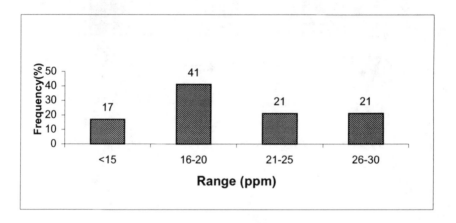

- Titanium in steel comes predominantly from the following sources
- Carried over BOF slag and
- From Fe alloying additions notably Fe-Cr.
- The following have been found effective in the control of titanium in bearing steel.
- Restricting slag carryover during tapping to reduce reversal of titanium.
- Increase in the slag volume through addition of fluxes at VAD stage so that TiO2 is effectively diluted in the slag under reducing conditions.
- A low treatment temperature to prevent reduction of Tio2 to Ti.
- Addition of aluminium just before degassing to minimise reversal of titanium during arcing.
- Implementation of a ladle recycling plan such that residual VAD slag, rich in titanium is diluted by some other grades.
- Use of imported Fe-Cr alloying additions having Ti content less than 0.20%.

Oxygen Content

The oxygen content distribution in low carbon and high carbon bearing steel is shown in Figure15 and 16, respectively.

Figure15- *Variation of oxygen in case carburising bearing steel grade*

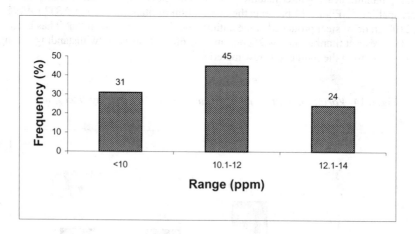

Figure16- *Variation of oxygen in through hardening bearing steel grade*

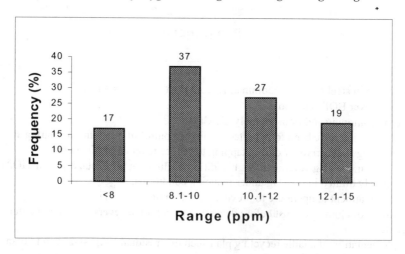

It can be seen that through a well-controlled processes the total oxygen content in the through hardening steel grade could be kept below 12 ppm in 80% of casts and in about

53% of the cases below 10 ppm. Also in low carbon grades 75% of casts had an oxygen content below 12ppm. The FeO content of final VAD slag has a significant bearing on the total oxygen content as shown in Figure – 16 and 17 .The following strategies have been adopted at the author's works to restrict oxygen content in bearing steel.

Figure 17 - *Variation of oxygen in finish product with FeO content of final VAD slag.*

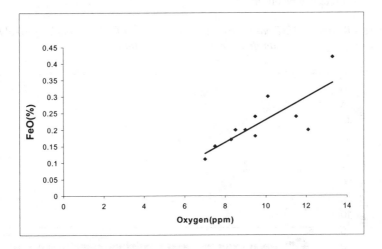

A modified oxygen blow profile and optimization of the duration of blowing.
Post blow stirring to scavenge out free oxygen in the bath.
    Addition of Al before de-gassing so that any remaining oxygen can form aluminium oxides early to ensure that these have enough time to coalescence and join in slag phase.
    Protection of the liquid stream during teeming.
    Protection of the liquid meniscus during uphill teeming by appropriately designed bottom pouring flux.

Evaluation by End users

Low carbon case carburising steel produced at the authors' works was evaluated by one of the leading bearing manufacturers in the United States. The results of an ultrasonic test carried out on races forged and rolled from bar at authors plant are shown in Figures18 (the result correspond to races produced from bars representing different positions of an ingot).It can be seen that the product from most parts of the ingot was equally clean. The count of detectable inclusions (> 13 microns) [21] was seen to be below 2 numbers per cubic inch which signifies and extremely high level of cleanliness . This can enable the bearing manufactures to reduce the size of the bearings for a given service rating .

It can also be seen that the components representing the bottom end of the ingot had the most inclusions . this is known as the " bottom cone" effect . Steelmakers need to take judicious bottom discard to prevent this relatively dirty portion of the solidified steel from getting into the antifriction bearing application. The bearing producers also carried out an international benchmarking exercise with case carburising steel procured from different sources . the results of this exercise are shown in figure 19 [22] . The superiority of the described BOF-VAD ingot casting process for carburized TRB core testing as compared to sources can be observed.

Figure18 – *Results of UST based cleanliness evaluation of case carburising steel for antifriction bearing application*

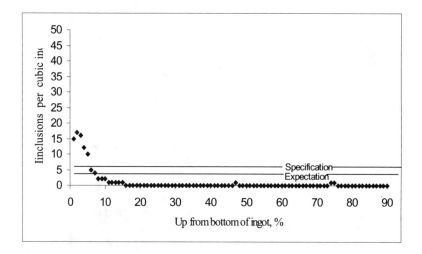

Figure 19-*Result of benchmarking exercise*

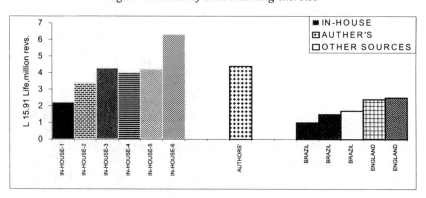

Compact fatigue testing rigs were used for benchmarking exercise.

Conclusion

1. The bearing industry requires increasingly higher levels of cleanliness in steel as a means to produce compact bearings having smaller envelope sizes.
2. With the high level of cleanliness in steel i.e. available at present , ultrasound based bulk scanning method provides for the most objective assessment with the results co-relating well with the life of bearings observed in simulated rig test.
3. The authors' works have developed the technology to produce clean steel that is in compliance with the expectations of the most discerning manufacturers of antifriction bearings.

References

[1]   Winder.R.L. "Value Creation Through Investment and Continuous Improvement", The Timken Co.

[2]   Leibeneperger.R.L. "Power Density: Product Design of 21st Century", IJTM Special Publication on the Role of Technology in Corporate Policy, 1991

[3]   Monnot.J., Heritier.B., and Cogne. J.Y., "Relationship of Melting Practice, Inclusion Type and Size with Fatigue Resistance of Bearing Steel", Effect of Steel Manufacturing Processes on the Quality of Bearing Steel, ASTM, STP 1987, J.J.C. Hoo, Ed., American Society for Testing and Materials, Philadelphia, 1988, p 149–165

[4]   Palmgren. A, "The Carrying Capacity and Life of Ball Bearing", The Ball Bearing J.SKF., Vol 3, 1937, p 34

[5]   Lundberg.G., Palmgren.A., "Dynamic Capacity of Roller Bearings", Applied Mechanics, Am. Soc. Mech. Eng. 1948, A-19.

[6]   Styri. H., "Fatigue Strength of Ball Bearing Races and Heat Treated 52100 Steel Specimen", 54 Annual Meeting of American Society of Mechanical Engineers, June 1951, 682.

[7]   Backstrom S., "Endurance of Bearings of Acid Open Hearth Steel and the Effect of Sulphide Inclusions of Endurance", ISI/BISRA, Phys. Met. Com, Cambridge, 1968.

[8]   Olund.L.J.P., Lund.T.B., Hedberg.B.H., "Fatigue Initiation and Endurance in Low Oxygen Ball Bearing Steel", Clean Steel 5, 1999, Vol.2, p.137-143.

[9]   Brooksbank, D., Andrews K.W., "Journal of Iron and Steel institute", Vol.210, April 1972, p. 246-255.

[10] Uhrus L.O., "Clean Steel", Special Report No. 77 of Iron and Steel Institute, London, 1962, p. 104-109.

[11] Narita.K., Onoye.T, Yamamoto.K., Transactions, Iron and Steel Institute of Japan, Vol.21 1981, p.198.

[12] Stover.J.D., Kolarik.R.V.II., "The Evaluation and Improvements in Bearing Steel Quality Using an Ultrasonic Macro Inclusion Detection Method', A Timken Company Technical Note, January 1987.

[13] Donze.JJ., "Discussion of ASTM Method for Rating Inclusions", Bearing Steels the Rating of Non-metallic Inclusions, ASTM, STP 575, American Society for Testing and Materials, 1975, p.3-9.

[14] Hoo.J.J.C., "Re-examination of Rating Methods of Non-metallic Inclusions in Bearing Steel", Bearing Steels the Rating on Non-metallic Inclusions, ASTM, STP 575, American Society for Testing and Materials, 1975, p.38-48.

[15] Burr, W.H., "Ultrasonic Rating of Bearing Steel Cleanliness", Bearing Steels the Rating of Non-metallic Inclusions, ASTM, STP 575, American Society for Testing and Materials, 1975, p.178-188.

[16] Attwood, B., "Steelmaking Proceedings", Pittsburgh, 1982, Vol. 65, p. 96.

[17] Huet.L., Jonsson.T., Reinholdsson. F., "The Effect of De-oxidation Praxis on Inclusion Characteristic in Bearing Steel Production", Steelmaking Conference Proceedings, Vol.639, 1997.

[18] Blank.J.R., "The Use of Bottom Teeming Techniques in the Production of High Quality Carbon and Alloy Steel Ingots", British Steel Corporation. Special Steel Division, Stockbridge Works, Sheffield, S30 5JA.

[19] McCauley.W.L., "Effect of Mold Powders on the Quality of Bottom Poured Ingots", Reprinted from "Iron and Steel Engineers".

[20] Stover.JD., Murlidharan.U., "Effect of Residual Titanium on Rolling Contact Fatigue Resistance of Bearing Steel, The Timken Company, Canton (reprinted).

[21] Stover,J.D., Kolarik ii, R.V., Keener.D.M., "The Detection of Aluminium Oxide Stringers in Steel Using an Ultrasonic Measuring Method", Mechanical Working and Steel Processings Proceedings, 1989, p 431-439.

[22] Undocumented correspondence.

Steel Technology and Bearing Component Manufacture

Thord Johansson and Henrik Sandqvist[2]

Machinability Control - A Topic of Great Importance to the Engineering Industry

Reference: Johansson, T., and Sandqvist, H., "**Machinability Control - A Topic of Great Importance to the Engineering Industry**," *Bearing Steel Technology, ASTM STP 1419,* J. M. Beswick, Ed., American Society for Testing and Materials International, West Conshohocken, PA, 2002.

Abstract: More complicated and expensive machine tools together with production with limited manpower requires disturbance free and safe manufacturing, to avoid expensive and unexpected stops. The result of a machining operation is based on the interaction between manufacturing method, the machine tool and the material. There exist few well-documented test methods. Mainly the ISO 3685 is referred to, at least in Europe. This single point turning test is, however, based on cutting tools no longer available and on rather long times in cut, as the test specimen has a length of 400 - 600 mm.

In order to reach good conformity between the test results and a production environment, the applied test methods need to be fine-tuned to better simulate reality. For that reason, the ISO 3685 test method has been slightly modified and new test methods have been developed to determine a raw material's machinability. Among others ways to evaluate the impact from short machining cycles, 1 - 15 seconds, through different discontinuous machining modes have been developed, which will be described here.

Important parameters affecting the manufacturing result are tool life / tool cost versus cutting data, chip formation to avoid chip jamming, surface roughness, and component distortion. This paper will present the relationship between certain parameters and the raw material properties; steel grade and composition and cutting forces evaluated through different methods.

Keywords: Machining, machinability, tool life, chip formation, surface integrity, bearing steel, cutting forces

Introduction

The analysis of *machinability* often means analysis of tool wear. In some cases, also the chip formation and the surface integrity are mentioned. But, for a full perception of the term *machinability*, the following aspects are included (see Figure 1.) Apart from tool wear, surface integrity and chip formation, also the process forces and related temperatures as well as the working environment are added.

---

[1]Manager Metal Cutting R&D, Ovako Steel AB, S-712 80, Hällefors, Sweden.
[2]Project Manager, Ovako Steel AB, Hornsgatan 1, HK3/4, S-415 50 Göteborg, Sweden.

When deciding whether the machinability of a certain material or condition is good or bad, one usually refers to one of these aspects. The machinability is however a balance between all five.

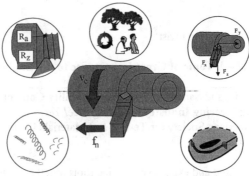

Figure 1 - *Aspects on machinability.*

Also, the part dimensions and tolerances could be included in the machinability term, but they are not really functions of the chip forming process. Geometry impact is more a general result of the metal cutting process. Cutting forces introduce tool holder deflection, and the tool continuously deteriorates, affecting both the part dimensions and tolerances. The cutting forces and the relation to clamping method and clamping forces heavily influence the part's dimensions and tolerances, including out-of-roundness.

The *machinability* is the output from a machining operation, and the input comprises the *process factors,* nine main parameters describing a machining operation, see Figure 2.

The machining method (1) describes the tool ways; the sequence and how a tool moves along the work-piece. Cutting data (2) describe the relative motion between the cutting tool and the work-piece. The insert type (3) is standardized, but the micro-geometry as well as insert substrate and the coating (4) are usually unique for each manufacturer of cutting tools.

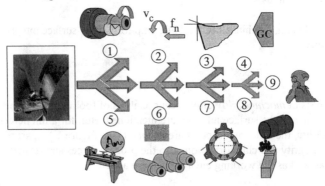

Figure 2 - *Process factors.*

A machine tool (5) with specific characteristics is used and the workpiece material (6) is described by its condition, the composition and physical properties. The material is clamped (7) in a specific way, and cutting media (8) are often used for cooling, lubrication and chip transport. The whole operation is laid out by the work preparation function and controlled by the operator (9).

All the main factors described above can be divided in a number of sub-groups. This is what has to be done when attempting to define test methods, which must simulate real production.

Test Methods

To simulate the various products machined in Ovako's steel grades, the test methods have been divided into continuous and discontinuous machining, the latter further specified in interrupted and intermittent machining, with different times in cut.

For continuous machining, there is a standardized test method, ISO 3685, "Tool life testing with single-point turning tools". It is mainly used for evaluating machinability when using longer times-in-cut. In the ISO test, flat inserts are used to avoid any influence from the chip breaker. This means that the correlation between test results and production is relatively low. To improve this, test methods using production inserts have been developed.

No standardized tests are available for discontinuous machining. Test methods have therefore been developed suitable for simulating various machining operations, mainly with shorter times in cut.

Continuous Machining Test

For continuous turning, a test method called *CET, Continuous External Turning,* has been developed. Chip formation, surface roughness and tool wear are analysed as a function of cutting data in rough, medium and fine machining. The workpiece length in this test is 400 mm.

The surface roughness, see the example in Figure 3, is presented as R_{max}-values as a function of the cutting speed at a pre-determined feed and depth of cut. This decides the optimum working area for the subsequent chip formation and tool life tests. The depth of cut is pre-set to 1 (fine), 2 (medium) and 4 (rough) mm.

Using the cutting speed where the surface roughness levels out, chip formation is evaluated and chip form diagrams, Figure 4, are established as a function of feed and depth of cut.

Finally, the tool wear is evaluated for rough, medium and fine machining. In these tests, the main insert wear should be flank wear. Flank wear is time dependent and can be predicted, whereas for example chipping and fracture can occur anytime, and do not represent a balanced wear curve.

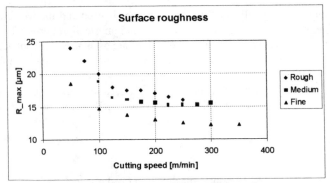

Figure 3 - *Example of surface roughness diagram.*

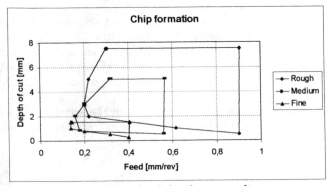

Figure 4 - *Example of chip formation diagram.*

Tool life tests are made at various positions in the chip formation diagram area. The cutting speed is selected so that a tool life of between 5 and 30 minutes is reached (see Figure 5.)

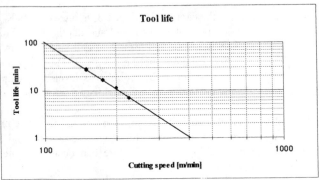

Figure 5 - *Tool life diagram.*

The obtained tool lives as a function of cutting data are put into a regression model, based on the assumption that the tool life can be written according to the extended Taylor equation, where tool life T is a function of cutting speed v_c, as well as feed f_n, depth of cut a_p and a constant C.

$$T = C \, f_n^{\alpha} \, a_p^{\beta} \, v_c^{\gamma} \qquad (1)$$

The coefficients are calculated through linear regression, and a calculation of tool life is done for the selected cutting data and plotted against the measured data when running a trial, see Figure 6.

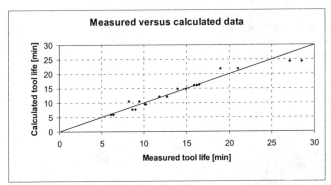

Figure 6 - *Example of measured tool life versus calculated tool life.*

In this example, the tool life equation can be written as

$$T = 7.00326 \, f_n^{-0.82652} \, a_p^{-0.08316} \, v_c^{-2.63865} \qquad (2)$$

A good correlation between the measured and calculated tool life data can be found. This means that for any combination of cutting data, within the selected area, the tool life can be calculated with good accuracy using the extended Taylor equation and the calculated coefficients. It is also possible, to some extent, to extrapolate the equation for a rough estimation of tool life outside the evaluated area.

The CET test gives a good overview of the material's machinability from a surface roughness, chip formation and tool wear point of view. In the real application these data are used as start values, and normally some adjustments have to be done. It can also be used in the set-up by the programmer or technician for tool life and cycle time calculations prior to actual machining.

Discontinuous Machining Mode (DMM)

Interrupted Machining Mode - On smaller parts, where it is normal to make one, two or three cuts, for example on a bearing ring where the face and the bore are machined with the same insert, the discontinuous machining test method has been very successful. In this test method, the pass sequence is divided in three cuts, with exit and entry in-between, a cycle which is then repeated throughout the whole evaluation, see Figure 7.

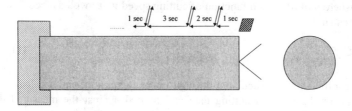

Figure 7 - *Interrupted machining mode.*

The test method can be adjusted for shorter or longer machining times, or instead of machining times, it can be turning lengths, e.g., 5, 10 and 15 mm. All depending on the products or product groups the evaluation is intended for.

Intermittent machining mode - Intermittent machining means machining with at least one interruption or slot per revolution, see Figure 8. This interruption represents slots like keyways or splines on shafts.

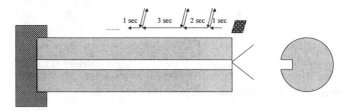

Figure 8 - *Intermittent machining mode.*

The problem when evaluating intermittent machining is that tool life usually is set by chipping and fracture, and not by a predictable flank wear. The machining is more similar to milling operations with heavy entries and exits.

Until now, this machining type has not been a focused operation. The manufacturing sequence today is usually soft turning prior to drilling, milling or spline cutting with subsequent heat treatment and grinding. The interest in intermittent machining will increase when grinding is replaced with finish hard turning, where keyways are milled, holes drilled etc. prior to hard turning.

Machinability Relationships

An evaluation of the influence from steel grade composition on tool life, cutting forces and chip formation has been performed. Eight heats of SAE 52100 with varied composition were produced, and the cutting forces were measured at different cutting data. The material compositions are shown in Table 1. The EDF factor shown in Table 1 is the sum of the elements mainly partitioning in the ferrite phase (Si, Mn, Ni). Usually, also the P, Mo and Cu elements are included, but in order to detect other possible correlations, they were separated in this study.

Table 1 - Material composition.

Variant		1	2	3	4	5	6	7	8
C	%	1,00	1,00	1,02	1,01	0,98	0,96	0,96	0,96
Si	%	0,30	0,32	0,32	0,29	0,08	0,07	0,10	0,06
Mn	%	0,35	0,38	0,37	0,36	0,27	0,27	0,28	0,26
P	%	0,021	0,023	0,005	0,014	0,007	0,006	0,020	0,018
S	%	0,013	0,003	0,002	0,012	0,013	0,005	0,003	0,013
Cr	%	1,39	1,38	1,40	1,39	1,38	1,39	1,39	1,39
Ni	%	0,19	0,20	0,19	0,22	0,16	0,15	0,15	0,17
Mo	%	0,06	0,05	0,02	0,01	0,05	0,04	0,01	0,01
Cu	%	0,22	0,24	0,04	0,02	0,22	0,20	0,04	0,04
Al	%	0,044	0,022	0,035	0,028	0,039	0,025	0,035	0,026
N	ppm	122	56	113	84	67	118	80	118
EDF	%	0,84	0,90	0,88	0,87	0,51	0,49	0,53	0,49
Hardness	HB	199	202	193	193	184	182	185	179

Tool Life and Hardness

Tool life as a function of hardness was evaluated using the ISO 3685 test as well as a DMM test, see Figure 9. In the ISO 3685 test, a slight increase in tool life can be seen when increasing the hardness. Though, the scatter is high and to verify this relationship, more machining tests have to be done.

In the DMM test, no real correlation between tool life and material hardness could be seen.

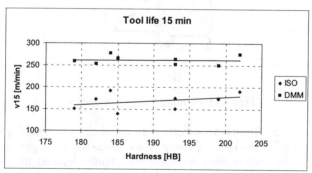

Figure 9 - *Tool life as a function of material hardness.*

Tool Life and Composition

Comparing the constituents, the largest influence on tool life came from the nitrogen content. In the ISO 3685 test, a correlation can be seen, but the scatter is relatively high. In the DMM test, a clear trend towards lower tool life at increased nitrogen content, see Figure 10.

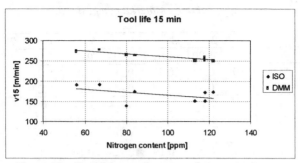

Figure 10 - *Tool life as a function of nitrogen content.*

Detailed regression analysis against all alloying elements and combination of elements provided no further correlations between tool life and the composition.

In an additional test, to verify if the influence from the nitrogen could be traced back to structural features, a TEM analysis was done. The results showed that in the material batch with low nitrogen, and longer tool life, only a few small nitrides were found. In the material batch with high nitrogen, more and larger particles were found, which affected the tool life in a negative way.

Cutting Forces and Composition

The three cutting force components are the vertical cutting force F_v, the feed cutting force F_f and the passive cutting force F_p, see Figure 11.

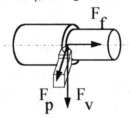

Figure 11 - *Cutting force components.*

There are three constituents that indicate some correlation to the cutting force levels in the experiment; the Cu-, EDF- and P-components. Increasing the copper and EDF levels decreases the vertical cutting force while the phosphorus increases the vertical cutting force. At higher feeds, the influence can clearly be seen, but at lower feeds, the influence is in some cases small, but the trend is the same for all selected cutting data. Figure 12 shows the vertical cutting force and Figure 13 the feed cutting force as a function of the EDF content.

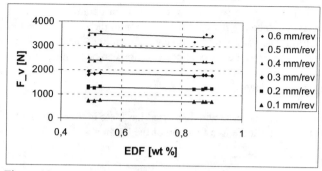

Figure 12 - *Vertical cutting force as a function of EDF-content.*

These six curves correspond to the six feed rates used in the experiment. Both the vertical cutting force and the feed cutting force decrease with increased levels for all the studied cutting data. For the passive cutting force, the trend is decreasing, but there are only very small differences between high and low levels.

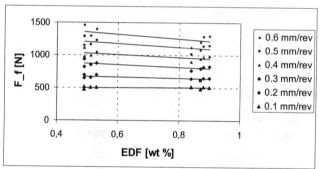

Figure 13 - *Feed cutting force as a function of EDF-content.*

A similar trend is also observed for the copper content. In Figure 14 it can be seen, that the vertical cutting force decreases slightly with increased copper content.

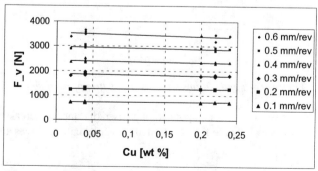

Figure 14 - *Vertical cutting force as a function of Cu-content.*

EDF and copper are the two largest composition parameters in this study, and this will probably also influence the results. The variation in the other parameters is very small. For the passive force, the variation is relatively high and the signal also includes cross-talk, why really no influence from the material composition can be confirmed.

Cutting Forces and Hardness

The cutting forces decrease with increased hardness in the studied interval. Figure 15 shows the vertical cutting force as a function of the hardness.

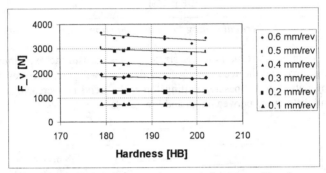

Figure 15 - *Vertical cutting force as a function of hardness.*

The material hardness depends to a large extent on the EDF-content and the copper content. Consequently, the cutting forces are found to decrease with increased hardness. The feed cutting force also decreases with increased hardness in the studied interval. As can be seen in Figure 16, the influence increases with increased feed.

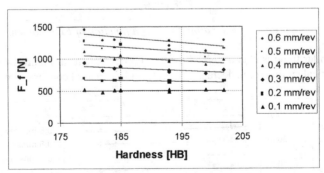

Figure 16 - *Feed cutting force as a function of hardness.*

Also for the passive force component, increased hardness decreases the cutting force. The influence is small, due to the variation in measured cutting forces and cross-talk.

Cutting Force Dynamics and Composition

Hot rolled annealed material is soft and when machined, it generates chips where the shear planes, i.e., the segment boundaries, can be seen but the segments are also deformed. This is typical when machining a soft material. Chip breaking occurs when the chips hit the workpiece and/or the tool and tool holder. The chips are more or less uniformly deformed, and they can be classified as continuous chips.

The same behaviour can also be found in the measurements of the cutting force dynamics. The signal is broad banded, the size of the generated segments varies around a mean value. Increased feed enhances the material segmentation.

When comparing the eight different batches a clear difference is observed in the material segmentation behaviour between the material with high and the material with low EDF-content (Table 1), see Figure 17. In the material with low EDF-content, left in Figure 17, there is a large spread in frequency at each cutting speed, which is equal to a large spread in undeformed segment length. High amplitudes can also be found at low frequencies, corresponding to chip breaking.

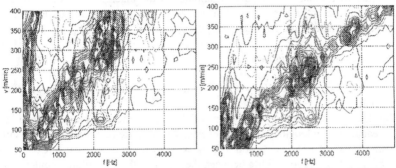

Figure 17 - *Frequency contour plot, a_p=3 mm, f_n=0.5 mm/rev, (a) EDF = 0,49 % and (b) EDF = 0,90 %.*

In the material with high EDF-content, right in Figure 17, the segmentation frequencies are higher for the same cutting speed, i.e. the generated segments are smaller when machining the material with high EDF-content. The segments are also more even in size and there is lower spread in the segmentation frequency when machining the material with high EDF-content, see Figure 17b. The segmentation will improve the chip breaking. No distinct influence from the other material parameters can be seen.

Surface Roughness and Composition

The relatively small variations in the material composition had no influence on the surface roughness in the chosen cutting data interval. This parameter is primarily set by the combination of feed and insert corner radius.

Chip Formation and Composition

No major difference could be seen between the different batches.

Sulphur Impact on Machinability

Throughout the years, several different elements have been added to the steel in order to facilitate the manufacturing of components. Unfortunately, these additives form inclusions of different types and sizes, which - in turn - will affect even other properties than machinability only. Today's demands on noise levels, fatigue life and load resistance can be met thanks to the technological development in steel making, which has led to a situation where extremely clean bearing steel grades can be produced.

If the additives used to enhance the machinability in earlier days are disregarded for obvious reasons, mainly oxides and sulphides are left. Certain types of complex oxides have a positive effect on machinability, however also a major negative impact on fatigue life, which is why there is a continuous striving to reduce the oxygen content in bearing steels. As the steel making technology allows for ever cleaner steels, the focus is now also on sulphide reduction.

In order to evaluate the impact of sulphur on the machinability of bearing steels, simulation tests have been performed using a DMM test method for turning and a through-hole test method for drilling and tapping.

Sulphur Influence on Turning

Two batches of SAE 52100 with different sulphur content S, 0.001 % and 0.010 %, were selected.

The test method used was a variant of the DMM method presented in Figure 7, based on equal cutting lengths of 84 mm cycles. The tool life reached was in principle the same, using standard P15 inserts and a flank wear of 0.3 mm as wear-out criterion, see Figure 18. No difference in tool life between the high and the low sulphur content material can be seen at these relatively high cutting speeds, relevant to CNC machining.

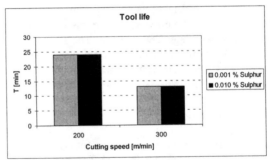

Figure 18 - *Tool life versus cutting speed and sulphur content.*

A certain difference in chip formation was however noted. The chips from the low sulphur heat were somewhat longer and more distorted compared to the chips from the other heat.

Sulphur Influence on Drilling and Tapping

To analyse if the sulphur content affects tool life at lower cutting speeds, drilling and tapping experiments were performed. Hot rolled bars in SAE1055 with a diameter of 90 mm, were cut in 12 mm thick slices to serve as test material. Relevant standard tools and cutting data were selected for the evaluation of the sulphur impact in drilling and tapping operations for a certain application range. The main difference in the compositions was the sulphur content from 0.009 % up to 0.022 %, see Table 2.

The bars were tested in the as-rolled condition. After air-cooling, the structure of such a steel grade varys somewhat, resulting even in variations in the hardness levels. Therefore, the heat A2 was normalized in a complementary study, to evaluate the hardness impact on machinability. The hardness level was 216 HB after normalization.

Table 2 - *Material composition.*

Heat	Composition [wt %] (* ppm)										Hardness
	C	Si	Mn	P	S	Cr	Ni	Mo	Cu	N*	
D6630	0,58	0,18	0,71	0,010	0,022	0,08	0,08	0,03	0,11	106	217
A2	0,59	0,18	0,74	0,007	0,009	0,17	0,13	0,04	0,20	96	236

A machining centre equipped with a force monitoring unit was used. The unit measures the torque in the drilling and tapping operations. Each drill was planned to make 800 holes and each tap 1600 holes. The crater wear of the drills was measured, while the wear of the taps was controlled using a "go/no-go" thread gauge throughout the whole test sequence.

The torque in Figures 19 and 20 is an average of six drills and three taps. However, one drill and one tap broke before the pre-set number of holes was reached due to high torque in the low sulphur heat. After normalization of the low sulphur heat, the torque was still higher compared to the material with high sulphur.

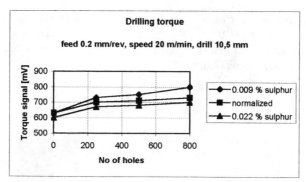

Figure 19 - *Torque versus number of holes in drilling.*

The mean crater wear on the drills was 0.7 mm in the high sulphur material, and 0.9 mm in the low, thus the average crater wear of the drills increased 30% in the low sulphur material.

Two drills were evaluated regarding tool wear in the normalized heat, resulting in an average crater wear of 0.86 mm.

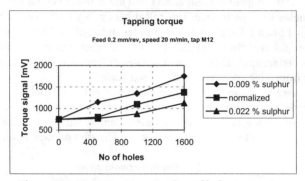

Figure 20 - *Torque versus number of holes in tapping.*

Tool Life in Hardened Material

Tool life in hardened material is evaluated using the same test methods as described earlier. Figure 21 shows the result from hard turning of three bearing steel grades with a boron-nitride insert, using a DMM-test method.

Table 3 - *Chemical composition.*

Grade	Composition [wt %]						
	C	Si	Mn	Cr	Mo	P	S
803	1,01	0,27	0,32	1,47	0,08	0,025	0,025
824	0,97	0,32	0,32	1,80	0,20	0,025	0,025
677	0,67	1,55	1,45	1,10	0,25	0,025	0,025

A solid PCBN insert is used in the evaluation. All three material grades have the same hardness level, 61-62 HRC, but the structure differs. The hardness is important for the machining operation, but this also shows the importance of the material composition and structure in hardened condition.

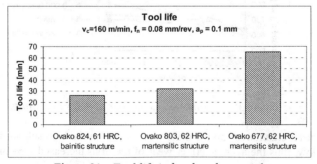

Figure 21 - *Tool life in hardened material.*

Conclusions

The following conclusions can be drawn.

- To reduce evaluation time and reduce the need for production disturbing tests, the development of relevant test methods is essential.
- Different test methods are necessary for different manufacturing processes.
- Turning tool life is increased when increasing the material hardness within the studied range in soft annealed SAE 52100.
- High nitrogen content decreases tool life. This is mainly a function of the nitrides formed in the material.
- The cutting forces decrease with the elements which increase the material hardness, in this study the Si, Mn, Ni and Cu elements.
- The dynamic behaviour is more distinct when increasing the material hardness.
- Modern cutting tools for CNC turning are made to work at elevated temperatures, which is where the sulphur content has less impact on tool life.
- The effect of sulphur is, however, evident when evaluating the chip formation, as the low sulphur heat chips are longer and more tangled.
- In low speed operations like drilling and tapping, the sulphur content shows greater importance.
- The tapping torque is between 40 up to 100 % higher in the low sulphur heat compared to the one with 0.022 % sulphur. A normalization of the 1055 material decreased the torque, but still remained considerably higher.
- The structure and the hardness of the raw material has great influence on the tool life in hard turning.

References

[1]   Ståhl, J-E., "Verkstadstekniska tillverkningsmetoder", Inst. f. Mekanisk Teknologi och verktygsmaskiner, LTH, Lund, 1997, in Swedish.

[2]   Andersson, M., "Ytor, dynamik och mikrogeometrier", Doktorsavhandling, Inst. f. Mekanisk Teknologi och verktygsmaskiner, LTH, Lund, 1993, in Swedish.

[3]   M'Saoubi, R., Chandrasekaran, H., "Grain size and phase effects in chip formation in orthogonal turning", No. IM-2000-046, Swedish Institute for Metals Research, Sweden.

Thore B. Lund[1] and L. J. Patrik Ölund[2]

Environmentally Friendly Bearing Steel With Reduced Hardening Distortion

---

Reference: Lund, T. B., and Ölund, L. J. P., "Environmentally Friendly Bearing Steel With Reduced Hardening Distortion," Bearing Steel Technology, ASTM STP 1419, J. M. Beswick, Ed., American Society for Testing and Materials International, West Conshohocken, PA, 2002.

Abstract: Environmental issues are becoming increasingly important as the costs of waste disposal increase and global climate effects of petroleum product usage become more evident. A major problem in the manufacturing of bearing components today is the distortion generated in the heat treatment quenching operation. The quenching is difficult to control and is a polluting fire and health risk due to the quenching media used. The hardening distortion causes excessive grinding, and large efforts have been made to reduce distortion and the excessive grinding costs caused by this. Major efforts have been made to develop gas quenching, but as the standard steels used for component manufacturing today have very limited hardenability, only a minor share of the component range can be effectively gas quenched.

By utilizing modern tools for material development, a family of low-alloyed steel has been designed which combine environmental friendliness, minimum hardening distortion and improved product performance for industrial components. The steels also have been designed in such a way that standard, high volume production routes can be utilized, and -with the advances in hard machining - in many cases can be used to design new and very cost efficient ways of component production with a minimal environmental impact.

This paper presents a concept where components can be martensitically hardened in a simple air cooling, even directly on cooling from a hot forming operation. These steels significantly reduce hardening distortion, improve working environment and are environmentally friendly. They also offer the potential to change component production routes drastically and as well provide high performance components for large volume production.

Keywords: bearing steel, heat treatment, quenching, distortion, environment, hard machining.

---

[1]Project Manager, Ovako Steel AB, SE-415 50 Göteborg, Sweden.
[2]Manager Materials Technology, Ovako Steel AB, SE-813 82 Hofors, Sweden.

The development work on the air-hardening steel family has tried to encompass all the technological tools available today. This in order to generate a family of steels designed to ensure cost efficient and environmentally safe production of high performance components.

Today's Steels Used for Components

The vast majority of the components used by industry today are hardened to a martensitic structure. Regardless of the hardness level desired, components that are case hardened, hardened and tempered, nitrided, carbonitrided, surface hardened or through hardened are all given a martensitic structure. The hardness level, or the hardness distribution through the component, is selected depending on the specific component usage. The steels used for these applications are invariably low alloyed steels with carbon contents adapted to the final hardness required from the components (Figure1).

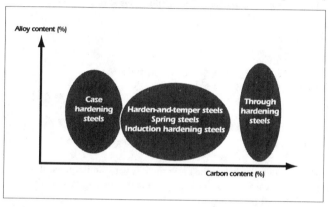

Figure 1 – *Steels used for large volume component production.*

Even for the limited range of steels, that are used for low-alloyed steel components there are hundreds of variants with minor variations in chemical composition, and what is common to all these variants is that they have a design concept that dates back at least one century [1]. By an improved alloy design, many of the compromises needed in today's component manufacturing can be avoided.

The Air-Hardening Steel Family

The air-hardening steel family has three members, one case hardening steel, one harden-and-temper steel through harden and tempered to high toughness and one through hardening steel. These three steel grades (Figure 2) can effectively replace the hundreds of variants in use today for component production with enhanced productivity, improved product performance and significant environmental benefits. (Table 1).

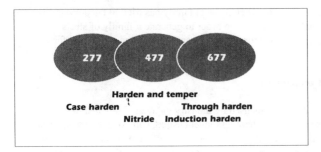

Figure 2 – *The air-hardening family.*

Table 1 – *Approximate chemical compositions*

	C	Si	Mn	Cr	Ni	Mo	V
277	0.15	0.1	1.3	2.2	0.5	0.5	0.2
477	0.4	1.7	1.5	1.5		0.45	
677	0.67	1.5	1.4	1.1		0.25	

Today's Manufacturing Routes

In the manufacturing of components today, the basic route is very similar regardless which alternative that is selected: carburising, hardening and tempering, surface hardening or through hardening (Figure 3).

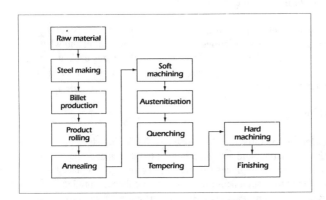

Figure 3 – *Typical component production route.*

Many steps in the production sequence generate problems, which need to be fixed in the subsequent manufacturing.

- Hot forming processes generate a pearlitic structure that requires a cumbersome softening process to enable soft machining.
- Hardening processes generate unpredictable quenching distortion which requires time consuming and costly grinding processes to restore geometry.
- The processing involved with softening and heat treatment require large energy consumption and involves use of media, which contribute to pollution and energy waste.
- The soft machining and grinding processes require immense amounts of polluting and health hazardous media and generate significant material losses in the processing.

Fundamental to all members in the air-hardening steel family is their ability to provide a component with a fully martensitic structure throughout the component by simply allowing the component to cool in air after austenitisation. With the design concept selected for the air-hardening family completely new processing routes become possible.

Hardening of Components

All steel grades used for large volume component manufacture today have very limited hardenability. This is not a design feature, but rather a consequence of the fact that it has not been possible to produce high hardenability steels in large volume steel production at low costs. There are a number of standardised steels available today with air-hardening capabilities, but they all belong to the tool steel category. These steels are produced in low volume, low productivity plants at cost and price levels that are not even possible to consider for the use for very price competitive, large volume component production. And, often, the quality levels are not on par with what is required for bearing type applications.

The air-hardening family of steels combine large volume production capabilities, high metallurgical quality and the possibility to use very slow quenching rates while still obtaining high performance products.

Quenching

To achieve a martensitic structure in today's low-alloyed steels a very high quenching rate is required. As the critical cooling times of today's case hardening, harden-and-temper and through hardening steels are very short, a drastic quench is required. The critical cooling time for today's steels for components is of the order of a few seconds, and this means that all parts of a component must be brought to the Ms temperature within a very short time. To allow a slower cooling, the transformation regions must be moved to longer times (Figure 4).

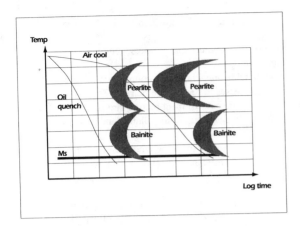

Figure 4 – *Critical cooling rates.*

This provides the fundamental advantage of the air-hardening family: the slow cooling ensures that the surface to core temperature gradient is very small at the point in time when the martensite transformation occurs. This has as consequence that the transformation occurs homogeneously and that unpredictable distortion generated in the quenching can be significantly reduced.

Bearing Ring Component Manufacturing Using the Air-Hardening Steel Concept

In the following, a direct comparison to the processing of ASTM A295 52100 for component manufacturing will be used.

Pre-Component Production

For almost all bearing components used today, a hot rolled tube, ring, wire or a hot forged pre-form is used. Common to all these preforms is that they give a pearlitic, hard to machine structure upon cooling. This means that a complex and time consuming soft annealing process must be used to enable soft machining of the components.

With the air-hardening concept, new opportunities open up. As the bars, tubes, rings and wire rod on the air-cooling after hot rolling will air-harden, the pre-components will generate full hardness martensitic structures on the cooling beds. This means that an option between a full soft annealing and a tempering back of a martensitic structure

opens up. The air-hardening steels are delivered in the tempered back condition as this generates the possibilities of:
- Reducing processing time,
- Reducing decarburization as the time at decarburization temperatures is significantly reduced, and
- Reducing the scaling as the time at scaling temperatures is significantly reduced.

The structure after a high temperature tempering will have a more fine grained carbide structure than a fully soft annealed 52100 has (Figure 5), and the hardness of the material will be slightly higher (Figure 6).

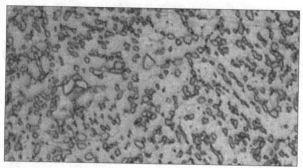

Figure 5 – *High temperature tempered structure of 677, magnification 1000X.*

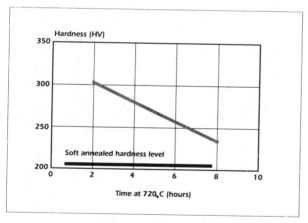

Figure 6 – *Hardness of soft annealed and tempered 677.*

In spite of this, the soft machining properties of a high temperature tempered 677 will be adequate and cold formability on par with a conventionally soft annealed 52100 due to the finer carbide size distribution and the lower total contents of carbides.

Austenitisation

The austenitisation of conventional 52100 and 677 is significantly different.

With increasing austenitisation temperatures, more and more of the base material carbon is brought into solution in the austenite, which is stable at high temperatures. It is very well-known that 52100 must be austenitised in a fairly narrow temperature range (855 +/– 5°C) in order to give full hardness and a reasonable amount of retained austenite. Any overheating will generate excessive amounts of retained austenite, and with increasing temperatures needle martensite with microcracks will form on quenching, and at high overheating massive amounts of retained austenite and severe cracking will occur (Figure 7).

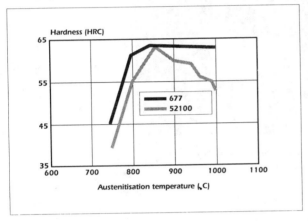

Figure 7 – *Austenitisation temperature and hardness*
of 52100 and 677.

The carbon content dissolved in austenite at the point in temperature where 52100 has optimum properties is about 0.7 % °C.

The carbon content of 677 has been selected to be at this level, and this means that when austenitising 677, the matrix will always have the same composition as the austenite of a 'perfectly' austenitised 52100.

Quenching

As the critical cooling time for 52100 is very short, the quenching required to achieve a martensitic structure must be extremely fast and requires the use of high power quenching media as oils or salts. The fact that the quenching must be made very fast generates a situation where uneven cooling of the components occurs, and the uneven cooling rates will generate a transformation situation where distortion will occur. With the alloy design of 677, the cooling can be affected in a much more homogeneous way

(Figure 8), and this will generate a situation where the martensite transformation will occur much more evenly.

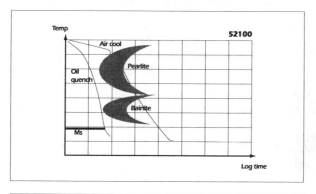

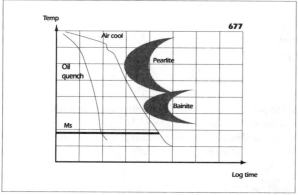

Figure 8 – *Critical cooling rates for 52100 and 677.*

Distortion

The distortion generated in quenching has been a major concern in component production for a long time due to the very negative impact it has on post heat-treatment operations. As the distortion generated in the quenching generates significant dimensional changes, large efforts have to be spent in to rectify the component geometry. This is very costly and time consuming and is one of the main drawbacks in today's heat-treating operations. In a comparative test, cylindrical bearing rings were produced by exactly the same processing route in 52100 and 677 with the only difference that the 52100 rings were oil quenched and the 677 rings were allowed to air cool on the transporter from the austenitising furnace to the tempering furnace.

The out of roundness generated in the hardening was reduced from an average 100 microns to an average of about 10 microns, roughly the same out of roundness that is generated in a high quality soft machining operation (Figure 9).

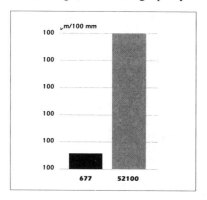

Figure 9 – *Out of roundness generated*
in heat treatment of bearing rings.

Through Hardenability

The 677 has been designed to provide the same through hardenability in a still air cooling as what 52100 steel has in a fast oil quench (Table 2).

The 52100 has a through hardenability in air-cooling, which probably is less than one mm, and, conversely, 677 will through harden sections well in excess of 100 mm in an oil quench.

Table 2 – *Through hardenability*

Maximum diameter or wall	52100 oil quenched	677 air-cooled
Bar	25 mm	30 mm
Ring or tube cut	15 mm	17 mm

Dimensional Stability

The 677 has been designed to provide a far better dimensional stability than what can be attained with 52100. The dimensional stability of 677 and 52100 have been compared in accelerated dilatometer tests and for both variants the starting condition is a 160° C/1 hour tempering (Figure 10).

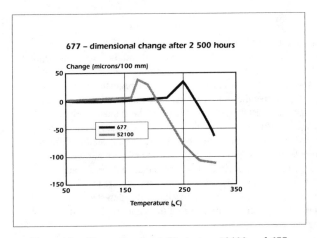

Figure 10 – *Dimensional stability test on 52100 and 677.*

Evidently, 677 is dimensionally stable up to much higher temperatures than 52100. To reach the same stability with 52100, an initial tempering which will reduce the hardness to about 58 HRC is required. This means that the combination of very high dimensional stability and high hardness, which is not possible to achieve in standard high-carbon bearing steels, easily is attained with 677.

The reason for this enhanced dimensional stability is the higher stability of the retained austenite generated in 677 compared to 52100, and the retained austenite remains untransformed up to fairly high tempering temperatures (Figure 11).

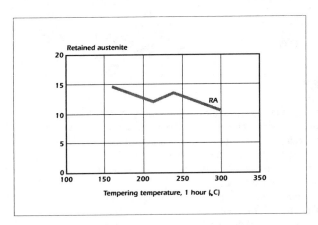

Figure 11 – *Retained austenite and tempering temperature in 677.*

Surface Hardening

The 677 is very well-suited for surface hardening. The cooling after the surface heating can simply be made in air without any additional cooling, and the hardening depth
can be adjusted to any desired level. A very significant advantage for 677 over other
high carbon steels is that the austenitisation does not need to be regulated as carefully.
With 677 an overheating does not give the significant negative influence on properties,
which occur with 52100 type steels. Rather, 677 will react as the standard induction-
hardening steels that tolerate significant overheating without any negative effect on
product properties. In one example, quenched-and-tempered 677 was heated to different
surface temperatures in one laser unit whereafter the material has been allowed to air
cool. Evidently, a large range of induction hardening depths can be attained with
maintained surface characteristics, simply by changing the temperature to which the
surface is heated (Figure 12). This obviously is not possible with such steels as 52100
as enhanced surface temperatures (other conditions being the same) would lead to rapid
over-austenitisation of the surface.

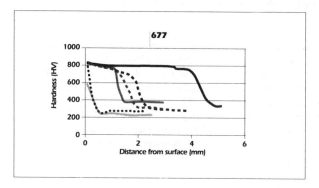

Figure 12 – *Laser hardening of 677 with varied energy input.*

Tomorrow's Processing Routes

As the air-hardening steels can be hardened from hot forming temperatures, new
possibilities to shorten the processing routes open up. Recent advances in hard machining have been very significant, and one very interesting aspect of the 677 steel is that
it hard machines very much better than conventional bearing steels.

The fact that 677 can be hardened directly from the hot forming temperature creates
entirely new possibilities for component manufacture (Figure 13). Combining a direct
air hardening from the hot forming makes it possible to conceive production
routes, which reduce the number of processing steps significantly. This also opens up
the possibility to generate completely new component production scenarios where the
number of processing steps are minimised and environmental impact is heavily reduced.

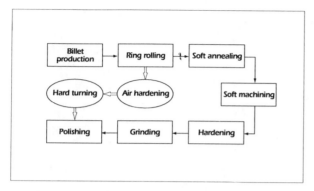

Figure 13 – *Production of a medium sized rolling bearing ring.*

For smaller bearing components, an austenitic warm forming operation followed by air hardening can provide components with a dimensional accuracy good enough to enable direct hard machining.

Conclusions

The low-alloy air-hardening family provide opportunities to improve the working environment significantly, reduce environmental disturbance in component production, significantly reduce hardening distortion, and in processing sequences where hot forming is made, drastically reduce the number of processing steps required to produce a high quality component.

In particular, combining the air-hardening steel concept with recent advances in hard machining opens exciting new possibilities to reduce cost and improve performance in high quality component manufacturing.

The new air-hardening steels provide a very high quality alternative to the steels currently used for large-scale component production.

References:

[1]   Stribeck, R., Glasers Annualen für Gewerbe und Bauwesen, Nr 577, 1. Juni 1901, s 2-9.

Developments in Bearing Steel Quality Assessment and Correlations with Bearing Life

Gilles Auclair[1] and Pascal Daguier[1]

Appropriate Techniques for Internal Cleanliness Assessment

Reference: Auclair, G., and Daguier, P., "**Appropriate Techniques for Internal Cleanliness Assessment,**" *Bearing Steel Technology, ASTM STP 1419*, J. M. Beswick, Eds., American Society for Testing Materials International, West Conshohocken, PA, 2002.

Abstract: In the steels used for bearing applications, one of the most important functional properties is fatigue endurance, which is closely related to the micro and macro cleanliness of the metal. Like other bearing steel producers throughout the world (Timken, SKF, Daïdo, Sanyo, etc.), Ascometal has expended considerable effort to attain the very high quality level required to ensure optimum performance in service. To obtain this quality level, the Ascometal philosophy has been to equip its bearing steel plants with appropriate systems for characterizing cleanliness levels both during melting and refining and for the semi-finished products. In particular, optical emission spectroscopy (OES-PDA), quantitative metallography (QM) and ultrasonic testing (high frequency US) were chosen to meet these goals. The equipment available in the different steel plants and the recent improvements made in OES-PDA and US testing procedures are widely described in this paper and examples of the use of this recent knowledge to predict endurance level on the semi-product are presented.

Keywords: bearing steel, nonmetallic inclusion, cleanliness, rolling contact fatigue limit

Introduction

The bearing steels commonly used in mechanical components (automotive and railway engineering, etc.) require high quality in terms of defect contents. In these materials, the most frequent defects considered by users to have deleterious effects on service properties (in this case particularly the fatigue endurance) are nonmetallic-inclusions. Steelmakers have made great efforts throughout the twentieth century to improve cleanliness levels, and have completely modified steel refining processes. Today's superclean steels contain very few and small inclusions, and have very low oxygen contents (5 ppm and less). If the trend observed over the last 40 years is to be continued, things will become difficult for steelmakers in the near future! Nevertheless, further improvements are necessary to meet the increasing demands of customers, due

[1]Research Engineer and Metallurgy Department Manager, and Research Engineer, Fatigue Mechanics Department, respectively; Ascometal CREAS, B. P. 70045, 57301 Hagondange, France.

essentially to component size reductions, more severe service conditions, and last but not least, the reduction of costs.

The guarantee that can be given to customers is directly related to the understanding and reliability of the melting and refining processes concerned. For this purpose, steelmakers have developed specific methods for the qualitative and quantitative evaluation of the cleanliness levels attained.

Nonmetallic Inclusions Distribution

At the cleanliness levels now attained in modern steel plants, the population of endogenous nonmetallic inclusions show log-normal distributions (Figure 1).

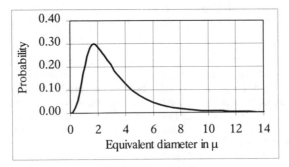

Figure 1 - *Example of endogenous nonmetallic-inclusion distribution for an oxygen content of 5 ppm, following a log-normal distribution (mean = 2.6, σ = 1.5).*

This curve was determined for a nominal oxygen content of 5 ppm, considering that the endogenous inclusions are globular alumina particles. Examination of this curve indicates that a large proportion of oxides (more than 95%) have a diameter less than 8 μm. In conventional inclusion rating methods, such as DIN 50602, for example, these sizes are not considered, except when data for K-1 or K-2 inclusions are to be collected. For this reason, modifications of the classical rating procedures have been proposed [1, 2], to include inclusions with smaller diameters and obtain a more accurate description of the complete nonmetallic inclusion population. It is also the principal reason why an approach based on the statistics of extreme values is recommended for evaluating the maximum inclusion diameter liable to be encountered in a steel [3].

Nevertheless, as regards the properties of bearings in service, many authors [4, 5] agree that the critical defect (inclusion) size can be considered to lie between 13 and 15 μm. It is therefore not normally necessary to collect such precise data, unless they provide information on the upper end of the distribution.

For this reason, calculations have been performed [6] to determine the level of confidence that can be attributed to the measurements and also to adapt the method to describe the distribution of the nonmetallic inclusions in the steel. For example (Figure 2), the confidence limits for different acceptable levels of measurement error are calculated for a described distribution (Figure 1).

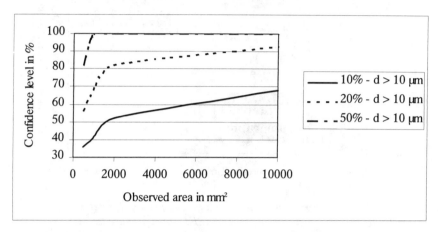

Figure 2 - *Surface area to be examined to obtain a given confidence limit for inclusions of different sizes with different acceptable levels of measurement error for nonmetallic inclusion with equivalent diameter (d) > 10 µm.*

For an accepted error of 20 % and for the population of inclusions with diameters greater than 10 µm, the confidence limit reaches 90 % if the observed area is around 8000 mm². The probability of observing these inclusions is very low using conventional rating procedures. This means that, in order to achieve greater accuracy, a much larger surface area must be examined with a high resolution.

The basic requirements for a reliable description of the nonmetallic inclusion population have not yet been fully met and can be summarised as follows :

    (1) accurate description of the endogenous inclusions, i.e. high resolution examination (d > 1.5 µm) with low measurement error ; and

    (2) large inspected volume to guarantee a high confidence limit for the data collected on large endogenous and scarce exogenous inclusions.

The techniques available for describing nonmetallic inclusions have been presented in previous papers [4, 7] and are summarised schematically in Figure 3.

This figure shows that no single technique is capable of describing the whole inclusion distribution and that an appropriate combination of methods is necessary to reach the specified goals. The inspection time can vary from a few minutes to 100 hours, for the analysis of 1 mg to several hundred grams.

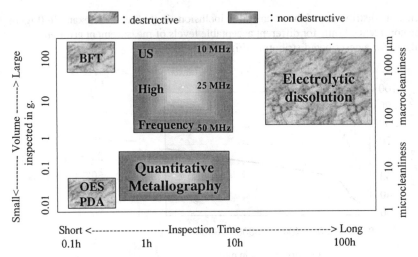

Figure 3 - *Schematic representation of the different methods for describing nonmetallic-inclusion distributions in steel (BFT : blue fracture test, US : ultrasonic testing, OES-PDA : optical emission spectroscopy with pulse discrimination analysis).*

It must be noted, that other techniques such as electron beam remelting (E.B.R.) and computer-controlled scanning electron microscopy (C.C.S.E.M.) are also used by steelmakers to control the cleanliness level of the design steels. These techniques are almost used to control the micro-cleanliness of the steel but in the case of very clean steels such as bearing steels, the control of the macro-cleanliness by these techniques is time consuming to analyse a big volume.

Over the last five years, Ascometal has focused attention on three of these methods and has equipped its steel-plants to enable them to make these measurements [8]. The methods chosen are optical emission spectroscopy and quantitative metallography to describe the distribution of endogenous inclusions, and ultrasonic inspection to evaluate approximately the distribution of macro-inclusions.

Further Developments

Experience gained with the everyday use of these techniques revealed that the distribution of nonmetallic inclusions is not described completely. Indeed, considering the resolution and the inspected volume for each of the techniques employed, there is a gap between 15 and 50 μm that is not correctly covered (Figure 4). Further development work has been conducted in order to improve the resolution and increase the volume inspected by ultrasonic testing and also to enhance the amount of information obtained from optical emission spectroscopy measurements.

OES-PDA

After a brief summary of the principles of this technique [9], a description will be given of the current development work to achieve the goals fixed for the determination of nonmetallic inclusion distributions.

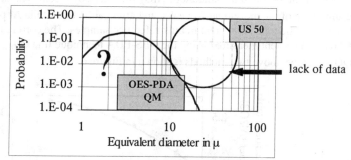

Figure 4 - *Example of distribution of a log-normal distribution (7 ppm oxygen, mean = 3.9, σ = 1.3) ; showing the resolution of the different methods used and the region where data is lacking.*

A massive sample is excited by a spark discharge composed in this case of 2000 elementary pulses generated during 20 seconds at a frequency of 100 Hz. The light emission is recorded after each individual discharge and gives a spectrum in which the light intensity varies as a function of acquisition time. Two types of pulses can be distinguished :

(1) low intensity pulses corresponding to elements in solid solution in the steel matrix, and
(2) high intensity pulses corresponding to elements contained in the nonmetallic inclusions.

The simultaneous emission of high intensity pulses for different elements shows that these elements are associated in the detected inclusion.

Considerable progress has already been made in this technique, which is regularly used by steelmakers [10, 11] to monitor melting and refining processes. The qualitative and quantitative evaluation of the inclusions contained in a steel now takes only a relatively short time.

Considerable effort has been expended [12] to gain a better understanding of the excitation phenomena involved when an inclusion emits a light pulse. The operating conditions were adapted to ensure a good correlation between elementary light pulses and the removal of individual nonmetallic inclusions resulting from deoxidation. The observations were made using a CCD camera with a very high temporal resolution (10 ns).

Taking into account the operating conditions and the weight of steel sputtered per pulse, it was demonstrated that the minimum diameter of nonmetallic inclusion (e.g. Al_2O_3) that can be detected by this technique is related to the total Al content of the steel matrix. This minimum diameter can be as small as 1.5 μm (Figure 5).

The size of the nonmetallic inclusions was determined after having first established the relationship between the amount of AlO_x measured by electrolytic dissolution and the amplitude of the individual Al peaks, and after calibration of the Al peak intensity as a function of the total Al content in bulk reference samples. The correlation between the total oxygen content measured using the OES-PDA technique (the O_{total} is related to Al_2O_3) and the above two methods is shown in Figure 6.

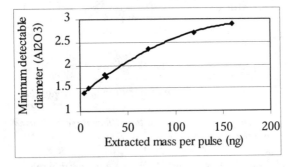

Figure 5 - *Minimum detectable inclusion diameter (Al_2O_3) versus the mass removed per pulse (total Al content = 30×10^{-3}).*

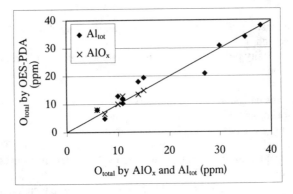

Figure 6 - *Comparison of the total oxygen content measured by OES-PDA and oxygen content measured by other techniques .*

The next step consists in correlating the distribution of nonmetallic inclusions measured by quantitative metallography with the distribution of the intensity pulses obtained using the OES-PDA technique, in order to obtain quantitative information on the size of the detected nonmetallic inclusions (Figure 7).

In this figure, a log-normal curve is fitted to the data, assuming that all the detected nonmetallic inclusions are globular pure alumina particles, to verify that the total oxygen content (O_{total} in ppm) is correctly described by the measured distributions (matter balance-sheet). The fitted curve gives information on parts of the distribution not covered by the observations, because they represent events that are either too rare (inclusions bigger than 15 µm) or too frequent (excessively numerous small inclusions).

These recent improvements show that the endogenous inclusion population is well described with this method, even when the inspected volume is not very large.

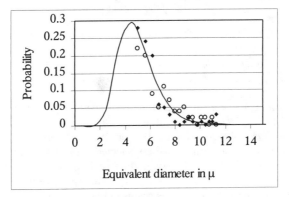

Figure 7 - *Correlation of the different methods.*
Circles: OES-PDA data. Diamonds: quantitative
metallography data. Curve : log-normal distribution
for O_{total} = 7ppm (mean = 4.8 ; σ = 1.1).

Ultrasonic Testing

During the last five years, considerable progress was made in ultrasonic testing by the use of very high frequencies (50 MHz and more). Steelmakers have asked suppliers of nondestructive inspection equipment to improve the resolution of US techniques to enable the detection of smaller inclusions in a larger volume. Sanyo Steel [13-15] and more recently Aïchi Steel [16, 17] have published the results of their developments and show that it is now possible to detect small inclusions with a good accuracy.

Ascometal has also chosen to use high frequency transducers (up to 100 MHz), but has developed an original approach consisting in recording not only the C-scans, but also all the A-scans on a predefined area, enabling off-line signal treatment.

To evaluate the performance of the transducers, a reference sample was made with artificial defects of sizes ranging from 10 to 100 µm. The measurement results are plotted in Figure 8. The signal to background noise ratio rises to about 12 dB for an artificial defect of 25 µm. During these experiments, it was also shown to be very difficult to detect artificial defects smaller than this size without specific treatment, due to the attenuation of the ultrasonic waves in both water and the steel.

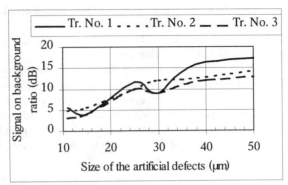

Figure 8 - *Performance of the three transducers tested, in terms of signal to background noise ratio (dB). The detection of the 30 μm diameter defect is not very good due to its poor definition.*

Similar measurements were also performed with natural defects, combining image analysis on polished surfaces at different depths with ultrasonic maps. The correlation between these results is shown in Figure 9, where it can be seen that all the defects with equivalent diameters greater than 20 μm are detected with a probability of 1. Indeed, the probability of detection varies not only with the size, but also with the nature of the defect and its orientation with respect to the ultrasonic waves. Some defects of 15 μm were detected but the probability for this size is only about 0.3.

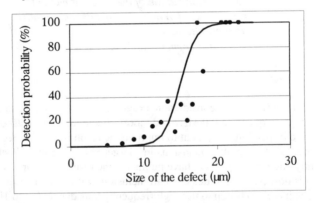

Figure 9 - *Variation of the detection probability versus the size of the natural defects.*

To improve the detection probability for small defects (10 to 15 μm), a system has been developed in which it is possible to perform signal treatment on the stored A-scan data. A number of signal treatments have been evaluated and encouraging results were obtained, with an increase of +6dB in the signal to background ratio. An example of this type of improvement is illustrated in Figure 10, which shows maps of a defect (nonmetallic inclusion) before and after signal treatment.

Instead of using the local approach described above, it is also possible to perform an overall statistical analysis of the A-scan data, to assess the quality of the steel in terms of cleanliness. An example of this type of treatment performed on three samples of different quality is shown in Figure 11. However, great precautions are necessary with treatments of this type, because the results are highly dependent on the operating conditions.

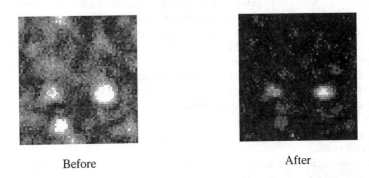

Before   After

Figure 10 - *Example of improvement of the signal to background ratio due to signal treatment (size of the scanned area 580 x 580 μm^2).*

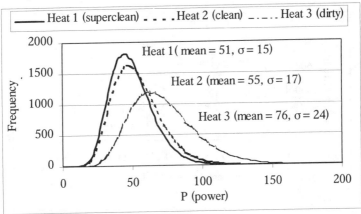

Figure 11 - *Intensity histograms of the A-scan signals for three different heats.*

Figure 11 shows that the three heats can be distinguished by their intensity histograms using this type of global treatment (statistical data can be calculated). Although this approach gives no precise information concerning the position of the defects, it provides a rapid indication of the cleanliness level without the need to scan the whole sample.

How To Use These Data - Conclusions

In parallel to such developments for the characterisation of cleanliness, a physical model was developed [*18, 19*] to predict the distribution of fatigue life in rolling contact fatigue test using the distribution of inclusions in steel. This model is based on the physical description of the mechanism of spalling on nonmetallic inclusions .

This model describes the formation of a fatigue « butterfly » around a nonmetallic inclusion in the stress field generated by the displacement of the ball on the raceway. The butterfly is formed above a critical hertzian pressure, by an accumulation of the dislocations. When the density of dislocations is above a critical value, a microcrack is nucleated and propagates toward the surface. The time to spalling corresponds to emergence of a crack at the surface.

For the validation stage, the model parameters are chosen to simulate flat washer fatigue test with sudden death type analysis. The data used to characterise the distribution of inclusions are those obtained by quantitative metallography and OES-PDA techniques (microcleanliness) and high frequency ultrasonic inspection (macrocleanliness). Figure 12 shows the comparison between simulation and fatigue test performed on various heat for several years.

The open circles represent simulation results based only on endogenous distributions, while the filled squares correspond to cases where whole of the distributions (micro + macro) are taken into account. This demonstrates the main influence of large inclusions on fatigue life and how it is useful to describe the total population of nonmetallic inclusions to get a realistic estimation of the in-service property.

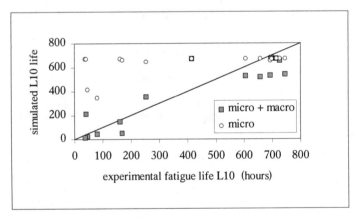

Figure 12 – *Comparison of experimental endurance level with simulated one by the physical model using the description of the nonmetallic population.*

Increasing user requirements in terms of cleanliness has led steelmakers to improve the quality of their steel. For this purpose, considerable efforts have been made to equip plants with melting and refining processes capable of achieving the necessary guaranteed quality. At the same time, appropriate techniques have been developed and are still being improved to describe defect distributions in steel as accurately as possible.

Recent developments work on OES-PDA and high frequency US inspection techniques have enabled the determination of continuous nonmetallic inclusion distributions in steel. Inclusion size distributions can now be measured quantitatively from 1.5 μm to hundreds of μm (Figure 13). The quantitative OES-PDA technique can also be used for monitoring the quality of melting and refining treatments and as a basis for process improvements.

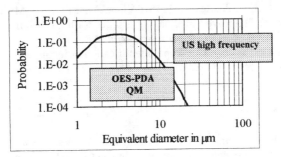

Figure 13 - *New state of the art in the description of nonmetallic inclusion populations following the recent developments described in the present paper.*

All these data also are particularly useful for evaluating the fatigue endurance in service for bearing steels using a physical model using the complete description of the nonmetallic inclusion distribution.

References

[1] Vander Voort, G. F.," Inclusions Ratings: Past, Present, and Future," *Bearing Steels Into the 21ˢᵗ Century, ASTM STP 1327*, J. J. C. Hoo and W. B. Green, Eds., American Society for Testing Materials, 1998, pp. 13-26.

[2] Vander Voort, G. F. "Measuring inclusion content by ASTM E 1245," *Clean Steel 5*, 1997, pp. 58-67.

[3] Murakami, Y, Toriyama, T. and Coudert, E. M., "Instructions for a New Method of Inclusion Rating and Correlation with the Fatigue Limit," *Journal of Testing and Evaluation*, Vol. 22, 1994, pp. 318-326.

[4] Auclair, G., Ruby-Meyer, F., Meilland, R. and Rocabois, P., "Cleanliness Assessment : A critical review and a Real Need to Predict Rolling Contact Fatigue Behaviour," *Bearing Steels Into the 21ˢᵗ Century, ASTM STP 1327*, J. J. C. Hoo and W. B. Green, Eds., American Society for Testing Materials, 1998, pp. 39-54.

[5] Tsubota, K., Sato, T., Kato, T., Hiraoka, Y. and Hayashi, R., "Bearings Steels in the 21st Century," *Bearing Steels Into the 21st Century, ASTM STP 1327*, J. J. C. Hoo and W. B. Green, Eds., American Society for Testing Materials, 1998, pp. 202-215.

[6] Hénault, E., "Simulation de la cotation inclusionnaire sur fil ou barre," *CREAS internal report*, n°38, 1998.

[7] Irving, B., "Methods for assessment of nonmetallic inclusion in steel," *Ironmaking and Steelmaking*, Vol. 21, No. 3, 1994, pp. 174-181.

[8] Berthou, A., Bellus, J., Charles, L., Falcoz-Vigne, M., Fiorese, J, Mancini, J. and Zbaczyniak, Y., "Improved steelmaking practice for high cleanliness bearing steels," *3ème Symposium Roulement Ascometal*, Arles 2000.

[9] Ruby-Meyer, F. and Willay, G., "Rapid Identification of Inclusions in Steel by OES-CDI technique," *Revue de Métallurgie*, CIT, Vol. 94, No. 3, Mars 1997, pp.367-378.

[10] Reinholdsson, F., Lind, A., Nilsson, R. and Jönsson, P., "Rapid Determination of Inclusion Characteristics in Bearing Steel Production," *Clean Steel 5*, 1997, pp. 96-106.

[11] Reinholdsson, F., Jönsson, P., Lind, A., Goransson, M., JoHansson, B. M. and Nilsson, R., "On-line determination of Inclusion Characteristics in bearing Steels," *Steel Time International*, Vol. 22, No. 2, March 1998, pp. 27-28.

[12] Pollino, L., "Etude des mécanismes en spectrométrie d'émission optique à source d'étincelles avec comptage des impulsions permettant la mise au point d'un modèle de quantification des inclusions dans les aciers," Thèse CIFRE, 1999, Lyon (ECL).

[13] Sanyo technical report, Vol. 4, 1997.

[14] Muraï, J., Ida, T., and Shiraiwa, T., "Detection of alumina no-metallic inclusion and void in steel by ultrasonic testing method," *Journal of NDI*, Vol. 47, No. 7, March 1998, pp. 498-503.

[15] Kato, Y., "Ultrasonic Flaw detection of Nonmetallic inclusion in Steel," *CAMP-ISIJ*, Vol. 12, 1999, p. 473.

[16] Nagayama, H., "Detection of inclusion by ultrasonic method (Influence of inclusion on rolling contact fatigue life-1)," *CAMP-ISIJ*, Vol. 11, 1998, p. 1323.

[17] Nagayama, H., "Phenomem of flaking by inclusion detected by ultrasonic method (Influence of inclusion on rolling contact fatigue life-2)," *CAMP-ISIJ*, Vol. 11, 1998, p. 1324.

[18] Piot, D., Lormand, G., Vincent, A., Baudry, G., Girodin, D. and Dudragne, G., "Fatigue life distribution model based on microstructure and cleanliness assessments in bearing steel," *3ème Symposium Roulement Ascometal*, Arles 2000.

[19] Fougères, R., Lormand, G., Vincent, A., Dudragne, G., Girodin, D., Baudry, G., and Daguier., P., "A new Physically Based Model for Prediction the Fatigue Life Distribution of Bearings," *Bearing Steel Technology, ASTM STP 1419*, J.M. Beswick, Eds., American Society for Testing Materials, 2001.

Yukitaka Murakami[1] and Naoko N. Yokoyama[2]

Influence of Hydrogen Trapped by Inclusions on Fatigue Strength of Bearing Steel

Reference: Murakami, Y. and Yokoyama, N. N., "Influence of Hydrogen Trapped by Inclusions on Fatigue Strength of Bearing Steel," *Bearing Steel Technology, ASTM STP 1419*, J. M. Beswick, Ed., American Society for Testing and Materials International, West Conshohocken, PA, 2002.

Abstract: The mechanism of fatigue failure, in the extremely high cycle regime, is studied on a bearing steel, ASTM A295 52100. Special focus was given to the optically dark area (ODA) in the vicinity of fracture origin (subsurface nonmetallic inclusion) of specimens QT that received the conventional heat treatment and quenching followed by tempering. Specimens having a longer fatigue life had a larger ODA. To investigate the influence of the hydrogen trapped by inclusions on fatigue properties, specimens heat treated in a vacuum (specimens VQ) were prepared. At the identical fatigue life N_f, specimens VQ had a slightly smaller ODA than specimens QT. Hydrogen was detected around the inclusion at fracture origin of both specimens. These results were compared with those for a Cr-Mo steel, SCM435. It can be concluded that the formation of ODA is closely related to hydrogen trapped by nonmetallic inclusions. The mechanism of duplex *S-N* curve is also discussed.

Keywords: Ultra-long fatigue failure, inclusion, bearing steel, $\sqrt{area}$ parameter model, hydrogen, optically dark area (ODA)

Introduction

Recent studies [1-7] have provided indications that fatigue failure can occur in the life regime exceeding $N=10^7$ and at stresses lower than the conventional fatigue limit. The mechanism causing the step-wise *S-N* curve from low-cycle to the extremely high cycle fatigue has been discussed by several researchers. Gigacycles ($N=10^9$) corresponds to the cycles that a Japanese Shinkansen train experiences during ten years of use. It is also very common that turbine blades experience more than $N=10^7$ stress cycles by vibration during their service life. It is important for fatigue and fracture research to focus on the mechanism of ultra-long fatigue failure of high strength steel. Fatigue strength of high strength steels is sensitive to small defects and to inclusions. The effect of internal hydrogen trapped by nonmetallic inclusions on high cycles fatigue was first indicated by Murakami et al [7-13].

Previous studies [7-13] have reported Cr-Mo steel SCM435 that was observed to have an optically dark area (ODA). The inclusion from which ultra-long fatigue fracture originated was observed, by optical microscope, and that to have formed an ODA which was influenced by hydrogen.

In this study, tension-compression fatigue tests were carried out with a bearing

[1] Professor, Department of Mechanical Engineering Science, Kyushu University, 6-10-1, Hakozaki, Higashi-ku, Fukuoka, 812-8581, Japan.
[2] Graduate student, Department of Mechanical Engineering Science, Graduate School of Engineering, Kyushu University, 6-10-1, Hakozaki, Higashi-ku Fukuoka, 812-8581, Japan.

steel ASTM A295 52100. Two series of specimens having two different hydrogen contents were prepared by changing heat-treatment as in the case of SCM435 [9-10, 12-13]. The fracture surfaces, especially in the vicinity of inclusions, were studied. The results are compared with those of SCM435. The results of ASTM A295 52100 also showed that hydrogen trapped by the inclusion has a critical influence on ultra-long fatigue failure depending on the hydrogen content. Aspects of the double S-N curve are also discussed in terms of experimental method, specimen size and statistical distribution of inclusions sizes.

Test Specimens and Experimental Method

Materials and Dimensions

A bearing steel, ASTM A295 52100 was used for this investigation. Table 1 shows the chemical composition. To investigate the influence of hydrogen, two different heat-treatments were specified.
(1)Specimens QT: The first series of specimens were quenched at 840°C and tempered at 180°C. These specimens are termed specimens QT (quenched and tempered). The hydrogen content was measured to be 0.80 ppm.
(2)Specimens VQ: The second series of specimens were heat treated in a vacuum at 840°C followed by quenching and tempering at 180°C. The hydrogen content was 0.07 ppm.

Table 1- *Chemical composition of ASTM A295 52100.*
(wt%) (ppm)

C	Si	Mn	Cr	P	S	O
0.97	0.18	0.27	1.33	0.016	0.007	8

Specimens QT were heat treated in a RX gas followed by quenching. This gas contained over 30 vol% hydrogen, and hydrogen is likely to diffuse into the material during heat treatment at 840°C. On the contrary, during tempering at 180°C some hydrogen leaves the material. Thus, final total hydrogen content became 0.80 ppm. Since Specimens VQ were heat treated in a vacuum (vacuum level of approximately 6.7 Pa), the hydrogen content 0.07 ppm was much lower than specimens QT (0.80 ppm).
Preliminary fatigue tests were carried out to investigate the influence of surface finish of the specimens. Initially, four specimens were tested with the as-heat-treated surface finish without polishing at the stress amplitudes σ =802 MPa, 763 MPa, 772 MPa, 709 MPa. The first two specimens failed due to internal inclusions while the third and fourth failed at the surface. Next, after electropolishing, one specimen QT was tested at σ =804 MPa and one specimen VQ was tested at σ =842 MPa. In this case the specimen VQ failed from a surface pit of about 20 μm diameter where the surface inclusion had fallen out. Following these tests the remainder of the specimens were polished to #2000 by emery paper.
Figure 1 shows the dimensions and shape of the tension compression fatigue specimens. The highly stressed control volume (the volume of the test part in which potential fracture origins exist) per specimen is $V_1 = \pi/4 \times 7^2 \times 20 \cong 770$ mm³. In case that inclusions become fatigue fracture origin, the fatigue strength depends on the specimen volume which is exposed to high stress. Therefore, comparison of the data obtained by different researchers must be made by taking into account the size of control volume based on specimen size, specimen shape and experimental method (tension-compression or bending).

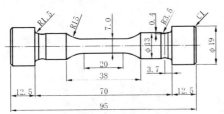

Figure 1- *Tension-compression fatigue specimen* (mm).

Experimental Method

Loading was tension-compression with R ratio = -1 and frequency 27~51 Hz. In a tension-compression fatigue test, specimen bending misalignment can easily lead to under-prediction of the measured fatigue limit. To avoid this difficulty, four strain gages were attached to each specimen. These were equally spaced around the circumference on one of the enlarged smooth sections of the specimen near the gripping fixture.

Measurement of Hydrogen

The hydrogen content was measured by thermal desorption spectrometry (TDS) with a quadrupole mass spectrometer (QMS). The basic principle of this method is as follows. A sample is heated in vacuum, and hydrogen gas coming out from steel is ionized in the QMS tube. The ionization current leads to desorption speed of hydrogen. The hydrogen content is calculated by dividing the total desorbed hydrogen by the specimen mass. At this moment desorption speed of hydrogen gas corresponds to PV in the gas equation as $PV=nRT$. The gas desorption is measured based on the calibrated standard leak.

To visualize hydrogen trapping sites at fracture surface, secondary ion mass spectrometry (SIMS) was used [*14-15*]. SIMS bombards primary ions on the solid sample, and detects secondary ions coming out of the sample surface. The secondary ions are analyzed to identify the elements existing at the sample surface. Hydrogen trapping sites can be visualized by analyzing secondary ion images. SIMS measures hydrogen trapped below the surface to approximately 0.01 μm depth.

Experimental Results and Discussion

Residual Stress of Surface and Hardness Distribution

A compressive residual stress, of approximately 500 MPa, was present on the specimen surface. This magnitude of residual stress cannot be ignored and has a strong influence on the allowable stress amplitude. To maintain equilibrium it is assumed that there are tensile mean stresses just below the specimen surface. Figure 2 shows the *HV* hardness distribution on the cross section of a Specimen QT measured along all four radial directions.

Results of Tension-Compression Fatigue Test

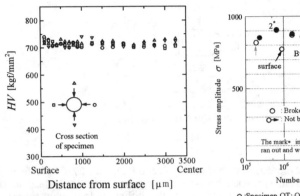

Figure 2- *Hardness distribution at specimen section (SUJ2).*

Figure 3- *S-N data (SUJ2).*

Table 2- *Results of fatigue test.*

♣Heat Treatment

♣	σ(MPa)	N_f	origin	√area (µm)	♣	σ(MPa)	N_f	origin	√area (µm)
QT	709	3.44×10^7	surface	?	VQ	652	5.34×10^7	Al, Ca, Mg	19.2
QT	763	4.41×10^7	Al, Mg	32.3	VQ	685	1.00×10^8	not broken	22.1
QT	772	9.13×10^5	surface	15.8		→906	6.62×10^5	Al	
QT	785	5.10×10^7	not broken	10.0	VQ	722	4.89×10^7	Al	27.4
	→ 835	4.56×10^6	Al, S		VQ	750	3.09×10^7	Al, Ca, S	25.1
QT	802	5.38×10^6	Ti	6.26	VQ	781	3.56×10^7	Al, Ca	24.3
QT	804	4.37×10^7	Al, S, Ca	27.5	VQ	799	4.55×10^7	Al, Ca	23.9
QT	817	1.92×10^5	? (inclusion)	28.0	VQ	819	5.23×10^6	Al, S, Ca, Mg	44.3
QT	831	2.65×10^7	Al, Mg	21.3	VQ	842	5.17×10^3	surface	13.8
QT	853	6.98×10^6	Al, Mg, Ca	23.7	VQ	855	2.38×10^5	Al, Mg, Ca	82.0
QT	857	1.35×10^7	Al	29.0	VQ	857	3.25×10^6	Al, Mg	24.3
QT	870	1.71×10^6	Al, Ca, S	25.1	VQ	879	1.72×10^6	Al, Ca	30.7
QT	883	2.09×10^7	Al	14.1					

Of the 23 specimens tested, 18 fractures occurred due to internal inclusions and 5 fractures occurred along the surface. Table 2 shows the results of the fatigue tests. When the fracture origin was an internal inclusion, a fish-eye fracture pattern was observed. Inclusion chemical composition was identified by means of X-ray analysis. Chemical compositions of inclusions were mostly Ti type, $Al_2O_3 \cdot (CaO)_x$ type globular duplex that contains Al and Ca, or Al_2O_3 type that contains Al. The shape of the fish-eye was nearly circular.

Figure 3 shows the *S-N* data. This data has significant scatter primarily because of the large difference in the inclusion characteristics leading to fatigue failure. The data with the mark No. 1* indicates that a specimen with the mark No. 1 ran out up to $N=5.10 \times 10^7$ cycles and then it was retested at higher stress level. The data with the mark No. 2* also indicates that a specimen with the mark No. 2 ran out up to $N=10^8$ cycles and then it was retested at higher stress level.

Because the residual stress state was not accurately known, specimens which failed at or near the surface were excluded from further analysis. Failure in two specimens QT having the upward arrow mark in Figure 3 originated from an inclusion only 18 μm below the surface (σ=802 MPa) and an inclusion next to surface (σ=817 MPa) where residual stresses are considered to have had an effect on the fatigue behavior. One non-polished specimen fractured due to a 5 μm deep turning scar and one electropolished specimen failed from an inclusion pit on the specimen surface.

Figure 4 shows the statistics of extreme distribution [16] of the inclusions leading to fatigue failure. Data is not distributed on a straight line, but this is not expected because the chemical compositions of the inclusions are different indicating several competing defect populations.

In order to evaluate the inclusions, the fatigue limit σ_w of each specimen was estimated by the $\sqrt{area}$ parameter model [16-17]. The effective stress ratio R was initially assumed to be R=-1, i.e., zero residual stress. It has been shown that when failure initiates from a small defect or inclusion, the fatigue limit can be estimated using the formula.

$$\sigma_w = 1.56\,(HV+120)\,/\,(\sqrt{area}\,)^{1/6} \qquad (1)$$

where
σ_w = fatigue limit (MPa),
HV = Vickers hardness number (kgf/mm^2) and
$\sqrt{area}$ = the square root of the projection area of a defect (μm).

Figure 5 shows modified S-N data of type 1 where the vertical axis is the ratio between the applied stress and the fatigue limit estimated from Eq. (1), σ/σ_w, vs. the cycles to failure N_f. Even though the specimen indicated as the data with the mark No. 1 in the figure has σ/σ_w < 1.0, it is expected that the specimen would have broken if the fatigue test had continued at the first stress level. This is based on the observed spread of the ODA as shown in Figure 8. Data presented indicates a trend that fatigue failure will occur even if the stress amplitude is below the estimated fatigue limit based on Eq. (1).

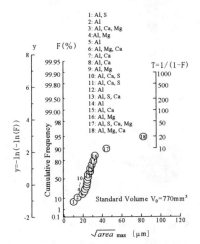

Figure 4- *Statistics of extreme distribution of the inclusions at fracture origin (ASTM A295 52100).*

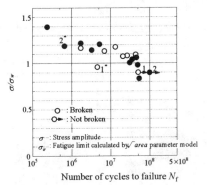

Figure 5- *Modified S-N data of type 1 (ASTM A295 52100).*

Observation of Fracture Surface

Figure 6 shows the optical photographs near the fatigue fracture origin for specimen QT. Figure 7 shows the optical photographs for specimens VQ. If the center of the fish-eye mark is carefully observed using an optical microscope, a dark area can be found in most cases in the vicinity of inclusion at the fracture origin. This dark area has been termed ODA (optically dark area) [7-13]. At longer fatigue lives the ODA size increases.

Figure 8 shows the relationship between ODA size and the cycles to failure N_f. At the identical N_f, the ratio of ODA to inclusion size for the lower hydrogen specimen VQ is smaller than for the conventionally heat treated specimen QT. This tendency is the same as has been previously reported for SCM435 [7-13], but the difference due to heat treatment is not as dramatic for ASTM A295 52100 as compared to SCM435. The fracture surface of the specimen, which ran out up to $N=5.10 \times 10^7$ and tested at higher stress level to failure was examined by optical microscope after failure indicated by the mark No. 1* in Figure 8. At the fatigue life of $N_f \cong 5 \times 10^6$, the ODA is much larger than other ODAs. Therefore, it is presumed that most of the ODA was made during the first fatigue test with lower stress. And likewise, it is also presumed for the mark No. 2 that most of the ODA was formed during the first fatigue test with a lower stress.

Effect of Hydrogen Trapped by Inclusions

Figure 9 shows the secondary ion images of hydrogen near an inclusion that led to fatigue fracture.

Figure 10 shows a similar image of SCM435 [12-13]. In the case of SCM435, hydrogen is trapped at the nonmetallic inclusions in specimen QT but almost no hydrogen is trapped in specimens VQ. On the other hand, Figure 9 indicates that

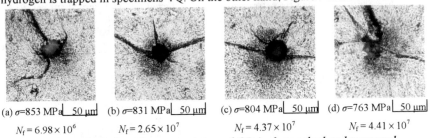

(a) σ=853 MPa 50 μm   (b) σ=831 MPa 50 μm   (c) σ=804 MPa 50 μm   (d) σ=763 MPa 50 μm

$N_f = 6.98 \times 10^6$ $N_f = 2.65 \times 10^7$ $N_f = 4.37 \times 10^7$ $N_f = 4.41 \times 10^7$

Figure 6- *Fatigue fracture origin and ODA of quenched and tempered specimens (ASTM 295 52100, Specimen QT).*

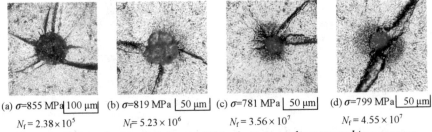

(a) σ=855 MPa 100 μm   (b) σ=819 MPa 50 μm   (c) σ=781 MPa 50 μm   (d) σ=799 MPa 50 μm

$N_f = 2.38 \times 10^5$ $N_f = 5.23 \times 10^6$ $N_f = 3.56 \times 10^7$ $N_f = 4.55 \times 10^7$

Figure 7- *Fatigue fracture origin and ODA of specimens heat treated in a vacuum followed by quenching and tempering (ASTM A295 52100, Specimen VQ).*

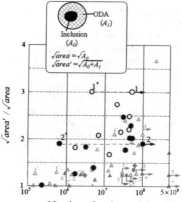

Number of cycles to failure N_f

ASTM A295 52100
○: Specimen QT: Quenched and tempered
●: Specimen VQ: Heat treated in a vacuum followed by
          quenching and tempering
SCM435 [13]
△: Specimen QT : Quenched and tempered
✦: Specimen VA1 : Annealed in a vacuum at 300C for 1h after QT
■: Specimen VA2 : Annealed in a vacuum at 300C for 2h after QT
▲: Specimen VQ : Heat treated in a vacuum followed by
          quenching and tempering

Figure 8- *Relationship between the size of
ODA and cycles to failure N_f.*

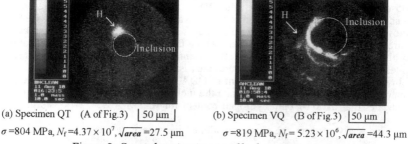

(a) Specimen QT   (A of Fig.3) | 50 μm | (b) Specimen VQ   (B of Fig.3) | 50 μm |
σ =804 MPa, N_f =4.37 × 10⁷, $\sqrt{area}$ =27.5 μm σ =819 MPa, N_f = 5.23 × 10⁶, $\sqrt{area}$ =44.3 μm

Figure 9- *Secondary ion image of hydrogen trapped
by the inclusion at fatigue fracture origin (SUJ2).*

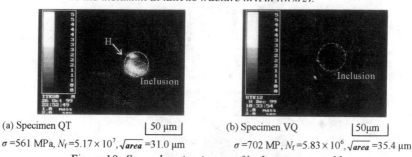

(a) Specimen QT | 50 μm | (b) Specimen VQ | 50μm |
σ =561 MPa, N_f =5.17 × 10⁷, $\sqrt{area}$ =31.0 μm σ =702 MP, N_f =5.83 × 10⁶, $\sqrt{area}$ =35.4 μm

Figure 10- *Secondary ion image of hydrogen trapped by
the inclusion at fatigue fracture origin (SCM435) [12-13].*

hydrogen is trapped in the vicinity of nonmetallic inclusions both in specimen QT and in specimen VQ of ASTM A295 52100.

As shown in Figure 8, in the case of ASTM A295 52100,the ratio of ODA to inclusion size at the identical N_f is smaller in specimens VQ than in specimens QT. However, the difference is not as dramatic as SCM435. The ODA size difference previously mentioned can be explained by considering the difference in hydrogen content for the materials. Table 3 shows the hydrogen content for all material/heat treatment combinations. During heat treatment, hydrogen is primarily trapped by inclusions that have a large trapping force. Hydrogen is saturated in the vicinity of inclusions, the remainder of the hydrogen is trapped by dislocations or at grain boundaries. Hydrogen content for SCM435 was 0.7~0.9 ppm in specimen QT and only 0.01 ppm in specimen VQ. In the later case the inclusions are not saturated with hydrogen, so significant difference must exist in the content of hydrogen trapped primarily by inclusions. For the ASTM A295 52100 steel, the specimen VQ (0.07 ppm) still has enough residual

Table 3   *Content of hydrogen in specimens*   (ppm).

Material	QT	VQ
SAE52100	0.80	0.07
SCM435	0.7~0.9	0.01

hydrogen to reach near saturation of the inclusions. The result is that there is only a small difference in behavior between the two heat treatments for ASTM A295 52100.

Because the hydrogen content contained in steels ASTM A295 52100 and in SCM435 causes a change in the size of the ODA, the ODA is a result of cyclic crack growth under the influence of hydrogen trapped by an inclusion [7-13]. In other words, ODA growth is not a pure fatigue mechanism but is a synergistic effect combining both cyclic stress and the hydrogen environment. Once the size of the ODA becomes large enough, the stress intensity exceeds the intrinsic threshold value and the fatigue crack propagates only due to cyclic loading without the assistance of hydrogen.

In order to prevent the development of ODA, and thus extend the fatigue life of actual machine parts, the trapped hydrogen at the inclusion must be reduced. The current study indicates that the 0.07 ppm hydrogen content for ASTM A295 52100 is still too great.

To indirectly confirm the above mentioned hypothesis, the effective size of an

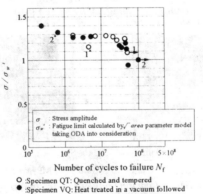

Figure 11- *Modified S-N data of type 2 (SAE52100).*

inclusion was evaluated by adding the size of the ODA to the original size of the inclusion, another modified *S-N* data of type 2 can be drawn and is shown in Figure 11. The value of σ / σ_w' for fractured specimens exceeded approximately 1.0 in all cases. The results imply that after very slow fatigue crack growth inside the ODA near the inclusion, the crack size exceeds the critical dimension for the mechanical threshold value estimated by the $\sqrt{area}$ parameter model. The fatigue crack then grows without the assistance of hydrogen and produces a fatigue fracture surface typical of a martensite lath structure. On the other hand, even if the size of inclusion is small enough to satisfy σ/σ_w < 1.0, specimens have a possibility of fail as the size of the ODA grows with number of cycles. For example, even though the applied stress for the specimen with the mark No. 1 in Figure 5 satisfies σ/σ_w < 1.0, the specimen is presumed to fail if the fatigue test is continued up to $N \cong 10^8 \sim 5 \times 10^8$ at the first stress level (see Figure 8). The prediction is based on the observation of the large ODA which was probably produced at the first low amplitude.

Effect of Dimensions of Specimens and Test Method on S-N curve

As previously mentioned, the controled volume of this specimen is $V_1 \cong 770$ mm^3. The control volume V(mm^3) of the rotating bending specimen (Figure 12), which is used by a Japanese research group [*18*], is computed by calculating the volume in which the applied stress exceeds a definite values such as $\sigma \ge \gamma \sigma_0$, as [*16, 19*]

$$d_1 = d/\sqrt[3]{\gamma}, \ z_1 = \sqrt{R^2 - \{R - 0.5(d_1 - d)\}^2}$$

$$V = 0.25\pi(1-\gamma)(d+d_1)^2 z_1 \qquad (2)$$

where
d = the minimum diameter of the test part (mm) and
R = the radius of curvature of the test specimen (mm).

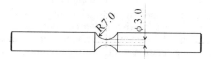

Figure 12- *Rotating bending fatigue specimen* (mm) [*18*].

The test specimen of the ASTM A295 52100 (with the critical dimensions d=3 mm, R=7.0 mm [*18*], and if $\gamma = \sigma/\sigma_0$=0.90 was assumed) has a critical volume $V_2 \cong 2.57$ mm^3. A comparison of these specimens gives $V_1/V_2 \cong 300$, so the control volume of a single tension-compression specimen is equal to that of 300 rotating bending specimens with diameter 3 mm. In other words, a single tension-compression specimen will have an inclusion as the fracture origin that corresponds to the largest inclusion leading to failure in 300 rotating bending specimens. The tension-compression specimen will also be broken in fewer cycles to failure, or at much lower stress amplitude, than for a rotating bending specimen. Conversely, a double *S-N* curve measured from rotating bending specimens with diameter 3 mm [*18*] would be significantly influenced by the small size and the large stress gradient. Therefore, it is possible that an *S-N* curve obtained from as many as 300 rotating bending specimens will not take on the same 2-step *S-N* curve. At least the double *S-N* curve will be not so pronounced. Such a possible variation is illustrated in Figure 13. Thus, the following inter-dependent factors that influence the

double *S-N* curve cannot be ignored:
(1) loading types, specimen size and shape (include the influence of stress gradient),
(2) distribution of inclusion (scatter of inclusion sizes),
(3) residual stress, and
(4) number of specimens.
Based on the above, the results of rotating bending specimen tests with diameter 3 mm should be treated carefully when applied to engineering design, as they are not necessarily suitable when considering the mechanism of ultra-long fatigue failure.

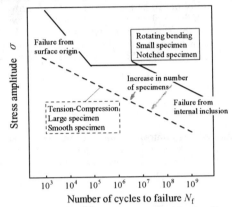

Figure 13- *Variation of S-N curve by loading types and specimen sizes.*

Conclusions

To investigate the influence of hydrogen trapped by inclusion on ultra-long fatigue failure of ASTM A295 52100, tension-compression fatigue tests were carried out with two different hydrogen content specimens by changing the heattreatments. These two kinds of specimens are specimens QT (hydrogen content 0.80 ppm) and specimens VQ (hydrogen content 0.07 ppm). The fracture surfaces, especially in the vicinity of inclusions, were observed, and the relation with hydrogen content was considered. The results compared with those of SCM435 were as follows,
(1) As the number of cycles increased, the ODA (optically dark area) size as compared to inclusion size also increased. This relationship is the same as previously observed for specimens QT of SCM435.
(2) Specimens VQ of ASTM A295 52100 have smaller ODAs at the idntical fatigue life N_f than specimens QT. This tendency is the same as for SCM435. However, the difference is not as dramatic as that of SCM435 (specimens QT with 0.7~0.9 ppm, specimens VQ with 0.01 ppm content of hydrogen).
(3) Even in the lower hydrogen specimens VQ for ASTM A295 52100, hydrogen was trapped in the vicinity of nonmetallic inclusions. This is because during heat treatment hydrogen is primarily trapped by inclusions that have large trapping force, and after hydrogen is saturated in the vicinity of inclusions, the remainder of the hydrogen is trapped by dislocations or grain boundaries.
(4) In order to avoid fatigue failure in machine parts it is necessary to reduce the trapped hydrogen content and thus eliminate the formation of ODA. A hydrogen content of 0.07 ppm for ASTM A295 52100 is still too large.
(5) In order to investigate the mechanism of ultra-long fatigue failure, small size rotating bending specimens are not suitable and it is best to test large size tension-compression specimens.

References

[1] Naito, T., Ueda, H. and Kikuchi, M., "Observation of Fatigue Fracture Surface of Carburized Steel," *Journal of Society of Material Science, Japan*, Vol. 32, No. 361, 1983, p.1162.

[2] Naito, T., Ueda, H. and Kikuchi, M., "Fatigue Behavior of Carburized Steel with Internal Oxides and Nonmartensitic Microstructure near the Surface," *Metallurgical Transactions*, Vol. 15A, July 1984, p.1431.

[3] Emura, H. and Asami, K., "Fatigue Strength Characteristics of High Strength Steel," *Transactions of the Japan Society of Mechanical Engineers*, A, Vol. 55, No. 509, 1989, p. 45.

[4] Kuroshima, Y., Shimizu, M. and Kawasaki, K., "Fracture Mode Transition in High Cycle Fatigue of High Strength Steel," *Transactions of the Japan Society of Mechanical Engineers*, A, Vol. 59, No. 560, 1993, p. 1001.

[5] Abe, T. and Kanazawa, K., "Influence of Non-metallic Inclusions and Carbides on High-cycle Fatigue Strength of Tool Steels," *Journal of Society of Material Science, Japan*, Vol. 45, No. 1, 1996, p. 1.

[6] Nakamura, T., Kaneko, M., Noguchi, T. and Jinbo, K., "Relation between High Cycle Fatigue Characteristics and Fracture Origins in Low-temperature-tempered Cr-Mo Steel," *Transactions of the Japan Society of Mechanical Engineers*, A, Vol. 64, No. 623, 1998, p. 1820.

[7] Murakami, Y., Nomoto, T., Ueda, T., Murakami, Y. and Ohori, M., "Analysis of the Mechanism of Superlong Fatigue Failure by Optical Microscope and SEM/AFM Observations," *Journal of Society of Material Science, Japan*, Vol. 48, No. 10, 1999, p. 1112.

[8] Murakami, Y., Nomoto, T. and Ueda, T., "Factors Influencing the Mechanism of Superlong Fatigue Failure in Steels," *Fatigue Fract. Engng. Mater. Struct.*, Blackwell Science Ltd., Vol. 22, 1999, p. 581.

[9] Murakami, Y., Nomoto, T., Ueda, T. and Murakami, Y., "Mechanism of Superlong Fatigue Failure in the Regime of $N > 10^7$ Cycles and Fractography of the Fracture Surface," *Transactions of the Japan Society of Mechanical Engineers*, A, Vol. 66, No. 642, 2000, p. 311.

[10] Murakami, Y., Nomoto, T., Ueda, T. and Murakami, Y., "On the Mechanism of Fatigue Failure in the Superlong Life Regime ($N > 10^7$ Cycles). Part 1: Influence of Hydrogen Trapped by Inclusions," *Fatigue Fract. Engng. Mater. Struct.*, Blackwell Science Ltd., Vol. 23, 2000, p. 893.

[11] Murakami, Y., Nomoto, T., Ueda, T. and Murakami, Y., "On the Mechanism of Fatigue Failure in the Superlong Life Regime ($N > 10^7$ Cycles). Part2: A Fractographic Investigation," *Fatigue Fract. Engng. Mater. Struct.*, Blackwell Science Ltd., Vol. 23, 2000, p. 903.

[12] Murakami, Y., Konishi, H. and Takai, K., "Effect of Hydrogen Trapped by Inclusions on Superlong Fatigue Failure," *Proceedings of the 49th Annual Meeting*, Society of Material Science, Japan, 2000, p.534.

[13] Murakami, Y., Konishi, H., Takai, K. and Murakami, Y., "Acceleration of Superlong Fatigue Failure by Hydrogen Trapped by Inclusions and Elimination on Conventional Fatigue Limit," *Tetsu-to-Hagané*, The Iron and Steel Institute of Japan, Vol. 86, No. 11, 2000, p. 777.

[14] Takai, K., Homma, Y., Izutsu, K. and Nagumo, M., "Identification of Trapping Sites in High-Strength Steels by Secondary Ion Mass Spectrometry for Thermally Desorbed Hydrogen," *Journal of the Japan Institute of Metals*, Vol. 60, No. 12, 1996, p.1155.

[15] Takai, K., "Visualization of Hydrogen in Steels by Secondary Ion Mass Spectrometry," *Zairyo-to-Kankyo*, Japan Society of Corrosion Engineering, Vol. 49, No. 5, 2000, p. 271.

[16] Murakami, Y., *Metal Fatigue: Effects of Small Defects and Nonmetallic Inclusions*,

Yokendo Ltd., Tokyo, 1993.

[17] Murakami, Y. and Endo, M., "Effects of Hardness and Crack Geometry on ΔK_{th} of Small Cracks," *Journal of Society of Material Science, Japan*, Vol. 35, No. 395, 1986, p. 911.

[18] Sakai, T., Takeda, M., Shiozawa, K., Ochi, Y., Nakajima, M., Nakamura, T. and Oguma, N., "Experimental Reconfirmation of Characteristic *S-N* Property for High Carbon Chromium Bearing Steel in Wide Life Region in Rotating Bending," *Journal of Society of Material Science, Japan*, Vol. 49, No. 7, 2000, p. 779.

[19] Murakami, Y., Toriyama, T. and Coudert, E. M., "Instructions for a New Method of Inclusion Rating and Correlations with the Fatigue Limit," *Journal of Testing and Evaluation*, JTEVA, Vol. 22, No. 4, July 1994, p. 318.

G. Shi,[1] H. V. Atkinson,[1] C. M. Sellars,[1] C. W. Anderson,[2] and J. R. Yates[1]

Statistical Prediction of the Maximum Inclusion Size in Bearing Steels

Reference: Shi, G., Atkinson, H. V., Sellars, C. M., Anderson, C. W. and Yates, J. R., "Statistical Prediction of the Maximum Inclusion Size in Bearing Steels," *Bearing Steel Technology, ASTM STP 1419*, J. M. Beswick, Ed., American Society for Testing and Materials International, West Conshohocken, PA, 2002.

Abstract: Large and brittle oxide inclusions may initiate fatigue failure in bearing steels. The size of the maximum inclusion in a large volume must be predicted by statistical analysis because only small samples can directly be analysed and there are limitations on non-destructive testing methods. A new method based on the Generalized Pareto distribution (GPD) was recently proposed by the Sheffield group. This allows data on inclusion sizes in small samples to be used to predict the maximum inclusion size in a large volume of steel. The method has advantages over other statistics of extremes methods. The number of sources of failure and the failure rate of practical bearings can be estimated from the predictions of the GPD and the stress distribution in the bearing. Here the GPD method is compared with the Statistics of extreme values (SEV) method developed by Murakami and co-workers. The application of predictions from the GPD in the safe design of bearings will be illustrated.

Keywords: bearing steels, inclusion rating, statistics of extremes, generalized pareto distribution

For engineering bearings where high fatigue strength and long lifetimes under dynamic loading are required, inclusions have been associated with the initiation of the failure process [1-3]. Failure of engineering bearings usually originates from the few large inclusions when the local stress amplitude is above a critical value. These few large oxide inclusions are randomly distributed in vast volumes of steel.

[1]Research Associate, [1]Reader and [1]Professor, respectively, in Engineering Materials Department, University of Sheffield, Mappin Street, Sheffield, S1 3JD, United Kingdom. G. Shi is now Section Leader at TWI Limited, Abington, Cambridge, CB1 6AL, United Kingdom. [2]Professor, School of Mathematics and Statistics, University of Sheffield, Hounsfield Road, Sheffield, S3 7RH, United Kingdom. [3]Professor, Mechanical Engineering Department, University of Sheffield, Mappin Street, Sheffield, S1 3JD, United Kingdom.

The combination of low concentration and relatively small size of inclusions requires the examination of unrealistically large areas or volumes of steel to give a statistically significant result. This is often difficult because small volumes can only be detected by conventional methods and the size of large inclusions is below the resolution of

non-destructive testing methods such as ultrasonic tests. The size and number of large inclusions in large volumes of steel, say 1 tonne, must be predicted by statistical analysis based on information from small samples.

Recently, the steel industry has started using statistics of extreme value (SEV) methods, which were initially developed by Murakami and co-workers [4-10], using the size of the maximum inclusion in each sample. Thus data on inclusion sizes in small samples can be used to predict the maximum inclusion size in a large volume of steel. A new method based on the Generalized Pareto distribution (GPD), which is a branch of statistics of extremes, has recently been proposed by the authors [11-13]. The methodology for the GPD method has been developed along with computer simulation of the effects of the parameters on the estimation and the confidence intervals [14-15] and the effectiveness of the method in discriminating between steels of different cleanness demonstrated [16]. Predictions from the GPD have been compared with the SEV method and extrapolating the log-normal distribution [11-12]. In addition, the authors have shown that results from cold crucible remelted samples and polished optical cross-sections are consistent [17]. One of the key features for the GPD method is that the estimated size is below an upper limit in some circumstances. It deals with the size distribution of inclusions above a certain size in a sample, not only the maximum inclusion in a sample areaone as in the SEV method. It has been found by the authors that the single largest inclusion is unlikely to lie in a highly stressed volume, but rather that the more frequently occurring slightly smaller inclusions have the highest probability of leading to a fatigue failure [14]. Therefore, successful design of bearing components must consider the size and distribution of large inclusions (and not just the largest) in a certain volume of steel. The GPD method developed by the Sheffield group is very powerful in this respect, in contrast with the SEV method, which does not have this capability given by the GPD method.

Here the application GPD method for estimating the size of the maximum inclusion in large volumes of bearing steels is summarised and the estimation is compared with the SEV method. These statistical methods focus on endogenous rather than exogenous inclusions. In addition, the use of the GPD to estimate the number of sources of failure and the safe design of steel components is illustrated for a bearing steel component.

Prediction of the Characteristic Size of the Maximum Inclusion in a Large Volume of Steel by the SEV and GPD Methods

The procedure for the SEV method has been standardized for the estimation of the maximum inclusion size by Murakami and co-workers [9]. The basic concept of the SEV method is that when a large number of data points following a basic distribution are collected, the maximum of each of these sets also follows a distribution. The distribution function was given by Gumbel [18] as follows

$$G(z)=exp(-exp(-(z-\lambda)/\alpha)\qquad(1)$$

where $G(z)$ is the probability that the largest inclusion is no larger than size z, and α and λ are the scale and location parameters.

The characteristic size of the maximum inclusion in a large volume of steel (z_V), which is defined as the size of inclusion which it is expected will be exceeded exactly once in V, can be estimated by the following equation [7,9,12]

$$z_V=\lambda-\alpha Ln(-Ln((T-1)/T))\qquad(2)$$

where T is the return period, defined as

$$T=V/V_0\qquad(3)$$

V is the volume of steel for the extrapolation and V_o is the standard inspection volume that can be estimated according to the size of the standard testing area and the size of inclusions [7-9]. The values of α and λ can be estimated by the maximum likelihood method [12] from the maximum sized inclusions (square root of the area) in N samples, $z_1, ..., z_N$.

The procedure for the GPD method has been standardised for the estimation of the maximum inclusion size in clean steels by the authors [11-12]. Suppose u is the threshold and x is the size ($\sqrt{area}$) of inclusions larger than the threshold. Then, the probability of finding an inclusion no larger than x, $F(x)$, given that it exceeds u, is approximated by the GPD with the following equation [19]

$$F(x)= 1-(1+\xi(x-u)/\sigma')^{-1/\xi}\qquad(4)$$

where $\sigma'>0$ is a scale parameter and ξ ($-\infty<\xi<\infty$) is a shape parameter. The range of $(x-u)$ is $0<x-u<\infty$ if $\xi\geq0$, and $0<x-u<-\sigma'/\xi$ if $\xi<0$.

The characteristic size of the maximum inclusion x_V in a large volume V (defined as the size expected to be exceeded by exactly one inclusion in V) can be estimated using [11-12]

$$x_V= u-\frac{\sigma'}{\xi}\{1-(N_V(u)V)^{\xi}\}\qquad(5)$$

where $N_V(u)$ denotes the expected number of exceedances of u in unit volume, which can be determined approximately according to the number of intercepted inclusions per unit area N_A on the polished surface [11].

When $\xi<0$, $(N_v(u)V)^{\xi}<<1$ when V is very large, then

$$x_V = u-\sigma'/\xi.\qquad(6)$$

$(u-\sigma'/\xi)$ will be the upper limit of the inclusion size in the steel, whatever the volume considered.

The data needed for the SEV and GPD method are different as shown in Table 1. There are three parameters in the GPD function (Equation 4), u, σ' and ξ. The authors have found in earlier work [11-12] that the estimated results from the GPD method are relatively insensitive to the choice of the critical threshold u. However, the choice of as low a threshold as possible leads to the most precise estimation [*14*]. The values of σ' and ξ at the chosen threshold were estimated by the maximum likelihood method.

The confidence intervals of the estimated result are estimated by the profile likelihood method [*19*].

Table 1 compares the SEV and GPD methods.

Table 1- *Comparison of the GPD and SEV methods*

Method	Data needed	Parameters	Size distribution	Upper limit
SEV	Size of the maximum inclusion in each sample	α and λ ξ is set to zero	Size distribution of the maximum inclusion	No upper limit
GPD	Size and number of inclusions above a certain size	σ', ξ and u	Distribution of large inclusions above a certain size	Upper limit when $\xi<0$

Experimental Method

The experimental material was air melted bearing steel from five different casts. Samples were cut from the rolled round bar. After being ground and polished, measurements of inclusion areas were made by quantitative image analysis on polished cross-sections using optical microscopy. The size of the maximum inclusion in each sample area was used for the SEV analysis (i.e., the method of Murakami and co-workers). The sizes of all inclusions larger than 5μm were determined for the GPD analysis.

Estimation of the Characteristic Size of the Maximum Inclusion in Large Volumes of Steel by the GPD method

Characteristic Size of the Maximum Inclusion Estimated by the GPD Method

Table 2 gives the parameters of GPD for different thresholds in one cast of the steel estimated by the maximum likelihood method.

Table 2 - *Parameters of GPD for different thresholds (Cast 4).*

Threshold, μm	5.0	5.2	5.4	5.6	5.8	6.0	6.2
σ'	1.48	1.37	1.26	1.25	1.17	1.09	1.04
ξ	-0.18	-0.16	-0.13	-0.13	-0.11	-0.09	-0.08
Upper limit, μm	13.3	13.9	15.1	15.1	16.3	17.8	19.2

The estimated values for the shape parameter ξ are all negative for different thresholds (Table 2). Therefore there is an upper limit for the estimated inclusion size. In all the steels investigated so far [11-17] the estimated value of ξ has been negative.

Figure 1a gives the estimated characteristic size and associated confidence intervals of the maximum inclusion in 1kg steel. The estimated size is relatively insensitive to the selection of threshold. However, the precision of the estimation decreases for higher thresholds (Figure 1a) because of the decrease of the number of data used in the estimation. The selection of the threshold value depends on the precision for the estimation needed and the convenience for measuring inclusion sizes.

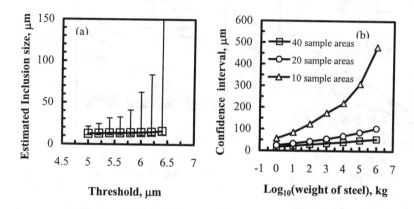

Figure 1 - *Characteristic Size of the Maximum Inclusion Estimated by GPD*
(a) Effect of threshold; (b) Effect of the number of samples on the confidence width.

What this means in practice is that when the GPD method is applied, the estimated size is similar for different number of data or samples, but the precision of the estimation will improve when more data are used for the estimation. The number of data or samples needed depends on the required confidence intervals for the estimation and the volume of steel for extrapolation as shown in Figure 1b. The confidence intervals narrow when the estimation is made with more data or in smaller volumes of steel. For a given volume of steel for extrapolation, the larger the number of inclusions collected or the more samples used, the higher the precision of the estimation. Quantitative relationships between the confidence intervals, volume of steel, number of inclusions and GPD parameters have been obtained by the authors using computer simulations [15]. The precision for a given number of inclusions measured or the number of inclusions needed for a certain precision can then be estimated.

Comparison of Estimation from the GPD and SEV Methods

Figure 2a is the comparison of the estimated characteristic size x_V in a large volume of steel from   the SEV and GPD in five casts of the same steel. The results from the GPD are similar to those from the SEV in small volumes of steel (<1 kg), but lower than the SEV for larger volumes of steel. The estimated x_V from SEV increases approximately linearly with the logarithm of the weight of steel, and there is no upper limit for the inclusion size. The difference of the maximum inclusion size between casts for the SEV method is larger than that for the GPD method. Even though Cast 2 is thought to be the least clean cast, it is difficult to discriminate Cast 2 from the others with the SEV method. For the GPD method, the results from the casts are similar apart from Cast 2 which gives a larger estimated x_V than for the other casts with the same volume of steel.

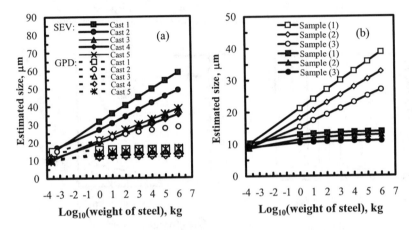

Figure 2 - *Comparison of the characteristic size of the maximum inclusion estimated by the SEV and GPD Methods in (a) Five different casts of steel and (b) One cast of steel repeated three times.*

Figure 2b is the comparison of the characteristic size of the maximum inclusion x_V in a large volume of steel by the SEV and GPD methods in the same cast (Cast 3) repeated three times. The variation of the estimated results of the SEV and GPD methods among the three experiments is less than for different casts. However, for the GPD method, the variation of the estimated size for the three repeated experiments is smaller than for the SEV method. For example, the maximum variation of the estimated size of the maximum inclusion in 10^6 kg steel is 3µm for the GPD method and 11µm for the SEV method

The results of SEV and GPD are different in a large volume of steel. The estimated size from SEV increases approximately linearly with the increase of the logarithm of the weight of steel. There is no upper limit for the estimated inclusion size. The larger the volume of steel, the larger the estimated inclusion size. However, for the GPD method, there is an upper limit for the estimated inclusion size. The estimated inclusion size increases only slowly up to about 1kg and then remains at the upper limit. The estimated inclusion size will not exceed the upper limit whatever the volume of steel.

The existence of an upper limit for inclusion size is in line with expectations in the steelmaking process because larger inclusions are expected to float out. With the estimation of the upper limit of the inclusion size, it is possible for steel makers and steel users to know the probability of finding inclusions larger than a critical size in steels, and for design engineers to predict the potential dangers caused by the worst inclusion in steel components. This is particularly important for steels used in critical situations where the inclusion size must be below a certain size. For different steel applications, a critical inclusion size is usually defined [20]. Inclusions above the critical size are dangerous and can cause the failure of steel products. This critical size is different for different properties of steel. The definition of the critical inclusion size for different properties and for different steel types sets a new challenge for steel cleanness assessment, i.e., the estimation of the maximum inclusion size in a large volume of steel and the probability of finding inclusions larger than a critical size. This information can be obtained from the GPD method. This is one of the crucial features for the GPD method.

Precision of the SEV and GPD Methods

Figure 3a compares the estimated size and confidence interval of the characteristic size of the maximum inclusion in a large volume of steel estimated by the SEV and the GPD methods. The confidence intervals in the plots are estimated from the observed data by the profile likelihood method [14]. The confidence intervals of the estimated size increase with the increase of the volume of steel. Figure 3a shows a fundamental difference between the two methods, with SEV predicting ever increasing values, with relatively narrow confidence intervals, and GPD converging on a maximum value, but with widening confidence intervals. The difference for the confidence intervals depends on the relationship between the two fitted distributions and the assumptions made in the SEV method, which is crucial for the interpretation and practical application of the two methods.

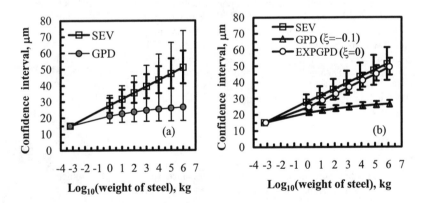

Figure 3 - *Comparison of the size and confidence interval of the maximum inclusion in large volumes of steel estimated by the SEV and GPD methods,(a) SEV and GPD with variable ξ; (b) SEV and GPD with fixed value for ξ.*

The Gumbel distribution used in the SEV method is derived from the GEV method by assuming $\xi \rightarrow 0$ [12, 14]. If the parameter ξ for the GPD is arbitrarily set to zero, the GPD becomes an exponential distribution (EXPGPD) [14] and the characteristic size of the maximum inclusion in a large volume of steel can be estimated by

$$x_V = u + \sigma' \ln(N_V(u)V) \quad (7)$$

The estimated characteristic size of the maximum inclusion is then similar to that for the SEV method but the confidence intervals are narrower as shown in Figure 3b. The confidence intervals for the GPD become very narrow if ξ is known to have a particular negative value (e.g. −0.1) as shown in Figure 3b. Therefore the difference between SEV and GPD results from the assumption in the SEV method that the parameter ξ is zero. It is not clear that there is a physical basis for fixing ξ to 0. If the assumption is made that ξ is zero in both approaches, then the difference between them is that the GPD-exponential (EXPGPD) approach utilizes all measured sizes greater than a threshold, whereas the SEV approach based on the Gumbel distribution uses only the sizes of the largest inclusions in separate sampled areas. Since the GPD-exponential method is therefore able to use more information, estimates from that should be more precise.

Application of the GPD for the Defect Tolerant Design of Components

Long life fatigue failures in engineering components often originate from large, brittle inclusions. The durability of components is strongly dependent on the size of the inclusions and the magnitude of the local stresses caused by the applied loads. A successful design must consider both the size and the number of large inclusions as well as the stress distribution arising from the geometry and loading of the component. A new approach to the safe fatigue design of steel components based on the size distribution of large inclusions in a component with a given stress distribution has been developed by the authors, which allows the estimation of the fatigue failure probability of a component by incorporating the size distribution of large inclusions from GPD and the volume distribution for stress under the applied stress [21].

If g is defined as the function for the boundary between failure and survival regions in the Kitagawa-Takahashi diagram and the function g is such that no failures result from inclusions smaller than a critical threshold size d_0, then the probability of failure of the component, is the probability that there is at least one such inclusion in the component [21]

$$\text{Pr(failure of the component)} = 1 - EXP(-\sum \lambda_i) \quad (8)$$

where λ_i is the expected number of inclusions in the size range (d_i, d_{i+1}), which coincides with a stress high enough to initiate a fatal crack. It is given by

$$\lambda_i = V\lambda_0 \tau_s(S \geq g^{-1}(d_i)) F_D(d_i < D \leq d_{i+1}, D > d_0) \quad (9)$$

where V is the volume of a component and d_0 is the smallest size of inclusions initiating failure under the maximum stress level for the given stress condition in the component. d_0 can be estimated according to the stress distribution and the Kitagawa-Takahashi diagram. Inclusions below d_0 will not cause fatigue failures under the given stress condition. $F_D(D)$ is the conditional probability of finding inclusions larger than D given by the GPD, which can be obtained from equation (1). $\tau_s(S_i)$ is the volume fraction of the component where stress S is at least $S_i = g^{-1}(d_i)$. λ_0 is the number of inclusions larger than d_0 per unit volume.

In Figure 4 are presented the results for a bearing steel component under fully reversed tension-compression loading. In Figure 4a, the left-hand axis and thick curve show the conditional probability of finding inclusions larger than a certain size estimated by the GPD method using the experimental data and Equation (4). It is noteworthy that, the probability of finding inclusions larger than the upper limit (26µm) is zero regardless of the volume of material considered. The right-hand axis and thin curve related to the upper stress state show the cumulative volume fraction of the component in which the local fatigue stress exceeds the particular stress level. The volume fraction for stress above 850MPa is very small. This curve has been calculated from the expected stress distribution in the component. The volume fraction of the component in which the stress range exceeds the critical value to initiate cracking for each inclusion size can be obtained from the curve.   The estimated expected number of inclusions that coincides with the stress condition to cause the fatigue failure in the component is given in Figure 4b. This is the solid thick curve bounding the shaded area. The area of the shaded area in Figure 4b is the expected total number of inclusions that will cause fatigue failure in the component.

The failure probability of the component caused by inclusions can then be estimated according to Equation (8).

It can be clearly seen from Figure 4b that the single largest inclusion is unlikely to lie in a highly stressed volume, whereas the more frequently occurring slightly smaller inclusions have the highest probability of leading to failure because of the localized stress concentration within a component. Knowledge of the shape of the size distribution of large inclusions in the highest size range is therefore essential. The principal difference between the GPD method and other descriptions of steel cleanness, such as the SEV method, is the additional information provided. If long life fatigue failure of engineering components is governed by the presence of oxide inclusions, then knowledge of the size distribution of the large inclusions, from the GPD method, is much more informative than knowledge of the size of the single largest inclusion.   It is clear from this example that the fatigue process is a combination of both the volume of stressed material and the likelihood of finding an inclusion, in that volume, that is large enough to lead to failure. The SEV method only deals with the size distribution of the single largest inclusion in a component which is relatively unlikely to appear in the highly stressed volume of a component. The other large inclusions that contribute more to the failure probability of a component are not included in the SEV method.

Changes in the design stress and steel cleanness will greatly affect the failure probability. Figures 4a and 4b also show the effect of a decrease in design stress amplitude from 275MPa to 240MPa on the failure probability. The thin curve is moved to the right in Figure 4a and clearly has a major effect in reducing the expected failure rate, Figure 4b. Also a small reduction in maximum inclusion size by increasing the steel cleanness, as shown in Figure 4a, shifts the thick curve to the left and has a similar impact in decreasing the failure probability of the component. This clearly demonstrates the interrelation between local stress distribution, inclusion size distribution and failure probability.

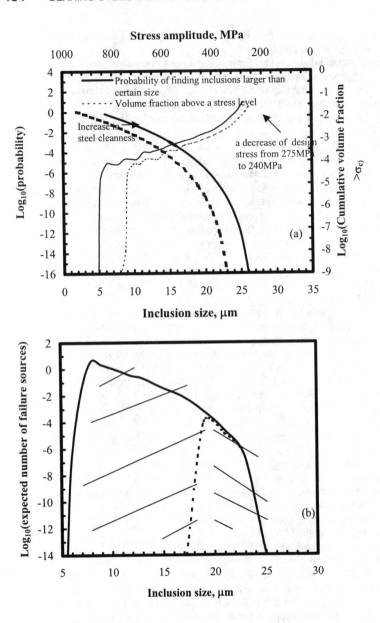

Figure 4 – *Illustration of effects of design stress and steel cleanness on the fatigue failure probability of a bearing steel component, (a)Volume distribution for stress and probability of finding inclusions; (b) Expected number of failure sources.*

Conclusions

The statistics of extreme methods are effective in discriminating the cleanness of steels. Both SEV and GPD discriminate between the cleanness of the five casts. For the repeatability on a particular cast, GPD gives better consistency than SEV. The confidence intervals for the estimated result from the SEV and GPD methods are different. Wider confidence limit intervals are obtained when the extrapolation is made for a larger volume of steel. The precision of the GPD method is higher than for the SEV method under the same assumptions as for the SEV method (i.e. $\xi=0$; but there is apparently no physical justification for this assumption). The probability of failure of a component depends on the stress distribution and the number and size distribution of large inclusions. The single largest inclusion is unlikely to lie in a highly stressed volume, whereas the more frequently occurring slightly smaller inclusions have the highest probability of leading to failure. Knowledge of the shape of the size distribution in the highest size range is therefore essential.

Acknowledgments

The authors wish to thank the Engineering and Physical Sciences Research Council (Project GR/M39756) for financial support.

References

[1]   T. Uesuigi, T., "Recent development of bearing steel in Japan," *Trans ISIJ* Vol. 11, 1988, No. 11, pp. 893-899.

[2]   Hampshire, J.M. and King, E., "Quantitative Inclusion Ratings and Continuous Casting: User Experience and Relationships with Rolling Contact Fatigue Life," *Effect of Steel Manufacturing Process on the Quality of Bearing steels*, ASTM STP 987, J.J.C. Hoo, Ed., American Society for Testing and Materials, Philadelphia, PA, 1988, pp. 61-80.

[3]   Lankford, J., "Effect of Oxide Inclusions on Fatigue Failure," *International Metals Review*, Vol. 22, 1977, No. 9, pp. 221-228.

[4]   Murakami, Y., Kawakami, K. and Duckworth, W. E., "Quantitative Evaluation of Effects of Shape and Size of Artificially Introduced Alumina Particles on the Fatigue Strength of 1.5Ni-Cr-Mo (En24) Steel," *International Journal of Fatigue* Vol. 13, No. 6, 1991, pp. 489-499.

[5]   Murakami, Y., Kodama, S. and Konuma, S., "Quantitative Evaluation of Effects of Non-metallic Inclusions on Fatigue Strength of High Strength Steel. I: Basic Fatigue Mechanism and Evaluation of Correlation between the Fatigue Fracture Stress and the Size and Location of Non-metallic Inclusions," *International Journal of Fatigue*, Vol. 11, 1989, No. 5, pp. 291-298.

[6]   Murakami, Y. and Usuki, H., "Quantitative Evaluation of Effects of Non-metallic Inclusions on Fatigue Strength of High Strength Steel II: Fatigue Limit Evaluation Based on Statistics for Extreme Values of Inclusion Size," *International Journal of Fatigue*, Vol. 11, 1989, No. 5, pp. 299-307.

[7]   Murakami, Y., "Inclusion Rating by Statistics of Extreme Values and Its Application to Fatigue Strength Prediction and Quality Control Of Materials," *Journal of Research of the Institute of Standards and Technology*, Vol. 99, No. 4, pp. 345-353.

[8]   Uemura, Y. and Murakami, Y., "A Numerical Simulation of Evaluating the Maximum Size of Inclusions to Examine the Validity of the Metallographic Determination of the Maximum Size of Inclusions," *Transactions of the Japan Society of Mechanical Engineering*, Vol. 56, 1990, No. 1, pp. 162-167.

[9]   Murakami, Y., Toriyama, T. and Coudert, E. M., "Instructions for a New Method of Inclusion Rating and Correlations with the Fatigue Limit," *Journal of Testing and Evaluation*, Vol. 22, 1994, No. 4, pp. 318-326.

[10] Toriyama, T., Murakami, Y., Yamashita, T., Tsubota, K. and Furumura, K., "Inclusion Rating by Statistics of Extreme for Electron Beam Remelted Super Clean Bearing Steel and its Application to Fatigue Strength Prediction," *Tetsu to hagane- Journal of the Iron and Steel Institute of Japan*, Vol. 81, 1995, No. 10, pp. 77-82.

[11] Shi, G., Atkinson, H. V., Sellars, C. M. and Anderson, C. W., "Application of the Generalized Pareto Distribution to the Estimation of the Size of the Maximum Inclusion in Clean Steels,"*Acta Mater.*, Vol. 47, 1999, No. 5, pp. 1455-1468.

[12] Shi, G., Atkinson, H. V., Sellars, C. M. and Anderson, C. W., "Comparison of Extreme Value Statistics Methods for Predicting Maximum Inclusion Size in Clean Steels,"*Ironmaking & Steelmaking*, Vol. 26, 1999, No. 4, pp. 239-246.

[13] Atkinson, H. V., Shi, G., Sellars, C. M. and Anderson, C. W., "Statistical Prediction of Inclusion Sizes in Clean Steels," *Materials Science & Technology*, Vol. 16, 2000, No. 10, pp. 1175-1180.

[14] Anderson, C. W., Shi, G., Atkinson, H. V. and Sellars, C. M., "The Precision of Methods Using the Statistics of Extremes for the Estimation of the Maximum Size of Inclusions in Clean Steels,"*Acta Mater.*, Vol. 48, 2000, No. 11, pp. 4235-4246.

[15] Shi, G., Atkinson, H. V., Sellars, C. M. and Anderson, C. W. and Yates, J. R., "Computer Simulation of the Estimation of the Maximum Inclusion Size in Clean Steels by the Generalized Pareto Distribution Method," *Acta Mater.,* Vol. 49, 2001, pp. 1813-1820.

[16] Shi, G., Atkinson, H. V., Sellars, C. M. and Anderson, C. W., "The Maximum Inclusion Size in Two Clean Steels: 1. Comparison of the Maximum Size Estimates by the Statistics of Extremes and Generalized Pareto Distribution Methods," *Ironmaking & Steelmaking*, Vol. 27, 2000, No. 5, pp. 355-360.

[17] Shi, G., Atkinson, H. V., Sellars, C. M. and Anderson, C. W., The Maximum Inclusion Size in Two Clean Steels: 2 Use of Data from Cold Crucible Remelted Samples and Polished Optical Cross-Sections," *Ironmaking and Steelmaking,* Vol. 27, 2000, No. 5, pp. 361-366.

[18] Gumbel, E.J., *Statistics of Extreme,* Columbia University Press, New York, USA,1958.

[19] Davison, A. C. and Smith, R. L., "Models for Exceedances Over High Thresholds," *J. R. Statist. Soc.,* Vol. 52B, 1990, No. 3, pp. 393-442.

[20] Kiessling, R., "Clean Steel-A Debatable Concept," *Clean Steels-Proceeding of the Second Int. Conf. on Clean Steels,* Held on 1-3 June 1981 at Balatonfured, Hungary, Ed. and Pub. by the Institute of Metals, London, 1983, pp. 1-9.

[21] Yates, J. R., Shi, G., Atkinson, H. V., Sellars, C. M. and Anderson, C. W., "Fatigue Tolerant Design of Steel Components Based on the Size of Large Inclusions", submitted to Fatigue and Fracture of Engineering Materials and Structures.

Jerry O. Wolfe [1]

Steel Supplier Evaluation Techniques To Assure Bearing Performance

---

Reference:
Wolfe, Jerry O., **"Steel Supplier Evaluation Techniques To Assure Bearing Performance,"** *Bearing Steel Technology, ASTM STP 1419,* J. M. Beswick, Ed., American Society for Testing and Materials International, West Conshohocken, PA, 2002.

Abstract:
The internal quality of steel is one of the critical factors in the performance of bearings. A multi- national company using steel from many sources around the world must have a detailed and comprehensive program for evaluating steel suppliers to assure ongoing, consistent bearing performance. There are many techniques that have been developed and used over the years such as blue fracture test, microscopic evaluation, oxygen analysis, sophisticated ultrasonic techniques and longer range tests such as fatigue life testing. The control of the process steps in making steel is a critical part of clean steel technology. Timken has developed an ultrasonic technique as well as specific sample preparation requirements to assure the quality of steel will meet the stringent requirements of bearing performance. Recent data from evaluation of many world steel suppliers will be summarized to demonstrate the importance of assuring clean steel. Ultrasonic data from several configurations of samples as well as reduction ratios will demonstrate the importance of a tightly controlled evaluation program.

Keywords: steel cleanness, ultrasonic testing, inclusions, fatigue life, steel suppliers, process evaluation

Introduction

Bearing fatigue performance is dependent upon clean steel and other critical factors such as geometry, surface finish and optimal heat treatment properties. The cleanness of steel is not a parameter that can be measured on a finished bearing directly like a hardness test or surface finish measurement to assure proper manufacture and excellent performance. Historically the cleanness of bearing steel has been measured on samples from heats of steel using many different techniques such as blue fracture

---

[1] Manager, Bearing Materials and Metallurgy, The Timken Company, Timken Research, Canton, Ohio 44706.

(British Standard BS 5710 or German Standard SEP 1584), microscopic inclusion measurement (ASTM E45), magnetic particle inspection (Aerospace Materials Standard 2301), and oxygen content. Timken has used these techniques but has not been satisfied with the correlation with performance and has developed an ultrasonic technique for measuring steel cleanness [1]. This technique not only can differentiate between various levels of steel cleanness, the results have demonstrated a correlation to bearing fatigue performance.   For this reason a comprehensive program has been established to assure that all our steel suppliers are evaluated using the Timken ultrasonic technique.   This program assures all material purchased by our bearing plants meet our stringent standards of cleanness.

Since we have extensive global bearing manufacturing facilities, many steel suppliers are required in every region of the world. These steel suppliers are continuously monitored to assure an ongoing acceptable level of steel cleanness for our bearing products. Potential new suppliers are evaluated using the Timken ultrasonic inspection technique.

Since many different processes are used to produce bearing steels, knowledge of the process is critical and the test sample location is selected based on historical knowledge of variation within the ingot or bloom after teeming. Since The Timken Company is an integrated company that produces both steel and bearings, the synergism of these two businesses gives a distinct advantage concerning the development of clean steel technology.   These clean steel improvements have been reported in previous technical papers.

Ultrasonic Technique

The ultrasonic technique developed at Timken Research and previously reported[2] is as follows:

- Programmable three-coordinate transducer movement system,
- Turntable with encoder for circular parts,
- 15MHz focused transducer,
- Inspected volume is from 2.3 mm to 4.6 mm below the surface, and
- Detection threshold - 0.6mm.

Steel Supplier Evaluation

There are many ways to evaluate steel suppliers to assure the quality of steel used in our product meets the requirements for fatigue life. A challenge is to identify what parameters are critical and how to measure them. Industry standards are not sufficient to assure the demanding performance requirements of most of our products. One of the critical parameters for bearing performance is the inclusion content in the steel and the distribution of those inclusions in the final product. The measurement of the inclusion content has been our challenge for over 20 years, and the technique has been perfected to a well-established procedure for steel supplier evaluation, as well as a steel process monitoring tool.

As previously described [2], the evaluation process starts with an ingot or bloom from the steel supplier that is converted into test samples. Samples can be machined from bars or tubing or forged from blooms. Heat treatment of samples is required to obtain consistent results. The test sample locations and number of samples are determined to obtain a statistically significant sample size for the process being evaluated. With most ingot processes, the bottom of the ingot can have a higher frequency of inclusions, and is the most significant location to interrogate with a significant number of samples. In a bloom cast process, samples are selected throughout the entire sequence of a multiple cast operation.

The size and shape of the ultrasonic test sample is an important parameter to establish for the size of the original as cast ingot or bloom. The volume of material ultrasonically tested is significant and in most samples this is greater than 70000 mm [2]. The ability to detect inclusions is dependent upon the reduction ratio [3] and was shown to be maximized at approximately 20 to 1 ratio [4]. The fiber direction or inclusion orientation is also important to maximize the response from the ultrasonic test. Figure 1 shows some typical conical shaped test samples that have been used to evaluate steel suppliers.

Figure 1 - *Samples used for ultrasonic testing.*

The following are examples of data from evaluations of various steel companies around the world.

Many steel suppliers produce steel using the ingot cast process. These processes are evaluated on an ongoing basis to assure the Timken specification is met for present suppliers and evaluated for potential new suppliers. Figure 2 shows a comparison of several steel suppliers who use ingot teeming, and suppliers A,B, C, D, E, and F met our specifications while suppliers W,X, Y and Z did not and were not approved to supply steel to the Timken bearing plants.

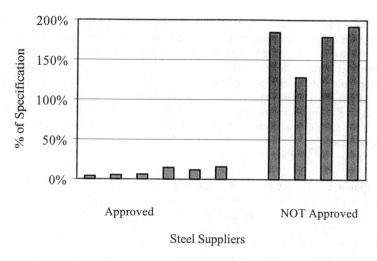

Figure 2 - *Ingot supplier evaluation.*

1.   Many steel companies also utilize a continuous casting process for producing bearing quality steels.   Figure 3 shows a comparison of several steel suppliers who use continuous cast teeming, and suppliers A, B, C, and D met our specifications while suppliers X, Y and Z did not meet our requirements, and their material is not approved for our bearing products.

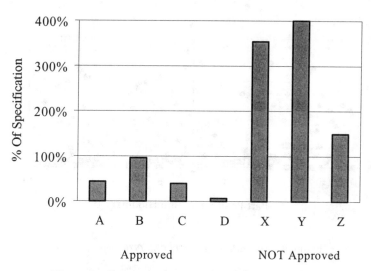

Figure 3 - *Continuous cast supplier evaluation.*

2.   One bloom cast supplier was confident the steel manufacturing process was capable of meeting our requirements. The blooms were converted into bearing rings and ultrasonically tested. As can be seen in Figure 4 the outside diameter of the rings met our specification 99% of the time; however the inside diameter of the rings did not meet our requirements (400% of specification). This demonstrates the fact that the testing program needs to be extensive enough to evaluate steel from all facets of the steel process. The inclusion distribution and how the product is manufactured from the blooms can have a significant impact on performance.

3.   One supplier added vacuum degassing equipment into their steel manufacturing process and felt very comfortable that the steel quality would improve by using the additional process to degas the liquid steel. Figure 5 shows the data before and after the process change and the effect this step had on the inclusion content of the steel.   The inclusion content went up to more than 500% of our specification. This points out the critical nature of ongoing monitoring of process changes in already approved steel suppliers.   This company later modified the degas process and was able to produce acceptable quality.

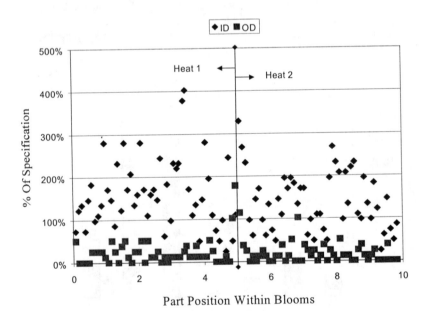

Figure 4 - *Evaluation of bloom cast process.*

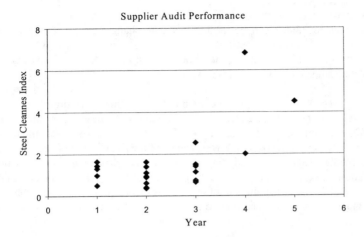

Figure 5 - *Evaluation of degas process.*

4. One of the techniques used to monitor quality of our steel suppliers is to obtain bearing cups and cones (inner and outer races) from the plants and ultrasonically test for inclusion content to confirm acceptable quality. Figure 6 shows an ongoing audit of steel plant ABC and the acceptable quality being produced.

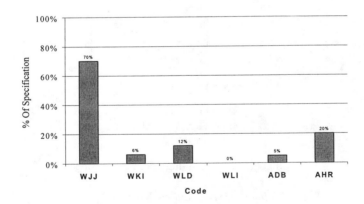

Figure 6 - *Ongoing ultrasonic evaluation – Plant ABC.*

Steel Process Evaluation

The ultrasonic technique can be used to evaluate changes in the steel process. Many times the process change seems satisfactory from a procedural and technical basis but will require verification using the ultrasonic test method. The following are examples of data from some process change evaluations.

1. A steel supplier (X) wanted to change the ingot size in their operation to improve the utilization of the blooming mill. We had established a base line of ultrasonic evaluation over several years of ingot size No. 1, so a comparison was made for the new ingot size. Ingot size No. 2 was evaluated for five different trials and was not acceptable from the standpoint of meeting our bearing steel practice specification. Figure 7 shows the evaluations of all three sizes of ingots. The ingot size No. 2 was acceptable so a third size ingot was developed. Ingot size 3 was evaluated on two occasions and this met our quality requirements.

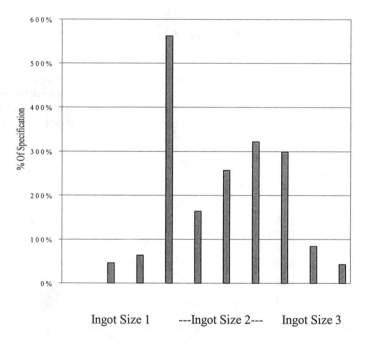

Ingot Size 1   ---Ingot Size 2---   Ingot Size 3

Figure 7 - *Ingot size evaluation – Supplier X.*

2. One of the advantages of monitoring internal quality of steel from suppliers is a determination of long term trends. Figure 8 shows data from audits conducted on one of our major steel suppliers. These data show that a process change occurred and the quality of steel changed. The internal quality was still within our control specification; however, when brought to the attention of the supplier, certain process parameters were modified, and the data came down to the historical lower

level of inclusion content.   The standard methods of evaluating steel using oxygen content or non-metallic inclusions would not detect this type of trend.

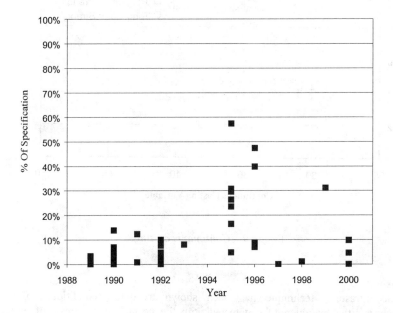

Figure 8 - *Ongoing evaluation of supplier process using rings from ingots.*

3.   In the continuous casting process, the amount of steel in the tundish is an important parameter to assure good quality steel. This is demonstrated on one of our supplier's casters when we tested various conditions during the casting operation. Figure 9 shows a relationship concerning this variable and cleanness.

Discussion
The ultrasonic technique is an invaluable tool to evaluate steel from potential suppliers and approved suppliers. This technique has been used for many years, and the improvements in steel quality in Timken bearings is being verified by our full scale bearing tests. Each year hundreds of bearings are tested and the L10 life is determined for various bearing groups from each producing plant. These tests are confirming that fewer and fewer bearings are having inclusion initiated spalls; therefore the steel quality program is giving our customers the excellent bearing performance expected.

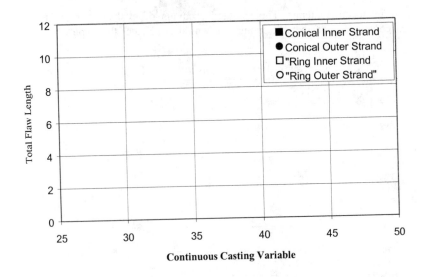

Figure 9 – *Continuous casting.*

Conclusions
The ultrasonic technique has been shown to detect conditions in steel manufacturing that would not be detected with the normal quality tests of oxygen content or non-metallic inclusion content. The ultrasonic test is an integral part of our steel evaluation process to approve suppliers and to audit the ongoing consistency of material.

References
[1]   Stover, Jack D., Robert V. Kolarik and Douglas M. Keener. "The detection of aluminum oxide stringers in steel using an ultrasonic measuring method." in 31<u>st</u> <u>Mechanical Working and Steel Processing Conference Proceedings</u> held in Chicago, IL 22-25 October 1989. Warrendale, PA: Iron & Steel Society, 1990 p. 431-440

[2]   Eckel, James A., Peter C. Glaws, Jerry O. Wolfe, and Bonnie J. Zorc. "Clean engineered steels – progress at the end of the Twentieth century", in <u>Advances in the production and use of steel with improved internal cleanliness,</u> ASTM STP 1361. edited by J. K. Mahoney Jr., West Conshohocken, PA: American Society for Testing and Materials, 1999 p. 1-1

[3] Stover, Jack D. and Robert V. Kolarik. "Evaluation of improvements in bearing steel quality using an ultrasonic macro-inclusion detection method." Timken Company Technical Note Canton, OH: The Timken Company, 1987

[4] Stover, Jack D. and Robert L. Leibensperger. "Inclusions rolling contact fatigue and power dense transmission design." presented at International Conference on Low Residual Steels (Organized by: The Indian Institute of Metals and Tata Steel) Jamshedpur, India February 8-9, 1999

Tomoaki Nishikawa,[1] Hironori Nagayama,[2] Shoji Nishimon,[2] Kiyokazu Asai,[2] Isao Fujii,[2] and Takuya Sugimoto[3]

Study of Evaluating Method for Non-Metallic Inclusions and Development of Slag Refining for Bearing Steel

Reference: Nishikawa, T., Nagayama, H., Nishimon, S., Asai, K., Fujii, I., Sugimoto, T., "**Study of Evaluating Method for Non-Metallic Inclusions and Development of Slag Refining for Bearing Steel,**" *Bearing Steel Technology, ASTM STP 1419,* J. M. Beswick, Ed., American society for Testing and Materials International, West Conshohocken, PA. 2002.

Abstract: The evaluation of the nonmetallic inclusions is very important to estimate the rolling contact fatigue life of bearing steel. The study of the ultrasonic testing as nondestructive testing made it clear that the nonmetallic inclusion over 10μm could be detected and there was a relationship between the flaking and the nonmetallic inclusions in the rolling contact fatigue life testing. On the extraction of the acid solution and Coulter counter method, the changes of the nonmetallic inclusions in molten steel was analyzed and the higher basicity · less SiO_2 slag refining reduced the quantity of the nonmetallic inclusions over 20μm size to 75% compared with the conventional refining method.

Keywords: ultrasonic tester, extraction of acid solution, nonmetallic inclusion, fatigue life

Introduction

The microscopic evaluation of the nonmetallic inclusions has been commonly used to estimate the rolling contact fatigue life of the bearing steel. But recently, the bearing steel has been getting such a high cleanliness level that it is difficult to estimate the fatigue life by the conventional method.   In this paper, it is shown that ultrasonic testing as nondestructive testing and Coulter counter method can be useful methods to evaluate the nonmetallic inclusions and estimate the rolling contact fatigue life.

Evaluating Method of Nonmetallic Inclusions

Characteristics of methods

Table 1 summarizes the characteristics of the evaluating methods for nonmetallic inclusions in comparison with conventional method and new methods.
In order to evaluate the size-distribution of the nonmetallic inclusions and estimate the rolling fatigue life, the U.T.(Ultrasonic tester) and the E.A.S./C.C.M(Extraction of acid solution and Coulter counter method) were effective, the U.T. especially was the useful way to estimate the rolling fatigue life as a nondestructive method.

[1] Chief of Staff, Parts Engineering Development Division, [2] Chief of Staff, and [3] Chief of Project, respectively, Production Engineering Division No.1, Aichi Steel Co., 1 Wanowari, Arao-Machi, Tokai-Shi, Aichi-Ken, Japan.

Table1-*Characteristics of evaluating methods.*

Method		Conventional	New	
		ASTM, JIS etc.	U T	E.A.S./C.C.M
Convenience		easy	nondestructive , quantitative	quantitative
Inconvenience		non-quantitative	cannot detect as cast T.P	destructive
Inclusion evaluation	As cast T.P	−	△	○
	Product	○	○	○
Fatigue life estimation		△	○	−
Detection size limit		−	$\geqq 10\ \mu m$	$\geqq 3\ \mu m$(flexible)

UT : Ultrasonic tester.   E.A.S./C.C.M : Extraction of acid solution and Coulter counter method

Ultrasonic Testing

Equipment-Figure 1 and Figure 2 show the schematic diagram of U.T., which is equipped with an ultrasonic pulsar-receiver, monitor, oscilloscope, water bath and personal computer. The characteristics of each unit are adjusted as much as possible for detecting the smaller defects. Especially, by using the focusing type probe and adopting the water bath immersion testing, it was possible to detect the smaller defects.

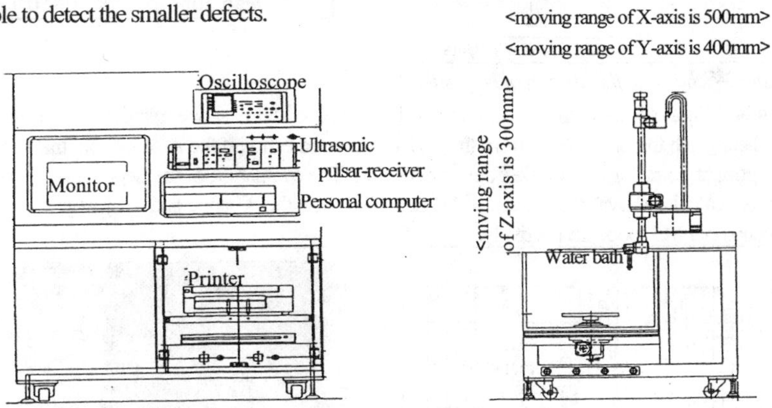

<moving range of X-axis is 500mm>

<moving range of Y-axis is 400mm>

Figure 1-*Schematic diagram of U.T.*

Test Piece- All test pieces were prepared for the rolling contact fatigue life testing. The rolled bar product of bearing steel (JIS:SUJ2) was quenched and tempered, and after that, machined into the shape of the life testing piece. The detection and life testing site was polished to a mirror surface.

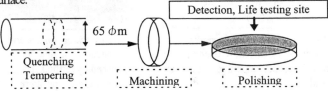

Figure 2-*Preparation of test piece.*

*Method-*In this detection, a special ultrasonic probe was used, the wave frequency was 80MHz and the focal length was 6.0 mm. Two detection methods were used, one was the normal incidence method (NI) and the other was the leaky surface acoustic wave method (L-SAW).

(1) *Normal Incidence Method* -Figure 3 and Table 2 show the schematic illustration and the test conditions of the NI-method. In this condition, the highest sound pressure and the smallest diameter of the sound beam were obtained at the focal point, so it detected the smallest defect possible. The gate length was adjusted to 150~260 μ m depth from the surface, so it could detect the defects existing in this range.

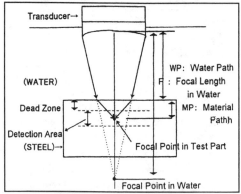

Figure 3-*Schematic illustration of NI- method.*

Table 2-*Test conditions of NI-method.*

Kind of wave	Longitudinal
Signal	Pulse
Wave frequency	80 MHz
Focal length	6.0 mm
Water path (WP)	4.5 mm
Material path(MP)	0.2 mm
Gate length (Detection area)	150~260 μm from surface
Dead zone	0~50 μm

Figure 4 and Figure 5 show the defect echo on the A scope and C scope, respectively. It was not easy to distinguish the defect echo from the surface reflected echo on the A scope, but that was the most important point for the smallest defect detection. The evaluation of the depth and size of the defect were calculated by the first peak of the defect echo on the A scope and the image size of the defect echo on the C scope, respectively.

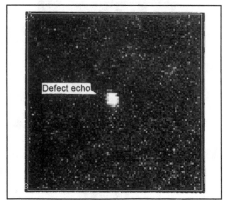

Figure 4-*Defect echo on A scope (example).*   Figure 5-*Defect image on C scope (example).*

Figure 6 shows the schematic flow of the proceeding for detection. At first, the test piece was treated with quenching and tempering, and its surface was polished by buffing. Then, the test piece was ultrasonically scanned over the whole surface, and the defect's positions were roughly determined. Precise scanning was carried out of each defect's position, and the depth from the surface and the surface and the size of the defect were evaluated on the defect echo image.

Figure 7 shows the example of the defect detected by the C scope, (a) shows the echo image in the rough detection, (b) shows that in the precise detection , and (c) shows the actually observed defect in the microscopic magnification, and it was a non-metallic inclusion.

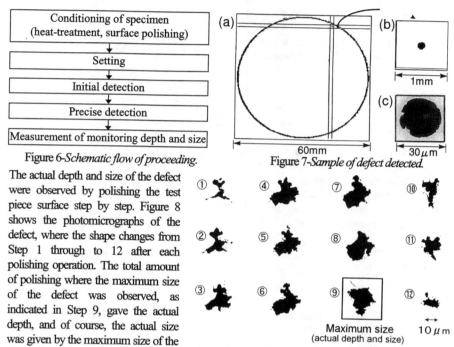

Figure 6-*Schematic flow of proceeding.*

Figure 7-*Sample of defect detected.*

The actual depth and size of the defect were observed by polishing the test piece surface step by step. Figure 8 shows the photomicrographs of the defect, where the shape changes from Step 1 through to 12 after each polishing operation. The total amount of polishing where the maximum size of the defect was observed, as indicated in Step 9, gave the actual depth, and of course, the actual size was given by the maximum size of the defect at this point.

Figure 8-*Shape changes of defect after polishing.*

Figure 9 shows the relationship between the evaluated depth by the U.T. and the actual depth, and Figure 10 shows the relationship between the evaluated size (inclusion diameter) by the U.T. and the actual size. There was good correlation between the evaluated value and the actual value, so the U.T. method was able to evaluate the nonmetallic inclusions.

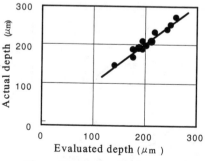

Figure 9-*Relationship between depth evaluatedby U.T. and actual depth.*

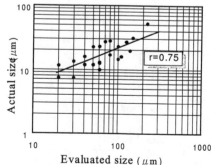

Figure 10-*Relationship between size evaluated by U.T. and actual size.*

Figure 11 shows an example of the evaluation of all inclusions detected by the U.T., which were classified every 10 μ m according to size, and drawn by a circle with the appropriate size in the proper position. This map was very useful for the rolling contact fatigue life testing to observe the behavior of the flaking caused by the non-metallic inclusion.

(2)*Leaky Surface Acoustic Wave Method-*
Figure 12 shows the schematic illustration and Table 3 shows the test conditions of the L-SAW method. In this method, the ultrasonic probe was inclined 29.9° and adjusted its position to bring the focal point just on the surface. In this condition, that made the high energy surface wave, and could easily defect the defects existing in the surface layer.

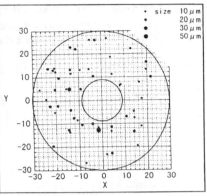

Figure 11-*Defects map evaluated by U.T.*

Table 3-*Test conditions of L-SAW.*

Kind of wave	Longitudinal
Signal	Pulse
Wave frequency	80 MHz
Focal length	6.0 mm
Incident angle	29.9°
Detection area (surface layer)	0∼37 μm from surface

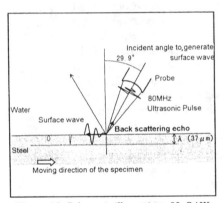

Figure 12-*Schematic illustration of L-SAW.*

Figure 13 shows the schematic flow of the proceeding for the detection. The conditioning of the test piece was the same as the NI method. Figure 14 shows the detection way and area. The ultra sonic probe moves in the Y-direction, and the specimen is turned full circle at the same time. So, it can examine the enough area around the race way of the rolling contact fatigue life testing.

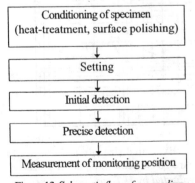

Figure 13-*Schematic flow of proceeding.*

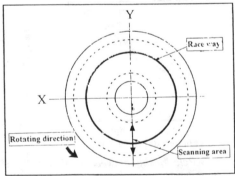

Figure 14-*The detection method and area.*

Figure 15 shows the defect image, which characteristically had a tail like a comet. This was characteristic of the L-SAW method and was different form the NI method. This characteristic was important to distinguish the real defects from contamination and stains on the test piece surface. The images of a contamination and stains had no tail at all, so they could easily be distinguished. But on the other hand, by this characteristic itself, the actual defect size could not be evaluated using the image size, only the position of the defect and the fact that its size was larger than about 8 μ m was indicated.

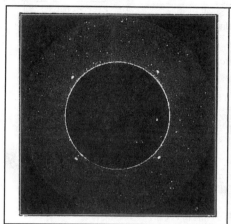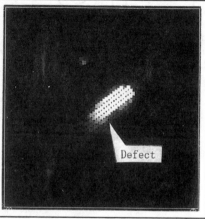

Figure 15-*Defect image of L-SAW method.*

Advantages of U.T.- The ultrasonic testing could indicate where the defects (nonmetallic inclusions) existed in the test piece and their size by using both the NI and L-SAW methods. It was very useful to know where the defects were and their size, before rolling contact fatigue life testing. It gave us useful information to make the mechanism of the flaking clear.

Extraction of Acid Solution (E.A.S) and Coulter Counter Method (C.C.M).

Method- Figure 16 shows the schematic flow of the proceeding for the E.A.S and Figure 17 shows the schematic diagram of the C.C.M. We applied heated sulfuric-acid solution for extracting the Al_2O_3 Inclusions in the Al-killed steel, including bearing-steel, and evaluated the distribution of the nonmetallic inclusions by C.C.M after the E.A.S. Figure 18 shows the principle of the C.C.M. The change of the electrical resistance when the dispersed particles in the electrically conductive liquid pass through the small aperture of the tube was measured, and it was converted to the particle size. The electrically conductive liquid was based on NaCl solutions and the diameter of the small aperture was 140 μm. Under this conditions, the range of the measurable particle sizes were from 3 μm to 80 μm.

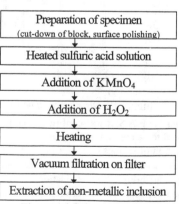

Figure 16-*Schematic flow of proceeding for the E.A.S.*

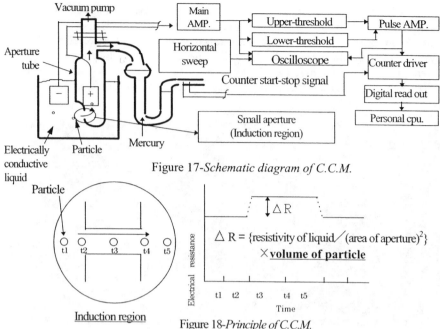

Figure 17-*Schematic diagram of C.C.M.*

Figure 18-*Principle of C.C.M.*

$$\Delta R = \{resistivity\ of\ liquid \diagup (area\ of\ aperture)^2\}$$
$$\times \textbf{volume of particle}$$

Results-Figure 19 shows an example of the size distribution of the nonmetallic inclusions evaluated by the C.C.M. after the E.A.S. The C.C.M. was useful to evaluate the size distribution of the nonmetallic inclusions because of its absolute value measurement of both size and number, and convenient as it was possible to evaluate them with a small quantity of the sample because of its high analytic ability based on the particle volume measurement.

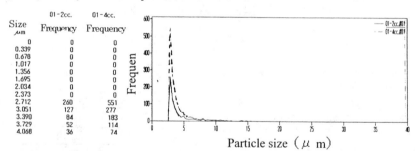

Size μm	01-2cc. Frequency	01-4cc. Frequency
0	0	0
0.339	0	0
0.678	0	0
1.017	0	0
1.356	0	0
1.695	0	0
2.034	0	0
2.373	0	0
2.712	260	551
3.051	127	277
3.390	84	183
3.729	52	114
4.068	36	74

Particle size $(\mu\ m)$

Figure 19-*Distribution of non-metallic inclusions by C.C.M after E.A.S. (example)*

After the E.A.S, it was confirmed that much block-type residue had remained, and these were found to be the SiO_2 gels by the EPMA analysis. In order to dissolve them, we tried the alkali solution of various conditions after the E.A.S, and it was confirmed that a suitable condition could decrease the SiO_2 gels and the remaining ones were under 10 μm. Figure 20 shows the reproducibility of the evaluation for the non-metallic inclusion by the C.C.M. There was a good correspondence between each amount of the evaluated specimen, so it indicated high reliability for the size distribution of the nonmetallic inclusions. Figure 21 shows that the pure-Al_2O_3 particles were not fused by the acid-alkali solution (called E.A.A.S.). So, it was confirmed that E.A.A.S/C.C.M. was able to evaluate the nonmetallic inclusion distributions.

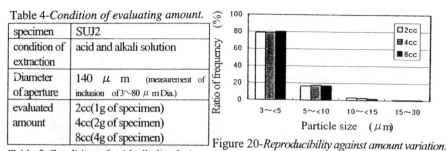

Table 4-*Condition of evaluating amount.*

specimen	SUJ2
condition of extraction	acid and alkali solution
Diameter of aperture	140 μ m (measurement of inclusion of 3~80 μ m Dia.)
evaluated amount	2cc(1g of specimen) 4cc(2g of specimen) 8cc(4g of specimen)

Figure 20-*Reproducibility against amount variation.*

Table 5-*Condition of acid-alkali solution.*

specimen	pure-Al$_2$O$_3$ particles
Procedure of evaluation	1) the sifting of two sizes of particles (5~10and 10~30 μ m) 2) after sifting, evaluation of each condition as follows ; (a):the evaluation of the distribution of the particle size by the C.C.M (b):after acid solution for particles, the evaluation of the distribution of the particle size by the C.C. M (C): after acid and alkali solution for particles, the evaluation of the distribution of the particle size by the C.C. M 3) the comparison with the distribution of the particle size for a, b, and c.

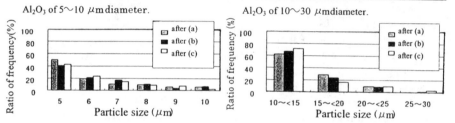

Figure 21-*Evaluation of fusion of Al$_2$O$_3$ by E.A.A.S using pure-Al$_2$O$_3$ particles.*

Application of Ultrasonic Testing on Rolling Contact Fatigue Life Testing

In order to clearly relate nonmetallic inclusions with rolling contact fatigue life, the experiments were carried out under the condition that the relative positions between the nonmetallic inclusions in the test piece and the race way on its surface were specified clearly.

Method

Experimental proceeding- Figure 22 shows the experimental proceeding. At first, the test pieces were detected precisely by the U.T., and all defects were registered with their size and depth. The position of significant defects were marked with the dent marks of the Vickers tester. After that, the relative position between the defect and the dent marks was reconfirmed by the U.T.. Fig.23 shows the reconfirmed image by the U.T.. Next, the depth of the defect from the surface was adjusted to the experimental condition by polishing the surface. In setting of the test piece on the fatigue life tester, the position of the significant defect was controlled just under the race way by the dent marks. Of course, it was possible to set the significant defect a little bit out of the race way, and careful setting was needed to avoid another defects existing under the race way. Finally, the rolling contact fatigue life testing was carried out.

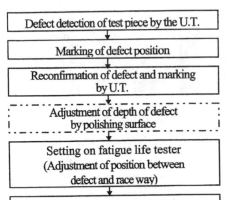

Figure 22-*Experimental proceeding.*

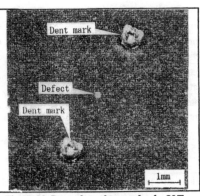

Figure 23-*Reconfirmed image by the U.T.*

Table 6-*Test conditions*

Type		Mori
Hertzian stress		5.3Gpa
Cycle rate		1500cpm
Ball	Steel grade	JIS-SUJ2
	size	3/8inch × 3ball
Lubricating oil		machining oil #10

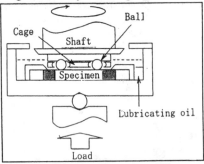

Figure 24-*Schematic illustration of life tester.*

Rolling Contact Fatigue Life Test- Figure 24 shows the schematic illustration of the life tester and Table 6 shows test conditions. Table 7 shows the various test conditions of the defect's size, depth, and the relative positions between the defect and the race way. Upon testing, the flaking occurrence was checked and, if no flaking was observed, the change of the defect images was observed after the life testing by the U.T. Furthermore, microscopic observation was made around the defect.

Table 7-*Test conditions of rolling contact fatigue life.*

Test type	Defect characteristics			Relative position between Defect and race wav	Detection method
	position	depth	size		
A	subsurface	75~250 μm	8~30 μm	just under/ little bit out	NI method
B	surface layer	0~37 μm	$\geqq$8 μm	just under/ little bit out	L-SAW

Results

Case of the Subsurface Defect (Type A)

(1) *Case 1 (flaking)-* Figure 25 shows an example of flaking, and Table 8 shows the defect characteristics evaluated by the U.T. before testing and the number of cycles when flaking occurred. Figure 26 shows the shape of the flaking measured by the depth meter. The collation of the relative position between the dent mark and the flaking with that between the dent mark and the defect, and the depth of the flaking with that of the defect, indicated that the flaking occurred by the defect.

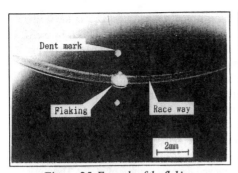

Figure 25-*Example of the flaking.*

Table 8-*Defect characteristics and fatigue life.*

Defect characteristics			Fatigue life
depth	size	position	cycles
150 μm	32 μm	just under	1.5×10^7

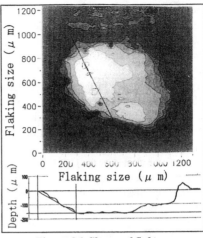

Figure 26-*Shape of flaking.*

(2) *Case 2 (Change of Defect Image)*- In this case, the life testing was finished after 1×10^8 cycles with no flaking, and after that, the defect was observed by the UT and the microscopic tester. Figure 27 shows an example of the defect image change from before to after life testing, and Table 9 shows the defect characteristics evaluated by the U.T. before and after life testing and the total number of cycles. Compared with the defect image before testing, the image after testing was remarkably different and the defect size in the image had grown to more than three times. That means that the actual size of the defect had grown to about twice in size. The image after testing had the white band at the defect position that looked like the Milky Way. That indicated the race way and appeared by the influence of the dent shaped by the rolling balls.

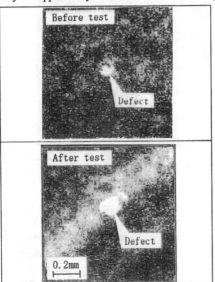

Figure 27-*Defect image change in testing.*

Table 9-*Defect characteristics and fatigue. life*

	Defect characteristics		
	depth	size	position
Before	80 μm	18 μm	just under
After	80 μm	38 μm	just under
Fatigue life cycles	1×10^8		

Figure 28-*Microscopic observation by SEM.*

Figure 28 shows the example of the microscopic observation of the actual defect after life testing by SEM. That defect had a nonmetallic inclusion and cracks and it was confirmed by SEM analysis that the nonmetallic inclusion was Al_2O_3-CaO complex. The remarkable point was that the cracks were connected to the nonmetallic inclusion and inclined at an angle of about 45 degrees against the surface. So, it was presumed that starting from the nonmetallic inclusion, the cracks were generated and grew by the shear stress during the life testing. The change of the defect image after life testing indicated the generation of the cracks.

(3) *Case 3 (No change of Defect Image)*- In this case, as in case 2, the life testing was finished after 1×10^8 cycles with no flaking, and after that, the defect was observed by U.T. Figure 29 shows an example of the defect image change from before to after life testing, and Table 10 shows the defect characteristics evaluated by the U.T. before life testing and the total number of cycles. There was no change of the defect image, and the microscopic observation found no cracks. Figure 30 shows the defect image of another case, in which the relative position between the defect and the race way was set a little bit out. In this case, there was also no change of the defect image.

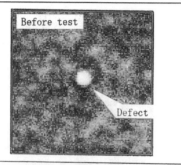

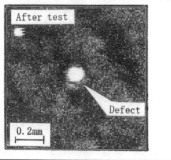

Figure 29-*Defect image change in testing.*

Table 10-*Defect characteristics and fatigue life.*

	Defect characteristics		
	depth	size	position
Before	180 μm	27 μm	just under
Before	180 μm	38 μm	little bit out
Fatigue life cycles			1×10^8

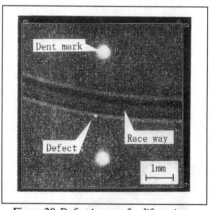

Figure 30-*Defect image after life testing*

(4) *Relationship Between Fatigue Life and Nonmetallic Inclusions* [3] -Figure 31 shows the relationship between the nonmetallic inclusions and the flaking on the bearing steel products. The size and depth from the sample surface of the nonmetallic inclusions were evaluated by the U.T. before life testing, and the flaking behavior was observed by rolling contact fatigue life testing, which was performed on the condition of adjusting the position of the evaluated nonmetallic inclusions just under the race way. It was confirmed that nonmetallic inclusions whose size was over 20 μm and whose depth was 100 μm to 150 μm under surface (the biggest shear stress range) could be the starting point of the flaking.

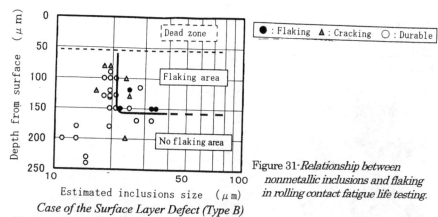

Figure 31-*Relationship between nonmetallic inclusions and flaking in rolling contact fatigue life testing.*

Case of the Surface Layer Defect (Type B)

(1) *Case 4 (Flaking)*- Figure 32 shows an example of the flaking, and Table 11 shows the defect characteristics evaluated by the U.T. before testing and the number of cycles when flaking occurred. Figure 33 shows the shape of the flaking measured by the depth meter. The same as Type A, the flaking point was presumed at the defect point, but the situation was remarkably different. The number of cycles at flaking was smaller than that of Type A, and the depth of the flaking reaches the maximum shear stress range about 150 μm beyond the defect size. Of course, it was beforehand confirmed that no defect existed in that range.

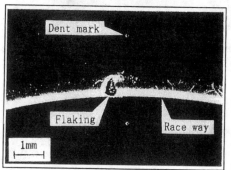

Figure 32-*Example of flaking.*

Table11-*Defect characteristics and fatigue life.*

Defect characteristics			Fatigue life
depth	size	position	cycles
~37 μm	-	just under	4.1×10^6

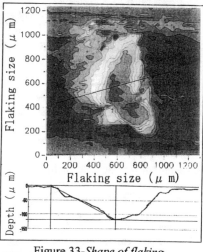

Figure 33-*Shape of flaking.*

Case 5 (Change of Defect Image)- Figure 34 shows an example of the defect image change. Table 12 shows the defect characteristics and the total number of cycles, and Figure 35 shows the microscopic observation. The change of the defect image and the defect type was the same as Type A, but the result of the microscopic observation was slightly different. In that observation, it was confirmed that the cracks ran vertically below the surface with the nonmetallic inclusion. So, it was presumed that the stress that generated the cracks was the tensile stress which registered the maximum in the surface layer. To return to Case 4, which had flaking, the mechanism of the flaking by the defect existing in the surface layer was presumed as follows. First, the crack was generated by the tensile stress starting from the nonmetallic inclusion existing in the surface layer toward the surface, and it grew vertically below the surface with the nonmetallic inclusion. When the crack approached the maximum shear stress range, the growing direction of the crack was changed to the horizontal by the shear stress, and finally it made the flaking.

Table 12-*Defect characteristics and fatigue life.*

Defect characteristics			Fatigue life cycles
depth	size	position	
~37 μm	-	little bit out	1×10^8

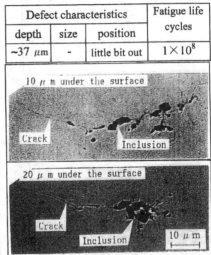

Figure 34-*Defect image change in life testing.*   Figure 35-*Microscopic observation.*

Considerations

The results shown above suggested that the most harmful inclusions to the bearing life was the Al2O3-CaO complex inclusions whose size was over about 20 μm, but the life of the bearing was strongly dependent on its position. So, the most important subject for the steel maker is how to decrease the Al2O3-CaO complex inclusions.

Improvement of Nonmetallic Inclusion

Process and Refining Improvement

Figure 36 shows the process flow of No.3 EAF-BL/CC line in Aichi Steel Co. The bearing steels are mainly produced on this line. Table 13 shows the details of the evaluated sample. One of the countermeasures to form fine nonmetallic inclusions is the slag basicity control. Two types of refining methods were applied for the evaluation of samples, one was the conventional refining method (called Method A), and the other, which was twice as high slag basicity was the improved refining method (called Method B). The samples were taken at each stage from refining to final rolling. Each sample was evaluated for the distribution and the composition of the nonmetallic inclusions by the U.T., E.A.A.S/C.C.M. and EPMA. In addition to these, the final rolled products were evaluated on the fatigue life by the rolling contact fatigue life testing.

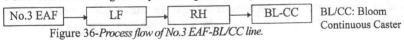

Figure 36-*Process flow of No.3 EAF-BL/CC line.*   BL/CC: Bloom Continuous Caster

Table 13-*Details of the evaluated sample.*

Specimen	Refining	Slag basicity	Sampling
SUJ2	Method A	CaO/SiO$_2$	metal during RH operation
	(conventional)	5	final rolled products
	Method B	CaO/SiO$_2$	metal during RH operation
	(improved)	$\geqq 10$	final rolled products

SUJ2 Chemical Composition(%)		
C	Si	Mn
1.00	0.25	0.35
Cr	S	Mo
1.45	0.002	<0.008

Results

Size Distribution of Nonmetallic Inclusions at Refining Stage-Figure 37 shows the size distribution of the nonmetallic inclusions evaluated by the E.A.A.S/C.C.M, and the total oxygen at each refining stage. As compared with Method A, the number of the nonmetallic inclusions and the total oxygen were both improved by Method B at each stage. Especially, the number of nonmetallic inclusions over 20 μm was reduced by that method.

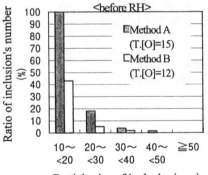

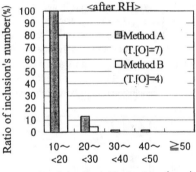

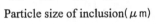

Figure 37-*Size distribution of the inclusions evaluated by E.A.A.S/C.C.M. at each stage.*

Size Distribution of Nonmetallic Inclusions in Final Rolled Products-Figure 38 and 39 show the size distribution of nonmetallic inclusions in the final rolled products of the bearing steel evaluated by the U.T and the E.A.A.S/C.C.M. As compared with Method A, the number of the nonmetallic inclusions was reduced by Method B. Its effect on reducing the nonmetallic inclusions over 20 μm size was especially remarkable.

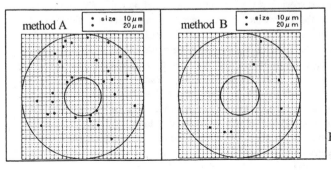

Figure 38-*Size distribution evaluated by U.T.*

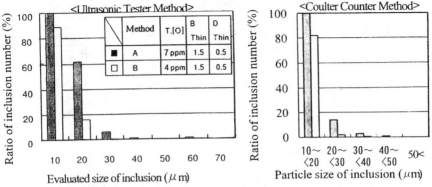

Figure 39-*Size distribution of non-metallic inclusions in the final rolled products.*

Relationship between Composition and Size Distribution of Inclusions- Figure 40 shows the ratio of the Al_2O_3 and $mCaO-nAl_2O_3$ inclusions after RH operation for each refining method. The composition of each inclusion was judged by the EPMA. As compared with Method A, the $mCaO-nAl_2O_3$ was remarkably reduced by Method B. Figure 41 shows the roughly indicated size distribution of the nonmetallic inclusions for each composition and producing stage. It was confirmed that the $mCaO-nAl_2O_3$ inclusion's sizes were larger than those of Al_2O_3 at each stage, and that might be caused by the difference of the melting points for each inclusion. So, it was confirmed that Method B had the effect of not only reducing the number of the nonmetallic inclusions but also making their sizes finer.

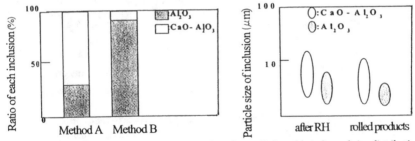

Figure 40-*Ratio of each composition of nonmetallic inclusions after RH operation.*

Figure 41-*Roughly indicated size distribution of each inclusion at each stage.*

Figure 42 shows the example of the size distribution of the nonmetallic inclusions evaluated by the E.A.A.S/C.C.M. The evaluated specimens were sampled during RH operation for each refining method. It was confirmed that the nonmetallic inclusions were distributed exponentially. Figure 43 shows the comparison of the calculated total oxygen and the analyzed total oxygen for each sample. The former was calculated assuming that the total oxygen was roughly equal to the sum of the oxygen contents including in the inclusions, and that the size and number distribution of the nonmetallic inclusions were to be exponential based on the evaluation by the E.A.A.S/C.C.M. Therefore the number of smaller inclusions under 3 μm that could not be counted by the C.C.M, also belonged to the exponential distribution from Figure 42. It was clear that the calculated total oxygen was lower than the analyzed total oxygen at every point from Figure 43, therefore the calculation was not so accurate. But on the comparison of the deviation from the equal line for both refining methods, the situation was remarkably different.

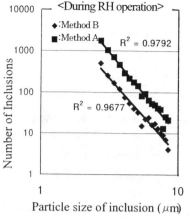

Figure 42-*Example of size distribution of nonmetallic inclusions by E.A.A.S/C.C.M.*

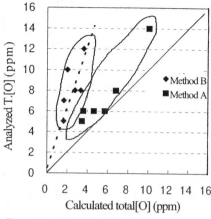

Figure 43-*Total oxygen comparison with calculated and analyzed.*

In the case of Method A, the calculated total oxygen was nearly equal to the analyzed one, and it might mean that most inclusions have sizes larger than 3 μm. In the case of Method B, the calculated total oxygen was quite different than the analyzed one, and it might mean that most inclusions had sizes smaller than 3 μm. So, it was assumed that the number of inclusions under 3 μ m in the specimen of Method B no longer followed the exponential distribution determined by the evaluation. From these results, method B might be more effective for making nonmetallic inclusion's sizes finer.

Improvement of Rolling Contact Fatigue Life-Figure 44 shows the result of the rolling contact fatigue life testing for the bearing steel products produced by each refining method. As mentioned above, Method B, by which the nonmetallic inclusions were reduced and minimized, improved the rolling contact fatigue life much better than Method A.

Conclusions

(1) We established method for the evaluation of the size distribution of the nonmetallic inclusions by the U.T and the E.A.A.S/C.C.M.

(2) We confirmed that refining Method B was effective to reduce the number and size of the non-metallic inclusions and improve the L_{10} life on the rolling contact fatigue life testing.

(3) We confirmed that non-metallic inclusions over 20 μm subsurface caused the flaking in the rolling contact fatigue life testing.

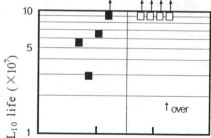

Figure 44-*Result of rolling contact fatigue life Testing.*

References

1)Nagayama, et al.:CAMP-ISIJ vol.11(1998)-1323

2)Nishimon, et al.:CAMP-ISIJ vol.12(1999)-1390

3)Nishikawa, et al.:CAMP-ISIJ vol.12(1999)-1388

Dieter Thiery[1] and Christof Delhaes[2]

Higher Macro-Cleanliness of Bearing Steels Needs More Accurate Measuring-Methods[3]

Reference: Thiery, D., and Delhaes, C., "Higher Macro-Cleanliness of Bearing Steels Needs More Accurate Measuring-Methods," Bearing Steel Technology, ASTM STP 1419, J. M. Beswick, Ed., American Society for Testing and Materials International, West Conshohocken, PA, 2002.

Abstract: Increasing requirements of trendsetter-industry (automotive and railway) on the performance of bearings demand also an improvement of the applied materials. That means principally to reduce macroscopic, non-metallic inclusions. Therefore, steel works need new targets to optimize metallurgical and casting techniques.
For this reason, ultrasonic examination methods are more and more applied to test bigger volumes instead of plains. Especially the immersion ultrasonic testing allows to detect smaller inhomogenities.
To get optimal testing conditions, SAARSTAHL AG and FhG-IZfP made pretests.
Then, the german steel industry in the VDEh made a circle examination to optimize and standardize the test conditions. The reproducible limit size of detectable defects seems to be an equivalent flat bottom hole of 300 to 400 µm for the chosen conditions.
All results of the circle examination were used to prepare detailed prescriptions for a test in form of a german standard (SEP 1927), presented in this paper.

Keywords: Bearing steel, Macro-cleanliness, Immersion ultrasonic testing, SEP 1927

[1]Senior Quality Manager, Saarstahl AG, Section WW-VK, 66330 Völklingen, Germany.
[2]Dr.-Ing., Quality Manager NDT Level III, Section WW-VK, Saarstahl AG, 66330 Völklingen, Germany.
[3]Joint Investigation Projekt of the German Steel Industry at VDEh (German Iron and Steel Institute) level in cooperation with the German Bearing Industry.

Introduction

Steel, like practically all products or services, is subject to ever severer quality requirements. Classical grade 52100 anti-friction bearing steel is an important indicator in this connection. Having existed for 100 years now, it is to be regarded as a mature product. Thanks to the permanent improvement of steel products, the performance of certain types of bearings made from these products has increased by 500% over the last 50 years. The reasons for this are manifold. They reach from geometrical optimization through improved lubrication methods to significant minimization of non-metallic inclusions in steel by permanently reducing oxygen levels or by aluminium-free steelmaking practices [1]. Warranty periods have increased from one to three or even four years in the automotive industry and from 500 000 to 2 000 000 km for railway rolling stock.

Already in 1994, there was a publication entitled "Clean Steel is Harder to Measure than Produce" [2]. Why? The traditional inspection methods for macroscopic cleanliness - step-machining and blue brittle fracture test - have lost their significance with today's quality standards. Inclusions have become smaller and less frequent. But with today's more demanding service conditions, they may nevertheless represent starting points for pitting. In the context of a continuous improvement program at steel plant level, new, more accurate and safe measuring methods are required in order to establish significant target values. Immersion ultrasonic testing obviously is such a method. Specialists in the Non-destructive Testing Industry know the manifold applications of this process as well as the influencing parameters which may have to be taken into account. It is, therefore, essential to specify the test conditions in full detail. It will be shown in the following that, based on immersion ultrasonic testing, a technique has been developed which gives fairly comparable results. Macroscopic cleanliness shall be determined by the immersion ultrasonic testing process. (Figure 1) schematically shows such a facility, where the search unit and the object under test are located in a tank containing the couplant (normally water).

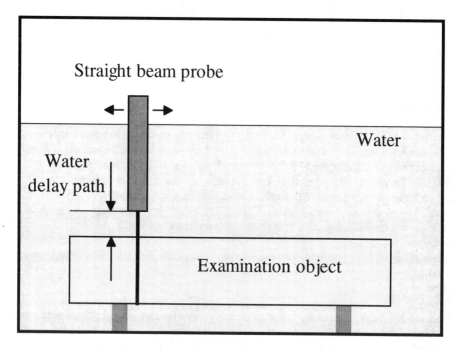

Figure 1 - *Principle of immersion ultrasonic testing.*

This inspection method guarantees a constant transmission of the sonic energy between the search unit and the object under examination. The ultrasonic wavelength decreases with increasing frequency so that very small discontinuities can be detected. At the same time, however, sound attenuation increases and, as a result, the cross-section that can be examined is reduced. In the manual or automated ultrasonic inspection of steel bars, search units with frequencies from 2 to 6 MHz are used in most cases. Cleanliness examination employs higher frequencies, usually between 10 and 25 MHz, depending on the aim of the inspection.

The inspection area and the material thicknesses to be examined at the highest sensitivity can be varied by selecting different water travel distances and types of search unit.

Preliminary Investigations at IzfP Saarbrücken and at Saarstahl

The results of immersion ultrasonic testing may be influenced by a great number of parameters. To determine appropriate test conditions for cleanliness inspection, preliminary investigations were conducted by the Fraunhofer Institute for Non-destructive Testing (IzfP), Saarbrücken.

The influence of different search units and different surface conditions (roughness, geometry) is described in the following.

Surface Roughness

If a surface presenting different sonic permeabilities is hit by an ultrasonic beam at a non-vertical angle, the beam will be refracted. The question how much of the beam is reflected and how much of it may penetrate into the material depends on the angle of incidence as well as on the density of the material under test multiplied by its sound velocity. With increasing roughness of the entry surface, the fraction of the beam that penetrates into the material becomes smaller and the untested near-surface area ("dead zone") increases in size.

For test purpose, a material surface was prepared so as to present six different roughnesses betwen 5.68 and 62.16 µm depth. (Figure 2) is a high-frequency signal representation of the A-scans for roughness depths of 5.68 µm and 37.76 µm.

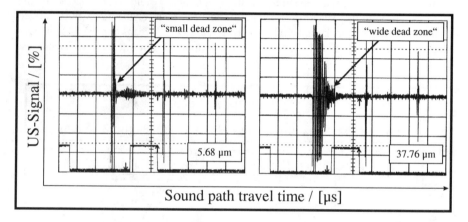

Figure 2 - *Comparison of different surface roughnessess (5.68 µm and 37.76 µm).*

The decay length was defined as the distance in steel in mm at which the entry signal has dropped to 5 % of the screen height. An evaluation of the A-scans gives the following (Table 1).

Table 1 - *Decay length of the entry signal for different roughness values.*

Roughness [µm]	Decay length [mm steel]
5.68	5.7
6.32	5.7
33.29	22.8
37.76	30.4
47.68	30.4
62.16	32.3

Inspecting the volume of a steel billet at metal distances from 5 mm is only possible if the surface roughness is 6.32 µm or smaller.

Surface Geometry

What is to be regarded as surface roughness at microscopic level may be described as surface geometry at macroscopic level. The different angles of incidence resulting from the geometry of the entry surface affect both the reflected and penetrating fractions of the sound wave beam. If the entry surface is not plane but curved, the sound field generated within the metal is deformed. The length of the near field, the focal point and the angle of divergence are modified.

In the case of a convex entry surface, e.g., the periphery of round bars, the sound beam is more or less de-focussed depending on the radius of curvature. The decrease of the sound pressure with the delay time is more pronounced than for the plane entry surface of, for instance, square or flat material. (Figure 3) shows the A-scans of slots of equal size (reflecting surface 0.2 mm x 2 mm) contained in a 55-mm square and round test specimen.

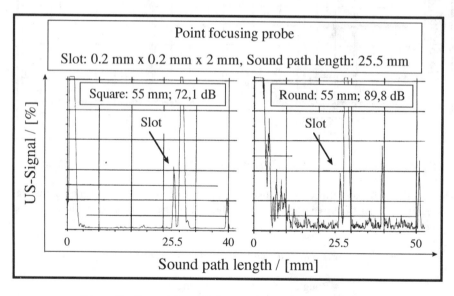

Figure 3 - *Comparison of plane and curved entry surfaces.*

For the same sound travel and grain structure, the gain of the ultrasonic instrument must be increased by approximately 18 dB, in order to amplify the slot signal from the round piece to the screen height of that from the square sample. The electrical and structural noise levels are also amplified, which markedly decreases the signal-to-noise ratio. Furthermore, the dead zone is extended. This geometrical influence is weaker for search units featuring a lesser degree of focussing.

Influence of the Search Unit

Inspection for cleanliness aims to detect small discontinuities over the cross-section in as much volume as possible at constant water travel distance and equal sensitivity. These are partly conflicting requirements, which is why it is necessary to determine an optimum combination of type of search unit, inspection frequency, transducer diameter and water delay path.

Using a point-focussed and a plane transducer, a square and a round sample with 80 mm diameter were examined by the immersion method. The 200 µm wide and 2 mm long spark-eroded slots at 18 mm, 28 mm and 73 mm metal distance could not always be detected by both search units. The search unit and process data are given in (Table 2).

Table 2 - *Search unit and process data.*

Search unit	$D_{Transducer}$ [mm]	Focussing	Focal length [mm]	Near field length [mm]	Water delay path [mm]
A	6	-	-	60 (H_2O)	22
B	19	point focus	150 (H_2O)	-	62

As shown in (Table 3), the search unit having a plane transducer detects the slots at greater sound path lengths than the point-focussed unit. The plane entry surfaces are more favorable for the detection of flaws than the curved surfaces.

Table 3 - *Comparison of different search units.*

Sound path [mm]	Specimen containing slots (Width 200 µm; length 2 mm; distance from backwall 200 µm)			
	Square specimen 80 mm		Round specimen 80 mm	
	Search unit A	Search unit B	Search unit A	Search unit B
8	detected	detected	detected	detected
18	detected	detected	detected	detected
28	detected	detected	detected	detected
38	detected	detected	detected	**not detected**
73	detected	**not detected**	**not detected**	**not detected**

Preliminary Tests at Member Works of the German Iron and Steel Institute (VDEh)

In a joint investigation project, the German steel industry has performed immersion ultrasonic examinations on defined samples in order to gain experience which is to serve as basis for specifying a unified inspection procedure. These tests were performed by the following works: Edelstahlwerke Witten Krefeld, Georgsmarienhütte, Krupp

Edelstahlprofile, Lechstahlwerke, Mannesmann Forschungsinstitut, Saarstahl and VSG Energie- und Schmiedetechnik.

Table 4 lists the solid-material test samples with either curved or flat test surface which were chosen for a joint investigation project. Nine different samples were chosen in order to determine the minimum detectable reflector sizes as well as the parameters influencing the test. The samples contained natural flaws as well as artificial flaws of different size and geometry.

Table 4 - *Samples used in the joint investigation.*

Specimen No.	Dimension [mm]	Reflector
1	round 50 length 60	natural defects
2	round 50 length 350	artificial defects
3	square 50 length 120	natural defects
4	square 55 length 250	artificial defects
5	round 97 length 250	natural defects
6 a (small) 6 b (large)	ASTM 588 Cal. Specimen	artificial defects
8 a 8 b	2 x round 45 length 240	natural defects

The samples were made available by the participating works without prior definition of inspection conditions. The requirement was that all discontinuities contained in the samples should be detected and evaluated.

The different influencing parameters, such as location and geometry of discontinuities, geometry of test samples, preparation of test samples, calibration blocks, search units and water delay path were investigated.

The results are given for the samples 2 and 4 (Figures 4 and 5). These samples contained spark-eroded defined slots representing discontinuities of known location, orientation and size. The ultrasonic inspection results, however, scatter over a very large range.

Sample No. 2, a round bar of 50 mm diameter, contains four slots at a depth of approximately 6, 25, 28 and 44 mm. According to the manufacturer of the samples, their ultrasonic response characteristics is equivalent to that of a 400 µm flat-bottom hole.

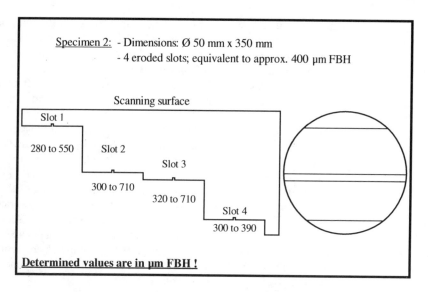

Figure 4 - *Results from round specimen No. 2.*

The near-surface slot was not always detected, which greatly depended on the search unit used. The artificial reflector was found to be equivalent to a 280 to 550 µm FBH. Slot No. 4 at 44 mm metal depth shows similar results. This slot was not always detected. It was evaluated equivalent to between 300 and 390 µm FBH. The slots at 25 and 28 mm distance were detected in each case. Their size is reported to range from 300 to 710 µm and 320 to 710 µm respectively.

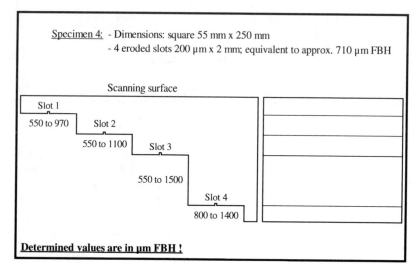

Figure 5 - *Results from square specimen No. 4.*

Figure 5 shows the results from specimen No. 4. This square specimen (55 mm) has four steps containing slots at metal distances of approximately 7, 16, 26 and 48 mm. According to its manufacturer, the slots are 200 μm x 2 mm in size, which gives an calculated ultrasonic response equivalent to a 710 μm FBH. The slots representing the shortest and the longest sound travel could not always be evaluated. The difference between the respective maximum and minimum values is very great. For slot No. 3 these values differ by a factor of almost 3.

Evidently, an ultrasonic examination is no absolute measuring method. It is based on comparison to known reflectors, the data of which have to be stated in each case. The reference reflectors used may be natural flaws or artificially produced, such as transverse holes, flat-bottom holes, slots or ball impressions.

In Germany, the flat-bottom hole, which is the basis of the DGS-diagram, is the generally employed reference reflector. This type of reflector, which is usually generated by drilling, is more difficult to produce in a calibration block than other reflectors. ASTM 588 standard specification uses ball impressions as reference reflectors. Along the lines of this standard, two specimens were introduced into the project. The test pieces and results are schematically shown in (Figure 6). Using a carbide-metal ball of 10 mm diameter, impressions of different depth were made in the specimens.

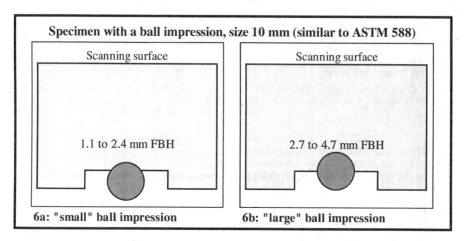

Figure 6 - *Results of specimen Nos. 6a and 6b.*

The depth of the impressions was supposed to be negligible so that the evaluation of specimens Nos. 6a and 6b should reveal no difference. The reflectors were evaluated to be equivalent to, respectively, 1.1 to 2.4 and 2.7 to 4.7 mm FBH. During the test, it was found to be difficult to scan the apex of the ball impression with maximum sound pressure and to clearly separate this signal from several backwall echos. This is the reason for the extremely different evaluation results. The details of the results are described in the literature (See References [3]).

The general conclusion to be drawn from the above is that it is essential to specify test conditions in full detail in order to obtain comparable results.

If test conditions, particularly the search unit data, are not specified, defect detectability and evaluation will be inconsistent. Ball impressions are considered unsuitable as reference reflectors. Testing square and flat specimens is more sensitive than testing round specimens. As it seems, the reproducible limit of the minimum defect size for automatic evaluation is eqivalent to a 300 to 400 µm flat-bottom hole (FBH).

The following theoretical considerations were made in order to improve the assessability of detectable flaw sizes. The reflecting area of the discontinuity in the sound beam is the decisive characteristic for the ultrasonic signal received. In (Figure 7) a plane "natural" flaw is compared to a flat bottom hole.

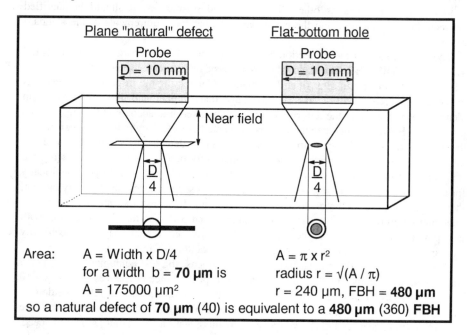

Figure 7 - *Comparison of defect detectability.*

Using a plane transducer with 10 mm diameter, a reflector is viewed within the range of highest sensitivity, i. e., in the focal point. The diameter of the sound beam (6dB drop) at this point is ¼ of the transducer diameter. The area of a planar defect of, say, 70 µm width is 175,000 µm². Consequently, an inclusion of 70 µm size, which is longer than the sound field, produces the same signal height as an artificial defect (FBH) of 480 µm. The ratio of the different geometries becomes greater, if the two reflectors are compared outside the focal point.

Draft of a German Preliminary Standard (Stahl-Eisen-Prüfblatt SEP 1927)

To unify test conditions and obtain reproducible test results, a tentative standard [4] was prepared on the basis of the above-mentioned findings, This standard (Stahl-Eisen-Prüfblatt SEP 1927), which will be adopted in 2001, has been coordinated between the German steel industry and steel users, particularly suppliers to the automotive industry.

The standard applies to automated immersion ultrasonic inspections of suitably prepared specimens from rolled or forged steel, except for austenitic, ferritic-austenitic, and free-machining steels. It is to be used for solid parts of simple geometry (e. g. square or round), having 20 to 100 mm diameter or side length, or for the inspection of the rim zone of larger parts at metal distances up to 50 mm. For application of the standard to non-transformable steels or other dimensions and geometries, it should be clarified between the manufacturer and the customers, whether the requirements of the standard can be met.

The qualification of the inspection personnel is specified in accordance with DIN EN 473 and ISO/FDIS 9712. The standard makes a basic difference between the inspection of a heat of steel before and after final deformation. Conducting the inspection on products in the as-delivered condition has the advantage that supplier and user ought to obtain identical results and that the deformation is already taken into account at the stage of the inspection.. However, the specimens to be inspected are often cylindrical, which means that radially oriented discontinuities are not necessarily detected by straight-beam search units. When testing steel products prior to final deformation, samples representing the same or a similar reduction ratio as the final product must be rolled or forged specifically for ultrasonic testing purposes. As the geometry of these test pieces can be freely chosen, they usually have a square cross-section presenting flat, easy-to-scan entry surfaces. Specimens with this geometry can be scanned from four sides, so that discontinuities with any possible orientation can be detected. Furthermore, a heat may be specifically earmarked for a particular use depending on the inspection findings.

The standard specifies the surface of the specimens, the test equipment (e. g., plane transducers with diameters chosen to match the respective metal distances and having 10 MHz nominal frequency), the calibration (geometry of reference blocks, reference defects of 1.0 mm FBH), the sensitivity levels, expection volume, the performance of the inspection (tranducer feed distance, scanning method, test ranges, gating, scanning speed, pulse repetition frequency, pulse distance, water delay path, evaluation method), the determination of acceptability limits, and the preparation of the inspection report.

To validate SEP 1927 standard specification, another joint investigation is scheduled. The results will probably be available already by the end of this year.

It can be assumed already now that the standard will have to be revised or extended, e. g. for higher transducer frequencies (15 MHz), once enough practical experience is available. Still, the a.m. standard allows to compare the results obtained in the meantime.

Summary

The cleanliness of steels, particularly of bearing steels, has continuously been improved in recent years. This is why conventional blue brittle fracture testing will be supplemented by the more sensitive immersion ultrasonic inspection method in determining macroscopic cleanliness. As a result, it will be possible to specify adequate target values to be taken into account by steelmakers.

This paper describes how a standard inspection sheet for ultrasonic testing came about. Members of the German Iron and Steel Institute (VDEh) and steel users, particularly bearing manufacturers, have prepared the tentative standard "Stahl-Eisen-Prüfblatt (SEP) 1927."

Various preliminary tests and a joint investigation at VDEh level have shown that a very detailed specification of the parameters affecting the inspection results is necessary in order to obtain reproducible and comparable ultrasonic inspection results. The experience gained went into SEP 1927 standard, which will be adopted in 2001. Another joint investigation is scheduled in order to validate SEP 1927. The results will probably be available by the end of the year. On the basis of the data obtained by this new investigation and of the then comparable inspections, the Standard shall be revised in the foreseeable future and possibly be transformed into a European or ISO standard.

References

[1] Thiery, D., Bettinger, R., Krumpholz, A., Valtentin, P., "Aluminiumfreier Wälzlagerstahl," *Verlag Stahleisen GmbH Düsseldorf*, Reprint 117, Number 8, 1997, pp. 79-89.

[2] Jacobi, D., "Clean Steel is Harder to Measure Than Produce," *Metallurgie und Werkstofftechnik hochreiner Stähle*, StuE 114, No. 11, 1994, pp. 45-56.

[3] Thiery, D., Delhaes, Chr., "Die Ultraschall-Tauchtechnik als Mittel zur Bestimmung des makroskopischen Reinheitsgrades von Stählen," *Härtereitechnische Mitteilungen Hanser Verlag München*", Issue 3, No. 55, 2000, pp. 160-165.

[4] Stahl-Eisen-Prüfblatt SEP 1927 "Ultraschall-Tauchtechnik-Prüfung zur Bestimmung des makroskopischen Reinheitsgrades von gewalzten oder geschmiedeten Stäben aus Stahl," *Verlag Stahleisen GmbH Düsseldorf.*

Yoshiyuki Kato,[1] Kaiko Sato,[1] Kazuhiko Hiraoka,[1] and Yoshio Nuri[1]

Recent Evaluation Procedures of Nonmetallic Inclusions in Bearing Steels (Statistics of Extreme Value Method and Development of Higher Frequency Ultrasonic Testing Method)

Reference: Kato, Y., Sato, K., Hiraoka K., and Nuri, Y., "**Recent Evaluation Procedures of Nonmetallic Inclusions in Bearing Steels (Statistics of Extreme Value Method and Development of Higher Frequency Ultrasonic Testing Method),**" *Bearing Steel Technology, STP 1419*, J. M. Beswick, Ed., American Society for Testing and Materials International, West Conshohocken, PA, 2002.

Abstract: Large microscopic inclusions from 20 to 100 μm in diameter have recently been paid attention from a viewpoint of fatigue strength of steel products. As the inclusion detection capability, or probability, is practically limited by a conventional optical microscopy, however, the evaluation of the distribution of these inclusions used to be feasible only by extraction method such as acid-solution procedure. It has been found that ultrasonic testing with 50 to 125 MHz frequency, focus-type transducers is suitable to evaluate the inclusions where the echo intensity is proportional to inclusion diameter. This paper will describe recent inclusion evaluation procedures and, as a main body, the results of the application of the new ultrasonic testing system. Included are:

The relationship between oxygen content in steel and maximum inclusion diameter in steel predicted by statistics of extreme value with the aid of microscopic image analysis, and

The inclusion diameter distribution measured directly by the ultrasonic testing

Keywords: nonmetallic inclusion, bearing steel, cleanliness, ultrasonic testing, micro inclusion, oxygen content, SAE 52100, statistics of extreme value method

---

[1] Reserch Engineer, Technological Research Laboratory, Sanyo Special Steel Co., Ltd..,
3007, Shikama-ku, Himeji-city, 672-8677 Japan.

Introduction

Demands on the reduction of weight and fuel consumption involved in motorcar technology stimulate the development of higher strength of materials and longer fatigue life of automotive parts. The improvement of the steel manufacturing process as greatly contributed in producing higher strength materials with better micro-cleanliness. The large size inclusion, which is often seen in the center of the fish eye of a fracture surface of rotary-bent fatigue test specimens, has significantly adverse effects on the fatigue property of materials[1-2]. The conventional evaluation methods for inclusions such as the optical microscopic and acid dissolution methods may not give detailed information of the large size inclusion with 20-200µm. There is an inclusion size range where the evaluation is not well done in the conventional methods as shown in Figure 1. The improvement in terms of reliable, quantitative and quick evaluation on the referred size inclusion is desired.

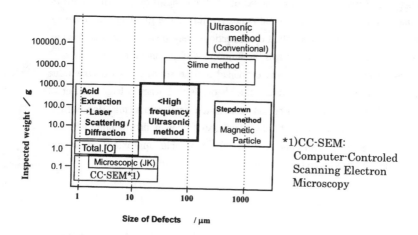

Figure 1-- *Size of defects and evaluation methods.*

An evaluating method for the inclusion in steel using the short focus (PF = 6.5-12.5 mm) probe with higher frequency of 50-125 MHz has been studied in Europe, the United States and Japan over the last five years. This evaluation method has been attracting attention as an epoch-making evaluation method because it was reported that small inclusions down to 10 µm could be found [3-4]. In this report, the distribution of the parameters (slope and intercept) and the maximum predicted diameter are described by two-dimensional statistics of extreme values obtained so far and the problems with statistics of extreme value are discussed. Further, the following items are described: 1) the outline of the system to evaluate the diameter of inclusion from echo amplitude by the focusing higher frequency ultrasonic detection method; and 2) the feature of the system, for instance, the direct observation of inclusion with C-scope imaging unit, the possibility of detection of extrinsic inclusion, the measurement of inclusion size by distance amplitude correction.

Calculation Condition and Experimental Procedure

Parameter and Predicted $\sqrt{area}$ $_{max(So,S)}$ of Statistics of Extreme Value Method

The experimental material was a round bar of 65 mm diameter forged from a rolled billet of 167 mm round. Sample areas of 10 mm (length) by 10 mm (width) by 10 mm (thickness) were cut from the mid radius position. After grinding and polishing, the cleanliness of inclusion on polished cross-sections were measured by microscope. The size of the maximum inclusion and the number of all the inclusions larger than 3 μm diameter in each sample area was examined for the statistics of extreme value analysis. The basic concept of extreme value theory is that when a large number of observations following a basic distribution, such as a normal, exponential, log-normal, etc., are collected, the maxima of these sets also follow a distribution, which is different from the basic distribution. A widely applicable approximation to this distribution function was given by Gumbel [5] as

$$G(z) = exp(-exp(-(z-\lambda)/\alpha))   \qquad (1)$$

where $G(z)$ is the probability that the largest inclusion is no larger than size z, and α and λ are the scale and location parameters. In the method of Murakami [6,7], a standard inspection area $So(mm^2)$ is defined. The area of the maximum inclusion in S_0 is measured. Then, the square root of the area $z = \sqrt{area}$ $_{max}$ of the maximum inclusion is calculated. This is repeated for N areas S_0. The cumulative probability $G(z_{(i)})$ of the ith largest maximum inclusion size $z_{(i)}$ can be calculated simply by

$$G(z_{(i)}) = i/(N + 1) = exp(-exp(-(z_{(i)}-\lambda)/\alpha))   \qquad (2)$$

where $z_{(i)}$ is the ith in the ordered series of $\sqrt{area}_{max,i}$ If the distribution of Equation (1) is correct and if inclusion size $z(i)$ is plotted against $-\ln(-\ln(i/(N + 1)))$, an approximate straight line of slope α and intercept λ on the vertical axis is obtained.

For the estimation of the distribution of inclusion size in a large area of steel S, the return period T, is defined as

$$T = S/So \qquad (3)$$

where So is the inspected area from a single sample area.

The characteristic size of the maximum inclusion (CSMI) in large area S (i.e., the size expected to be exceeded exactly once in area S), which is denoted by z, can be defined by solving the equation $G(z) = 1-1/T$ to give

$$(z-\lambda)/\alpha = -\ln(-\ln(T- 1)/T)) \qquad (4)$$

Hence, the characteristic size of the maximum inclusion in the large area S, z, can be estimated from Equation (4) once α and λ are estimated. In this report, the calculate conditions of predicted $\sqrt{area}_{max(So,S)}$ are $S_0=100\ mm^2\square\ S=30000\ mm^2$, $\square=30$.

Evaluation of Oxide Inclusion by Focusing Higher Frequency Ultrasonic Detection Method

Scanning Conditions-- A large microscopic inclusion in steel was examined for the possibility of evaluation by ultrasonic detection. It was found that a 100 MHz probe allowed to evaluate inclusions more than 20μm while 50 MHz prove could evaluate ones more than 30μm. Conditions of ultrasonic detection is shown in Table 1. The schematic diagram of the device is shown in Figure 2. The procedure and the outline of focusing higher frequency ultrasonic detection methods developed by the authors so far is described below.

The Review of Higher Frequency Ultrasonic Detection [8]

Probe and Detection Sensitivity of Defect-- Detection sensitivity of focusing higher-frequency probe (PF=12.5, Frequency 50, 80, 100 and 125 MHz) is to be approximately 1/4 of a wavelength.

Scanning Method of Detection, Two-Phase Scanning - Scanning mode is basically

plane. Scanning path interval is usually set to 30-100 μm, which is smaller than the beam diameter from the probe. Two-phase scanning is conducted consisting of the rough detection for the determination of the coordinate position in the first stage and the precise detection right above inclusions for the second stage.

Table 1--*Condition of ultrasonic detection.*

Item	Distance(mm)
Focal Point in Water	12.5
Water Path	6.5
Dead Zone	0 to 0.5
Gate Range Below Surface	1.0 to 2.0 or 1.0 to 1.5
Focal point Below Surface	1.0 to 1.5

Wavelength*1)	Frequency(MHz)			
	50	80	100	125
1/2-Wavelength(μm)	59	37	30	24
1/4-Wavelength(μm)	30	18	15	12

*1) Wavelength = Sound velocity
/ Frequency (Hz)x10^6
(Sound velocity =5900m/sec in steel)

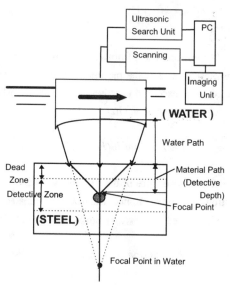

Figure 2--*Immersion transducer and condition of ultrasonic detection.*

The reason why two-phase scanning is necessary is that inclusions will not come in the center axis of the probe during scanning. Since the beam diameter from the probe is narrow with 100-200 μm and the attenuation in the radius direction is large, it is difficult to give the correction equation of echo amplitude. Accordingly, measurements should be made right above the inclusion.

Amplitude Correction Detection Area in the Axis Directions -The position (z)

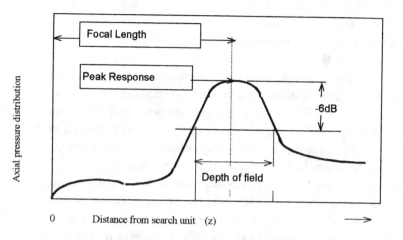

Figure 3-- *On-axis profile parameters from focused search unit.*

of inclusions in the axis direction can be obtained from the beam path length. Echo amplitude in the axis direction becomes the maximum at the focal point as shown in Figure 3, and decreases in the front and back position of the focal point in accordance with ASTM Standard Guide for Evaluating Characteristics of Ultrasonic Search Unit (E1065). Approximately, a quadratic equation with zero at the focal point is applied as the distance amplitude correction in the axis direction. Since the frequency of middle-large size inclusions is low, it is necessary to increase the scanning volume for their evaluation by an increase of the area or the depth. The scanning area, however, should be increased because the detection area of the focusing type probe in the axis direction (z) becomes small due to the attenuation.

Influence of Heat Treatment and Correction of Echo Amplitude - The micro/macro structure of steel affects echo amplitude. The echo amplitude in quenched steel is higher by 10-20 % than that of tempered or normalized steel. As the echo amplitude from as-rolled steel is 50 % lower than that of quenched steel, it is not suitable for the inclusion measurement. Accordingly, the correction of echo amplitude was made in this work using echo amplitude in quenched steel as a standard.

Surface Roughness and Inclination of Specimen Surface--The surface roughness is kept to maximum coarseness (R_{max}) smaller than 5 µm. The specimen plane is to be parallel with the scanning direction. Changes of beam path give a big error to distance amplitude correction because the focal point in steel greatly changes with specimen inclination. It is necessary to set the focal point correctly at the center of the measurement range in the course of examination from the initial to terminal point.

Relation of Defect Diameter and Echo Amplitude--The echo amplitude is corrected by the equation mentioned above. In order to relate the echo amplitude with the inclusion diameter, the small inclusion is extracted by acid dissolution and observed by SEM to measure the size. For the medium-large size inclusions larger than 50 μm, which are not frequently found, the maximum size of the inclusions are measured by an optical microscope through repeated polishing. The calibration line with the relation between inclusion diameter and echo amplitude is thus constructed.

Differentiation between Voids and Inclusions - There are two problems involved in the ultrasonic testing. One is the difficulty with the recognition of inclusion morphology since size of inclusions is measured through the image data by the echo amplitude with the minimum detection lattice unit of 5μm. The other problem is the difficulty with differentiating between voids and inclusions. It has been reported by Murai [9], that the phase of reflection wave turns over at an interface of steel and air. Because of this indication, the differentiation has become feasible with the index of P/A (P/A= positive echo amplitude / all (= positive + negative) echo amplitude). In the case of P/A≤0.45, the echo shows an inclusion, and P/A ≥0.55 corresponds to a void. But the differentiation for the case of the intermediate value (P/A =0.45-0.55) may be difficult. Under the conditions of the coexistence of voids and inclusions, the evaluation based on the image observation with smaller detection lattice is necessary. In this study the signal with P/A larger than 0.45 is treated as the void.

Inclusion Evaluation Result

Inclusion Evaluation with Optical Microscope

Relation between oxygen content in steel and number of inclusions - The number of inclusions increases in proportion to oxygen contents in steel as shown in Figure 4. To date oxygen contents are used for the quality index of cleanliness of steel and correlated with total number of inclusions observed with the optical microscope.

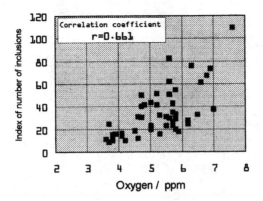

Figure 4--*Relationship between oxygen content and*
number of inclusion detected by microscopy
(Inclusion diameter $\geq$ 3 μm, SAE52100).

Predicted $\sqrt{area}$ max(100,30000) in Statistics of Extreme Value Method and Oxygen
Content

Relationship between Predicted $\sqrt{area}$ max(100,30000) and Oxygen Content--
Relationship between Parameter α and λ is shown in Equation 6. The regression are
the following expressions: $y = (x-\lambda)/\alpha$. Predicted maximum diameter $\sqrt{area}$ max(100, 30000) is calculated by

$$\sqrt{area}\,_{max(100,30000)} = \alpha y + \lambda \qquad (6)$$

Values of predicted $\sqrt{area}$ max of SAE52100 heats with outlying observation
(abnormally large value, which is called isolated island) are larger than those of heats
without it. The outlying observation is defined as an observation in the case where the
difference between {the maximum value of mth} and {the value of $(m-1)$th } or
between { the value of $(m-1)$th data} and {the value of $(m-2)$ data} is 5 μm and larger.
The values of predicted $\sqrt{area}$ max with and without outlying observation were
separated as shown in Figure 5, and the group without outlying observation is well
related to oxygen contents.

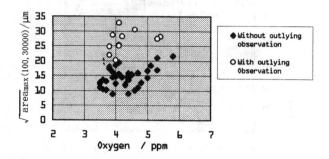

Figure 5-- *Relationship between oxygen content and* $\sqrt{area}_{max(100,30000)}$ *of SAE52100.*

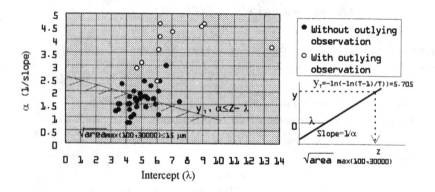

Figure 6-- *Relationship between α (reciprocal of slope)and λ (intercept at y=0)*
in the estimation of statistics of extreme values of SAE52100.

Relationship between Parameter α and λ -- α (a reciprocal number of slope) is related with a value of intercept λ. Excepting for the data with a large outlying observation, predicted $\sqrt{area}_{max}$ is in proportion to α. α with an outlying observation becomes a large value as shown in Figures 6. The most suitable condition range for the cleanliness steel in production was specified by α and λ. When given the aim of extreme value, it is necessary to keep the province of y_T x α ≤ z-λ . These parameter value should be set to α ≤ 2.0 and λ ≤ 5.0 to get the supreme cleanliness heat of predicted $\sqrt{area}_{max(100, 30000)}$ ≤ 15 μm.

Examination of Calculate Conditions of Statistics of Extreme Value Method--Large-size inclusion(50-100 μm) was found in fish eye of fractured surface by fatigue test. It is necessary to study the basic conditions (S_0, S and N) to calculate the predicted $\sqrt{area}$ $_{max(So.S)}$ of statistics of extreme value. The relationship between standard inspection area (S_0) and predicted $\sqrt{area}$ $_{max(So, 30000)}$ is shown in Figure 7. At the first step, 120 pieces of the maximum inclusion in $S_0=100$ mm^2 are measured (total test area is 12,000 mm^2). 120 data are divided into nine groups, n=120, 60, 40, 30, 24, 20, 15, 12 and 10. When total area is the standard inspection area, respectively, as $S_0 =$ 100, 200, 300, 400, 500, 600, 800, 1000 and 1200 mm^2, the predicted $\sqrt{area}$ $_{max}$ $_{(So.30000)}$ is likely to saturate to a constant value at 500 mm^2. Even with this inspection area, predicted $\sqrt{area}$ $_{max (So.30000)}$ is still affected by the outlying observations. At least 20 samples are necessary to obtain a stable extreme value since the extreme value fluctuates even under the conditions of $S_0 = 500$ mm^2, N=5 to 30.

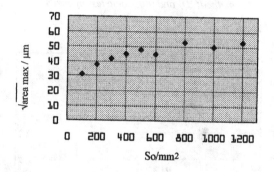

Figure 7-- *Relationship between S_0 and $\sqrt{area}$ $_{max(So,30000)}$.*

Evaluation of Inclusion by Higher-Frequency Ultrasonic Method

Microscopic Method and Higher Frequency Ultrasonic Method--As to the number of inclusions, the comparison of microscopic method(1/mm^2) with ultrasonic testing method {1/(mm^{2}x0.5mm)} is shown in Figure 8. The inspection area of the former is 200 mm^2 and a volume of the latter are 200 mm^2 x 0.5= 100mm^3. The detection capability of the ultrasonic method is considered to be several hundred times greater than that of the microscopic method in the same analysis area.

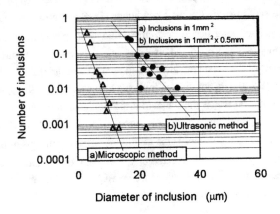

Figure 8-- *Comparison of the number of inclusions by between microscopic method(2D) and ultrasonic testing method(3D).*

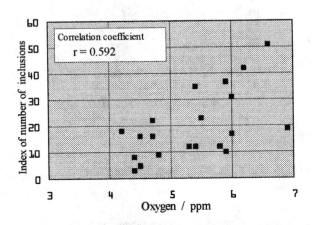

Figure 9--*Relationship between oxygen content and number of inclusions by ultrasonic testing. (Inclusion size $\geq 25\,\mu m$, $50\,MHz$)*

Particle Size Distribution by Ultrasonic detection Method - The relation between oxygen content and number of inclusions detected by ultrasonic testing (more than 25 µm) is shown in Figure 9. The number of inclusions increases proportionally as oxygen contents in the three-dimensional ultrasonic testing method as in the two-dimensional microscopic method as shown in Figure 6. Furthermore, the obvious difference in the distribution between the supreme cleanliness steel and ordinary steel is seen in Table 2.

Table 2 - *Distribution of inclusions detected by focusing-ultrasonic probe (100 MHz).*

Heat		Inclusion size (μm)									
		25-	30-	35-	40-	45-	50-	55-	60-	65-	Sum
	A	5	1								□
Supreme	B	7	2								□
Cleanliness	C	12	2	1							15
SAE52100	D	8	1								11
	E	10	1		1						12
(mean)		(8.4)	(1.8)	(0.2)	(0.2)						(10.6)
	F	21	4	2		1					28
Conventional	G	31	10	2	1	2					46
SAE52100	H	16	2	3	2						22
	I	29	8	2	2	1					42
	J	50	15	4	2	2	1				74
(mean)	(	29.4)	(7.8)	(2.6)	(1.2)	(1.2)	(0.2)				(42.4)

Specimen size: Round 65, Scanning path interval: 30 μm, Probe: 100 MHz, PF = 12.5 mm, Normal beam.

Relationship between the Inspection Volume and the Maximum Inclusion Diameter

The relation between the inspection volume and the maximum inclusion diameter found by means of increasing standard inspection volume is investigated. Extreme values of a supreme cleanliness heat by the microscopic method and the ultrasonic method are shown in Figure 10. The data of both methods do not contain outlying observations, and especially, the data of the ultrasonic methods shows a tendency to converge to a constant value. Testing area of microscopic method is 100 mm^2/piece, provided that one layer of microscopic observation is 10 μm for the volume conversion. Accordingly, the equivalent volume of image analysis is 100x0.01=1 mm^3. On the other hand, the standard inspection volume of ultrasonic testing method is 65 x 65 x 0.5= 2 113 mm^3/piece. $\sqrt{area}_{max(100,633,000)}$ for 2 113mm^3 x 30 pieces (total area: 6 339 000 mm^2) is 30.8 μm obtained by the microscopic method, and this value is very close to 29.0 μm by the ultrasonic method. The ratio of the inspection area in the two methods is approximately 2 100, and the distribution of the actual maximum diameter of statistics of extreme value are 5-15μm by the microscopic method and 25-30μm by new ultrasonic method. Accordingly, the values of the latter are two times larger than those of the former.

Size of inclusions are smaller with the supreme cleanliness steel than that with the ordinary steel as shown in Figure 11. It is noted that an outlying observation still exists in an ordinary heat although the total testing volume is very large such as 2113mm³ x 30 = 63 390 mm³ (=507g). Accordingly, an increasing of the inspect volume shall be considered.

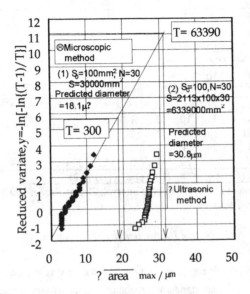

Figure 10 - *Comparison of $\sqrt{area}_{max}$ of each inspection area (or volume) by image analysis(2D) and by ultrasonic method(3D).*

Discussion

Problems of Statistic of Extreme Value Method

There is a problem with a prediction of maximum inclusion by statistic of extreme value method; 1) Outlying observations (isolated value), 2) Setting of calculation basis condition of S_0, S, N,

Outlying Observations - Firstly, as to microscopic method, predicted $\sqrt{area}\ _{max}$ is affected by the presence of an outlying observation even under the same calculation conditions, here $S_0=100$, $S=30000$, $N=30$. The slope of the regression and $\sqrt{area}\ _{max}$ value are significantly affected by the data deviated from the regression line. In other words, when an isolated value is too large, it should be treated specially. And, two parameters of α and λ are related with oxygen content in steel, and their values are desired to be as small as possible to produce supreme cleanliness steel. For the case of no isolated value (outlying observations) found, λ as well as oxygen content is useful for administrative index for micro-cleanliness of heats. For the case of outlying observations found, the contamination by extrinsic inclusions and out-of-control in the process may be involved, so that it is necessary to judge by increasing number of sampling.

Secondly, the inspection area of the present microscopic condition ($S_0=100$, $S=30000$, $N=30$) is not sufficient since the occurrence of large inclusions (outlying observation) is frequent. The result of statistics of extreme values of microscopic method (2D) and ultrasonic detection scanning (3D) is shown in Figure10. These two data are obtained from the same heat. The data of the ultrasonic methods clearly demonstrate a different distribution from those of the microscopic method and show a tendency to converge to a constant value. This indicates that the predicted $\sqrt{area}\ _{max(S_0,S)}$ by the microscopic method, based on measurements without an outlying observation, can be compared with the measurements by the ultrasonic method for the same inspection area even though the most suitable inspection area S has not been determined yet.

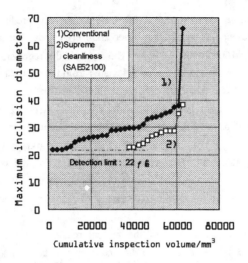

Figure 11 - *Relationship between maximum size*
of inclusion and inspection volume.

Figure 11 shows the maximum inclusion diameter of each specimen in order of size, by use of measurement data of supreme cleanliness steel and ordinary steel through ultrasonic detection method. For the inspection volume below 60 000 mm³ (=480g), the value of $\sqrt{area}_{max,i}$ is gradually increased as shown in Figure 11. But, for over 60 000 the outlying observation appeared suddenly. It is found that the large inspection volume is important to the evaluation of large size inclusions and the ultrasonic method with the distance correction of the focal point is useful because of the direct evaluation of maximum inclusion diameter.

Inclusion Evaluation by Ultrasonic Method

The characteristics and operating conditions of focusing type higher frequency ultrasonic method are shown in Table 3.

Detection Limit - Detection sensitivity decreases because the echo amplitude of detection decays with increasing the distance between the focal point and inclusions. For this reason, the echo amplitude from the inclusions away from the focal point is weaker than that from the inclusions close to it even if they have the same size.

Accordingly, the inclusions away from the focal point may not be evaluated because the echo amplitude before the correction is too low to be detected. In order to evaluate the distribution and size of inclusions existing at the same frequency in the entire inspection volume, it is necessary to consider the appropriate area to be corrected, and it may be required to alleviate the detection limit from 20 to 25 µm.

Scanning Time - Scanning time takes longer in proportion to scanning area of detection. For a long time scanning, the operation will be practiced at night with no one attended.

Differentiation between Void and Inclusion - The differentiation between voids and inclusions is made by the magnitude of an index P/A. However, in case of intermediate value (P/A=0.45-0.55) at which inclusions and voids may coexist, it is difficult to identify the type of defects. It is necessary to construct the calibration line corresponding to P/A.

Forging Ratio - Deformation of inclusions in the rolling direction influences the echo amplitude. In other words, the size and shape of inclusions are changed, depending on the rolling size even with the same billet. It is, therefore, necessary to prepare specimens under the similar conditions. Further, it is recommended that sufficient forging ratio enough to reduce micro-porosity be taken because they lead to anomalous signals which indicate numerous number of defects and extremely long imperfections.

Evaluation of Large Size Inclusions in Steel

There is a distinct correlation between oxygen content and number of inclusions larger than 25 µm in steel (Figure 9). Further, as shown in Table 2, there was the clear difference of distribution between the supreme cleanliness steel and ordinary steel in distribution, but the apparent correlation between the distribution and the other operating conditions of steel making has not been found. The relation between predicted $\sqrt{area}_{max(100\square30000)}$ by the microscopic method and the maximum inclusion size detected by the ultrasonic method is not still evident since outlying observations possibly exist as shown in Figure 11, where large inclusions of outlying observations (large globular oxide) come out suddenly even with large testing volume of 63 390 mm^3 (507g).

The advantages of the ultrasonic method are the direct observation of defect and the measurement of distribution with large inspection volume. Therefore, it is important to study how to treat outlying observations, and for this, the development of more sensitive probes and detectors for the larger inspection volume and so on will be the next subject. Further, to evaluate accurately the size and morphology of individual inclusions by the conversion system from echo amplitude to inclusion information, the development of detecting system that can deal with high speed scanning with a finer lattice and high speed processing of data is desired.

Table 3 - *Operating condition and specimen preparation of ultrasonic testing.*

Item	Measurement condition
Total detection limit	100 MHz: 25 μm (PF=12.5mm) 50 MHz: 30 μm (PF=12.5mm)
Heat treatment (Recommended)	Quenched or Quenched & tempered
Surface roughness	Rmax. $\leq$ 5.0 μm
Scanning area x depth	Rough scanning: Max: 100mm x 100mm x (0.5 to 1.0) mm =5000 to 10000 mm³ (40 g to 80 g / piecce) Precise scanning: 1.0 x 1.0 x ((0.5 to 1.0) mm³
Focal position	Center of the gate
Incline	Less than 0.1 mm / 100 mm
Distance amplitude correction	Quadratic equation
Diameter of inclusions	>100μm: d=(Size of image dia.)-(Beam dia.) $\leq$ 100μm: Regression d = ax + b
Frequency	50 to 125 MHz
Scanning time	100 x100 : 40 to 60 minutes / piece
Discrimination between voids and inclusions	P/A: P(Positive echo amplitude), A (Total echo amplitude) P/A$\leq$0.45: Inclusions, P/A$\geq$0.55: Voids P/A= 0.45 to 0.50 intermediate value
Calibration	Reference block (0.40 mm FBH)
Evaluation (ASTM E45 chart)	A type: impossible B type(cluster): possible, imperfect. D type(globular oxide). possible

Conclusion

As to the evaluation of the distribution and three-dimensional locations of inclusions approximately 20 to 100 μm, the automated system is developed to allow long-time operation for the examination of inclusions contained in a relatively large volume by the high frequency focusing-type ultrasonic method.

The conventional statistics of extreme value method by optical microscopy has a problem in view of accuracy for predicting maximum inclusions in each heat because it has been based on data observed by an optical microscope with a small specimen. The accuracy of the evaluation of microscopic large inclusions is improved by the application of the ultrasonic method because the inspection volume is increased by thousands of times. Further, it is advantageous that an extrinsic, large-size inclusion may be detected by this method.

This ultrasonic method, however, is not perfect, at present as long as the treatment of outlying observations, which occur unexpectedly, is not established. For this reason, the development of more sensitive probes and higher-performance testing system to examine larger volumes efficiently, and inclusion morphology will be the next subjects.

References

[1] Murakami, Y., Toriyama T., and Coudert, E.M., "Instructions for a New Method of Inclusion Rating and Correlation with the Fatigue Limit," *Journal of Testing and Evaluation*, Vol. 22, No. 4, 1994, pp. 318-326.

[2] Monnot, J., Heritier, B., and Congne, Y., "Relationship of Melting Practice, Inclusion Type and Size with Fatigue Resistance of Bearing Steels," *ASTM STP 987*, 1986, pp.149 -165.

[3] Kato, Y., Sato, S., Nuri, Y., and Takemoto, S., "Ultrasonic Flaw Detection of Non-Metallic Inclusion in Steel," *Current Advances in Materials and Processes -ISIJ*, Vol. 12., 1999, pp. 473.

[4] Nagayama, H., Nasu, H., Noguchi, T., Sugimoto, T., Nishikawa, T., and Asai, M., "Detection of Inclusion by Ultrasonic Method (Influence of Inclusion Rolling Contact Life-2)," *Current Advances in Materials and Processes -ISIJ*, Vol.11, 1998, pp.1323.

[5] Murakami, Y., "Inclusion Rating by Statistics of Extreme Values and its Application to Fatigue Strength Prediction and Quality Control of Materials," *Journal Research of the National Institute of Standards and Technology*, Vol. 99, No. 4, July-August, 1994, pp. 345-351.

[6] Murakami, Y., *"Metal fatigue-Effect of Small Defects and Nonmetallic Inclusions,"* 1993, Yokendo Ltd., Tokyo.

[7] Gumbel, E. J., *"Statistics of Extreme,"* Columbia University Press, New York, 1958.

[8] Kato, Y., Takemoto, S., Sato, K., and Nuri, Y., "Development of Evaluation Technique of Non-Metallic Inclusions in Steel by High-Frequency-Ultrasonic Detection", *Sanyo Technical Report*, Vol. 7, No. 1, 2000, pp. 35-48.

[9] Murai, J., Ida, T., and Shiraiwa, T., "Detection of Alumina Non-Metallic Inclusion and Void in Steel by Ultrasonic Testing Method," *Journal of the Japanese Society for Non- Destructive Inspection*, Vol. 47, No. 7, 1998, pp. 498-503.

Developments in Bearing Service Life Testing

R. Fougères,[1] G. Lormand,[2] A. Vincent,[3] D. Nelias,[4] G. Dudragne,[5] D. Girodin,[6] G. Baudry,[7] and P. Daguier[8]

A New Physically Based Model for Predicting the Fatigue Life Distribution of Rolling Bearings

Reference: Fougères, R., Lormand, G., Vincent, A., Nelias, D., Dudragne, G., Girodin, D., Baudry G., and Daguier, P., **"A New Physically Based Model for Predicting the Fatigue Life Distribution of Rolling Bearings,"** *Bearing Steel Technology, ASTM STP 1419*, J. M. Beswick, Ed., American Society Testing and Materials International, West Conshohocken, PA, 2002.

Abstract: The available models are unable to estimate the fatigue life distribution of bearings explicitly taking into account material parameters. This paper presents a new model, that has been developed from a detailed analysis of damage mechanisms, for the prediction of the failure of rolling bearings operating under rolling fatigue conditions. The new approach introduces both nucleation and growth of microcracks present, or not, at the surface of the contact in the presence, or not, of inclusions. The distribution of fatigue lives is given for different loading conditions corresponding to smooth, rough or indented contacts. A good agreement is observed between the theoretical and experimental results.

Keywords: modeling, rolling fatigue, material parameters, roughness, indent

Introduction

Since rolling bearings are important components of various machines, mechanisms and engines, there is an increasing demand for predicting the fatigue life of such systems. A great number of factors influence rolling bearing life such as steel quality, bearing geometry, loading conditions, bearing kinematics, surface finishing, lubricant conditions,

[1] R. FOUGERES, Professor, INSA LYON, roger.fougeres@insa-lyon.fr
[2] G. LORMAND, Assistant Professor, INSA LYON, gerard.lormand@insa-lyon.fr
[3] A. VINCENT, Professor, INSA LYON, alain.vincent@insa-lyon.fr
[6] D. GIRODIN, Senior Engineer, SNR, daniel.girodin@snr.fr
[5] G. DUDRAGNE, Senior Engineer, Head of the SNR Laboratory and test center, gilles.dudragne@snr.fr
[4] D. NELIAS, Assistant Professor, INSA LYON, daniel.nelias@insa-lyon.fr
[7] G. BAUDRY, Senior engineer, Head of Ascometal fatigue group, g.baudry@ascometal.lucchini.com
[8] P. DAGUIER, Senior Enginner, Ascometal fatigue group, p.daguier@ascometal.lucchini.com

chemical environment, contamination, and thermal effect. Due to the high number of influencing factors the fatigue life of rolling bearings is widely distributed. Weibull [1] was the first to develop a statistical theory of fatigue life for high strength materials. A recent paper [2] indicated that design lubrication, and contamination are dominant causes of rolling contact fatigue failure. In fact, the material is always involved in the process of rolling bearing fatigue life degradation. For instance, the resistance to indentation seems to be very dependent on the material response, which is itself dependent on the steel microstructure. Exhaustive reviews of fatigue life modeling, including all factors affecting the lifetime of bearings have been made in the past, see for instance Tallian [3]. However, such modeling does not mention in an explicit manner if material physics assumptions are introduced, or not, in the models. The present paper aims at presenting a new physically based model for predicting the rolling fatigue life in bearing steels. Before presenting the new model, a brief review of damage mechanisms involved in rolling fatigue, is presented as well as an analysis of previous models. Applications of this new model, to the prediction of the contact fatigue life, for different loading conditions, are also presented.

Brief Review of Damage Mechanisms in Bearing Steel

Before presenting the damage mechanisms in bearing steels, we refer to usual uniaxial fatigue loading. Fatigue of materials is a very old problem that has been the subject of numerous studies over the last three decades. From a physical point of view, it is usually accepted that fatigue damage occurs in three successive steps :

1. Very short cracks (1 to 10 μm long) are initiated within the material, generally in regions where there are inhomogeneities : inclusion, porosity, large size precipitates, high plastically strained zone, slip bands, grain boundaries... These inhomogeneities are regions of the material with mechanical and/or physical properties different from those of the matrix in which they are present.

2. Short crack growth. From a general point of view, it is worth noting that the short crack growth rate is largely dependent on the microstructure of the material.

3. Paris law large crack growth. Once microstructural barriers are overcome, the crack growth can be considered from linear or nonlinear fracture mechanics. The dependence of the crack growth rate on the stress intensity factor is generally described by means of a Paris law.

In the case of fatigue under contact loading conditions the three previously described steps are generally observed. Therefore, depending on the operating conditions, various types of damage may be observed such as pitting or microspalling, surface initiated deep spalling (SIDS) and sub-surface initiated deep spalling (SSIDS). Pitting or microspalling is often a result of poor lubrication conditions, poor surface finish, or high sliding ratio between contact surfaces. SIDS is typical in the presence of tensile hoop stress. Finally, SSIDS is predominantly observed when bearings operate under elasto-hydro-dynamic (EHD) conditions, low roughness of contact surfaces and low sliding ratio [4, 5]. When the two last conditions are not satisfied, SIDS damage is generally observed. Understanding the material fatigue process, responsible for each type of damage, is also a difficult problem due to the complexity of the microstructure of bearing steels. When

SSIDS damage is considered, it is well established that, most often, spalling originates from cracks that are initiated in the vicinity of material inhomogeneities such as non-metallic inclusions located below the contact surface [4, 6]. Observing this sub-surface region after nital etching has shown that specific white etching areas (WEAs), also called butterflies owing to their shape, take place around such inclusions [7, 8]. Moreover, it seems that these butterflies, in which crack initiation occurs, could be identified as ferrite [9]. Finally, it has been shown that when loading conditions enable a micro-crack to grow, the crack grows to the surface, resulting in spalling [10, 11]. This damage process originates from the strain misfit between inclusions and the martensitic matrix, that occurs under loading, due to the difference in their elasto-plastic properties. This misfit is responsible for the local stress concentration, which can be partially relaxed by local plastic flow, corresponding to the creation and movement of dislocations [12]. Under cyclic loading the repeated interaction of dislocations with carbide precipitates would be responsible for the local decay of martensite, thus leading to the WEA [13]. It has been suggested by Champaud et al [14] that crack nucleation would occur when a critical density of dislocations is reached in this region. Following crack nucleation within the WEA, a period of crack growth has been observed [11] and, finally, spalling occurs once the crack has reached the surface. Depending on the location of inhomogeneities in the volume beneath the contact, large variations can be expected in the ratio between the time for a crack to nucleate and the time for a nucleated crack to reach the surface. In a recent paper Nelias et al [15] analysed the role of inclusions, surface roughness and operating conditions on rolling contact fatigue. From tests performed on a two disk machine with 52100 and M50 bearing steels, the role of dominant parameters has been summarised as follows : 1) Inclusions act as stress raisers and they are responsible for SSIDS but they may also contribute to surface micro-spalling when the local stress fields due to surface asperities (rough surface case) and inclusions interact. 2) Crack nucleation may also results from the interaction between several inclusions (M50 case). 3) Depending on the surface topography, and the lubricant film thickness, sliding is assumed to be at the origin of the transverse micro-cracks observed on the contacting surface through a local increase of the friction coefficient. The lubricant may help to propagate surface cracks by hydraulic pressure effects.

Background of Main Fatigue Models for Prediction of Rolling Bearing Life

Despite two levels of complexity, namely due to the fatigue loading conditions and the material microstructure, many authors have proposed models and methods for assessing bearing life. Tallian [3] and Zaretsky et al [16] have presented reviews of such engineering and research models. From our point of view, the main models, to predict fatigue lifetime, can be divided into two categories, depending on the importance attributed to physical factors, i.e. phenomenological models and semi-analytical models.

Phenomenological Models

In this group we classify the models that are mainly based on a statistical analysis of many rolling bearing life endurance tests. Such an approach, which was first proposed by Weibull [1] and then modified by Lundberg and Palmgren [17] (hereafter noted LP), has lead to the well-known relationship between the probability of failure of a bearing, its load capacity and the applied load, is still used in present methods of calculating load rating and rating life of bearings. Thus, the international standards ISO 281 (1977) have been developed based on the LP equation, and modified in the course of time by inserting life adjustment factors in their original relationship, in order to account for the improvements in steel quality and lubrication conditions. At this stage, it has to be noted that this model predicts a finite life whatever the loading level, even when it is very low, so that no threshold effect is accounted for. On the other hand, Zwirlein and Schlicht [18] have noted that, with high quality bearing steels and under appropriate operating conditions, it is not unusual to get an actual service life considerably longer than calculated. Therefore, various modifications of the above theory have been proposed, since the eighties, to account for improvement of endurance properties of bearings [19, 20, 16]. The improvement proposed by Ioannides and Harris [19] (hereafter noted IH) is an extension of the LP theory, that is based upon the use of a steel fatigue limit σ_u. Accordingly, this modification specifically includes the concept of infinite life. In addition, in this theory, the risk of failure is defined locally, such that the probability of survival must be expressed as an integral over the risk volume V. The merit of this IH theory is to account explicitly for, on the one hand, the infinite life of bearings and, on the other hand, stress fields differing from Hertzian, especially those produced by rough contact surfaces or sliding contacts. However, the IH approach is dependent on the concept of an unclear material fatigue limit, from a fundamental point of view and under complex loading condition. In a recent paper, Harris and Mc Cool [21] have done a statistical comparison of LP and IH life predictions, and it has to be noted that for both methods, ratios between predicted and experimental fatigue lives are largely distributed. This indicates that the quality of the fatigue life prediction could be improved.

Semi-Analytical Models

The models classified in this group include some (but not all) features of the damage mechanism responsible for rolling bearing failure.
In two companion papers, Blake and Cheng [22,23] have proposed models for life prediction and failure probability prediction, in the case of surface pitting. These authors assume that there are initial cracks at the contact surface. This means that the time to nucleate micro-cracks is neglected. Crack lengths are fitted to a normal distribution and progression of damage is due to the growth of cracks according to a Paris law. When a crack becomes large enough, for unstable growth to occur, a pit is then created. Predicted trends are consistent with in-service behaviour. However, the predicted lives are generally shorter than those obtained experimentally. In 1994, Cheng and Cheng [24] published a significant paper concerning the modeling of crack initiation under contact fatigue. It is assumed that micro-cracks are nucleated in slip bands located in grains of the material. The slip band is modelled as two dislocation pileups of opposite signs. The length of each pileup is equal to the grain size. During the fatigue loading, dislocations are assumed to be accumulated in the pileups by considering movements of dislocations

partially irreversible. Due to this dislocation accumulation the free energy of the system is increased. When the free energy is large enough to balance the surface energy required to create a micro-crack, the crack nucleation is assumed to be achieved. Slip bands can appear in grains at the surface contact. Under this condition, image effects due to the contact surface influence the stress field of edge dislocation pileups. Cheng and Cheng [24] take these effects into account. This model takes the microstructure of the material partially into account but the microstructural state that is assumed, corresponding to perfectly homogeneous grains in the material, is not very realistic with respect to the actual microstructure described in the previous section. In addition, the presence of multiple martensite variants within each grain probably reduces the role of prior austenite grain boundaries. However, in order to predict failure probability, Cheng and Cheng [25] have combined this crack initiation model with a postulated Weibull distribution of fatigue lives, which is the weak point of this model.

At this step, the following can be identified:
- In models involving microstructural elements, it should be noted that the inhomogeneous nature of a material is rarely taken into account.
- The concept of infinite lifetime is not based on physical arguments and, hence, the definition of the corresponding fatigue limit and its experimental determination have not really been addressed.
- Micro-crack nucleation and crack growth stages are not introduced in the models.
- In the case of models predicting the distribution of fatigue lives, a Weibull law is systematically postulated. As a matter of fact, deviations from this statistical law have been reported [20].
- In phenomenological models, the probability of survival is calculated through different multiplying factors, each of them corresponding to the effect of material, lubrication, contact geometry, and so on. Such approaches lead to real difficulties in independent analyses, since some interactions are really expected to occur between the aforementioned effects.
- These adjustment factors are most often defined from many contact fatigue tests, which leads to high costs. In addition, such "adjusting" methods make it difficult to validate the models.

All these observations motivate the development of a new completely analytical model, hereafter called physically based model, based on bearing steel microstructure and the smallest possible number of adjustment parameters. This model is presented in the following section.

A New Physically Based Model

General Considerations

Most parts of the SSIDS model presented here have been successively developed from the pioneer work of P. Champaud et al [14], as described in References [26-28]. In addition, in this paper, we describe an extension of the model to crack nucleation and growth without the presence of inclusions but including eventual damages nucleated from the contact surface.

The approach used in this work can be divided in three steps, namely:

1) the first aiming at identifying damage mechanisms and determining the value of characteristic parameters involved in the fatigue phenomenon ;

2) the second step concerned with the development of crack nucleation and crack propagation models and their statistical application ;

3) the third devoted to the experimental validation of the model.

The New Model

Two cases are considered according to the presence of inclusions, or not:

Damage in the Presence of Inclusions - In the following sections the model is presented in the case of SSIDS. However, it should be noted that this general approach can be applied to other damage mechanisms, as well, such as surface initiated damage in the presence of inclusions. The deterministic and the statistical aspects have to be distinguished.

a) Deterministic aspect: According to the SSIDS mechanism described above, the following successive calculations have to be performed:

1)   The macroscopic stress field must be initially calculated, this being dependent on many factors namely, including lubrication regime, roughness of the surface, contact loading, contact geometry, hoop stress, residual stress, thermally induced stress field, and so on. In fact, in this model, we consider this stress field as an input that can be supplied, for instance by a refined tribological approach.

2)   When an inclusion is present, a stress concentration is developed in the surrounding martensitic matrix. The resulting local stress field is calculated from Eshelby's theory by assuming elastic and plastic eigenstrains. Such a calculation requires knowledge of the size, shape, position, orientation, and elastic modulus of the inclusion. This last parameter is determined from nano-indentation measurements. If the inclusion is very near the surface, image effects should be considered as in the Cheng et al model. In addition, clusters of inclusions can also be taken into account.

3) Plastic zone size and crack nucleation: The size of the butterfly is obtained by studying the partially reversible movement of edge dislocations in the matrix, which are emitted from the inclusion interface [26]. It is worth noting that dislocation movements can be activated only if the driving shear stress due to the contact loading is higher than the micro-yield stress of the martensitic matrix. As the cyclic process progresses dislocations are accumulated in the butterfly region. At a given cycle number the edge dislocation density reaches a critical value and a micro-crack, of order of the butterfly size, is nucleated. The cycle number for crack nucleation is noted N_a.

4)   Crack propagation model: Two ways have been used to calculate the crack growth rate:

-    The crack length can be obtained at a given cycle number by integrating a Mode II Paris law that gives a relationship between the crack growth rate and the stress intensity factor range under Mode II conditions.

-    In order to introduce microstructural parameters, a model has been developed

[26], where the emission and the thermally activated movement of dislocations from the crack tip are responsible for the crack growth. Here again an irreversibility factor has to be introduced. The cycle number for the crack to reach the surface is noted N_p. Finally, the cycle number to spalling, N, is given by the sum : $N=N_a+N_p$

Depending on both the inclusion position beneath the contact and the inclusion size, it has been experimentally observed that N_a and N_p may exhibit very different values [28]. Furthermore, the model shows that depending on the inclusion position in the contact, a crack can begin to grow and then stop. By means of ultrasonic observations, such a crack behaviour has been experimetally detected. Finally, with this model it is possible to take damage accumulation into account whatever the contact fatigue loading complexity.

b) Statistical aspect: failure probability prediction

The computation of the fatigue lives distribution requires the knowledge of the inclusion size distribution and the volume fraction within the bearing steel. Sophisticated methods have been recently developed to get these data [29, 30] and, by using a Monte Carlo method, inclusion distributions in the volume affected by the fatigue contact can be established for every bearing. For each detrimental inclusion, N_a and N_p are systematically calculated using the above models for crack nucleation and crack growth. Finally, for each bearing specimen, we consider only the inclusion, and the corresponding cycle number N, leading to the smallest cycle number to spalling (weakest link concept). The distribution of fatigue lives is then obtained for the bearing batch.

Damage Without the Presence of Inclusions - Due to cyclic loading, plastic strains can be developed in the bearing steel without the presence of inclusions. The cyclic plasticity is then assumed by means of slightly irreversible movements of dislocations. Dislocations are accumulated in the material and at a given cycle number, N_a, the dislocation density can reach a critical value and a microcrack is then nucleated. The size of the microcrack may be assessed to be the length of the cyclic plasticity region, where the value of the critical dislocation density is reached, while the microcrack direction may be defined from the locus of the Tresca shear stress maxima. From these different assumptions the following relation can be drawn:

$$\Lambda_c = \Lambda_i + \sum_{k=1}^{k=N_a} \Delta\Lambda_k \qquad (1)$$

where Λ_c and Λ_i are the critical and initial dislocation densities, respectively, N_a is the cycle number to nucleate a microcrack, and $\Delta\Lambda_k$ is the increase of the dislocation density from cycle number k to $k+1$. By assuming that dislocations are arranged according to a square network it is easy to relate the cycle number to crack nucleation:

$$N_a=(A-B\tau_{fe})/((\tau^2-\tau^2_{fe})f^* \qquad (2)$$

where A and B are material dependent constants, τ is the Tresca shear stress due to the rolling fatigue loading, τ_{fe} is the corresponding micro-yield stress resulting from a previous plastic deformation and f^* the irreversibility factor. Once a microcrack is nucleated the crack propagation can be calculated in a way similar to that used for determining the growth of a microcrack nucleated within a butterfly (see above).

Applications

This paragraph aims at presenting three domains where the model has been applied: definition and evaluation of endurance limit (aeronautic applications), statistical distribution of the fatigue lives (automotive applications) and surface damage in the presence of artificial indents on the raceway (gear box applications).

Infinite Lifetime

Definition - From this model we deduce that an infinite lifetime [*31*] can be assessed in different ways. In terms of contact pressure H we can define four criteria for an infinite lifetime, hereafter called endurance limit. The following definitions are given in the case of inclusions present in the material, but the following concepts can be easily extended to the case without inclusions. Thus, at increasing contact pressures:

- H_1 : The Hertzian pressure, for which the first dislocation emissions occur at the inclusion–matrix interface, is H_1, i.e. the maximum local shear stress, at the interface, is equal to the micro-yield stress of the martensitic matrix. H_1 is the lower bound of the infinite lifetime. It is obtained for the most harmful inclusion position. It depends on the triaxiality of the stress field and inclusion characteristics (modulus, shape, and orientation). The microyield stress is deduced from static tests in compression (proof strain of 20×10^{-6} defined with respect to microstructure considerations). By comparing the predicted H_1 value with results of experimental tests a very good agreement has been observed [*31*]. Effects of hoop stress, residual stress, Hertzian pressure, nature and shape of inclusions have also been studied [*31*].
- H_2 : This endurance limit value corresponds to the development of the plasticity around the inclusion but no crack nucleation would occur. However as an infinite number of cycles is considered in this work, H_2 is expected to tend towards H_1.
- H_3 : As the contact pressure is increased, accumulation of dislocations occurs and a micro-crack can be nucleated. But, if conditions for crack propagation are not fulfilled the micro-crack is expected to remain quiescent. H_3 is the maximum contact pressure for which this situation is met.
- H_4 : Beyond H_3, a crack can grow at the beginning of the fatigue process but, as mentioned previously, after some growth it can be arrested. This corresponds to the upper bound of the endurance limit.

Effect of the Surface Roughness on the Infinite Limit H_1 - Based on the half space assumptions, many models have been proposed to solve different types of contact problems (line or point contacts, smooth or rough surfaces, normal loading or both normal and tangential loads, purely elastic or elastic-plastic behaviour, steady-state or transient operation, etc..). In this work we only consider the normal contact between two elastic bodies, one being flat, the other presenting a perfectly sinusoidal roughness. Following the numerical procedure proposed by Kalker [*32*], the normal contact problem can be described by a set of equations that must be solved simultaneously in an iterative procedure. These equations are concerned with the load balance, the surface separation and the contact conditions. Depending on the amplitude / wavelength ratio of the roughness, the contact can be discontinuous or discrete. Figure 1 shows the variation of the Tresca shear stress, determined beneath the surface, along the axis passing through the center of the contact, for different values of amplitude roughness. The smooth contact curve corresponds to the lower line in Figure 1. These results show that secondary stress peaks appear near the contact surface when the amplitude of roughness is increased. In the case of high roughness, the secondary stress peak value is higher that the one of the Hertzian stress peak. In Figure 2 the effect of roughness on the infinite limit H_l is shown. (i.e. : different values of the amplitude / wavelength ratio: a/w ratio). It has to be noticed that the H_l value can be strongly reduced in the presence of a large roughness amplitude or small wavelength values. Moreover, as it can be seen in Figure 2, the H_l −a/w ratio curve exhibits a threshold value. Below this threshold it appears that the value of the roughness has no effect on the H_l limit.

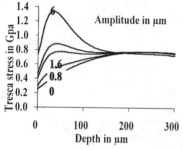
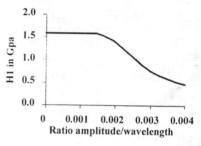

Figure 1 - *Tresca shear stress values as a function of the depth beneath the center of the contact surface, for different values of the amplitude roughness in μm,(Hertz pressure 2.5 GPa, contact radius 500 μm, roughness wavelength 125 μm).*

Figure 2 – *Effect of the amplitude wavelength ratio of the roughness on the H_l infinite limit. 52100 steel.*

Statistical distribution of lifetime in the case of smooth contact

The results of a simulation for a large batch of 5 000 flat washers, performed with an arbitrary but reasonable inclusion distribution, are shown in Figure 3a [28]. These results show that the failures are not distributed according to a two-parameter Weibull law. It is worth noting that the cumulative failure % vs time curve exhibits the same shape as the experimental curve obtained from the gathering of experimental fatigue data carried out on rolling bearings manufactured in the 1970s (Figure 3b). However, a quantitative comparison with the simulated curve cannot be achieved since the low cleanliness of this old steel, which lead to numerous failures, is not available.

Comparison between computed and experimental distributions of lives are reported in Figures 4a and 4b for two 52100 steels exhibiting a difference in cleanliness (A and B). Fatigue tests were carried out on SNR FB 2 thrust type test machines [33] with a contact pressure of 4.2 GPa. A and B steels contained mainly Al_2O_3 inclusions with an exponential distribution of size (mean diameter Φ= 2.7 μm and 2.4 μm for A and B steels, respectively). Due to the experimental fatigue test procedure (so-called sudden death method [28]), experimental results are presented according to lower and upper bounds. In the case of the lower bound, it is assumed that a surviving specimen would fail immediately after the fatigue test interruption. In contrast, the upper bound is obtained by assuming that an unfailed specimen would exhibit an infinite lifetime. It can be seen in Figure 4 that simulated curves show a good fit with the two experimental limit curves.

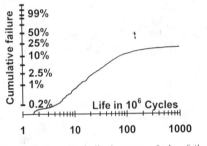

Figure 3a) – *Weibull diagram of the failures simulated for a batch of 600 flat washers.*

Figure 3b) - *Weibull diagram of fatigue life measured on a batch of 450 specimens machined from a bearing steel manufactured in the 70s.*

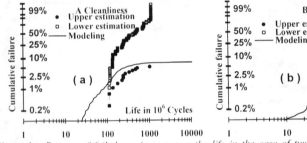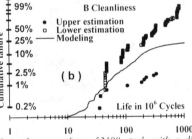

Figure 4 - *Percent of failed specimen versus the life in the case of two 52100 steels with a different cleanliness (A and B).*

Finally, the simulated and experimental results for the Hertz pressure have been plotted in Figure 5 as a function of the L_{10} lifetime, for a 6309 type ball bearing [34]. It can be seen that there is a very good agreement between experimental and simulated results, indicating the very good capability of this methodology.

Effect of Indents at the Contact Surface

It is generally established that the presence of an indent on a rolling contact surface strongly reduces the fatigue strength of bearings. In order to estimate the indent effect on the bearing damage, SNR FB 2 rolling fatigue tests have been performed in the presence of artificial indents on the surface of flat washers [33]. Generally, damages corresponding to surface initiated deep spallings are observed on the surface of the raceway. SIDS are usually located behind the indent side, about 20 μm distant from the indent side [33]. The results of finite element calculations are now presented as well as the prediction of lifetime in the presence of artificial indents.

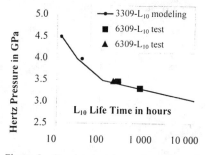

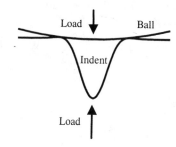

Figure 5 - *Simulated and experimental results in the case of a 6309 type ball bearing under pure radial loading conditions (one hour = 5x10⁵ cycles).*

Figure 6 - *Schematic configuration of the ball and indent for calculation of the rolling stress-strain fields by FEM.*

Stress Field in the Neighborhood of a Surface Indent - Stress and strain fields due to an indent, having a spherical segment shape, can be easily calculated by means of FEM (axisymmetrical case) and from knowledge of constitutive elastoplastic laws of the material. In the neighborhood of the indent a significant plastic strain is introduced as well as a residual stress field. Due to this, the micro-yield stress is increased all the more since the plastic strain is large, as it has been experimentally observed from compression tests performed on a previously plastically strained 52100 steel. In the case of indented contact surfaces, it is very difficult to calculate the stress field due to a rolling loading. In order to roughly estimate this field, we have considered the situation of a ball pressed on the indented surface. It is believed that the resultant stress field may be not too different from the one obtained under dry contact conditions. It seems that the position of the ball, with respect to the indent which is defined in Figure 6, corresponds to the most stressed situation for the bearing steel [35].

Figure 7 shows the Tresca shear stress value in a cross section perpendicular to the contact surface. This stress is the result of an applied load of 720 N between a ball of 10 mm in diameter and an indented surface (indent depth = 22 μm, indent radius = 200 μm). O_x and O_y axes correspond to the depth beneath the contact surface and the rolling direction, respectively. A very important stress peak is observed just at the edge of the indent.

With the same coordinate system, Figure 8 represents the variation of the difference between the effective Tresca shear stress, i.e. resulting from the ball contact and the residual stress field introduced by the previous indentation, and the micro-yield stress of the material that depends on the plastic deformation.

A stress peak is again observed at the surface contact but it is located in a very different position to that existing in Figure 7. As a matter of fact the surface stress peak is behind the indent edge at a distance of about 70 μm from the indent edge. This is not too different from damage locations observed during experiments reported in [*33*]. Once the damage is initiated at the surface, the crack growth is observed to be in a direction perpendicular to the contact surface [*33*]. This is in good agreement with the locus of maxima in the stress difference in Figure 8 which is also perpendicular to the contact surface. In fact this locus of maximal stress difference in Figure 8 coincides exactly with the interface between the plastically and the nonplastically strained regions induced by the indentation process.

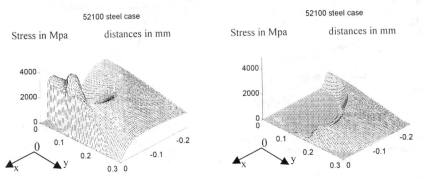

Figure 7 - *Tresca shear stress field due to a ball on an indented surface. FEM calculations.*

Figure 8 - *Stress field corresponding to the difference between the Tresca shear stress and the corresponding microyield stress.*

Prediction of Lifetime for Indented Contacts - Generally speaking, two types of sites are expected to be responsible for the nucleation of a microcrack in the material. That is to say, inclusions present in the matrix and new surface regions where the difference between the applied Tresca shear stress and the corresponding micro-yield stress exhibits a maximum (see Figure 8).

In order to compare these two types of damage mechanisms, Figure 9 illustrates the variation of the cycle number to nucleate a microcrack depending on either the inclusion size or the indent depth. For inclusion type nucleation, calculations are carried out at the maximum of the Hertzian stress field in the case of a smooth contact. The number of cycles for nucleating a crack has been calculated according to the previously described methodology (in the presence of inclusions). For indented contacts the number of cycles has been calculated at the contact surface according to Eq. 2 by assuming that loading conditions are those defined in Figures 7 and 8. Obviously the minimum number of cycles to rupture corresponds to the region of the surface where the stress field is maximum in Figure 8. For the low indent depth range (depth <7μm) a very strong decrease in the number of cycles to nucleate a microcrack is observed. For the high indent depth range the lifetime decreases more slowly and values of the number of cycles to failure are of the order of those obtained for failures due to very large size inclusions. These results show clearly the detrimental effect introduced by an indent.

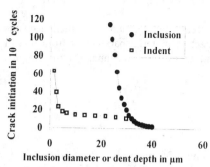

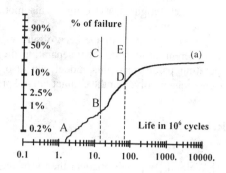

Figure 9 - *Variation of cycle numbers to nucleate a microcrack as a function of either the size of Al_2O_3 inclusions or the depth of an indent.*

Figure 10 - *Percentage of failure versus life time of flat washers. The vertical straight lines BC and DE correspond to damage with indents having a depth of 22 and 1.5 μm, respectively.*

Moreover it is possible to calculate the distribution of fatigue lives by including the two types of damage. Figure 10, shows the results obtained from this assertion. The curve (a) represents the life time distribution due to inclusions which are distributed in the contact volume by means of a Monte Carlo method in the case of a 52100 steel. Loading conditions are similar to those used in Figure 4. All indents have been considered as having the same depth and, therefore, they induce the same number of cycles to rupture. In the plot of Figure 10, indent damage points are placed on a straight line perpendicular to the cycle number axis. Results for two indent depths have been reported in Figure 10. Depending on the indent depth and by considering the concept of the weakest link, the resulting distribution could be either ABC or ABDE as it can be deduced from Figure 10. Such distributions, with a marked jump in the variation, have been actually observed in rolling fatigue tests with artificial indents. In conclusion, these results show that the fatigue endurance of bearings with indents is strongly dependent on the relative sizes of inclusions and indents. Moreover, the present analysis shows that failures from inclusions and indents cannot be described by single multiplying factors.

Concluding Remarks

In this paper a new model for predicting the distribution of bearing lifetime has been presented. The heterogeneous nature of bearing steels is a very important factor that must be taken into account in modeling the fatigue life, as well in the crack nucleation regime and in the crack growth behaviour. Different models have been analysed and it appears that none of established models is able to predict the life distribution law from the relevant microstructural features of bearing steels. A new analytical model, the so-called physically based model, has been developed. The relevant features of microstructure and damage mechanisms are included in the new model. The main advantage is the prediction of the failure distribution without adjustment parameters. That is all values of parameters involved in the model are experimentally determined almost independently of

the contact fatigue tests results. This model has been applied to smooth, rough or indented contacts.
Very good agreements have been observed between simulated and experimental results for different applications. By separating the effect of material parameters from that of operating parameters, this model can also lead to the accurate analysis of complex phenomena involved in the contact fatigue process.

References

[1] Weibull, W., "A statistical theory of the strength of materials," *Proceedings of the Royal Swedish Institute for Engineering Research*, N° 151, 1939, pp. 4-45.

[2] Ioannides, E., "Life prediction in rolling elements bearings, a new direction in tribology," Published by Mechanical Engineering Publications limited for the Institution of Mechanical Engineers. *Invited papers from the First Tribology Congress*, London,1997, 8-12 September, pp. 281-289.

[3] Tallian , T., E., "Simplified Contact Fatigue Life Prediction Model-Part I : Review of Published Models," *ASME, Journal of Tribology*, Vol. 114, N°2, 1992, pp. 207-213.

[4] Littman, W. E., and Widner, R.,L.; "Propagation of Contact Fatigue From Surface and Subsurface Origins," *ASME, Journal of Basic Engineering*, 1996, pp. 624-636.

[5] Furuma, K., Shirota, S., and Hirakawa, K., "The Subsurface-initiated and the Surface-initiated Rolling Fatigue Life of Bearings Steels," *Proceedings of the JSLE-ASLE* International Conference on Lubrication, Tokyo, 1975, pp. 475-483.

[6] Monnot, J., Tricot, R., and Gueussier, A., "Résistance à la fatigue et Endurance des Aciers de Roulements," *Revue de Métallurgie*, 1970, pp. 165-638.

[7] Schlicht, H., "Über die Entstehung von White Etching Areas (WEA) in Walzelementen," *Härterei-Tech. Mitt.*, HTM 28, Heft 2, 1973, pp. 112-123.

[8] Marze, A., Vincent, L., Coquillet, B., Munier, J., and Guiraldenq, P., "Evolution et Dégradation par Fatigue de la Structure Martensitique d'un Acier Semi-Rapide," "Memoires Scientifiques *Revue Métallurgie*, 1979, pp. 165-173.

[9] Becker, P.C., "Microstructural Changes Around Non-metallic Inclusions Caused by Rolling-Contact Fatigue of Bearing Steels," *Metals Technology*, June, 1981, pp. 234-243.

[10] Miller, G. R; and Keer, L. M. " On the Mechanics of Fatigue Contact Growth due to Contact Loading," *ASME, Journal of Applied Mechanics*, Vol. 105, 1983, pp. 615-620.

[11] Guy, P., Meynaud, P., Vincent, A., Dudragne, G., Baudry, G., "Subsurface Damage

Investigations By High Frequency Ultrasonic Echography on 100Cr6 Bearing Steel," *Tribology International*, Vol. 30, N° 4, 1996, pp. 247-259.

[*12*] Chiu, Y.P., Tallian, T.E., and McCool, J.I., "An Engineering Model of Spalling Fatigue Failure in Rolling Contact ; I The Subsurface Model," *Wear*, Vol.17, 1971, pp. 433-446.

[*13*] Moreira de Freitas, M., and François, D., " Formation de Phase Blanche en Fatigue de Roulement," *Scripta Metallurgica*, Vol.17, 1983, pp. 683-686.

[*14*] Champaud, P., Esnouf, C., and Fougères, R., "Proposition d'un Critère d'Amorçage des Fissures en Fatigue de Contact Hertzien à partir des Evolutions Microstructurales du Matériau Fatigué," *Procedings of the Spring Meeting of the S.F.M. Fatigue et Contacts Mécaniques*, Paris, 1989, pp. 159-170.

[*15*] Nélias D., Dumont M.L., Champiot F., Vincent A., Girodin D., Fougères R., Flamand L., "Role of Inclusions, Surface Roughness and Operating Conditions on Rolling Contact Fatigue," *ASME, Journal of Tribology* Vol.121, April, 1999, pp. 240-251.

[*16*]Zaretsky, E., V., Poplawskiy, J.V., and Peters, S.M., "Comparison of Life Theories for Rolling-Element Bearings," *STLE* Preprint N° 95-AM-3F-3, 1995.

[*17*] Lundberg, G., and Palmgren, A., "Dynamic Capacity of Rolling Bearings," *Acta Polytechnica, Mech.Eng.Series* I, Royal Swedish Academy of Engineering Science, N°3, Vol. 1, 1947, pp. 1-50.

[*18*] Zwirlein, O., and Schlicht, H., "Rolling Contact Fatigue Mechanisms-Accelerated Testing Versus Field Performance," *ASTM STP* 771, J.J.C. Hoo, ed., 1982, pp. 358-379.

[*19*] Ioannides, E., Harris, T.A., " A New Fatigue Life Model for Rolling Bearing" *ASME, Journal of Tribology*," Vol.107, 1985, pp. 367-378.

[*20*] Lösche, T., "New Aspect in the Realistic Prediction of the Fatigue Life of Rolling Bearings," *Wear*, Vol. 134, 1989, pp. 357-375.

[*21*] Harris T.A., Mc Cool J.I., "On the Accuracy of Rolling Bearing Fatigue Life Prediction," *ASME, Journal of Tribology*, Vol.118, N°2, 1999, pp. 637-669.

[*22*] Blake J. W., Cheng H.S., "A Surface Pitting Life Model For Spur Gears : Part I Life Prediction," *ASME, Journal of Tribology*, Vol. 113, 1991, pp. 712-718.

[*23*] Blake J. W., Cheng H.S., "A Surface Pitting Life Model For Spur Gears" : Part II Failure Probability Prediction," *ASME, Journal of Tribology*, Vol. 113, 1991, pp. 719-724.

[*24*] Cheng W., Cheng H.S., Mura T., Keer L.M., "Micromechanics Modeling Crack

Initiation under Contact fatigue," *ASME, Journal de Tribology*, Vol. 116, 1994, pp. 2-8.

[25] Cheng W., Cheng H.S., "Semi-Analytical Modeling of Crack Initiation Dominant Contact Fatigue Life for Roller Bearings," *ASME, Journal of Tribology*, Vol. 119, 1997, pp. 233-390.

[26] Vincent A., Lormand G., Lamagnère P., Gosset L., Girodin D., Dudragne G., and Fougères R., "Iron white etching areas formed around inclusions to crack nucleation in bearing steels under rolling contact fatigue," *Bearing Steels: Into 21st Century, ASTM STP.1327*, J. J. C. Ho and W. B. Green, Eds., American Society for Testing and Materials, West Conshohocken,PA, 1998, pp. 109-123.

[27] Lormand G., Meynaud P., Vincent A., Baudry G., Girodin D., Dudragne G., "From Cleanliness to Rolling Fatigue Life of Bearings - A New Approach," *Bearing Steels: Into 21st Century, ASTM STP.1327*, J. J. C. Ho and W. B. Green, Eds., American Society for Testing and Materials, West Conshohocken,PA, 1998, pp. 55-69.

[28] Piot D., Lormand G., Vincent A, G. Baudry, Girodin D., et Dudragne G., "Prediction of Fatigue Life Distributions for Bearings Based on the Inclusion Population in the Steel," Bearing Steels at Millennium, Third Ascometal Bearing Steels Symposium, Arles-sur-Rhône, France, June 27th & 28th 2000, pp. 55-63.

[29] Auclair G., Ruby-Meyer F., Meilland R., Rocabois P., "Cleanliness Assessment : a Critical Review and a Real Need to Predict Rolling Contact Fatigue Behaviour," *Bearing Steels: Into 21st Century, ASTM STP 1327*, J. J. C. Ho and W. B. Green, Eds., American Society for Testing and Materials, West Conshohocken,PA, 1998, pp. 39-54.

[30] Auclair G., Bele B., Louis C., and Meilland R. "Appropriate Technique for Cleanliness Assessment," *Bearing Steel Technology ASTM STP 1419*, J.M. Beswick, Ed., American Society Testing and Materials, West Conshohocken, PA, 2002.

[31] Lamagnère P., Fougères R., Lormand G., Vincent A., Girodin D., Dudragne G., Vergne F., "A Physically Based Model for Endurance Limit of Bearing Steels," *ASME, Journal of Tribology*, Vol.120, July 1998, pp. 421-426.

[32] Kalker J.J., "Three-Dimensional Elastic Bodies in Rolling Contact," *Kluwer Academic Publishers*, Dordrecht, 1990, 314 p.

[33] Girodin D., Ville F., Guers R., Dudragne G., "Rolling Contact Fatigue Tests to Investigate Surface Initiated Damage using Surface Dents," *Bearing Steel Technology ASTM STP 1419*, J.M. Beswick, Ed., American Society Testing and Materials, West Conshohocken, PA, 2002.

[34] Dudragne G. private Communication 2001.

[35] Lubrecht T. Private Communication 2001.

Hiromasa Tanaka[1]   and   Noriyuki Tsushima[2]

Estimation of Rolling Bearing Life under Contaminated Lubrication

---

Reference: Tanaka, H. and Tsushima, N., "**Estimation of Rolling Bearing Life under Contaminated Lubrication**," *Bearing Steel Technology, ASTM STP 1419*, J. M. Beswick, Ed., American Society for Testing and Materials International, West Conshohocken, PA, 2002.

Abstract: The failure mode assumption of Lundberg-Palmgren's bearing life theory is that cracks initiate below the rolling contact surface. Therefore, modification is required to predict surface originated flaking life under contaminated lubrication. A new life estimation method, which can also be applied to surface originated flaking, is described. This method comprises the calculation of a volume element life, which is related to the local stress below the contact area, and then calculating the total life of the contact stressed region. The theoretical result was compared with experimental endurance test results, and both results showed that the lower the bearing load, the greater the life was reduced from the basic rating life. Additional groups of bearing test lives, gathered from references, were also analyzed and the same trend was observed. From these results, an appropriate diagram for the life modification factor is obtained against P/C (P : equivalent bearing load, C : basic dynamic capacity) under various contaminated lubrication conditions.

Keywords: rolling bearing, rolling contact fatigue, bearing life, contaminated lubrication, life calculation, local stress

---

Bearing steel quality has been greatly improved over the past 20 years by reducing not only the amount of inclusions but also their size. Currently, mass-produced bearings made of clean steel have several times longer lives than their basic rating, when the oil is clean and other operating conditions are favorable [1].

---

[1] Senior Engineer, Bearing Engineering R&D Center, NTN Corporation, (511-8678) 3066, Higashikata, Kuwana, Mie, Japan.
[2] Project Manager, Engineering Administration Department, NTN Corporation,

On the other hand, as long as endurance testing of rolling element bearings has been carried out, the influence of surface defects on fatigue life has been reported. Irrespective of whether these surface defects were formed by rolling over contaminants in the oil, from handling damage or caused by the manufacturing process, their influence on life is detrimental. The defects from handling damage can easily be avoided by careful handling, and also, the defects caused by the manufacturing process should be eliminated by the product quality control. However, it is hard to avoid the contamination of a lubricant in an actual application unless fine filtering systems are used. Even if the bearings were manufactured from high quality steel, the surface originated flaking life caused by surface defects tends to be shorter than the required life determined from the ratio of dynamic capacity of the bearing and the equivalent load applied to the bearing. In order to prevent unexpected problems, establishing a more accurate bearing life estimation method is fundamental for rolling element bearing engineering. An estimation method to determine the rolling element bearing life, caused by both subsurface and surface dent originated flaking, is described in this paper by calculating an elemental volume life from the local stress. The stress concentration around a dent due to rolling over a debris particle is modeled by applying a high local stress on the surface. A comparison between this parametric study and the results of bearing life tests under contaminated lubrication show the validity of this bearing life estimation method. In addition, with the data from this test along with other published bearing life test data, a useful and convenient life estimation curve for contaminated lubrication conditions was made.

Bearing Life Equation

Equation(1) is the basic equation of the Lundberg-Palmgren(L-P)[2] theory.

$$\ln 1/S \sim (N^e \cdot \tau_0^c \cdot V) / z_0^h \qquad (1)$$

In *Equation(1)*,

S = probability of survival of stressed volume V,
N = number of stress cycles endured,
e = Weibull slope of life distribution,
τ_0 = maximum orthogonal shear stress, and
z_0 = depth beneath the contact surface at which τ_0 occurs.

Exponents c and h depend upon exponents e and p, which are determined empirically.

Equation(2) is the basic equation of the Ioannides-Harris (I-H) new life theory [3].

$$\ln 1/\Delta S_i \sim \left\{\ N_i^e \cdot (\sigma_i - \sigma_1)^c \cdot \Delta V_i\ \right\} / z_i^h \qquad (2)$$

In *Equation(2)*, ΔS_i is the probability of survival of a volume element ΔV_i, sufficiently large to contain many defects. z_i is the depth at which stress σ_i occurs and σ_1 is an endurance limit stress.   *Equation(2)* only applies if the stress σ_i exceeds σ_1 ; otherwise, $\Delta S_i = 1$ for ΔV_i.   Using the orthogonal shear stress (τ_0) for τ_i and setting $\tau_1 = 0$, reverts *Equation(2)* to *Equation(1)*.

Contrary to L-P theory *Equation(1)*, in the I-H theory *Equation(2)* , the effective stressed volume can be taken into account by including an endurance limit.   Even though the I-H theory includes a fatigue limit and may well predict modern bearing life, some assumptions are required to determine the most appropriate stress for causing rolling contact fatigue [4], and the appropriate fatigue limit stress.   The concept of local stress on a subdivided volume element of stressed volume is significant in order to predict the bearing life under both clean and contaminated lubrication because the failure can originate at any site, surface or subsurface.

In this paper, the local stress was determined as the von-Mises stress σ, and its value was calculated by Muro's program [5].   The calculation to obtain the local stress in the program was based on K. L. Johnson's method [6].   In *Equation(3)*, the von-Mises stress σ was used as a substitute for τ_0 in *Equation(1)*.   When we consider the probability of survival ΔS_i is constant, volume element life (ΔL_i), which is equivalent to the number of stress cycles endured (ΔN_i), can be described as *Equation(4)*.   The total life of stressed volume can be calculated by using *Equation(5)*.

$$\ln 1/\Delta S_i \sim (\ N_i^e \cdot \sigma_i^c \cdot \Delta V_i\ ) / z_i^h \qquad (3)$$

$$\Delta L_i = \Delta N_i \sim (\sigma_i^{-c} \cdot \Delta V_i^{-1} \cdot z_i^h)^{1/e} \qquad (4)$$

$$L = (\Delta L_1^{-e} + \Delta L_2^{-e} + \cdots\cdots + \Delta L_n^{-e})^{-1/e} \qquad (5)$$

Figure 1 shows an example output from this program.   The σ / Pmax distribution in the yz-plane at x = 0 is illustrated, where x : rolling direction, y : axial direction, z : depth direction.   The maximum of σ / Pmax occurred at z / b = 0.7 .   Under this calculation, the contact ellipse's aspect ratio was set as a / b = 10 (a : semimajor axis, b : semiminor axis, a / b = 10 is typical of ball bearing contact).   The volume element life can be calculated from the local stress at each point of y / a and z / b.   Subsequently, the total life of the stressed volume can be calculated by *Equation(5)* .   By setting the local volume element life on the surface element properly according to contamination level, an estimation of surface failure life of a bearing is possible.

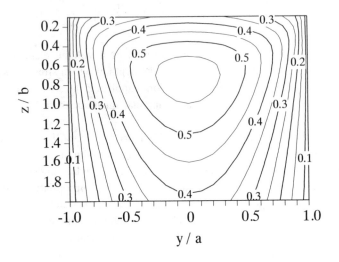

Figure 1   —   σ / Pmax distribution in the yz-plane at x=0.

Life Estimation under Contaminated Lubrication

Many dents on a bearing raceway can easily be seen after operating in heavily contaminated lubrication.   It is assumed that the stress concentration around the dents will inevitably occur when the rolling element rolls over the dent.   This is quite a different phenomenon from that of a smooth Hertzian contact.   Local plastic deformation created by the stress concentration should be the dominant reason for early flaking failure of bearings.

Although research on the effect of stress concentration on actual bearing raceways in the field is significant, it is by no means clear because the results vary greatly.   A better way to simulate the stress concentration is to apply a high local stress on the volume element near the surface.   A presumed value of local stress is applied on the center of the surface region.   Next, a local life for each volume element is calculated.   The total life is then obtained from *Equation(5)*.

The total life obtained from this calculation is converted into a radial ball bearing life.   Figure 2 shows the results from a parametric study of life estimation when the bearing load and stress concentration were changed.   The result was compared against the L-P theory.   In Figure 2, S.C. stands for "Stress Concentration".   In order to represent "small", "medium", and "large" stress concentrations, the appropriate local stress that matches the estimated life to the actual life was applied to the volume element near the surface.

This analytical result showed that the life reduction from the basic life rating was greater when the bearing load was light compared to the heavily loaded condition. This was especially true when the loading condition was low (Pmax = 2000MPa). The estimated life under heavily contaminated lubrication was one-tenth the basic life rating.

This life estimation method is still being investigated continuously. The more precise model of stress concentration around the dent will be discussed in a future report.

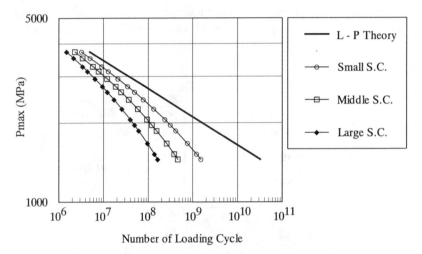

Figure 2 — *Result of bearing life estimation method.*

Endurance Tests under Contaminated Lubrication

The validity of the life estimation method described above was verified through bearing fatigue life tests.   Endurance tests under solid contaminated lubrication conditions were conducted on deep groove ball bearings of type 6206 (bore diameter : 30mm, outer diameter : 62mm, width : 16mm).   The bearings were made from SUJ2 (ASTM A295-98 52100) and conventionally heat-treated (Hardness Rockwell C 62).   The solid contaminant in the oil was gas-atomized high-speed steel powder or steel beads.   The hardnesses of the contaminants were Vickers 770, 560, 390, and 200.   The hardest contaminant was in the "as received" condition and the others were tempered or annealed in a furnace to lower their hardness.   The amount of contaminant used was 0.4 gram or 0.04 gram per 1 liter (1×10^{-3} m^3) of oil.

Figure 3 shows a schematic drawing of the bearing life tester, and the test conditions are shown in Table 1. Oil bath lubrication was used in this test. The solid contaminant was mixed in the oil prior to testing. Once the test bearings were in operation, the contaminated oil made its way into the bearing raceway. The shaft rotation speed was 2000 revolutions per minute. After testing, many dents were observed on the bearing raceways and dent originated flaking was the dominant failure mode. The test results were plotted using a Weibull distribution. The L_{10} life was then calculated. Figure 4 shows the relationship between Bearing Load and L_{10} life. The basic life rating based on the L-P theory is also shown in Figure 4 as a reference. These tests showed the same tendency that the lower the bearing load, the greater the life reduction from the basic life rating. It should be noted that the low hardness contaminants (Vickers 200) also decreased the bearing life. These test results show good agreement with the analytical results described in Figure 2.

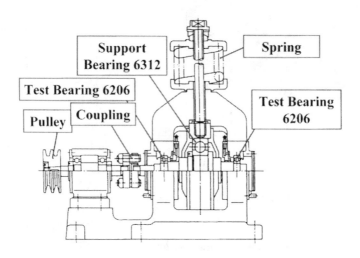

Figure 3   —   *NTN bearing life tester.*

Table 1   —   *Endurance test condition.*

Test Machine	NTN Rolling Contact Fatigue Test Rig			
Load	P / C = 0.04 to 0.5			
Shaft Speed	2000 rev. / minute			
Contaminant	Gas Atomized High Speed Steel			
Oil	Turbine VG56			VG68
Hardness of Contaminant	HV770	HV560	HV390	HV200
Amount of Contaminant	0.4 g / L [1]	0.4 g / L	0.4 g / L	0.04g / L

[1] 0.4 g / L means 0.4 gram per 1 liter (1x10^{-3} m^3) of oil

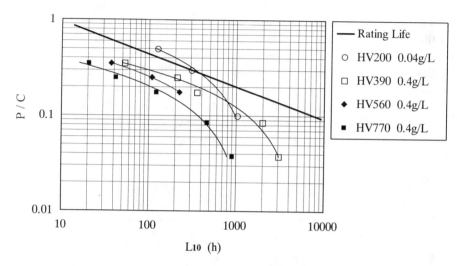

Figure 4   —   *Endurance life results of tested ball bearings.*

Analysis of Published Data

Bearing operating conditions in the field are quite diverse. So far the life analysis only evaluated the test lives of radial deep-groove ball bearings. Therefore, the examination of test results from as many different types of endurance life testers as possible is beneficial.   Fortunately, there are many published life test data of deep groove ball bearings under contaminated lubrication. Sixty-eight (68) data points from 4 published papers, including the data shown in Figure 4, could be identified regarding their relative lives, lubricating conditions and oil contamination levels.   These data are summarized in Table 2.   The bearing load was normalized by the dynamic capacity of each test bearing, and its range was from $P / C = 0.04$ to $P / C = 0.5$.   The lubricating condition is expressed by the viscosity ratio (kappa).   This ratio (kappa) was determined as the actual lubricant viscosity at the operating temperature divided by the required viscosity at the operating temperature.   It ranges from 0.10 to 3.01.   Additional information in Table 2 includes contamination particle size, hardness and amount.

It is recognized that there is a good correlation between kappa and bearing life under clean lubrication conditions.   When the kappa value is equal to one, the lubricating condition is satisfied as the required condition.   The relation between kappa and relative life under contaminated lubrication based on Table 2 is shown in Figure 5.   It seems that there is no relationship between kappa and life ratio under contaminated lubrication.   These results are due to the difference between the contaminant size and oil film thickness, the contaminant being much larger than the oil film thickness.   Also, it is related to the change in surface roughness of the bearing raceway during operation under contaminated oil lubrication.

Based on the analyzed results described above, it is felt that the effect of viscosity ratio can be neglected when estimating bearing life under contaminated lubrication.   The bearing life estimation method using 2 parameters, bearing load and the level of oil contamination without kappa value, will be a simple and convenient guide for rating bearing life under contaminated lubrication from an engineering viewpoint.

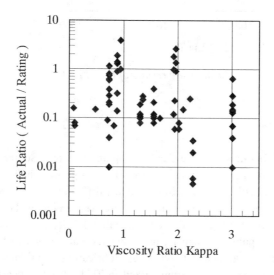

Figure 5   —   *Relationship between kappa and life ratio under contaminated lubrication.*

Table 2 — *Summary of life test results from published data and in-house data.*

Test Group No.	Load (P/C)	Speed (rpm)	Lubricant	Viscosity Ratio	Contaminant Size mm(x10⁻³)	Contaminant Hardness HV	Contaminant Weight g/L	Relative Life (Ratio)
1 (6206)	0.04 ~0.35	2000	VG56 oil	1.30 ~2.28	104~177	770	0.4	0.005 ~0.12
2 (6206)	0.04 ~0.35	2000	VG56 oil	1.35 ~2.28	104~177	390	0.4	0.02 ~0.40
3 (6206)	0.18 ~0.35	2000	VG56 oil	1.30 ~2.10	104~177	560	0.4	0.15 ~0.21
4 (6206)	0.10 ~0.50	2000	VG68 oil	1.92	less than 25	200	0.04	0.12 ~1.82
5 (6206)	0.18 ~0.35	2000	VG56 oil	1.30 ~2.02	less than 32	770	0.4	0.08 ~0.11
6 (6206)	0.18 ~0.35	2000	VG56 oil	1.30 ~1.94	104~177	770	0.2	0.06 ~0.12
7 (6206)	0.35	2000	VG56 oil	1.35	104~177	770	0.04	0.24
8 (6206)	0.18 ~0.35	2000	VG22 oil	0.48 ~0.82	104~177	770	0.4	0.07 ~0.15
9 (6206)	0.18 ~0.35	2000	VG2 oil	0.08 ~0.10	104~177	770	0.4	0.07 ~0.16
10 (63/22)	0.46	2500	VG68 oil	0.88	100~150 44~63	720~760	0.025 ~2.0	0.14 ~1.90
11 (6306)	0.46	2200	VG68 oil	0.94	44~63	720~760 2300~2700	0.25	1.0 ~3.9
12 (6304)	0.25	2400	90 Gear oil	3.01	less than 88	710	0.0005 ~0.09	0.1 ~0.65
13 (6304)	0.25	2400	90 Gear oil	3.01	less than 45	710 370 230	0.03	0.04 ~0.16
14 (6304)	0.25	2400	90 Gear oil	3.01	45~88 16~45 less than 16	710	0.09 ~2.1	0.07 ~0.29
15 (6206)	0.16 ~0.46	3000 3900	VG68 oil	1.96~ 2.23	44~74	540~730	0.005	0.25 ~2.64
16	0.32	4500	Gear oil 75W-90	0.73	100~150 26~50 11~25 less than 10	700~750	0.01 ~0.4	0.01 ~1.17

Group No.1, 2, 3, 4 are from Figure 4
Group No.5, 6, 7, 8, 9 are from reference [7]
Group No.10, 11 are from reference [8]
Group No.12, 13, 14, 15 are from reference [9]
Group No.16 is from reference [10]

Bearing Life Estimating Guide under Contaminated Lubrication

From the summary of life test results shown in Table 2, it is clear that not only the size of the contaminant but also the total amount of contaminant in the oil affects the bearing life. K. Shimizu et al. [10] reported experimental results regarding the relationship between the amount and size of solid contaminants and ball bearing life. *Equation(6)* represents its relationship.

$$L \sim (\text{Contaminant Size})^{-0.48} \times (\text{Contaminant Amount})^{-0.56} \qquad (6)$$

By using this relationship, the quantitative definition of lubricant contamination can be expressed as shown in Figure 6.   The contamination level was divided into four classes.   If there is information about the size and density of a contaminant, one can determine the contamination level.   The "normal cleanliness" region in Figure 6 was determined as the region where the basic life rating will be achieved when P / C is about 3 GPa under the test conditions.   "Moderate contamination", "heavy contamination" and "very heavy contamination" means 50%, 25%, and 10% of the basic life rating will be achieved respectively.   Of course the effect of the magnitude of loading is significant and must be included in the life estimation.

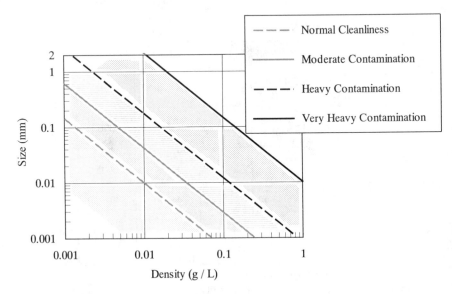

Figure 6   —   *Classification of contamination level in the bearing lubrication.*

Figure 7 is a recommended guide for estimating life under contaminated lubrication conditions.   When we estimate bearing life, a contamination level is identified from Figure 6, and then by using Figure 7, a life modification factor a $_{xyz}$ can be determined.   The estimated L_{10} under contaminated lubrication is represented as *Equation(7)*.   The effect of contaminant hardness on life is recognized under very heavy contamination as shown in Figure 4.   However, the effect of low hardness contaminant on bearing life is also shown in the same figure. Figure 8 shows the relationship between contaminant hardness and the life obtained from the analysis of the published data.   It shows that the milder the contamination level, or the lighter the bearing load, the smaller the effect of contaminant hardness has on bearing life.   Also, Xiaolan et al. [11] has shown that ductile debris is more detrimental.   From these facts, it is concluded that the effect of contaminant hardness on life seems to depend on the amount of contaminant in the oil and loading conditions.   Therefore, from a conservative estimation standpoint, it does not seem necessary to have an adjustment factor for contaminant hardness, even if an adjustment for contaminant hardness under "very heavy contamination" condition may be justifiable.

$$L_{10est.} = a_{xyz} (C / P)^3 \qquad (7)$$

Figure 9 shows the comparison between the estimated life ratio a $_{xyz}$ obtained from the data in Table 2 using Figure 7 and the actual life ratio based on the basic life rating.   Only six estimated lives are in the risk region for the estimated life ratio, whereas the conventional method (basic life rating) includes many risk estimates.   Therefore, the diagram shown in Figure 7 is a useful guide for obtaining the bearing life modification factor under contaminated lubrication.

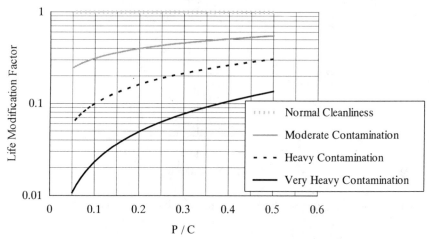

Figure 7   —   *Life estimating diagram under contaminated lubrication.*

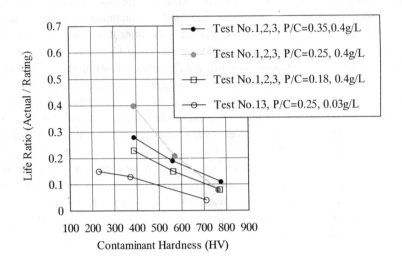

Figure 8   —   *The effect of contaminant hardness on test results.*

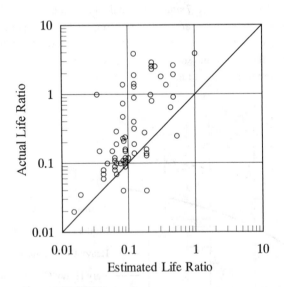

Figure 9   —   *Comparison between the estimated life and actual life.*

Conclusions

Research and testing were performed in order to obtain an accurate estimation of ball bearing life under contaminated lubrication.

(1) Calculation of local stress under the contact surface and application of stress concentration only at the surface element, showed that the smaller the bearing load, the larger the reduction of bearing life from the basic life rating under contaminated lubrication.

(2) Endurance test results validated the life estimation method.

(3) The bearing life estimation guide under contaminated lubrication conditions was developed with a quantitative definition of lubricant contamination level.

References

[1] Tanaka, H., Maeda, K., and Nakashima, H. : Proceedings of JICAST'98/CPST'98, Hamamatsu, 1998, pp.20.

[2] Lundberg, G. and Palmgren, A. : IVA Handlingar, 196, 1947, pp.1.

[3] Ioannides, E. and Harris, T.A. : ASME Journal of Tribology, Vol.107, 1985, pp.367.

[4] Harris, T. A. and Yu, W. K., : Trans. of the ASME Vol. 121, 1999, pp.85.

[5] Muro, H. : Proceedings of JAST Rolling Contact Fatigue Symposium 1993, pp.31.

[6] Johnson, K. L., " Contact Mechanics ", Cambridge University Press Reprinted 1989, pp.45.

[7] Tanaka, H., Maeda, K., and Nakashima, H.: Proceedings of JAST Tribology Conference, Tokyo, 1998, pp.502.

[8] Fujita, Y. and Hoshino, T.: Koyo Engineering Journal No.126, 1984, pp.28.

[9] Murakami, Y., Takemura, H., Fujii, A., and Furumura, K.: NSK Technical Journal No.655, 1993, pp.17.

[10] Shimizu, K., Hirota, T., Makino, K., and Itakura, T. : Proceedings of JAST Tribology Conference, Toyama, 1989, pp.229.

[11] Ai, X. and Nixon, H.P., : Tribology Transactions, Vol.43 , 2000, pp.311.

Yoichi Matsumoto,[1] Yasuo Murakami,[1] and Manabu Oohori[1]

Rolling Contact Fatigue Under Water-Infiltrated Lubrication

Reference: Matsumoto, Y., Murakami, Y., and Oohori, M., "**Rolling Contact Fatigue Under Water-Infiltrated Lubrication,**" *Bearing Steel Technology, ASTM STP 1419*, J. M. Beswick, Ed., American Society for Testing and Materials International, West Conshohocken, PA, 2002.

Abstract: This paper describes bearing life under water-infiltrated lubrication, which is often much shorter than the calculated bearing life. Bearings that failed in the field under water-infiltrated lubrication were analyzed to identify the mechanism. However, this was difficult due to insufficient information of the failure process. New fatigue life test methods were then developed to reproduce short life under water-infiltrated lubrication, to precisely observe the flaking process, and to study what material parameters affect the bearing life. It was found that failure under water-infiltrated lubrication initiates from nonmetallic inclusions on the rolling contact surface and propagates initially following grain boundary and then cutting through the grain, which eventually results in flaking. Higher cleanliness, which means less failure initiations, and nickel (Ni), which strengthens grain boundaries, improves bearing life under water-infiltrated lubrication. Hydrogen-induced failure is also experimentally studied to further understand water-induced failure. Hydrogen-induced failure is different from water-induced failure in the mechanism.

Keywords: Bearing, rolling contact fatigue life, water-infiltrated lubrication, boundary lubrication, flaking, peeling, elastohydrodynamic film parameter (lambda), hydrogen embrittlement, delayed fracture

[1]Manager, executive chief engineer, and general manager, respectively, Research and Development Center, NSK Ltd., 1-5-50, Kugenuma-shinmei, Fujisawa-shi, Kanagawa-ken, 251-8501, JAPAN.

Introduction

Bearing manufacturers have been improving bearing quality for many years. Consequently, problems with short bearing life are unusual under good operating conditions [1]. However, improved long-life bearings are still in demand for severe operating conditions such as debris-contaminated or water-infiltrated lubrication and high temperatures. In response, we studied rolling contact fatigue in various severe operating conditions. We found that higher retained austenite content and higher hardness of bearing steel extends life under debris-contaminated lubrications and that carbo-nitrided steel containing a special combination of elements extends bearing life at high operating temperatures up to 200°C. Today, bearings with these special specifications are widely used in the field [2].

Conversely, short life under water-infiltrated lubrication remains a problem and its mechanism is still unknown. Although probable mechanisms are estimated to be one or more of the following, there is no actual proof.

- Water reduces viscosity of oil and consequent metal contact causes flaking
- Corrosion pits cause flaking
- Water reduces steel strength chemically and causes flaking
- Hydrogen made by corrosion reduces the steel strength and causes flaking

The most important thing is that effective countermeasures on the basis of the mechanism should be taken for extending bearing life under water-infiltrated lubrication. To study the mechanism of, and the countermeasures for water-induced flaking, we have analyzed past experiments, including bearings that actually failed in the field. However, the analyses were not able to clarify the flaking mechanism due to insufficient information of the failure process. Therefore, we began with the development of fatigue life test methods that reproduce short life under water-infiltrated lubrication to precisely observe the flaking process and to study what parameters affect the bearing life.

This paper reports on the flaking mechanism under water-infiltrated lubrication and countermeasures for extending bearing life.

Flaking Under Water-Infiltrated Lubrication

Bearing life is greatly affected by the lubrication condition. Table 1 shows a summary of bearing life under various lubrication conditions [3-6]. In the table, bearing life is indexed as 100 when lubricant is clean and forms sufficient oil film thickness ($\Lambda \geqq 3$, $\Lambda =$ elastohydrodynamic film parameter = Oil film thickness / composite surface roughness). Index 100 of bearing life is equal to about 20 times the calculated life based on ISO 281:1990. Even when oil film thickness is insufficient, such as when Λ is small, bearing life decreases only by a factor of two or three provided that bearing surface roughness is within bearing quality specifications. When surface roughness is out of bearing quality specifications, the failure mode changes from flaking to peeling (Figure 1 [2]). Therefore, as far as the lubricant is clean and bearing surface roughness is within bearing quality specifications, problems with short life will not generally of concern.

Table 1 - *Bearing life under various lubrication conditions.*

	Lubrication condition		Life ratio	Failure mode	Surface roughness
	Lubricant	Λ^{1}			
1	Lubricant only	$\geqq 3.0$	100	Flaking	Bearing quality
2	Lubricant only	1.5	92	Flaking	Bearing quality
3	Lubricant only	1.0	43	Flaking	Bearing quality
4	Lubricant only	0.4	36	Flaking	Bearing quality
5	Lubricant only	1.2	4	Peeling	Ball is out of bearing quality
6	Lubricant + debris	$\geqq 3.0$ if no indentation	$0.5 \sim 20$	Flaking	Bearing quality
7	Lubricant + water	-	$5 \sim 40$	Flaking	Bearing quality
8	Water only	-	$\fallingdotseq 0.01$	Wear	Bearing quality

^{1} $\Lambda =$Oil film thickness / composite surface roughness

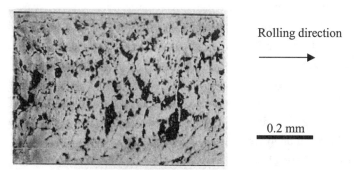

Rolling direction

0.2 mm

Figure 1 - *Peeling on raceway caused by balls with exceedingly bad surface roughness under boundary lubrication condition ($\Lambda =1.2$).*

When the lubricant is debris-contaminated, the bearing life decreases is significant. Cracks initiate from the edge of indents and eventually causes flaking as shown in Figure 2 [7]. The bearing life is affected not only by lubricant contamination level but also bearing material factors such as surface retained austenite content and hardness [2]. Material cleanliness has little connection with bearing life under debris-contaminated lubrication [5]. Bearings, for which countermeasures have been taken for debris-contaminated lubrication, are widely used in the field [2].

Rolling direction

Figure 2 - *Flaking initiated from the edge of an indent under debris-contaminated lubrication.*

When lubricant is water-infiltrated, as is the main subject of this paper, bearing life decreases from 5% to 40% with flaking. When lubricant is water only, bearing life decreases to approximately 0.01% with a wear failure mode. Although flaking initiation under water-infiltrated lubrication would be at the rolling contact surface due to metal contacts, the mechanism and related material factors are unknown.

Figure 3 shows typical flaking of roller bearings used under water-infiltrated lubrication in the field. The flaking is estimated to initiate from the center of the circled area in the figure. Beach marks can be seen surrounding the circle. The initiation was elementally analyzed with an electron probe micro Analyzer. However, it is difficult to conclude: either initiation occurs in metal, or occurs in an inclusions, but this inclusion is not yet present, due to relative slipping of fracture surfaces, that can pulverize inclusion. Conventional theory of lubrication implies that the initiation under water-infiltrated lubrication is at the surface because direct metal contact occurs between rolling elements and rings.

We thought the flaking of Figure 3 was too propagated for analyzing the cause. Therefore, we obtained bearings from the field with early stage flaking. Figure 4 shows a very early stage of flaking. A small pit exists on the raceway surface and the area around the pit is slightly depressed. The cross-section view shows the existence of a crack reaching the surface. However, it is still difficult to understand what the flaking mechanism is.

We therefore began the development of fatigue life test methods that reproduce short life under water-infiltrated lubrication to precisely observe the flaking process and to study what material parameters affect the bearing life.

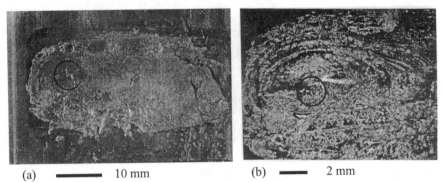

(a) ━━━━ 10 mm   (b) ━━ 2 mm

Figure 3 - *Flaking of roller bearings used under water-infiltrated lubrication in the field; (b) is a magnification of the initiation of the flaking (a).*

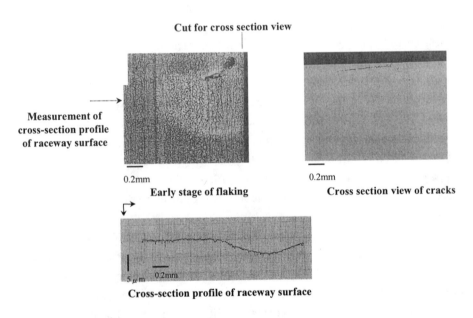

Figure 4 - *The early stage of flaking found in the field with water-infiltrated lubrication.*

Development of Fatigue Life Tests Reproducing the Water-Induced Flaking

Figure 5 shows a schematic diagram of a fatigue test machine for taper roller bearings with water-infiltrated lubrication. This test simulates roll neck bearings of work rolls in a steel mill, which are typically used under water-infiltrated lubrication. The test condition is as follows,

Test bearing:	Taper roller bearing HR32017
	(bore dia.=ϕ85, outside dia.=ϕ130, width=29)
Infiltrated water:	20 ml / 7 hrs
Lubricant:	Lithium soap grease (60g)
P/C:	0.25
Fr:	35.8 kN
Fa:	15.7 kN
Rotation speed:	1 500 rpm

Figure 6 shows the bearing life comparison between pure grease lubrication and grease plus water contamination. The bearing rings and rollers are made of through hardening steel (100Cr6, SAE 52100). The bearing life under water-infiltrated lubrication is shorter than that with pure grease lubrication by a factor of more than 30. The failure mode is flaking, as shown in Figure 7, which has very similar morphology to flaking in the field as shown in Figure 3. Almost all the failed parts are outer rings. This is equivalent to what we have found in the field. We pursued the process from crack initiation to flaking with this test machine as described in the next section.

To further understand the flaking mechanism under water-infiltrated lubrication, we also tested bearing life under water-infiltrated lubrication using thrust ball bearings. The schematic diagram of this test rig is shown in Figure 8 and the test condition is as follows:

Test bearing:	Thrust ball bearing 51305
	(bore diameter=ϕ25, outside diameter=ϕ52, height=18)
Infiltrated water:	30 ml / 24 hrs
Lubricant:	VG10 oil (70 ml)
P/C:	0.35
Pmax:	3.1 GPa
Rotation speed:	1 250 rpm

The thrust ball bearing life with oil plus water lubrication is much shorter than that with oil lubrication (Figure 9). Water-induced flaking with short life occurs regardless of ball or roller bearing type and despite oil or grease lubrications.

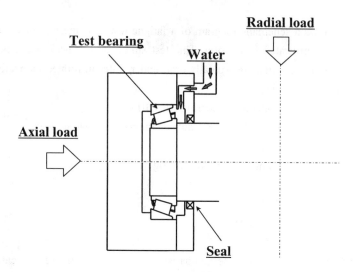

Figure 5 - *Schematic diagram of a taper roller bearing life test machine with water-infiltrated lubrication.*

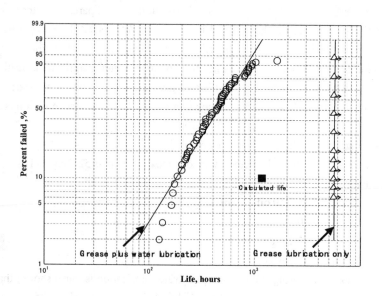

Figure 6 - *Bearing life comparison between grease lubrication only and grease plus water lubrication (taper roller bearings).*

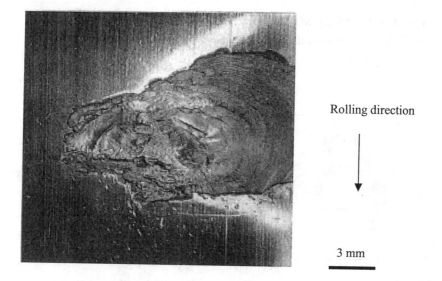

Rolling direction

3 mm

Figure 7 - *Flaking caused in a taper roller bearing with water-infiltrated lubrication.*

Process of Water-Induced Flaking

Figures 10 and 11 shows the early stage of flaking and respective cross section views of taper roller bearings tested under water-infiltrated oil lubrication. The cracks initiate from the surface. Figure 10 is of the earliest stage and the cracks may be propagating through the austenite grain boundary. However, what caused surface initiation could not be determined. The rolling surface was slightly worn out at a sub-micron depth. This shows the existing metal contact. Corrosion pits were not observed. This indicates that flaking initiation is not due to corrosion. Figure 12 shows the fatigue life test results of thrust ball bearings made of X108CrMo17(SAE 440C) martensitic stainless steel compared to 100Cr6(SAE 52100) bearing steel under oil plus water contamination. For this test, a superiority of the stainless steel was not observed. This means that corrosion resistance has no influence on bearing life under water-infiltrated lubrication. What is the origin of initiation under water-infiltrated lubrication? Weaker points in steel strength on the rolling contact surface could be the initiation. They might be nonmetallic inclusions or grain boundary. To verify the effect of nonmetallic inclusions, we carried out fatigue life tests using steels with different cleanliness: normal cleanliness using usual mass production steel and high cleanliness using vacuum arc re-melted steel. The results are shown in Figure 13. Higher cleanliness steel has longer life. Therefore, nonmetallic inclusions are the flaking initiation even under water-infiltrated lubrication, which has very poor oil film thickness causing wear.

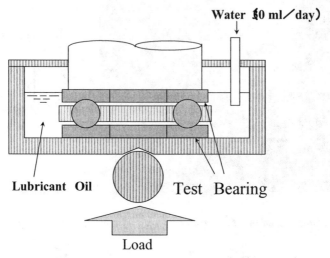

Figure 8 - *Schematic diagram of a thrust ball bearing life test rig with oil plus water lubrication.*

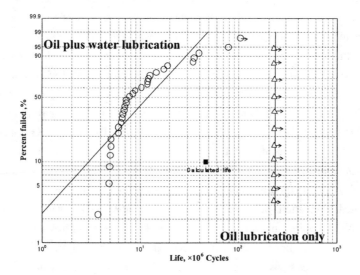

Figure 9 - *Bearing life comparison between oil lubrication only and oil plus water lubrication (thrust ball bearings).*

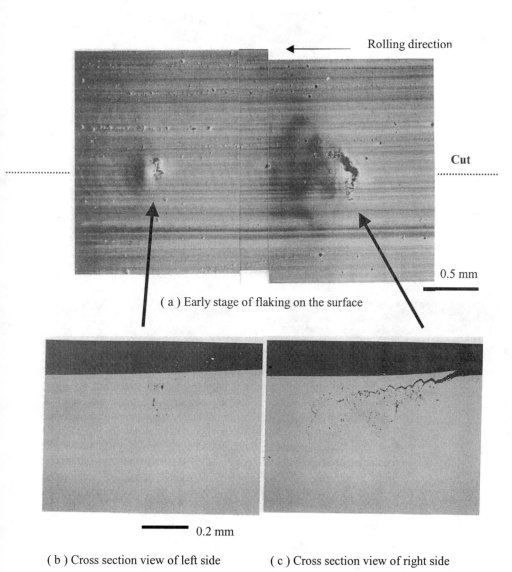

(a) Early stage of flaking on the surface

(b) Cross section view of left side   (c) Cross section view of right side

Figure 10 - *Early stage of flaking and cross section views of taper roller bearings tested under water-infiltrated lubrication condition.*

Rolling direction

→

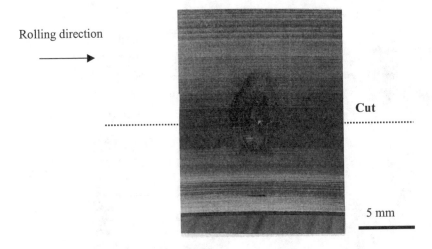

Cut

5 mm

(a) Early stage of flaking on the surface

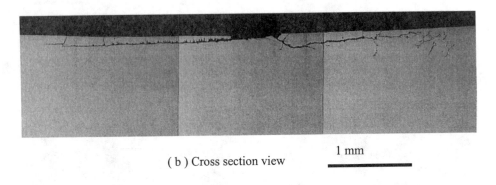

1 mm

(b) Cross section view

Figure 11 - *Early stage of flaking and cross section views of taper roller bearings tested under water-infiltrated lubrication condition.*

In addition, we looked at the effect of grain boundary strength because the cracks of Figure 10 seem to propagate through the austenite grain boundary. Ni improves delayed fracture strength in water as shown in Figure 14, which compares the strengths between no Ni steel (20CrMo4, SAE 4120 modified) and 3.3% Ni steel (18NiCrMo14-6 modified, SAE 9315 modified) at the tension stress of 1.5 GPa. Both steels are vacuum arc re-melted and carburized to be a proper steel with HRC=60 for rolling contact fatigue life tests. The delayed fracture in water initiates from the austenite grain boundary on the surface. It can be understood that the delayed fracture strength shows the grain boundary strength in water. Although delayed fracture in water is not fatigue, they present both surface initiation and water-induced failure.

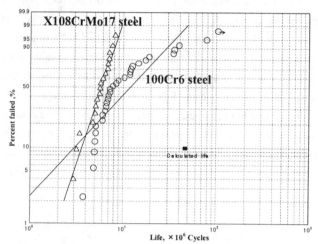

Figure 12 – *Comparison of rolling contact fatigue life under water-infiltrated lubrication between X108CrMo17(440C) martensitic stainless steel and 100Cr6(52100) bearing steel.*

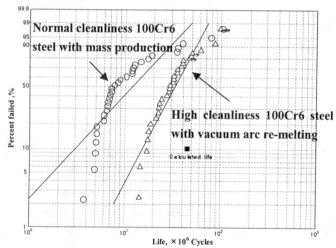

Figure 13 - *Comparison of rolling contact fatigue life under water-infiltrated lubrication between high cleanliness 100Cr6(52100) steel with vacuum arc re-melting and normal cleanliness 100Cr6(52100) steel with degassing.*

Therefore, the delayed fracture strength can be extended to the rolling contact fatigue life with water-infiltrated lubrication if the cracks caused by rolling contact fatigue with water-infiltrated lubrication propagate following the grain boundary. Figure 15 shows rolling contact fatigue life of vacuum arc re-melted steels with different Ni contents (20CrMo4 and 18NiCrMo14-6 modified). Ni improves slightly the rolling contact fatigue life under water-infiltrated lubrication condition when steel cleanliness is good. This might mean that the cracks caused by rolling contact fatigue with water-infiltrated lubrication propagate following the grain boundary.

It was concluded that high steel cleanliness, and preferably, the combination of high steel cleanliness with Ni, can improve bearing life under water-infiltrated lubrication. The process of water-induced flaking is summarized in Figure 16.

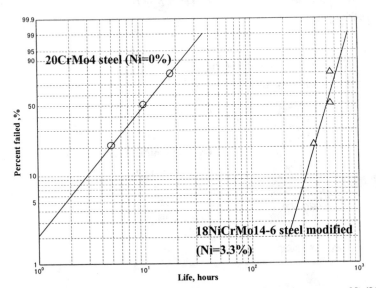

Figure 14 – *Comparison of delayed fracture strength in water between no Ni (20CrMo4, SAE 4120 modified) and 3.3% Ni (18NiCrMo14-6 modified, SAE 9315 modified) steels, both are vacuum arc re-melted and carburized.*

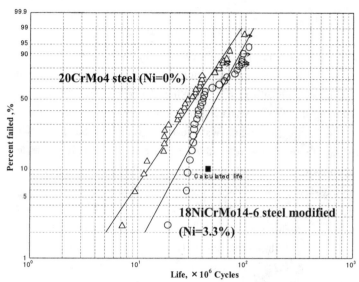

Figure 15 – *Comparison of rolling contact fatigue life under water-infiltrated lubrication between no Ni (20CrMo4, SAE 4120 modified) and 3.3% Ni (18NiCrMo14-6 modified, SAE 9315 modified) steels, both are vacuum arc re-melted and carburized.*

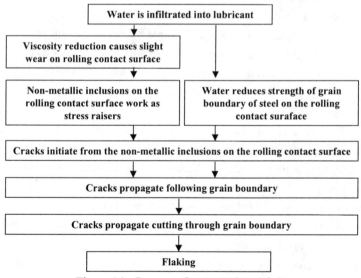

Figure 16 - *Process of water-induced flaking.*

Effect of Hydrogen

Failure under water-infiltrated lubrication initiates from nonmetallic inclusions and propagates initially following the prior austenite grain boundary. It then cuts through the grain and eventually results in flaking. Water promotes this failure.

Considering the role of water, does it promote failure directly or indirectly? The meaning of "indirectly" is that water causes hydrogen, and that the hydrogen promotes failure. To verify the role of water we carried out fatigue life tests in a hydrogen gas atmosphere. The test condition was as follows:

Hydrogen pressure: 1.5×10^5 Pa

Test bearing: Thrust ball bearing 51305 made of 100Cr6(52100) steel

(bore diameter= ϕ 25, outside diameter= ϕ 52, height=18)

Lubricant: Lithium soap grease (2g)

P/C: 0.21

Pmax: 2.4 GPa

Rotation speed: 1 000 rpm

The test result is shown in Figure 17. Bearing life in the hydrogen atmosphere is reduced to at least 10% of that in normal air atmosphere. The reason is hydrogen weakens the steel strength (i.e. hydrogen embrittlement). Figure 18 shows the microstructure of the tested bearings. The martensite has numerous cracks with structural change around the depth of the maximum shear stress. Figure 19 shows hydrogen content analysis using Thermal Desorption Spectrometry of tested thrust ball bearings in water-infiltrated lubrication, hydrogen atmosphere, and a delayed fracture test piece in water. The bearing under water-infiltrated lubrication and delayed fracture test piece in water do not contain hydrogen while the tested bearing in the hydrogen atmosphere contains hydrogen.

Figures 17 and 18 show the definitive difference between water- and hydrogen-induced failures in the mechanism, i.e. the former is surface-initiated and the latter is subsurface-initiated. Hydrogen diffuses into steel and is fixed around the depth of the maximum shear stress, at which the hydrogen weakens steel strength and causes cracks at a lower stress than fatigue in air atmosphere. Water cannot diffuse into steel and therefore stays at the surface, at which water weakens steel strength and causes cracks at a lower stress than fatigue in air atmosphere.

It can be concluded that water and hydrogen-induced failures are different in the mechanism.

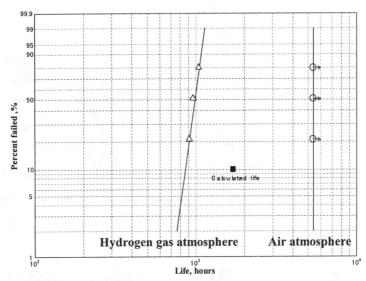

Figure 17 – *Comparison of rolling contact fatigue life between in a hydrogen gas and an air atmospheres.*

Figure 18 - *Microstructure with numerous cracks and structural change at the depth of the maximum shear stress of a tested bearing in the hydrogen gas atmosphere.*

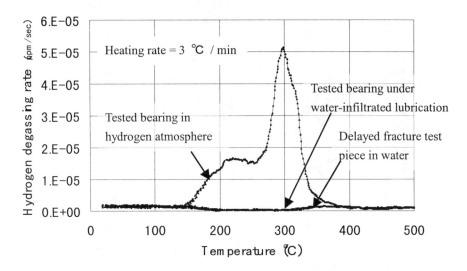

Figure 19 - Hydrogen content analysis using thermal desorption spectrometry of a tested bearing in water-infiltrated lubrication, hydrogen atmosphere, and a delayed fracture test piece in water.

Conclusion

To analyze the mechanism of water-induced failure of rolling bearings, fatigue life tests reproducing short life under water-infiltrated lubrication were carried out. We observed the flaking process precisely and studied what material parameters affect the bearing life. As a result, failure under water-infiltrated lubrication initiates from nonmetallic inclusions on the rolling contact surface and propagates initially following the grain boundary and then cutting through the grain, and then eventually results in flaking. Ni improves the grain boundary strength and extends bearing life in combination with high steel cleanliness under water-infiltrated lubrication.

Water- and hydrogen-induced failures are different in the mechanism. The former is surface-initiated and the latter is subsurface-initiated. Hydrogen diffuses into steel and is fixed at the depth of the maximum shear stress, at which the hydrogen weakens steel strength and causes cracks at a lower stress level than fatigue run in air atmosphere. Water cannot diffuse into steel and therefore stays at the surface, at which water weakens steel strength and causes cracks at a lower stress than fatigue in air atmosphere.

References

[1] Furumura, K., Abe, T. and Murakami, Y., "Progress in Through-Hardening Bearing Steels: User's Experience," *Bearing Steels: Into the 21st Century, ASTM STP 1327*, J. J. C. Hoo and W. B. Green, Eds., American Society for Testing and Materials, West Conshohocken, PA, 1998, pp. 249-264.

[2] Furumura, K., Murakami, Y. and Abe, T., "Case-Hardening Medium Carbon Steel for Tough and Long Life Bearing under Severe Lubrication Conditions," *Bearing Steels: Into the 21st Century, ASTM STP 1327*, J. J. C. Hoo and W. B. Green, Eds., American Society for Testing and Materials, West Conshohocken, PA, 1998, pp. 293-306.

[3] Takemura, H., Mitamura, N., Kawabe, Y. and Murakami, Y., "Rolling contact fatigue under low Λ lubrication," *Proceedings of JAST Tribology Conference*, Oosaka, November, 1997, pp. 324-326.

[4] Mitamura, N. and Murakami, Y., "Development of NSJ2 Bearing Steel," *Motion & Control*, No. 8, May, 2000, pp. 27-34.

[5] Furumura, K., Shirota, S. and Hirakawa, K., "The Surface-initiated and Subsurface-initiated Rolling Contact Fatigue," *NSK Bearing Journal*, No. 636, 1977, pp. 1-10.

[6] Sugi, H., Nagato, T., and Narai, H., "Rolling Contact Fatigue Life of Thrust Ball Bearings in Water," *NSK Technical Journal*, No. 657, 1994, pp. 22-27.

[7] Mitamura, N., Murakami, Y., and Krieger, F., "A New Method for Studying Surface-Initiated Bearing Failure," *SAE TECHNICAL PAPER SERIES 972714*, International Off-Highway & Powerplant Congress & Exposition Milwaukee, Wisconsin, September 8-10, 1997, pp. 1-10.

H.-Jürgen Böhmer[1], and Reiner Eberhard[2]

Microstructural Optimisation of Bearing Steels for Operation Under Contaminated Lubrication by Using the Experimental Method of Dented Surfaces

Reference: Böhmer, H.J., and Eberhard, R., "**Microstructural Optimisation of Bearing Steels for Operation Under Contaminated Lubrication by Using the Experimental Method of Dented Surfaces**," *Bearing Steel Technology, ASTM STP 1419*, J. M. Beswick, Ed., American Society for Testing and Materials International, West Conshohocken, PA, 2002

Abstract: The damage mechanisms of antifriction bearings operating under debris contaminated lubrication have been investigated experimentally. A particular experimental procedure has been designed to simulate natural foreign particle indentations and to allow a quick reproducible fatigue test comparison on material and heat treatment variants. Additionally, the scattering of the fatigue test results could be reduced significantly.

The different phases of the damaging process are described. From these results measures have been derived to increase the bearing performance and lifetime under these stress conditions, which are governed by geometrical notch effects and localized metal-to-metal-contact and plastic deformation. The effectiveness in laboratory tests has been checked versus field applications.

An optimization of the materials microstructure was found to be an efficient means to counteract such problems. This was done by modifying the alloying content of the bearing steel and the surface composition respectively and changing the heat treatment in a way to generate a certain amount of very stable retained austenite. This particular microstructural component could be proved to have inherent self-healing capabilities against indentations produced by the overrolling of debris particles and the subsequent re-flattening of the raised edges around the dents. This effect can be demonstrated by base-alloying of through-hardening grades as well as by surface alloying of case-hardenable steels.

The actual amount and the stability of the retained austenite against mechanical or thermal-induced transformation are important properties to achieve the tolerance to dent effects. Results of laboratory fatigue tests of different development routes and field experiences are presented. The consequences of these measures on the dimensional stability of the bearings are explained.

Keywords: rolling contact fatigue, contaminated lubrication, bearing performance, material optimization, heat treatment optimization

[1]Material scientist, FAG Industrial Bearings AG, D-97419 Schweinfurt, Germany
[2]Material research and development, FAG Industrial Bearings AG, D-97419 Schweinfurt, Germany

Commercial Relevance of Contaminated Lubrication

Failures due to contaminated lubrication cover an significant partition among the list of failure causes for antifriction bearings (Figure 1) [1]. Consequently, much effort is taken to ensure bearing operation in a clean lubrication system or to seal the bearings to avoid contamination from the environment. Yet, it is not always possible to take such measures or their efficiency will decrease with the operating time of the bearings. This leads to a rising demand for contamination-tolerant bearings. Additionally, this performance improvement should be achieved with low additional manufacturing costs while reducing the operation costs for the whole system in which the bearings are running.

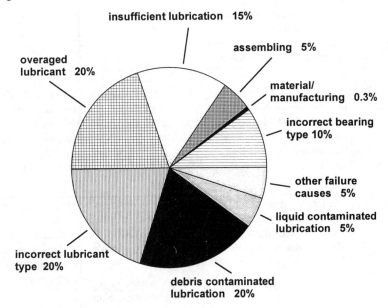

Figure 1 — *Percentage share of bearing failure causes.*
(Due to rounding errors the share values will sum up to an amount slightly above 100%).

The contamination of the lubricant may be caused by liquids or by solid particles called debris. Liquid contamination will reduce the efficiency of the lubricant and may cause corrosive attack of the bearing material. Such a kind of contamination requires different countermeasures than debris contamination and is not a subject of this paper. Very fine and hard solid particles will act abrasively causing wear instead of raceway dents. This process is also not investigated in the frame of this paper.

Failure Mechanism due to Debris Contaminated Lubrication

Table 1 — *Damage process due to debris contaminated lubrication.*

Stage	Process	Portion of lifetime	Relevance
Formation of the indentation	Particles, harder or softer than the bearing material, are overrolled. Soft particles are mostly deformed, hard ones fracture. They are pressed into the surface, leaving characteristic indentations. Often they are subsequently moved away by the lubricant, vibrations or inertial forces	Mostly only one or a few number of cycles of overrolling	Minor for the whole failure process and the development of counter measures
Plastic deformation of the raised edges	Raised edges around the indentations surmount the lubricant film thickness and cause metal to metal contact and friction. They become deformed in the subsequent operation	Brittle materials: A few number of cycles up to some few percent of the whole lifetime. Tough materials: 70% to 100% of the lifetime	Dominant for the further progress of the failure process – Very appropriate for influencing bearing performance
Crack initiation	The increased stressing at/within the raised edges mainly induces the formation of cracks due to material fatigue	Brittle materials: A few number of cycles up to some few percent of the whole lifetime. Tough materials: Crack initiation takes a longer time and may even be suppressed	High: optimization of material to withstand fatigue and crack initiation increases bearing performance
Crack propagation	Cracks generated at the raised edges propagate below the raceway in a shallow bow form before they reach the surface again	1% to 20% of the lifetime	Medium: The bearing is already damaged - but a slow crack propagation rate will increase bearing life
Spalling	The crack propagation finally results in the break out of near surface material	A short period at the end of the bearing life	Minor: the bearing life has already come to an end

To check for the possibilities of improving the bearing behavior under debris contaminated operation, the resulting damage process has been thoroughly investigated. Five different stages are described to represent the whole failure process (Table 1).

Examples for the indentations caused by hard and soft debris particles respectively are shown below (Figure 2). Soft particles generate a shallow indentation in which most of the grinding marks from hard machining can still be seen. Hard particles form deeper and jagged indentations because they do not plastically deform but fracture into many parts during overrolling. In both cases raised edges are formed around the indentations that become subsequently stressed and deformed by sliding effects as it can be seen in both pictures.

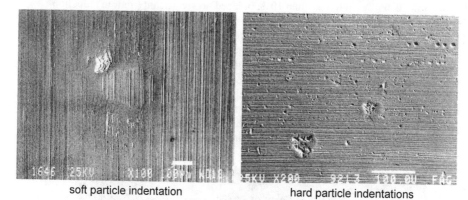

soft particle indentation   hard particle indentations

Figure 2 — *Typical appearance of debris particle indentations.*

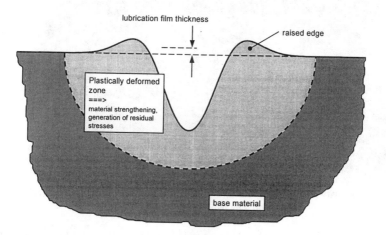

Figure 3 — *Schematic cross sectional view through an indentation.*

A schematic cross sectional view through such an indentation reveals the changes in the local geometry and material condition (Figure 3). The most eye-catching effect is the hole created when the debris particle is overrolled. The displaced material causes a plastically deformed zone around this hole and raised edges at the surface. The height of the raised edges is significantly higher than the lubricant film thickness. These changes of the local geometry lead to corresponding local disturbances in the lubrication conditions and in the dynamic rolling behavior of the rolling elements as well as to a local stress raising with metal to metal contact and shear forces. Experiments have shown that the raised edges to be the most detrimental effect of the complete indentation [2-4]. Experiments made on a two disk test rig showed that indentations that reduced the lifetime of the disks down to less than 10%, induced no significant lifetime reduction after the raised edges had been carefully honed away, in spite of the fact that the indents and the plastically deformed zones were still present. Indentations without raised edges need to be much bigger to have an impact on the rolling contact fatigue life [4,5].

Due to the steadily repeated overrolling of the raised edges, the trailing part of the dent results in crack initiation. These cracks propagate in a shallow angle of about 10° to 25° into the material. Thereafter, the material between these cracks and the surface will break away stepwise, leaving a spall growing with continued overrolling, whereas the crack continues to propagate in the rolling direction (Figure 4). The result will be a typical v-shaped spall immediately behind the indentation (Figure 5).

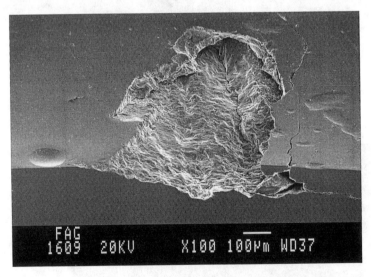

Figure 4 — *Raceway and surface near circumferential cut section at a v-spall (rolling direction was from left to right).*

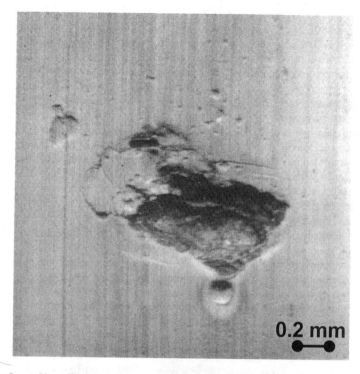

Figure 5 — *V-spall behind an indentation(rolling direction was from bottom to top).*

Related investigations can be found in the literature. Extensive experimental and theoretical work for a lot of different operational conditions is described in [6-9]. The circumstances under which debris particles will be transported into the contact area and the related consequences are given in [10]. The effect of the generated indentations on the situation in the contact area (lubricant film thickness and load distribution) is described in [11]. There may be operating conditions that change the location of pitting initiation from the trailing to the leading edge of the dent [4,9,12,13], but in most standard applications of antifriction bearings v-spalls behind the indentations will develop. This paper deals mostly with the possibility of improving material behavior to achieve an increased lifetime under these circumstances. Consequently, the most important phenomena for the authors becomes the overrolling of the raised edges around the indentations, the re-flattening thereof and the resultant material response.

Test Method for the Investigation of the Bearing Performance under Debris Contaminated Lubrication

Experiments to investigate the influence of debris contaminated lubrication in rolling contact fatigue are usually very difficult. You have to decide which kind of debris you use and how to add it to the lubrication system in a way that you can be sure it will be transported to the Hertzian contact area and become overrolled. You have to ensure that each of the tested bearings is damaged by a similar amount and type of particles at each cycle during the whole testing time. Even if you succeed in these efforts, you must realize a much higher scatter in the results compared to conventional rolling contact fatigue experiments. These are bad preconditions to compare different batches of bearings in relation to their behavior under debris contaminated operation.

To improve the situation the authors developed a test method to allow an easy inexpensive experimental way to distinguish different bearing designs and materials with respect to their debris contamination tolerance. Based on the initial investigations of the damage mechanism it becames evident that the material reaction at the raised edges around indentations mainly determines the bearing performance under these circumstances. Consequently the authors developed a reproducible method to create well defined artificial indentations at the raceway. A device was built that uses a diamond cone of a HRC-tester to form raceway indentations at precisely controlled locations, indent directions and indent forces. Because the necessary indentations should be small, only the ball-shaped tip of the diamond cone was pressed into the raceway.

The angular contact ball bearing type 7205B and the FAG test rig L17 were chosen for the experiments (Figure 6). In this test rig, the bearings are subjected to pure axial loading leading to equal stressing conditions for all Hertzian contact areas over the whole circumference. A lot of former experiments have been performed with this test rig such that a huge results database is available for comparison and assessment of the results.

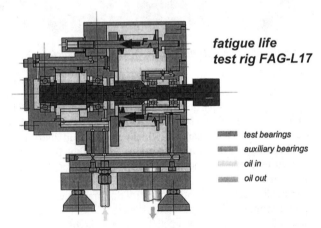

fatigue life
test rig FAG-L17

test bearings
auxiliary bearings
oil in
oil out

Figure 6 — *FAG test rig L17 for angular contact ball bearing type 7205B.*

Only the inner rings of the test bearings 7205B received artificial indentations to simulate debris contaminated lubrication. The deformation of the raised edges is strongly influenced by the local slip situation. Because the sliding speed is not constant across the raceway, eight indentations at different lateral positions were produced (Figure 7). The shaded area in the lower part of the figure shall indicate the running track width as determined by the long axis of the contact ellipse. On the right-hand side a schematic plot of the p*v-value (local pressure multiplied by the local sliding speed) is shown to inform roughly about this important parameter and the resulting shear forces.

The sliding effects were found to play a significant role in the behavior of the raised edges.

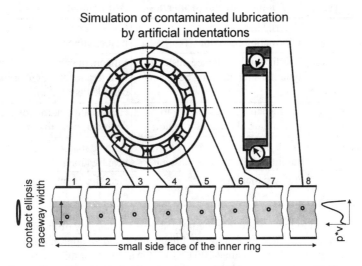

Figure 7 — *Set of locations for the simulation of debris contaminated rolling contact fatigue.*

A very good simulation of the material behavior under debris contaminated lubrication could be achieved by the application of this technique. Furthermore, the scatter of the experimental results could be reduced drastically compared to the afore mentioned bearing test methods using contaminated lubrication. This is because the shape (refer to Figure 5) and the location of the indentations and the resulting impact on the material properties can be precisely controlled by this technique. Thus, a very useful tool for the material optimization in this context has been developed.

Material Optimization

Using the tool mentioned in the preceding chapter a project for systematic optimization of bearings operating under debris-contaminated lubrication was launched. Considering the previous mentioned damage accumulation process (Table 1), a list of possible and easily applied solutions was created (Table 2).

Table 2 — *Influencing parameters on the damage process due to debris contaminated lubrication.*

Damage process	Dominant material properties	Adjustment
Formation of the indentation	Material hardness, deformation behavior	Carbon/nitrogen content, heat treatment
Plastic deformation of the raised edges	Stability of the retained austenite, dynamic strengthening behavior	Silicon, manganese, nickel, heat treatment, microstructure, carbide distribution
Crack initiation	Fatigue strength, capability to accumulate plastic deformation	Heat treatment, microstructure, degree of cleanliness
Crack propagation	Crack propagation rate, stability of the retained austenite	Silicon, manganese, nickel, heat treatment
Spalling	Fracture toughness	Heat treatment, microstructure, carbide distribution

It was decided to investigate first the influence of the stability of the retained austenite, achieved by an increased amount of manganese and an appropriate heat treatment. A German steel grade called 100 Cr Mn 6 was used for this purpose (Table 3). It was estimated that the amount and the stability of the retained austenite is increased due to the higher manganese content, and this was promoted by a specially applied heat treatment. The main aim was to check the impact of the retained austenite on the formation of the raised edges during the initial indent formation and the subsequent overrolling deformations in comparison to the correspondent behavior of standard bearing material SAE 52100. The potential influence of microstructure and retained austenite and different means of material optimization for debris contaminated conditions are mentioned in literature [2-5,14-16].

Table 3 — *Composition of the German steel grade 100 Cr Mn 6, an alloy similar to SAE 52100 with an increased amount of manganese and silicon.*

Element	C	Si	Mn	P	S	O	Cr	Cu	Mo	Ni	Al	Ti
Min:	0,90	0,55	1,10				1,40					
Max:	1,05	0,70	1,20	0,025	0,008	0,0015	1,65	0,25	0,1	0,3	0,05	0,004

The different materials showed no significant differences in the shape and macroscopic dimensions of the indentations measured directly after their creation. Yet, at the raised edges different microscopic appearances were found to be dependent on the material (Figure 8, Figure 9). The standard bearing steel revealed a more wrinkled structure and sometimes even small initial cracks could be observed in these areas. Whereas for the optimized 100 Cr Mn 6 material cracks could never be detected and the surfaces of the raised edges were less wrinkled. These are observations at artificial

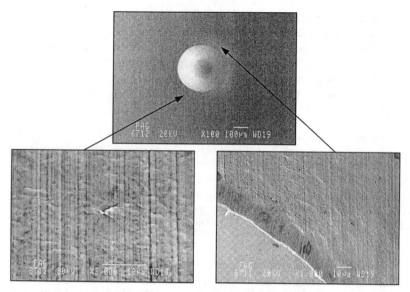

Figure 8 — *Appearance of a newly created indentation in a inner ring made from SAE 52100 (62,0 HRC, 14% retained austenite).*

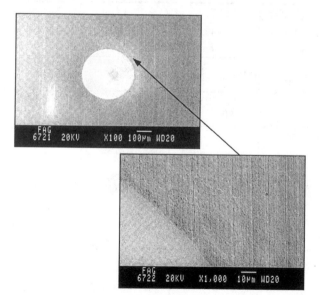

Figure 9 — *Appearance of a newly created indentation in a inner ring made from 100 Cr Mn 6 (61,5 HRC, 15% retained austenite).*

indentations with a diameter of about 0,35 mm. No wrinkling and crack formation could be found for both materials with indentations of about 0,16 mm diameter, which was the usual indentation size for most of our experiments. These observations are caused by the different stability of the retained austenite that also promotes different levels of stress-induced transformation under high loads.

The different material behavior as already found during the creating of the artificial indentations promised benefits for the later operational behavior. Yet, the ultimate proof has to be the rolling contact fatigue behavior. Based on the above reflections and initial observations an experimental programme was set up to check the performance of different materials in different heat treatment conditions (Table 4) in rolling contact fatigue with simulated debris contaminated lubrication. It was planned to test the behavior of the material 100 Cr Mn 6 with different amounts of retained austenite in comparison to the standard bearing steel SAE 52100. Also the significantly more expensive material Cronidur 30 (Table 5) was included in the test as well as carbonitrided SAE 4320 (Table 6) in different tempered conditions.

Table 4 — *Material and heat treatment.*

Material	Heat treatment before hardening	Austenitising	Quenching media	Tempering
SAE 52100	---	850°C	salt bath	180°C
100 Cr Mn 6 standard	---	830°C	salt bath	190°C
100 Cr Mn 6 low austenite	---	830°C	salt bath	240°C
100 Cr Mn 6 carbide network	970°C 30 min > 780°C 4 h	830°C	salt bath	190°C
Cronidur 30	---	1020°C	nitrogen	180°C
SAE 4320 standard	carbonitrided 930°C 10 h	830°C	oil	170°C
SAE 4320 15% RA	carbonitrided 930°C 10 h	830°C	oil	240°C
SAE 4320 2% RA	carbonitrided 930°C 10 h	830°C	oil	260°C

The resulting material properties for the different batches of bearings are summarized below (Table 7). Its last column describes the residual stresses due to the heat treatment without any effects of the final hard machining.

Table 5 — *Composition of Cronidur 30.*

Element	C	Si	Mn	P	S	O	Cr	Cu	Mo	Ni	Al	Ti	N
Min:	0,28	0,3	0,30				14,5		0,95				0,35
Max:	0,34	0,8	0,60	0,020	0,010	0,0025	16,0	0,15	1,10	0,30	0,015	0,003	0,44

Table 6 — *Composition of SAE 4320.*

Element	C	Si	Mn	P	S	O	Cr	Cu	Mo	Ni	Al	Ti
Min:	0,15	0,15	0,40		0,010		0,35		0,20	1,55	0,015	
Max:	0,23	0,35	0,80	0,025	0,025	0,0014	0,65	0,35	0,35	2,00	0,050	0,005

Table 7 — *Material properties after heat treatment.*

material	retained austenite at surface	surface hardness	case depth	Residual stress at surface
SAE 52100	14%	62 HRC	n.a.	< 100 MPa
100 Cr Mn 6 standard	15%	61.5 HRC	n.a.	< 100 MPa
100 Cr Mn 6 low austenite	4%	60.5 HRC	n.a.	< 100 MPa
100 Cr Mn 6 carbide network	15%	61.5 HRC	n.a.	< 100 MPa
Cronidur 30	10%	59 HRC	n.a.	< 100 MPa
SAE 4320 standard	32%	61 HRC	1.5 mm	-80 MPa
SAE 4320 15% RA	15%	60.5 HRC	1.5 mm	-156 MPa
SAE 4320 2% RA	2%	60 HRC	1.5 mm	-210 MPa

Because the inner ring contacts are subjected to a higher Hertzian pressure than the outer ring contacts, the inner rings are considered the test elements and consequently only they were artificially indentated to simulate the debris contaminated lubrication. The remaining elements of the bearings were taken from standard series production, and if it should happen that one of these failed first, the bearing was treated as suspended at the related running time for the inner ring. The material properties for the used standard balls were 64±2 HRC and 12% to 18% retained austenite, for the outer rings 60,5±2 HRC and max. 5% retained austenite, both made from SAE 52100.

Test Results

The first test runs were aimed to quantify the benefits of the 100 Cr Mn 6 material (Figure 10). It was found, that the L_{10} lifetime could be increased by a factor of about three compared to standard bearings and the scatter is less for the 100 Cr Mn 6 material. The 90% confidence intervals are also included in Figure 10 as thin lines to allow a better assessment of the tests. The tests were performed with a fairly good lubrication leading to a κ-value of about 2.4, which allows a satisfactory separation of the contact surfaces.

The investigation of the failed inner rings showed that most of the failures occurred at the indentations at the positions 2 or 3 (refer to Figure 7), occasionally also at positions 4 and 5. Obviously, the higher sliding rates (p*v-values) in the environment of positions 6 and 7 help to redeform the raised edges of the indentations and therefore delay the damage development in this area of the raceway. The outmost positions 1 and 8 are too low loaded to play a significant role in failure initiation.

Because there is an interaction between sliding effects and the behavior of the raised edges all further tests have been carried out with a less viscous oil called NL2 leading to a κ-value of about 0.14 to represent more severe operating conditions.

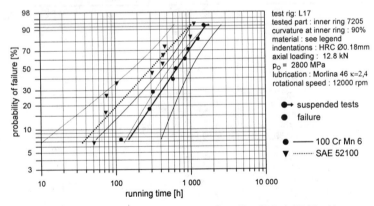

Figure 10 — *Lifetime of 100 Cr Mn 6 (variant "standard" from* Table 4) *compared to standard material under simulated debris contaminated lubrication.*

To check for the contribution of the retained austenite on the performance improvement, two test series with different amounts were performed (Figure 11). It was proved that the L_{10} lifetime decreases and the scatter increases, if the amount of retained austenite becomes too low. A certain amount of stable retained austenite within and in the neighborhood of the raised edges is necessary to allow a quick, easy deformation without any crack formation.

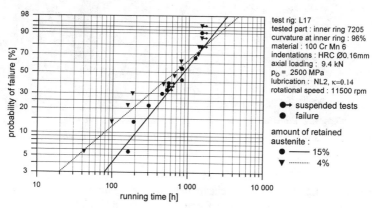

Figure 11 — *Influence of retained austenite in 100 Cr Mn 6 bearing rings under simulated debris contaminated lubrication.*

It was checked, if a bad carbide distribution gives a limiting life under such circumstances. However, produced carbide networks of the rating NH 2 according to ISO 5249 (= CN 5.2) within a lot of inner rings made from 100 Cr Mn 6 gave comparable results relative to rings without networks (Figure 12). Only the scattering

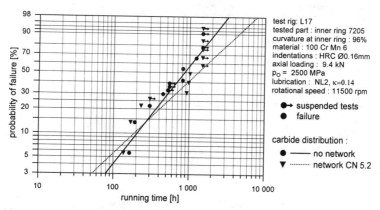

Figure 12 — *Influence of carbide network in 100 Cr Mn 6 bearing rings under simulated debris contaminated lubrication.*

was slightly higher for the lot with the carbide networks. SEM investigations proved further that crack propagation and pitting generation seemed to be uninfluenced by the presence of carbide network (Figure 13).

Figure 13 — *Cracks and pitting at an artificial indentation and their relation to carbide networks.*

The use of 100 Cr Mn 6 to optimize the bearing performance under debris contaminated lubrication is a relatively cheap method. Further improvement is possible, if cost is of less importance. For example, the nitrogen alloyed Cronidur 30 gives further performance improvement (Figure 14). Additionally, some other benefits like corrosion and heat resistance are provided.

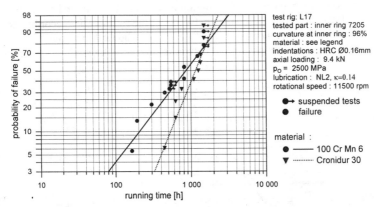

Figure 14 — *Lifetime of Cronidur 30 compared to 100 Cr Mn 6 under simulated debris contaminated lubrication.*

A similar effect of the retained austenite could be found with case hardened materials. This is demonstrated by the Weibull lines for three different lots of bearings with inner rings made from SAE 4320 (Figure 15). The tempering temperature for the inner rings of each lot was different to achieve a different amount of retained austenite. As found already in the 100 Cr Mn 6 experiments described above, again with an increasing content of retained austenite the lifetime under simulated debris contaminated lubrication increases.

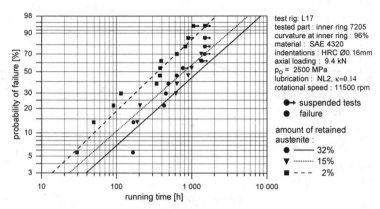

Figure 15 — *Lifetime of SAE4320 under simulated debris contaminated lubrication.*

Dimensional Stability

Although the retained austenite could be shown to be very beneficial for tolerance to debris contaminated lubrication, it may have severe detrimental consequences on the dimensional stability of the bearings. This depends on the actual operating conditions and mainly on the operating temperature. Also, stress induced transformation of the retained austenite has to be considered. The dimensional changes of rings made from 100 Cr Mn 6 at 130°C and 160°C after 1500 h soaking time in combination with hoop stresses due to interference fits are shown below (Figure 16). It is obvious that if the dimensional changes approach the values of the interference, this effect becomes increasingly important because of the risk of loosing the fit.

These dimensional changes are naturally caused by the stress-temperature induced transformation of retained austenite to martensite. Consequently, the initial amount of retained austenite determines the extent of the ring growth (Figure 17).

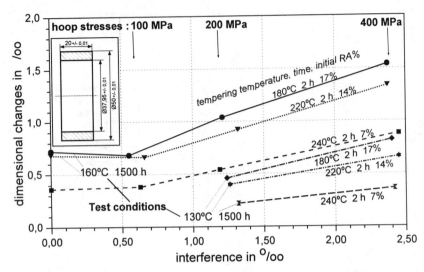

Figure 16 — *Dimensional changes of 100 Cr Mn 6 rings due to operational temperature and hoop stresses.*

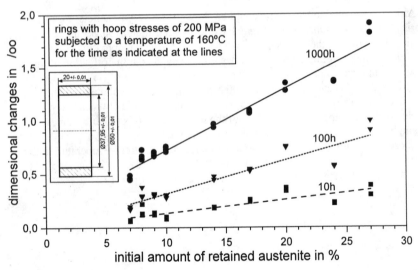

Figure 17 — *Influence of the initial amount of retained austenite on the dimensional changes (hoop stresses = 200 MPa).*

Conclusions

The failure mechanism due to debris contaminated lubrication was found to be dominated by the overrolling and plastic deformation behavior of the raised edges generated around the indentations of debris particles. This deformation behavior can be influenced by the composition of the materials microstructure, mainly by the amount and stability of the retained austenite. A certain minimum amount of stable retained austenite of about 5% seems to be necessary to achieve benefits for bearings made from 100 Cr Mn 6. This is not a recommendation to set up this amount of retained austenite. It shall just be emphasized that below 5% retained austenite there is the risk of achieving no benefits at all. With an increasing amount of retained austenite the lifetime under debris contaminated lubrication operation increases as long as the stability of it can be assured under the operating conditions. For standard bearing steel SAE 52100 the retained austenite is too unstable to cause any beneficial effects in this context.

To allow a quick and inexpensive assessment of rolling contact behavior of different alloys and heat treatments under debris contaminated conditions, the use of artificial and well defined raceway indentations is recommended. If sliding effects differ across the raceway width, dents should be located in all regions of distinguished sliding. Regions with sliding and normal loading conditions may be present, where flattening of the raised edges occurs without producing further damage. It would be worthwhile to investigate this phenomena and its material dependence in more detail in the future.

The materials with higher levels and higher stability of retained austenite that demonstrated benefits are only applicable if the operational temperature is not too high to avoid unacceptable dimensional changes of the bearing elements. Further work on the stabilization of retained austenite has to be done to increase the limiting temperature in this context.

References

[1]   Nierlich, W., Volkmuth, J. "Schäden und Schadensverhütung bei Wälzlagern," *Antriebstechnik 40,* Nr.1, 2001, pp.48-52.

[2]   Toda, K., Mikami, T., Johns, M., "Development of Long Life Bearing in Contaminated Lubrication," *SAE Technical Paper Series 921721,* Sept. 1992.

[3]   Beerbower, M. R., Shiratani, T., Murakami, Y., Abe, K., "Fighting Debris: Increasing Life with HTF Bearings for Transmissions," *SAE Technical Paper Series 940728,* Feb. 1994.

[4]   Volger, J., "Ermüdung der oberflächennahen Bauteilschicht unter Wälzbeanspruchung," *Dissertation RWTH Aachen,* 1991.

[5]   Leng, J., "Minderung der schädigenden Wirkung von Oberflächendefekten durch gezielte Auswahl von Werkstoff, Restaustenit und Gefüge," *Abschlußbericht FVA-Forschungsvorhaben Nr. 148/II,* 1994.

[6]   Ville, F., Nelias, D., "Influence of the Nature and Size of Solid Particles on the Indenetation Features in EHL Contacts," *Proceedings of the 24th Leeds-Lyon Symposium "Tribology of energy conservation, "* Tribology series 32, Elsevier, 1998, pp.399-410.

[7]   Ville, F., Nelias, D., "An Experimental Study on the Concentration and Shape of Dents caused by Spherical Metallic Particles in EHL Contacts," *Tribology Transactions,* Vol 42, n° 1, 1999, pp.231-240.

[8]   Ville, F., Nelias, D., "Early Fatigue Failure due to Dents in EHL Contacts," *Tribology Transactions,* Vol 42, n° 4, 1999, pp.795-800.

[9]   Ville, F., Nelias, D., "Detrimental Effects of Dents on Rolling Contact Fatigue," *ASME Journal of Tribology,* Vol. 122, n° 1, 2000, pp.55-64.

[10]   Kang, S. Y., Sadeghi, F., Ai, X., "Debris Effects on EHL Contact," *ASME Journal of Tribology,* Vol. 122, n° 1, 2000, pp.711-720.

[11]   Xu, G., Nickel, D.A., Sadeghi, F., Ai, X., "Elastoplastohydrodynamic Lubrication with Dent Effects," *ImechE Proc Instn Mech Engrs,* Vol. 210, 1996, pp.233-245.

[12]   Xu, G., Sadeghi, F., Hoeprich, M.R., "Dent Initiated Spall Formation in EHL Rolling/Sliding Contacts," *Abstract Papers from World Tribology Congress* Sept. 1997, p.107.

[13]   Xu, G., Sadeghi, F., " Spall Initiation and Propagation Due to Debris Denting," *Wear 201,* 1996, pp.106-116.

[14]   Rofes Vernis, J., Baudry, G., Auclair, G., Daguier, P., Bellus, J., Dudragne, G., Girodin, G., Jacob, G. "An Improved Steel Grade for Demanding Bearing Applications," *Bearing Steels at the Millenium, proceedings of the 3rd Ascometal Bearing Steels Symposium,* Arles-sur Rhone, France, 2000, pp.137-142.

[15]   Nelias, D., Dumont, M.-L., Couhier, F., Dudragne, G., Flamand, L., "Experimental and Theoretical Investigation on Rolling Contact Fatigue of 52100 and M50 Steels under EHL or Micro-EHL Conditions," *ASME Journal of Tribology,* Vol. 120, 1998, pp.184-190.

[16]   Luty, W. "Vergleichende Untersuchung an carbonitrierten Einsatzstählen und dem Stahl 100Cr6 unter dem Gesichtspunkt ihrer Anwendung für Wälzlager," *Härtereitechnische Mitteilungen 28,* Heft 4, 1973.

Daniel Girodin,[1] Fabrice Ville,[2] Roger Guers,[1] and Gilles Dudragne[1]

Rolling Contact Fatigue Tests to Investigate Surface Initiated Damage and Tolerance to Surface Dents

Reference: Girodin, D., Ville, F., Guers, R., and Dudragne, G., "**Rolling Contact Fatigue Tests to Investigate Surface Initiated Damage and Tolerance to Surface Dents,**" *Bearing Steel Technology, ASTM STP 1419,* J. M. Beswick, Ed., American Society for Testing and Materials International, West Conshohocken, PA, 2002.

Abstract: The improvement in steel cleanliness has resulted in a large reduction of subsurface damage initiated on inclusions. As a consequence surface initiated failure related to lubricant contamination has become the main cause of damage in most commercial applications. Debris contaminants can produce dents on the raceways, which generate stress concentrations, leading to failure.
This paper describes experimental procedures developed to study the surface initiated damage mechanisms using two types of pre-damaging processes to simulate debris contaminant effects:
- dents printed on the raceway using a diamond indenter,
- natural dents obtained using a lubricant contaminated by fine hard particles
Three-dimensional surface topography was used to characterise dent morphology and to compare the influence of materials. The test results show that the pre-denting method using hard powder is more efficient to reproduce surface morphology and damage mechanisms observed under practical operating conditions.

Keywords: rolling contact fatigue life, contaminated lubrication, surface initiated failure, bearing steels, stress analysis

Introduction

Bearing performance is profoundly influenced by the environment within which the bearings operate. Depending on the manufacturing quality of bearings (cleanliness of the steel, surface roughness, surface defects) and of the operating conditions (rolling speed,

[1] Senior Engineers and Manager, respectively, SNR Roulements, Direction du Produit, BP 2017, 74010 Annecy Cedex, France.
[2] Assistant Professor, Laboratoire de Mécanique des Contacts, INSA de Lyon 20, Av. Albert Einstein, 69621 Villeurbanne Cedex, France.

load, clearance, sliding, contact geometry, type of lubricant, temperature, lubricant contamination), the rolling contact fatigue can be initiated either in the subsurface or on the surface of the contacting parts.

Subsurface fatigue damage occurs when a hard non metallic inclusion is located in the zone of the maximum shear stress and acts as a stress raiser. If the local shear stress that results from this exceeds the micro-yield shear stress of the steel matrix, the cyclic plasticity associated with the stress - strain cycling originates for a cyclic movement of dislocations and the formation of a fatigue butterfly. When the loading conditions are high enough to let the accumulated dislocations reach a critical dislocation density, then a crack may initiate within the butterfly and is propagated until the surface is reached [1,2]. The fatigue failure appears generally as a spall on the raceway, limited in depth to the zone of the maximum shear stress.

Nevertheless, improvements in steel manufacturing processes over the past years have resulted in very clean steels and as a consequence rolling fatigue life has increased (even if heavier Hertzian contact stresses have been used in the same time for bearing applications). Thus, due to the high quality of steel used in rolling bearings, subsurface inclusion initiated failure normally observed under ideal operating conditions (smooth surfaces, fully flooded EHD conditions) has been progressively replaced by surface initiated failure, which has become nowadays one of the main causes of premature fatigue damage (the other one corresponding to starvation) in engineering practice. Particularly, even with thick EHD lubricating films, surface initiated failure due to debris contamination of the lubricant is of importance insofar as solid particles, from various origins (coming from either external or internal sources) can not be completely eliminated in most commercial applications. These particles cause surface damages that create stress concentrations large enough to shorten the bearing life considerably. Debris can get into the contact, deform elastoplastically or fracture and generate dents on the contacting surfaces. The subsequent overolling of dents will generate high pressure spikes superimposed on the Hertzian stress distribution. These pressure spikes that occur at dent edges are much higher than the Hertzian pressure and bring the maximum stress very close to the surface where cyclic plasticity initiates a surface crack that propagates into a large fatigue spall. A typical dent initiated spall has a characteristic V-shaped propagation extending from the dent edge along the rolling direction (opposite to the roller motion) with an unspalled ledge between the edge and the spall in most of cases.

Contact fatigue related to dents and surface distress has received a particular interest from bearing manufacturers and many research works have been conducted on this topic either experimentally or analytically.

The major factors that influence surface initiated fatigue have been experimentally studied: the debris nature, its size and distribution, the morphology of the generated dents, the level of filtering, the type of contact and the bearing materials.

The effect of debris contaminants entering the contact on the shape and size of the subsequent dents has been observed experimentally [3-7]. Even if it is small, a debris material is much larger than the lubricant film thickness and when coming into the contact is submitted to very high loads, so that deformation occurs. This deformation process can take different forms (either ductile or brittle) depending on the material properties and the effect on the nature of the subsequent damage can have a major influence on the fatigue life of the bearing. Ductile materials trapped in the inlet will be laminated and plastically deformed into platelets and finally ejected (they can be embedded in the surface when sliding occurs). They will leave on the contacting elements well-defined surface dents whose shape depend on the surface and particle hardness, the Hertzian stress, the rolling speed and the sliding/rolling ratio. On the contrary, brittle particles will fracture into several fragments that print several small dents on the surface. The fragment can also embed into the element surface.

Specific tests and characterisation techniques have been developed to study the detrimental effects of contaminants on fatigue life. Artificially produced surface defects, to simulate grinding or honing scratches, nicks from handling or dents from contaminants, have been widely used to study the conditions of crack initiation and propagation or to evaluate the dent resistance of materials. Among them, scratched furrows obtained by scratching a diamond tip and dents printed on the rolling surface using diamond hardness indenters prior to testing were used by many authors [8-11]. Several morphological parameters have been mentioned to be detrimental with regard to the fatigue life. Either the height of the raised built up shoulder, the slope of the indent or the ratio r/c (r = radius of the built up shoulder, c = half value of the dent width) have been mentioned to be the more prevalent parameters [11-13].

Extensive test programs were also carried out using a variety of lubricants and contaminants with controlled sizes, types and concentrations with and without filtration or seals, to determine their effects on the fatigue life of ball and tapered roller bearings [13-17]. Some research investigations were also dedicated to develop new steels or heat treatments able to resist surface initiated failure better [18-20].

Theoretical studies performed in recent years were focused on the effect of dents associated to contaminants debris on the pressure distribution, the internal stresses and the plastic deformation in the contacting bodies around the dent including residual stress effects due to the indentation of the raceway and to the overrolling of the dents [21-27].

Facing the demand for performance improvement of bearings in the car and aeronautic industries as well as for industrial equipment, it is of particular interest to improve fatigue life of bearings when they may possibly operate in contaminated lubricants. It is important to get a comprehensive interpretation of the damaging mechanism and of the parameters that influence the resistance of materials and bearings to indentations in order to design them in the best way.

In this paper test procedures used to simulate the effect of debris contaminant using artificially induced surface dents are described.

Two test methods have been developed, one by pressing a diamond indenter on the rolling surface to impress deliberate dents, the other by pre-denting bearing rings with contaminated oil prior to fatigue testing them under clean oil lubrication.

These methods were applied to study the damaging mechanisms of surface initiated fatigue, to determine the influencing parameters and to evaluate the behaviour of various bearing steels to surface defects (bearing steels used to manufacture differential or transmission bearings in car engines and aircraft engine bearings.)

Experimental Testing Methods

Examinations of bearings returned from service after extensive life in the field show that they are covered with debris dents having a large size range. As a result, the most frequent fatigue mode is surface initiated and the bearing manufacturers have developed test procedures that aim at reproducing the surface dents generated by debris particles in order to simulate the effects of contaminated lubrication on the fatigue life.
Two test methods have been used at SNR Roulements to reach the following targets:
  - Reproduce surface damages observed in actual applications (automotive transmissions for example) on simple test rigs using well controlled methods,
  - Separate and evaluate the respective effects of factors that have an influence on the surface initiated fatigue life: steel, morphology and amount of surface dents, lubricant, loading conditions.

Denting of Rolling Surface Using Diamond Indentures

Depending on the type of test sample, two specific devices have been developed to impress dents on the rolling surface using diamond indenters.
The test bench, the type of bearing and the indentation device are described hereafter.

Indentation of Flat Washers Used on the FB2 Test Rig - The SNR FB2 test rig developed from the original Unisteel test method [28] is used at SNR and by some of the steel manufacturers for the qualification and the quality audits of the material performance under well controlled lubricating and loading conditions [29]. The test equipment is schematically presented in Figure 1.

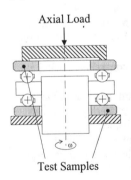

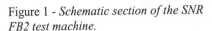

Test Samples

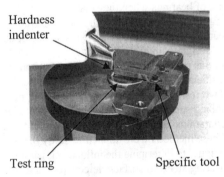

Figure 1 - *Schematic section of the SNR FB2 test machine.*

Figure 2 - *Specific tool used to centre dents on FB2 test rings.*

The two test rings (flat washers, outer diameter 62 mm, inner diameter 42 mm) are the outer components of a double thrust bearing. The shaft whose speed is 1500 rpm drives two intermediate rings of 15 balls (diameter 9.922 mm) and the raceway diameter is 54 mm. The lubricant temperature could be regulated between 40°C and 80°C. The surface roughness of balls and test rings is Ra ≤ 0.03 μm, which is representative of those of actual bearing components. Under these conditions the effectiveness of the lubricant defined by the lubricant film parameter $\lambda = h_{min} / (\sigma_1^2 + \sigma_2^2)^{1/2}$ depending on the lubricant used for the tests ($\lambda = 5.5$ with HLP ISO 46 oil, $\lambda = 3$ with MIL-L-23699 oil at 40°C) is such that a full EHD regime is ensured.

The Hertzian stress could be varied and the contact conditions are presented in Table 1.

Table 1 – *Contact conditions of FB2 test rig.*

Hertzian Stress, MPa	Contact Width, mm	Max. Shear Stress, MPa	Depth of Max Shear Stress, μm
2750	0.372	850	89
3000	0.406	930	98
3200	0.434	1000	104
3500	0.474	1090	114
400	0.542	1250	130
4200	0.570	1310	137

The dents were printed on the rolling surface using a specific tool fastened on the plate of a Rockwell hardness machine (Figure 2), so that indentations are regular and well positioned in the centre of ring raceways. Discontinuous loads are used to press the indenter on the rolling surface (150, 300, 450 and 600 N). Diamond sphero – conical Rockwell type indenters (cone forming a 120° angle) with spherical tip of various radii (200, 400, 600 and 800μm) have been manufactured in order to get the possibility to vary the indent morphology.

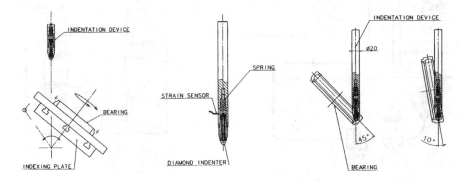

Figure 3 - *Functional diagram of the indentation device.*

Indentation and Test on Bearings - Specific equipment has also been developed to dent the surface of flat or bearing rings (inner and outer ring) using a Rockwell indenter fitted on a jig boring machine. The design of the equipment is such that the location of the indentation and the applied load should be controlled with a great accuracy. The bearing component is fastened on a rotateable and adjustable plate so that the indenter could be pressed at the required location on the raceway. The necessary indentation load for getting the required indentation morphology is adjustable by means of a load cell sandwiched between the diamond holder and the tappet rod (Figure 3). The dented components could be then tested on the FB2 test rig (flat washers) or on a standard "S" bench described further on (ball or roller bearings).

Pre-Damaging of Rolling Raceways Using Contaminant Debris Powders

This test method has been developed to reproduce accurately the damaging conditions of bearings operating under contaminated lubrication.
The functional surfaces of the bearings are pre-damaged using a contaminated lubricant prior to life testing under clean oil lubrication.
For this purpose, a specific equipment adapted from the one developed by the INSA of Lyon [*30*] was used (Figure 4).
It provides the possibility to control the flow, the particle content and the homogeneity of the contaminated oil in order to accurately adjust the size, density and uniformity of dents impressed on the bearing surface in such a way that the pre-damaging level should be as reproducible as possible.
This equipment is composed of a tank, a mixing pump, a free way gate, a pair of cleaning filters ($\beta_{12\mu m} = 200$ and $\beta_{3\mu m} = 200$) and a by-pass to divert the contaminated oil to the test rig. It works independently of the test rig when circulating the contaminated lubricant for homogenisation or when cleaning the lubricant between two tests through the filters.

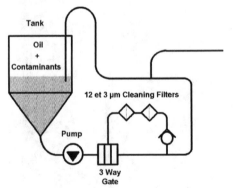

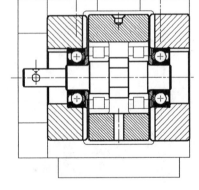

Figure 4 - *Schematic of the contamination equipment.*

Figure 5 - *Schematic of the standard "S" bearing test rig.*

Two bearings are pre-dented at the same time on a test rig able to run either ball or roller bearings (Figure 5).

After the races have been pre-damaged, the bearings are cleaned and then fatigue life tested on a similar test rig in clean oil. The same rotating and loading conditions are used for the pre-damaging and fatigue life test in order to be sure the bearings operate with the same contact angle (for ball bearings) or with the same deflection (for roller bearings), and that the rolling elements run over the most damaged pre-dented zone.

Assessment of Dent Morphology

The morphology of the dented surface was determined using a three-dimensional (3D) tactile profilometer and the typical dimensions of the dents were measured along two perpendicular directions.
An example of a dent produced by Rockwell and Vickers type indenters is presented in Figure 6.

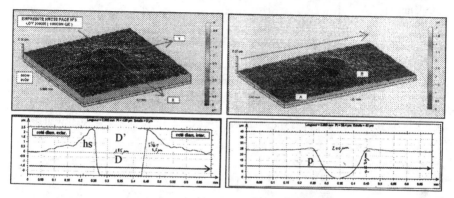

Figure 6 - *Typical 3D surface topography of Rockwell and Vickers indents and profiles of a Rockwell indent impressed on a FB2 test ring (100Cr6 steel, R200).*

Test Results

Thrust Bearing Test with Hardness Indentations

A Vickers indenter with a pyramidal 136° angle and Rockwell type diamond indenters with spherical tips of different radii (R = 200 μm to 800 μm) were used to impress indents of various morphology on the rolling surface.
The evolution of indent size characteristics, typically the diameter (or the diagonal) D, the depth d, and the height of the raised shoulder hs for different steels used in automotive and aerospace bearings (grade given in Table 2) were measured in relation to the indentation load (L = 150 N to 600 N).

Table 2 - *Material characteristics and shoulder height for different steels.*

	100Cr6 (52100)	100Cr6 Mod (high retain. austenite content)	32CrMoV13 (nitrided steel)	M50NiL (case hardened steel)	80MoCrV40 (M50)	XD15NW (martens. nitrogen steel)
Surface Hardness, Rc	62	63	62	62.5	62	59
Retained Austenite via X-ray, %	7	15		<1	<1	8
hs / R200 – L150, μm	0.7	0.65	1.3	1.7	0.8	0.7
hs / R200 – L300, μm	2.4	2	2.7	3.3	2.2	2.2
hs / R400 – L150, μm	0.4	0.3	0.5	0.5	0.5	0.35
hs / R400 – L300, μm	0.6	0.7	1	1.1	0.6	0.7

As expected, the dimensions of the dents increase when the indentation load increase and the morphology is related to the strain hardening properties of the steel. Nevertheless, the type of indenter and the tip radius of the Rockwell type indenter has a significant effect on the evolution of the indent morphology, particularly on the shoulder height and on the indent depth as shown in Figure 7 for 100Cr6 steel and Rockwell dent type.

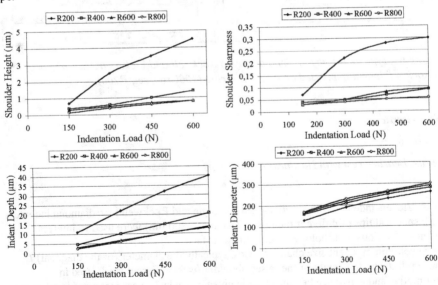

Figure 7 - *Evolution of indent dimensions vs indentation load (100Cr6 steel).*

It could be noticed that the height of the shoulder and the shoulder sharpness (ratio: hs / [(D' − D) / 2]) vary in the same way.
Rockwell type indents were preferably used to perform fatigue life tests because of their symmetrical morphology, which is useful for modelling and calculation. The other reason that leads to this choice is linked to their likeness with the surface dents observed on bearings returned from service.

Damaging Mechanism – In order to study the damaging mechanism of dented surfaces and determine the more influent parameters, rolling fatigue tests with scheduled stops after 10 min, 1h30, 15h, 60h,150h and / or after spalling were performed to follow the evolution of the rolling surface around indents.
For each steel, two flat rings were indented with four indents produced on the raceway using Rockwell type indenters with tip radius 200 µm (R200), 400 µm (R400), 600 µm (R600) and 800 µm (R800) and two indentation loads, 150 N (L150) and 300 N (L300). Tests were run under 3.5 GPa and 4 GPa Hertzian stress with ISO 46 oil lubrication at 40°C.
The results presented in Table 3 show that the Hertzian stress is the main parameter that influences the fatigue life as all the rings failed before 150 h under 4 GPa.
The indents produced using the 200µm radius indenter seem to be the more harmful, probably because of the higher shoulder.

Table 3 – *Results of the stopped tests.*

| Steel Grade | Fatigue Life up to spalling / indent linked to spalling, h | | | |
	3.5 GPa / L150	3.5 GPa / L300	4 GPa / L150	4 GPa/ L300
100Cr6	>150	>150	>150	95 / R200
100Cr6 Mod	>150	>150	>150	107 / R200
XD15N	>150	57 / R600	>150	69 / R600
32CrMoV13	>150	75 / R400	169 / R200	46 / 200
M50Nil	>150	122 / R400	>150	50 / R400
M50	>150	>150	>150	102 / R400

The indent damage development illustrated in Figure 8 can be summarised as follows:
- Whatever the steel and the Hertzian stress may be, the raised shoulder is flattened by the high pressure spikes generated when the rollers move on the dent edge. The shoulder height decreases quickly during the first 10 minutes with cycle accumulation and becomes quite stable at roughly half the initial level.
- Due to the accumulated plastic strain resulting from the high pressure spikes and the high stress concentration in regions beneath the dent edge, cracks are initiated on or close to the surface at the dent edge.
- These cracks propagate into a large spall whose depth and size depends on the contact stress and on the morphology of the dent. The propagation time is related to the steel, the morphology of the dent shoulder and the contact stress.
      Initiation and spall propagation that occur after the dent in the direction of the ball motion (B.M) is the most frequent case (more than 80%), but in a few cases, microcracks or incipient spalls were observed on the two sides of dents (Figure 8b). The location of

the crack initiation that may appear as microcracks or microspalls is very close to the dent tip (5 to 10 μm). After crack propagation and spalling the remaining edge is then slightly flattened so that a larger ledge could be observed on macrographic examinations. The topographic recordings of the Figure 9 show the shape of a spall with respect to the indent after 150h under a 3.5 GPa Hertzian stress. The top of the ledge is a few microns beneath the initial surface and the depth of the spall 40 μm, that is, less than the depth of the maximum shear stress. The propagation profile is sharper opposite the dent than close to the dent ledge.

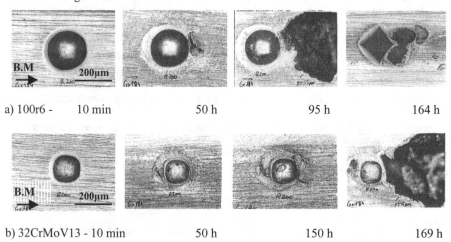

a) 100r6 -   10 min   50 h   95 h   164 h

b) 32CrMoV13 - 10 min   50 h   150 h   169 h

Figure 8 - *Typical features of dent initiated damage process for 100Cr6 steel (a) and 32CrMoV13 steel (b).*

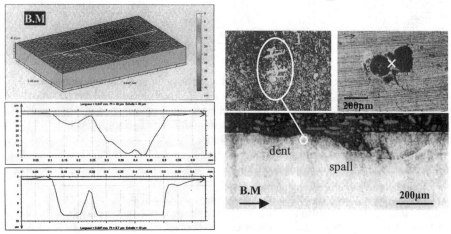

Figure 9 - *Typical profile of a spall (100Cr6 steel, R200 – L30 indentation, hs = 2.4 μm).*

Figure 10 - *Microstructural modification on carbides beneath the ridge of a fatigued M50 ring.*

Metallographic cross sections through the indent and the spall on a M50 fatigued ring showed that structural modifications occur (white butterfly on carbides in a segregated band) beneath the dent shoulder where the pressure spike is maximum (Figure 10).

These observations are in keeping with the numerical simulations performed for 100Cr6 steel using an elastic model applied on indents produced with a 200 µm radius Rockwell indenter loaded at 150 and 300N. The raised shoulders are respectively 0.7 µm and 2.4 µm in height.

Figure 11 illustrates the dimensionless pressure (pressure spike / maximum Hertzian pressure) at the dent edges for pure rolling conditions and the corresponding high stress regions beneath the surface. The pressure spikes are more than two to three times the value of the maximum Hertzian pressure for the raised shoulders taken into consideration (initial shape after denting). The Von Mises stress is for every case greater than the yield stress of the steel so that cyclic plasticity is generated during the rolling fatigue test, driving more or less quickly the initiation and propagation of surface initiated cracks. Due to the large local plastic deformation and residual stresses generated by the indentation around the dent together with those resulting from the subsequent overrolling of the dents, the local properties of the material as well as the local stress field could be modified in a different way depending on the material. As a consequence, the knowledge of these effects is of particular importance to understand and estimate the dent initiated fatigue. It makes it all the more important that in actual contacts the indentation process and running conditions are more complex.

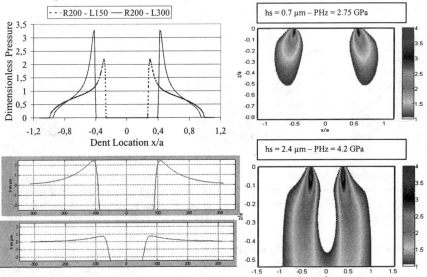

Figure 11 – *Pressure spikes and Von Mises stress compare to yield stress.*

Fatigue Life Tests – Rolling fatigue tests were performed under various loads (2.75 GPa to 4.2 GPa) and on various dent sizes obtained with a classical Vickers and a Rockwell type indenter with a 200 µm radius tip. The aim was to select the dent

dimensions that led to reasonable lives in order to allow a correct interpretation of results when material or running parameters are varied.
The ring raceways were printed either with a single dent or with four dents evenly distributed. The individual life of each ring has been recorded and Weibull statistics were used to determine the L10 fatigue life. Samples comprising 10 to 15 test rings were used to determine the L10 fatigue life when a single dent is printed instead of five rings when four dents are used. In the former case, the sudden death methodology was applied taking into consideration the first dent initiating spall on a given ring.

The Hertzian contact stress has a significant influence on the fatigue life of dented rings as soon as the level exceeds 2750 MPa as shown in Figure 12 for 100Cr6 steel and Figure 14 for the comparison of various steels. The larger the Hertzian stress, the shorter the fatigue life as a result of the high pressure spikes generated by large contact stresses. The fatigue life is also related to the height of the raised shoulder (or the shoulder sharpness). The higher the raised shoulder, the larger the pressure spikes and hence the lower the fatigue life for a given contact pressure (Figure 13). The evolution of the fatigue life is similar with regard to the contact pressure, but the life level changes a lot between 3.5 and 3.2 GPa.
It is to be noticed that results obtained using a Vickers indenter are in accordance with those obtained with a Rockwell indenter.
The number of dents printed on each ring (1 or 4) did not have a marked influence on the fatigue life, except under high Hertzian pressure for which ball failures were observed more frequently.

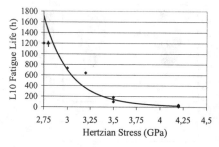

Figure 12 - *Relationship between Hertzian stress and fatigue life of dented rings (100Cr6 steel –Rockwell R200 indenter, load 300 N).*

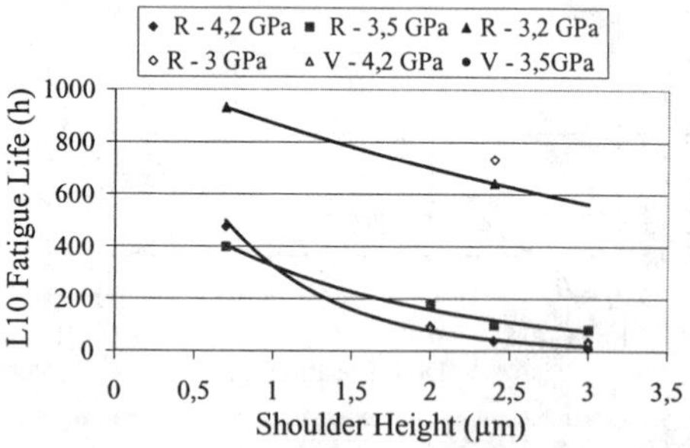

Figure 13 - *Relationship between dent shoulder height and fatigue life (100Cr6 steel –Rockwell (R) and Vickers (V) dents.*

Comparative tests were also performed on rings made of different steels using a standard 200 μm diameter Rockwell indenter loaded with a 300 N pressing load.
ISO 46 oil lubrication was used to test bearing steels for automotive transmission applications and MIL-L-23699 oil for aerospace bearing steels.
The results reported in Figure 14 show that the applied Hertzian stress is the predominant parameter that influences the fatigue life of dented surfaces when the materials are treated for the same range of hardness.
The precise effect of the material is difficult to appraise and it could be thought that dent initiated fatigue depends on complicated mechanisms in which interactions occur

between the influent parameters. It seems there is for each material and for a given dent morphology a minimum Hertzian pressure in relation to the lubricant that leads to a significant life reduction.
When a high contact pressure is applied the difference in fatigue life between the steels is reduced. The strain hardening at which the material is submitted during the indentation process around the dent probably modifies their local properties in such a way that they have quite the same behaviour when they are fatigued.
Some differences related to the type of lubricant were also observed with a tendency for ISO 46 oil to reduce the fatigue lives contrary to MIL-L-236999 oil. This shows the determinant influence of the lubricant on the damage process.

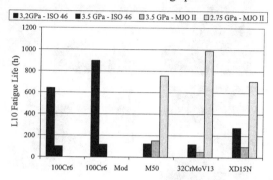

Figure 14 - *Comparison of test results for various steels.*

Fatigue Tests under Contaminated Lubrication

When inspecting the rolling surface of automobile gearbox bearings returned from service, countless large and smooth indents distributed in a wide range of sizes are observed all around the raceway together with incipient spalls (Figure 15).
Furthermore, large surface spalls are associated with these defects (not necessarily the larger one) and induced the bearing decay, even under relatively low operating contact stress (2500Mpa).
The size of the indents ranges from 50 to 400 – 500 μm, but these last probably result from large catastrophic spalls developed at the end of the bearing life. The spalls are initiated in most cases on dents, generally V shaped, between 100 and 200μm in diameter and 5 to 12μm in depth. No shoulders are observed on these indents because of the long over-rolling. The origin of these dents is probably due to metallic debris resulting from wear or spalls of gears that are deformed and flattened in the contact.
Various metallic and ceramic powders were considered as debris contaminant (silicon oxide SiO_2, silicon carbide SiC, M50 steel). M50 particles were selected because they produced surface dents similar to those observed on gearbox bearings described previously whereas brittle particles were fractured and printed too small and sharp indents. The conditions to pre-dent bearing surfaces were established using hardened M50 steel powder (hardness 53 – 61 Rc) particles with different size ranges (30 - 50μm,

50 – 100 µm and 125 – 200 µm). The concentration of particles in the oil, the contamination time and the loading conditions were also varied.

For ball bearings made from 100Cr6 steel, the best compromise between the number of dents produced on the surface and their size was obtained under the following conditions:
- Size range ≤ 50 µm
- Concentration : 0.1 g / l
- Running time : 1 min at 2250 rpm
- Maximum Hertzian Stress : 3300 or 2800 MPa (ratio radial load / axial load = 2)
- Lubricant : ISO46 at room temperature gear oil at 80°C

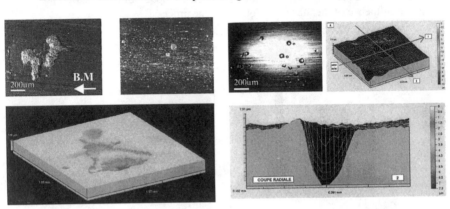

Figure 15 - *Visual aspect and 3D topography of defects on a gearbox bearing.*

Figure 16 - *Visual aspects and 3D morphology of natural dents performed using calibrated ≤ 50 µm M50 steel powder.*

Under these conditions the difference in applied load has a small effect on the indent size and the typical indents are about 100 – 120 µm in width, 6 – 7 µm in depth and 90 – 100 µm in width, 5 – 6 µm in depth in the central contact zone for a 3.3 GPa and 2.8 GPa Hertzian pressure, respectively. The shoulders are often higher in the rolling direction (Figure 16) and a small hole is sometime observed in the middle of the dent as reported previously [*10-14*].

The test procedure has been validated on 2 groups of commercial deep groove ball bearings (bearing A: O.D 59 mm, bearing B : O.D 130 mm) made in 100Cr6 steel heat treated according to different specifications for 2 levels of hardness.

The H.T1 heat treatment has been performed using a low tempering temperature (170°C) that produced a 62 Rc hardness with a structure that consist of hard tempered martensite and 6 - 8 % of retained austenite. For the H.T2 a higher tempering temperature was used, leading to a much softer structure free from retained austenite (59 Rc)

The L10 life of each group of bearings was evaluated without surface damaging and after pre-damaging.

The bearing characteristics and the maximum Hertzian stress on the most heavily loaded ring (inner ring) are given in Table 4.

Table 4 - *Bearing description and test conditions.*

Bearing type	Heat Treatment	Hardness, Rc	Applied Hertzian stress, GPa
A	H.T1	62	3.3
A	H.T1	62	2.8
B	H.T1	62	2.8
B	H.T2	59	2.8

The test results are presented in Figure 17.

When the bearing surfaces are pre-dented, a large life reduction is observed and the only mode of fatigue systematically observed is surface initiated spalling at the trailing edge of a dent as shown in Figure 18. This fatigue mechanism is the same that prevails on actual automotive gearbox bearings.

It could be observed that for a given size of dents, the fatigue life strongly depends on the applied load and on the material structure as obtained with different heat treatments.

The depth of the spall may reach the depth of the maximum Hertzian shear stresses.

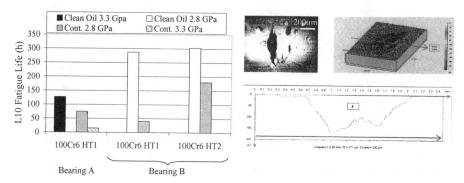

Figure 17 - *Fatigue life results of pre-dented ball bearings.*

Figure 18 - *Examples of spalls observed with pre-dented surfaces (bearing A).*

In the case of tapered bearings of various sizes and internal geometries, a lower Hertzian pressure should be used to obtain similar fatigue live and life reduction than for ball bearings, this probably in relation to the more complex kinematics and the possible sliding that may occur so that the dent initiated fatigue process speed is increased (Figure 19 a).

A similar tendency has been observed, but less marked when the operating temperature is increased (gear oil at 40°C and 120°C) as shown in Figure 19 b.

So, depending on the morphology of the dents obtained using a calibrated hard steel powder as contaminant, the type of rolling contact, the lubricant and the rolling conditions, the dent initiated fatigue life could be related to the material.

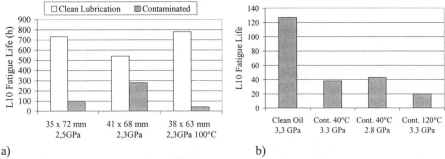

a)   b)

Figure 19 – *Fatigue life results for tapered bearings (a) and influence of the operating temperature for ball bearing (b).*

Conclusion

The effect of dents resulting from contaminated lubrication on the fatigue life of bearings was experimentally simulated either by pressing a diamond hardness indenter on the raceway or using a lubricant contaminated with calibrated metallic particles prior to fatiguing bearings in clean oil.

- In both methods the feasibility and the efficiency to produce surface dents on the rolling track in a reproducible way has been shown. The dent morphology could be controlled in order to obtain surface dents and damage mechanism (initiation and propagation of a spall at the trailing edge of the dent) comparable to those observed on actual applications returned from service. The fatigue life could be obtained in a reasonable time depending on the loading conditions in relation to the contact type and the lubricant.
- The fatigue life is shortened significantly when dents are printed on the rolling surface. The height (or the sharpness) of the raised shoulder, the applied load, the lubricant and the material have an effect on the fatigue life, but their respective influence is not easy to determine. However, the critical level related to the dent morphology seems to be different depending on the Hertzian pressure, the material, the type of contact and the type of lubricant.
- The method using hardness indents made it possible to identify the mechanism of the dent initiated fatigue that could be summarised as follows:
  - The raised shoulder is flattened very quickly when overrolled by the rolling elements.
  - Microcracks are initiated close to the edge of the raised shoulder in the region where the internal stresses generated by the large pressure spikes resulting from the overrolling of the dent are maximum. It is the resulting cyclic plasticity and the plastic strain accumulation that is responsible for the initiation of a crack and then its propagation.

- A large spall occurs almost systematically after the dent in the direction of the rolling element motion even if microcracks have also been initiated on the other side of the dent.
- The pre-denting method using metallic powder is more representative of the reality and makes it possible to discriminate heat treatments. Nevertheless, the pre-damaging conditions and the operating conditions for the fatigue tests as well must be controlled in a very accurate way. Although it should be confirmed by testing the same variants with the different methods, this method seems to be the most efficient to simulate the effect of contaminated lubrication and to determine the tolerance of materials to surface dents.

At the moment a few remaining questions are to be solved, particularly those linked to the respective influence (and / or the interactions) of the dent morphology in relation with the material and of the contact pressure on the fatigue life. Particularly, the modification of the mechanical characteristics of the material in the vicinity of the dent due to the indentation process and to the subsequent overrolling of the dent is of great importance. In the same way, the residual stresses generated by these processes are to be considered. Once these stress and strain parameters will be determined, the calculation of the fatigue life could be carried out using the physically based model described by R. Fougères et al. [*31*]. This model that takes into account the relevant features of the material and the operating parameters could be applied to indented contacts in order to predict the fatigue life distribution of rolling bearings.

As a consequence, the material and operating parameters need to be thoroughly studied in order to confirm the eventual existence of:
- A size or morphological limit for dents (or a plastic deformation limit around dents induced by the indentation process) which makes uniform the behaviour of the materials when submitted to subsequent fatigue.
- The operating conditions limits (applied load, sliding, type of lubricant, temperature…) that lead for a given dent morphology depending on the material to a significant reduction of fatigue life.

References

[1]   Lormand, G., Meynaud, P., Vincent, A., Baudry, G., Girodin, D. and Dudragne, G., "From Cleanliness to Rolling Fatigue Life of Bearings – A new Approach," *Bearing Steels : Into the 21st Century, ASTM STP 1327*, J.J.C. Hoo, Ed., American Society for Testing and Materials, West Conshohocken, PA, 1997, pp 55-69.

[2]   Lamagnère, P., Fougères, R., Vincent, A., Lormand, G., Girodin, D., Dudragne, G. and Vergne, F., "A Physically based Model for infinite Life of Rolling Bearings," *ASME, Journal of Tribology*, Vol.120, July 1998, N°3, pp. 1-6.

[3]   Ville, F. and Nelias, D., "Influence of the nature and size of solid particles on the indentation features in EHL contacts", *Proc. of the 24th Leeds-Lyon Symposium on Tribology*, Tribology Series, Vol 34, 1998, pp. 399-409.

[4]   F. Ville, D. Nelias, "An experimental study on the concentration and shape of dents caused by spherical metallic particles in EHL contacts", *Tribological Transactions*, Vol 42, 1999, N° 1, pp. 231-240.

[5]   Dwyer-Joyce, R.S., Hammer, J.J., Sayles, R.S. and Ioannides, E., "Surface damage effects caused by debris in rolling bearing lubricants, with an emphasis on friable materials", *Proc of ImeChe seminar, Rolling elements bearings – Towards the 21st century*, MEP Ed., 1990, pp.1-8.

[6]   Cann, P.M.E., Hamer, J.C., Sayles, R.S., Spikes, H.A. and Ioannides, E., "Direct observation of particle entry and deformation in rolling EHD contact", *Proc. of the 22nd Leeds-Lyon Symposium on Tribology*, Tribology Series, Vol 31, 1996, pp. 127-134.

[7]   Dwyer-Joyce, R.S., Heymer, J., "The entrainment of solid particles into rolling elastohydrodynamic contacts", *Proc. of the 22nd Leeds-Lyon Symposium on Tribology*, Tribology Series, Vol 31, 1996, pp. 135-140.

[8]   Cheng, W., Cheng, H.S., and Keer, L.M., "Longitudinal crack initiation under pure rolling contact fatigue", *Tribology Transactions*, Vol 37, 1994, N°1, pp. 51-58.

[9]   Weveden, L.D. and Usano, C.C., "Elastohydrodynamic film thickness measurementsof artificially produced surface dents and grooves", *ASLE Transactions*, Vol 22, 1979, N° 4, pp. 369-381.

[10]   Holzhauer, W., "Surface changes around large raceway indentations during run-in of tapered roller bearings", *Tribology Transactions*, Vol 34, 1991, N° 3, pp. 316-368.

[11]   Toda, K., Mikami, T. and Hoshino, T., "Effect of dents on rolling fatigue life", *Japanese Journal of Tribology*, Vol 38, 1993, N° 6, pp. 781-790.

[12]   Chiu, Y.P. and Liu, J.Y., "An analytical study of the stress concentration around a furrow shaped surface defect in rolling contact," *Trans ASME, Journal of lubrication technology*, Vol.92, 1970, pp. 258-263.

[13]   Moyer, C.A. "The influence of debris on bearing performance", *SAE Technical Paper Series 891906*, 1989.

[14]   Mitamura, N., Murakami, Y. and Krieger, F., "A new method for studying surface initiated bearing failure", *SAE Technical Paper 972712*, 1997.

[15]   Nixon, H.P. and Zantopulos, H., "Fatigue life performance comparison of tapered roller bearings with debris damaged raceway", *Lubrication Engineering*, Vol 51, 1995, N° 9, pp. 732-736.

[16]   Sayles, R.S. and MacPherson, P.B., "Inlfluence of wear debris on rolling contact fatigue", *ASTM STP 771, Rolling contact fatigue testing of bearing steels*, Hoo, J.J.C Ed., American Society for Testing and Materials, West Conshohocken, PA, 1982, pp 255-274.

[17]   Loewenthal, S.H. and Moyer, D.W., "Filtration effects on ball bearing life and condition in a contaminated lubricant", *Journal of Lubrication Technology*, Vol 101 , 1979, N°2, pp. 171-179.

[18]   Furumura, K., Murakami, Y. and Abe,T., "The development of bearing steels for long life rolling bearings under clean lubrication and contaminated lubrication," *ASTM STP 1195, Creative use of bearing steels*, Hoo, J.J.C Ed., American Society for Testing and Materials, West Conshohocken, PA, 1993, pp. 199-210.

[19]   Beerbower, M.R., Shiratani, T., Murakami, Y. and Abe, K., "Fighting debris: Increasing life with HTF bearings for transmissions," *SAE Technical Papers Series 940728*, 1994.

[20]   Mitamura, N., Murakami, Y., Dodd, A. and Scholz, A., "Bearing fatigue mode analysis and development of Hi-TF (HTF), Super-TF (STF) and New-TF (NTF) bearings," *Proceedings, 4th world congress on gearing and power transmission*, 1999, pp. 1193-1204.

[21]   Nelias, D. and Ville, F., "Detrimental effects of debris dents on rolling contact fatigue", *Journal of Tribology*, Vol 122, 2000, N° 1, pp. 55-64.

[22]   Xu,.G , Sadeghi, F. and Hoeprich, M.R., "Dent initiated spall formation in EHL rolling/sliding contact", *Journal of Tribology*, Vol 120, 1998, N° 3, pp. 453-462.

[23]   Xu .G., Sadeghi, F. and Hoeprich, M.R., "Residual stresses due to debris effects in EHL contacts", *Tribology Transactions*, Vol 40, 1997, N° 4, pp. 613-620.

[24]   Ozen, M., "Analysis of a surface crack subject to a rolling/sliding contact", *SAE Technical Paper Series 891905*, 1989.

[25]   Ko, C.N. and Ioannides, E., "Debris denting – The associated residual stresses and their effect on the fatigue life rolling bearing: an FEM analysis", *Proc. of the 15th Leeds-Lyon Symposium on Tribology*, 1988, pp. 199-207.

[26]   Hamer, J.C., Lubrecht, A.A., Ioannides, E. and Sayles, R.S., "Surface damage on rolling elements and its subsequent effects on performance and life", *Proc. of the 15th Leeds-Lyon Symposium on Tribology*, 1988, pp. 189-197.

[27]   Kang, Y.S., Saddeghi, F.and Ai, X. "Debris effects on EHL contacts", *Journal of Tribology*, Vol 122, 2000, n° 4, pp. 711-720.

[28]   Johnson, R.F. and Sewell, J.F., *Journal of Iron and steel Institute*, 1960, pp. 414-444.

[29]   Baudry, G., Saleil, G., Giroud, G., Duplomb, G., Bulit, J.H., Girodin, D., Dudragne, G. and Jacob, G., "Fatigue property evaluation of bearing steel issued from rotary continuous casting", *La revue de Métallurgie - CIT*, 1992, pp.877-886.

[30]   Ville, F., "Pollution solide des lubrifiants, indentation et fatigue des surfaces", *Thesis*, Mécanique, INSA de Lyon, 1998, 163p.

[31]   Fougères, R., Lormand, G., Vincent, A., Nelias, D., Dudragne, G., Girodin, D., Baudry, G. and Daguier, P., "A new physically based model for predicting the fatigue life distribution of rolling bearings", *Bearing Steel Technology, ASTM STP 1419*, J. M. Beswick, Ed., American Society for Testing and Materials, West Conshohocken, PA, 2002 (this symposium).

Bearing Metallurgy Developments for Improved Service Life

Masamichi Shibata,[1] Masao Goto,[1] Atsuhiko Ohta,[1] and Kazutoshi Toda[1]

Development of Long Life Rolling Bearings for Use in the Extreme Conditions

Reference: Shibata, M., Goto, M., Ohta, A., and Toda, K., "**Development of Long Life Rolling Bearings for Use in the Extreme Conditions**," *Bearing Steel Technology, ASTM STP 1419*, J. M. Beswick, Ed., American Society for Testing and Materials International, West Conshohocken, PA, 2002.

Abstract: As the service conditions of automobiles and industrial machines are becoming more extreme in recent years, higher bearing performance has been required for those applications. Especially, a demand for maintenance-free bearings is really high, that is, a demand for the extension of bearing life has been increasing. To satisfy those customers' demands, various measures as to materials and heat treatment have taken, those of which are KE bearings developed for automobiles and KUJ7 steel for semi-high temperature bearings. The characteristics in material and heat treatment necessary to extend bearing life and the direction of measures to each factor are described, then the characteristics of KE bearings and KUJ7 steel are also described.

Keywords: rolling bearing, rolling contact fatigue, contaminated lubrication semi-high temperature, temperature resistance, retained austenite

Introduction

As machine performance has been enhanced and machines are being downsized in recent years, service conditions for rolling bearings have become increasingly more extreme. For this reason, a major theme for bearing manufacturers is how to enhance the reliability and performance of bearings themselves.

In terms of structure, rolling bearings consist of raceways, rolling elements, and cages. They fulfill their function with the help of lubricants. Enhancement of bearing reliability therefore requires technological and theoretical progress of tribology in general, such as progress in performance of materials and lubricants, progress and development in manufacturing technologies, and reform of design concepts.

[1]Assistant general manager, assistant manager, manager and assistant manager, respectively, Koyo Seiko Co., Ltd, 24-1 Kokubu Higanjo-cho, Kashiwara-shi, Osaka , Japan

Higher bearing performance will be required, such as longer life, ability to handle heavier loads, lower friction and lower vibration, as well as corrosion resistance, and the ability to withstand high and low temperature and vacuums. Among these requirements, longer life is a perpetual theme for bearing makers. Figure1 shows the needs of bearing users and technological measures to satisfy those needs.

Measures to extend bearing life cah be divided into (1) common measures such as materials, heat treatment, and lubrication, which are common to all the bearings and applications, and (2) individual measures suitable for individual applications.

In this paper, the extreme service conditions of bearings such as lubricant containing debris (contaminated lubricant) and semi-high temperatures are mentioned. KE bearings and KUJ7 steel have been developed according to their respective application requirement. In the following, processes of the developments and performance are mentioned.

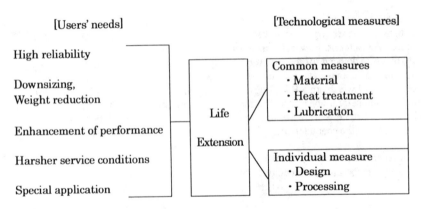

Figure 1 — *Needs of bearings and measures.*

Basic Problems to Extend Bearing Life

Process of Rolling Fatigue

Subsurface initiated flaking occurs by fatigue due to repeated overrolling stress cycles leading to subsurface crack initiation and then, propagation at non-metallic inclusions, inhomogeneous microstructure and carbides.

Surface initiated flaking occurs, on the other hand, when rolling elements roll over the ridge of dents formed by the crushing of debris in the lubricant or tangential force is produced by sliding, resulting in a surface crack which eventually develops into flaking.

Problems Concerning Measures for Extending Bearing Life

Table 1 shows general problems as to materials and heat treatment, expected result, and specific measures to solve those problems[1]. In the following section, the characteristics of KE bearings and KUJ7 steel are mentioned.

1) Foreign-matter resistant bearing series(KE bearing) ⟶ Measure No. ④

2) Bearings for semi-high temperature(KUJ7 steel)   ⟶ Measure No. ⑥

Debris Resistant Bearing (KE Bearing)

Bearing Life with Lubricant Containing Debris

Bearing life generally deteriorates sharply when the lubricant contains debris. Figure 2 shows the correlation between debris concentration and the life of tapered roller bearings when the following two debris are mixed in the lubricant[2].

1) 830HV in average hardness and 27 μ m in average particle diameter
2) 700HV in average hardness and 125 μ m in average particle diameter

The mixture of merely 0.01 mass% of debris in the lubricant makes the bearing life radically shorter than 1/6 of the bearing life with clean lubricant. When the debris concentration is 0.05 mass% or higher, the increase of concentration has an extremely slight effect on the bearing life, keeping it almost constant.

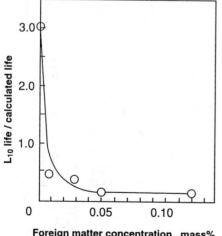

Test condition
Bearing: Tapered roller bearing
ϕ 72mm× ϕ 30mm×20.750mm
Load   :   Axial   Fa/C=0.24
                    Radial   Fr/C=0.36
Rotating speed   :   2000rpm
Lubrication   :   Oil bath
                    Gear oil 85W-90
Foreign matter   : 0.12mass%
          830HV   27 μ m ave,
          700HV 125 μ m ave

Foreign matter concentration , mass%

Figure 2 — *Correlation between debris concentration and bearing life* .

Table 1 — *Problems and measures as to materials and heat treatment.*

Theme	Effect			Measures to be taken
	Improvement of bearing life with clean lubricant	Improvement of bearing life with contaminated lubricant	Improvement of bearing life in high temperature atmosphere	
① Reduction of non-metallic inclusion	○			① Reduction of non-metallic inclusions in materials
② Enhancement of matrix strength	○	○	△	② Development of strong materials (Addition of Si and Ni)
③ Enhancement of hardness	△	○	△	③ Carbonitriding treatment
④ Formation of compressive residual stress	○	△		④ Development of heat treatment method(case hardening) → To optimize hardness and amount of retained austenite
⑤ Optimization of the amount of retained austenite	△	○		⑤ Development of high-concentration cemented steel and heat treatment method
⑥ Enhancement of high temp. hardness and strength		△	○	⑥ Development of steels for bearings for semi-high temperature (Si, Mo, C,V)

○ : **Effective**   △ : **Slightly effective**   — : **Ineffective**

Damage to bearings used with lubrication containing debris can be roughly divided into two types:

1) Rubbing damage caused by small and hard particles   (surface layer peeling),
2) Damage induced from dent formed by large and hard particles (dent-induced flaking).

In the following subsections, measures to extend bearing life for each type of damage are mentioned.

Countermeasure Against Surface Layer Peeling

Small, hard debris getting in the lubrication produces surface layer peeling, which is a type of abrasive wear.

Figure 3 shows the correlation between the bearing life and the surface hardness of the inner ring when the bearings with inner rings of 62~66HRC surface hardness were tested using the lubricating oil that contains 0.12 mass% of the debris of 830HV(65HRC) in hardness and 27 μ m in average particle diameter.

The bearing life increased as the hardness of the inner ring surface increased. The bearing   life increased sharply when the inner ring surface hardness exceeded the hardness of the debris. This indicates the surface hardness of the bearing must be equal to or greater than that of the debris.

Countermeasure Against Dent-Induced Flaking

Flaking is caused by dents formed by large, hard foreign matter mixed in the lubrication. FEM analysis and experiments show that the flaking is caused by concentrated stress produced at the ridge around dents[3]. The way to prevent dent-induced flaking therefore is to reduce the size of the ridge. Figure 4 shows the correlation between surface hardness and ridge height.

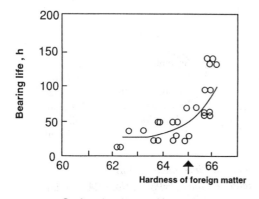

Test condition

Bearing: Tapered roller bearing
ϕ 72mm× ϕ 30mm×20.750mm
Load   : Axial   Fa/C=0.5
Rotating speed: 2000rpm
Lubrication: Oil bath
                 Gear oil 85W-90
Foreign matter :   0.12mass%
       830HV   27 μ m ave,

Figure 3 — *Correlation between surface hardness of inner ring and bearing life.*

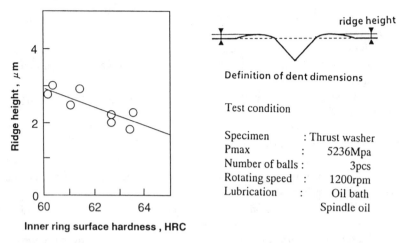

Figure 4—*Correlation between inner ring surface hardness and ridge height of dents (Dents were made under indentation load P=980N).*

The figure shows that ridge height decreases as surface hardness increases. Figure 5 shows the change in ridge height over time due to repeated rolling over dents formed on the surface of specimens that have approximately the same surface hardness but contain different amount of retained austenite.

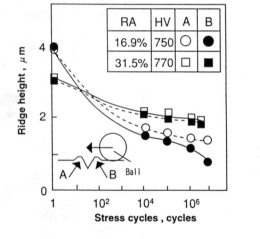

RA	HV	A	B
16.9%	750	○	●
31.5%	770	□	■

Test condition

Specimen	:	Thrust washer
Pmax	:	5236Mpa
Number of balls	:	3pcs
Rotating speed	:	1200rpm
Lubrication	:	Oil bath
		Spindle oil

Figure 5 —*Change in ridge height of dents over time due to rolling (Dents were made under indentation load P=980N, Note:RA =retained austenite).*

In the initial period, the ridge height of the specimen containing more retained austenite is lower than that of the specimen containing less retained austenite. The ridge height gradually decreases by repeated rolling, but Figure 5 shows that the more retained austenite is contained, the less the ridge height decreases. It was confirmed by X-ray diffraction analysis that the ridge hardness increased and work hardening was promoted as the amount of retained austenite increased[4]. In other words, a large amount of retained austenite induced the work hardening of ridges, prevented early reduction of ridge height, and led to a shorter bearing life.

Measures to Extend the Bearing Life with Lubricant Containing Foreign matters. (KE Bearing)

As mentioned in the previous subsection, the following measures are effective in extend in a bearing life with lubricant that contains debris.

1) Improve wear resistance by increasing surface hardness.
2) Improve dent resistance by increasing surface hardness.
3) Early reduction of ridge height by optimizing the amount of retained austenite.

There have been following different theories concerning the measures to extend the bearing life with lubricant that contains debris[5][6].

1) Improvement of surface hardness is the most effective.
2) Optimization of retained austenite is the most effective.
3) Improvement of core hardness is the most effective.

Practical tests have recently proved that surface hardness and optimal amount of retained austenite are effective to extend the bearing life of which the lubricant contains foreign matters.

It has been believed that it is technologically difficult to secure both high surface hardness and the proper amount of retained austenite because the increase in surface hardness means the increase in the proportion of martensite, in other words, the decrease in retained austenite content.

Development of new carburizing heat treatment technologies has however solved this problem, enabling development of the KE bearing which made from SAE5120. Figure 6 shows the result of life test of KE bearings with the lubricant containing debris. The KE bearing exhibits a life approximately ten times greater than that of conventional bearings.

Development of Steels for Bearings for Semi-High Temperature (KUJ7)

If using conventional bearings in the semi-high temperature range(up to 200℃), it is thought that bearing function generally deteriorates through the process shown in Figure 7 [7].

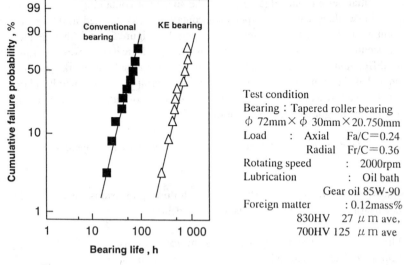

Test condition
Bearing : Tapered roller bearing
ϕ 72mm$\times$ ϕ 30mm$\times$20.750mm
Load   : Axial   Fa/C$=$0.24
              Radial   Fr/C$=$0.36
Rotating speed   :   2000rpm
Lubrication   :   Oil bath
              Gear oil 85W-90
Foreign matter   : 0.12mass%
              830HV   27 μ m ave,
              700HV 125 μ m ave

Figure 6 — *Result of life test of KE bearings with contaminated lubricant .*

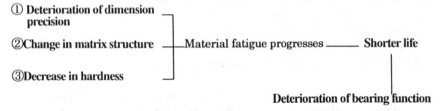

Figure 7 — *Deterioration Process of Bearing Function at Semi-High Temperature .*

The following is the explanation of functional deterioration shown in Figure7,

① "The deterioration of dimension precision" is caused by the decomposition of retained austenite by high temperature. This deterioration can be prevented if the microstructural change during operation is controlled and the amount of initial retained austenite is reduced by tempering the steels in advance at a temperature higher than the operating temperature (This is heat-resisting treatment for stabilization of dimension).

② Change in matrix structure occurs due to rolling fatigue especially under high temperature and high surface pressure condition. This change can be controlled by heat-resisting treatment, but not so effective.

③ Decrease in hardness is mainly attributable to the components of steels. Especially when heat resisting treatment is performed, initial hardness becomes low, resulting in a shorter bearing life. So, high speed tool steels such as M50 have been used for bearings for semi-high temperature,

This suggests that the following are needed to extend bearing life in the semi-high temperature range:

1) Enhanced resistance to softening by tempering and
2) Stabilization of structure

From a standpoint of cost, JIS SUJ2 steel was used as a base and the KUJ7 steel was developed by optimizing the alloy components of SUJ2. The alloy contents of KUJ7 is shown in Table 2 and the chemical composition of this steel is shown in Table 3.

Table 2 —*Alloy components of KUJ7 steel* .

Theme	Element to be added
Enhanced resistance to softening by tempering	Si, Mo
Enhanced strength of matrix	Si
Stabilization of residual carbide	Cr, Mo
Stabilization of structure	Mo

Table 3 —*Chemical composition of KUJ7 steel (mass%)* .

C	Si	Mn	Cr	Mo
1.0	1.0	0.5	2.0	0.5

The correlation between tempering temperature and hardness of KUJ7 is shown in Figure 8. KUJ7 shows better resistance to softening by tempering at 200°C or higher than SUJ2.

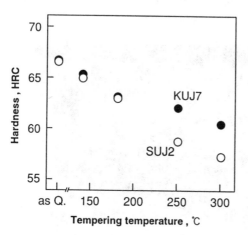

Figure 8—*Correlation between tempering temperature and hardness* .

KUJ7 can obtain the same hardness as SUJ2 even though heat resisting treatment is performed on KUJ7. Figure 9 shows the result of rolling life test using thrust bearing washers made of KUJ7 on which heat resisting treatment (S1 treatment) was performed.Figure 9 shows at which stress cycles microstructural change occurred in SUJ2 and KUJ7 at a test temperature of 150℃. The figure shows KUJ7 needs more stress cycles than SUJ2 for microstructural change. Figure 10 is a typical example of microstructural change. Figure 11 shows the comparison of life of deep groove ball bearings at 150℃. The comparison shows that life of bearings made of KUJ7 is seven times longer than that of bearings made of SUJ2.

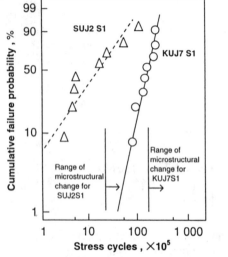

Test condition

Specimen	:	Thrust washer
Pmax	:	5236Mpa
Number of balls :		3pcs
Rotating speed	:	1200rpm
Lubrication	:	Oil bath
		ASTO#500
Test temperature:		150℃

Figure 9 —*Occurrence of microstructural change .*

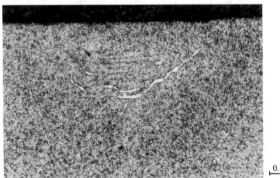

Figure 10 —*Example of microstructural change (cross section of thrust washer in the axial direction).*

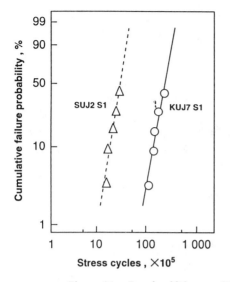

Test condition
Bearing   :   6206
Load   :   Fr/C＝0.46
Rotating speed   :   1200rpm
lubrication   :   Circulated oil
                                ASTO# 500
Test Temperature :   150℃

Figure 11 *—Result of life test of bearings made of KUJ7 steel* .

Summary

In this paper, the measures to extend bearing life through examination of rolling life under more extreme service conditions such as lubricant containing debris and semi-high temperature range are discussed, and are explained the performance of KE bearing series and new steel KUJ7 as specific examples. In the attempt to find a way to extend bearing life, a solution to one problem is still incompatible with a solution to others with current technologies. For example, it is quite hard to give high hardness and high toughness to steels at the same time. For such problems, heat treatments mainly to harden steel surface is an effective measure. As computer control technology progresses, new heat treatment method including surface refining will be developed in the near future to meet customers' needs.

Reference

[1] Shibata. M., " Technology for Extending the Life of Rolling Bearings" , *MOTION ENGINEERING JAPAN ' 95 symposium* , 1997- 4 , pp. 6-3-1.

[2] Toda. K., Mikami. T., Shibata. M., and Hoshino. T., " Effect of Debris on Life of Tapered Roller Bearings in Contaminated Lubricant ", *Journal of Japanese Society of Tribologists*, Vol.41 , No3 , 1996 , pp. 232-239.

[3] Toda. K., Mikami. T., and Hoshino.T.," Effect of Dent on Rolling Fatigue Life", *Journal of Japanese Society of Tribologists*, Vol. 38 , No.6 , 1993 , pp. 526-532.

[4] Toda. K., Mikami. T., and   Hoshino.T., " Effect of Ridge around Dent and Retained
     Austenaite on Rolling Fatigue Life", *Journal of Japan Institute of Metals*" , Vol.58 ,
     No.12 , 1994 , pp. 1473-1478.

[5] Murakami.Y., Matumoto.Y., and Furumura. K., " Long Life TF Bearings under Debris
     Contaminated Llubrication" , *NSK Technical Journal*, Vol. 650 , 1989 , pp. 1-11.

[6] Tsushima.N., Nakashima.H., and Maeda.K.," Improvement of Rolling Contact Fatigue
     Life of Caburized Tapered Roller Bearings" *SAE Technical Paper* No 860725 , 1986.

[7] Ohta.A., Johns.M.T., Amano.K., and Yasumoto. S., " Medium- Heat-Resistant Bearing
     Steel", *SAE Technical.Paper*   No 961831, 1996.

Sun-Joon Yoo,[1] Sang-Woo Choi,[1] Seung-Kyoo Han,[1] Jae-Sung Lee,[2] Byung-Jin Jung,[2] Bok-Han Song,[2] and Chang-Nam Park[2]

The Effect of V, Al and N on the Fatigue Life of a Carbonitrided Bearings

Reference: Yoo, S. J., Choi, S. W., Han, S. K., Lee, J .S., Jung, B. J., Song, B. H. and Park, C. N., **"The Effect of V, Al and N on the Fatigue Life of a Carbonitrided Bearings,"** *Bearing Steel Technology, ASTM STP 1419*, J. M. Beswick, Ed., American Society for Testing and Materials International, West Conshohocken, PA, 2002.

Abstract: The effect of chemical composition on microstructure and mechanical properties was investigated. Optimum contents of Al and N for appropriate prior austenite grain size were determined to avoid the formation of microcracks during oil quenching after a carbonitriding heat treatment. The microhardness and fatigue life of microalloyed steels based on SAE 5140H were compared with those of conventional steels. The surface hardness was increased due to finely distributed V-carbonitrides precipitated during double reheat process at the range of intercritical temperatures. The fatigue life was increased due to a large amount of retained austenite in the steel obtained by a carbonitriding heat treatment.

Keywords: carbonitriding bearing steel, fatigue life under contaminated lubricant condition, retained austenite, microcracks.

Introduction

The bearing steels are classified into two kinds, the low carbon case hardening steel containing about 0.2% carbon and the through-hardening steel containing about 1.0 % carbon. The case hardening bearing steel exhibits excellent fatigue life under the contaminated lubricant environment because of the large amounts of retained austenite if compared with that of through hardened bearings. But it shows unfavorable properties as regards steel cleanliness because of lower carbon content in the matrix. The medium carbon steels containing 0.3~0.6 wt % carbon, on the other hand, can have both the advantages of low carbon case hardening steel and high carbon through-hardening steel. With such medium carbon steels it is possible to reduce the carburizing (or carbonitriding) time to get a certain case depth and also

---

[1]Senior researcher, researcher, section manager Plate, Rod and Welding Research Group, Technical Research Laboratories, Pohang Iron and Steel Co., 1 Goedong-dong, Pohang, 790-785, Korea.
[2]Researcher, senior researcher, senior researcher and director, research institute, FAG Hanwha Bearing Corp., 851-5 Oei-Dong, Changwon-city, Kyung-Nam. Korea 641-020.

it is possible to increase the load capacity of bearings because of the higher core hardness.

Carburizing (or carbonitriding) time can be further economized in medium carbon steels with more elevated heat-treatment temperatures. But, the grain size becomes larger as the temperature increases, and that may cause microcracks during the quenching process. In this study, using different amount of Al and N in medium carbon steel, appropriate austenite grain size was determined to avoid the formation of microcrack during oil quenching process. And, also the mechanical properties of medium carbon microalloy steels manufactured by different heat treatment processes were compared with those of a conventional case hardening steel of 0.2% carbon and a through hardening bearing steel of 1.0% carbon.

Experimental procedures

As shown in Table 1 as S4, S5, and S6, to modify chemical composition of steels after carbonitrided heat treatment process 1.2% C steels containing various Al and N contents were austenitized at 950°C in a salt bath with different holding time and their resultant austenite grain sizes were investigated in order to quantify the effects of Al and N.

Table 1-*Chemical composition of used steels (O and N in wt ppm, the others in wt %).*

	C	Mn	Cr	Al	V	O	N	Remark
SAE5210	0.20	0.70	1.25	0.020	Tr	20	120	Conven.
S1	0.41	1.10	1.21	0.032	0.15	22	180	
S2	0.40	1.12	1.24	0.022	0.20	23	170	
S3	0.44	1.13	1.36	0.022	0.10	20	141	
S4	1.20	1.11	1.35	0.022	0.12	22	170	Mod.carbonitriding process
S5	1.22	1.13	1.33	0.017	0.11	23	141	Mod.carbonitriding Process
S6	1.22	1.11	1.31	0.032	0.10	20	180	Mod.carbonitriding Process
SAE52100	0.98	0.34	1.36	-	-	8	-	Conven.

Three laboratory steels based on SAE 5140H but modified with Mn and V were prepared with different Al and N contents as shown in Table 1 as S1, S2, and S3. Al and N have main influence on austenite grain size and consequently formation of microcrack during oil quenching [1,2]. The conventional steels, SAE5120 and SAE 52100, were used to compare the mechanical properties with those of the modified ones.

The laboratory steels were gas carbonitrided at 950°C for 5 hours. Two different post-carbonitriding heat treatments, as shown in Table 2, were applied. Treatment A, the direct oil quench from the carbonitriding temperature, was for the investigation on prior austenite grain size. Treatment B, double reheat treatment, was for the investigation on microstructural and mechanical properties.

Table 2- *Summary of heat treatment.*

Designation	Description
A. direct quench	Carbonitriding (950°C)/5hours -> oil quench (100°C) ->tempering (180°C)/2hours -> air cooling
B. double reheat	Carbonitriding (950°C)/5hours -> oil quench (100°C) ->Reheating (860-900°C)/40minutes-> oil quench (100°C) ->tempering (180°C)/2hours -> air cooling

To reveal the prior austenite grain boundaries, samples were etched using a boiling solution of 25g NaOH, 2g picral acid, and 100ml H20 for 90secs. The prior austenite grain size was measured with image analyzer. The same specimens were subsequently etched in 1% nital to observe the martensite microstructures and microcracks. Retained austenite was measured by X-ray diffraction.

Scanning and transmission electron microscopy were used to characterize microstructure and morphology of precipitated particles on the double reheated specimens. The microhardness and the amount of austenite as a function of depth from the surface were measured. Using the disk sample, fatigue tests were performed under two kinds of lubrication environment, that is, with clean and contaminated oils. The test conditions and the testing are shown in Table 3 and Figure 1, respectively.

Table 3- *Rolling contact fatigue conditions.*

Lubrication	Max Hertzian Stress	Rolling Contact Frequency
Clean spindle oil (C60)	5860 Mpa	2700 cpm
Contaminated spindle oil (C60)+200ppm of 50~100µm SiC powder	2645 Mpa	2700 cpm

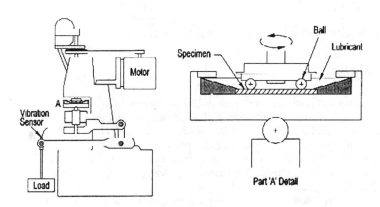

Figure 1-*Schematic diagram of fatigue test equipment.*

Results and Discussion

The Effect of Austenite Grain Size on Formation of Microcracks

The purpose of this experiment was to characterize the maximum prior austenite grain size and consequently the minimum amount of Al and N to avoid microcacks caused by martensite impingement during quenching. In general, as the grain size is increased, the grain boundary area is reduced, and more martensite plates are capable of causing intragranular cracking from martensite 'needle' impingement [1].

Figure 2 shows the effect of austenite grain size on total crack length in an examined area of 28500μm^2 for the 1.2%C steels i.e. S4, S5 and S6. It is evident that the total length of microcracks increased with austenite grain size. These microcracks were formed mainly in the martensite plates within prior austenite grains, as shown in figure 2. It was difficult to observe microcracks for the specimens having a prior austenite grain size less than 45μm.

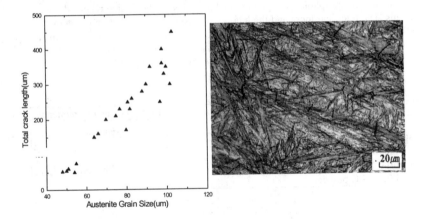

Figure 2 -*The total crack length as a function of prior austenite grain size and a photograph showing typical microcracks in 1.2% C steel (Steel: S4) (A.G.S.: 60μm).*

It is well-known that prior austenite grain size is closely related to the amount of Al and N because aluminum nitride particles inhibit austenite grain growth at high temperatures. However, large amounts of Al and N cause lower fatigue life and surface cracking of steel during continuous casting process, respectively.

Aluminum nitride dissolves in austenite to form a solid solution of Al and N, AlN(solid) <-> Al + N. The solubility limit can be represented by log[%Al][%N]=(-7400/T) +1.95.

Figure 3 shows the effect of the value, log [Al][N], on the austenite grain size after heating at various temperature for 5hours. The austenite grain size decreased smaller than 45μm when log [Al][N] was −3.4 for the specimens which were carbonitrided at 950°C. The results shown in figures 2 and 3 indicate that the total crack length will be zero for the steels containing Al and N with log [%Al][%N] of – 3.4.

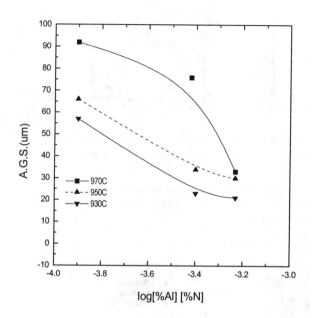

Figure3-*The effect of log [%Al] [%N] on austenite grain size after heating at various temperatures for 5hours. (Steel: S 1, S2 and S3).*

Microstructures

It is well-known that the microstructure of direct quenched specimens consists of coarse martensite and retained austenite. As the prior austenite grain size increases, the sizes of plate martensite and retained austenite become coarser. The double reheat process results in a finer martensite plates and lower retained austenite. It means that the intermediate austenitizing treatment results in very fine austenite grains restricting the grain growth by finely precipitated spherical carbides and nitrides[3].

The purpose of this experiment was to investigate the carbonitriding effect on the morphology of precipitates after double reheat treatment. As shown figure 4, Cr-carbides were observed in the conventional carburizing steels, while V-carbonitrides and Cr-carbides were observed in the carbonitrided steel S 3.

♦ SAE5120-Carburizing   ♦ S 3-Carbonitriding

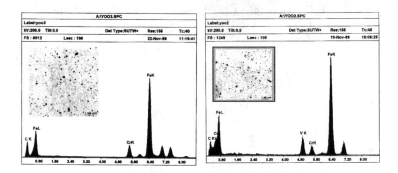

Figure 4-*Comparison of TEM replicas, and EDAX analyses of carbides in conventional carburized and carbonitrided laboratory steels.*

Figure 5 shows a quantitative size distribution of the precipitated particles.   The modified and carbonitrided steels contain a lager number of fine particles than those measured in the conventional steels.

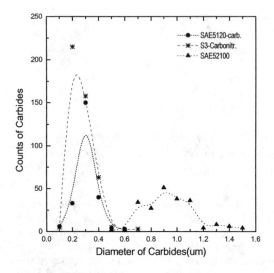

Figure 5 -*Comparison of the amount of carbide size distribution in modified/carbonitrided steel versus conventional steels.*

When double reheat temperature increased from 860°C to 900°C, the particles became coarser and the number of particles decreased as it was repeated in previous work [3].

Evaluation of the Amount of Retained Austenite

Since retained austenite lowers the stress concentration at the edge of indentations, it is effective to increase rolling contact fatigue life under contaminated lubricant conditions[4,5]. In this experiment, the influence of austenite grain size and the heat treatment method on the amount of austenite was investigated. After single quenching at 950°C, the amount of retained austenite decreased when the prior austenite grain size increased, as shown in figure 6.

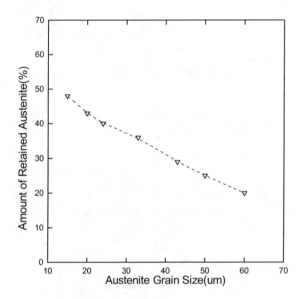

Figure 6 -*Effect of austenite grain size on the amount of retained austenite for 1.2% C steel (Steel S4).*

Figure 7 shows the change in amount of retained austenite as a function of distance from the surface for the double quenched and single quenched specimen. The difference in the amount of retained austenite between these specimens was about 10% in the surface area.

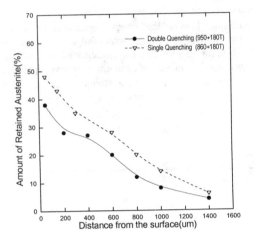

Figure 7 -*Change of retained austenite with different heating
temperature (Steel: S 3).*

The amount of retained austenite in steel S 3 was compared with that of
carburized steel in figure 8. Here it is possible to see that the change in case
hardening method from carburizing to carbonitriding leads to an increase in the
amount of retained austenite i.e. by about 5% in the surface area.

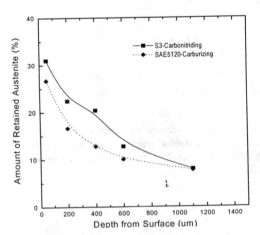

Figure8-*Comparison of the amount of retained austenite between
S3-carbonitriding and SAE5120-caburizing.*

Mechanical properties

In general, it is difficult to produce a material that contains both high hardness and high amount of retained austenite. Generally the hardness of steel containing large amount of retained austenite becomes lower. The modified laboratory steel in this study, however, exhibited high hardness level in spite of a large amount of retained austenite as shown in figure 9.

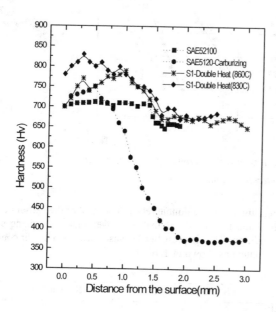

Figure 9 -*Comparison of   microhardness of*
various steels .

During fatigue tests under clean lubricant condition, the flaking is subsurface initiated at a material defects such as oxide inclusions. Therefore it is possible to increase fatigue life by decreasing the amount of oxide inclusions. Under a contaminated environment, on the other hand, the debris causes a surface defect and consequently leads to a site with a stress concentration. To relieve this stress concentration, a soft microstructure, for example retained austenite, is effective. Fatigue life of modified/carbonitrided steel was evaluated under clean and contaminated lubricant environment and compared with those of conventional ones as shown in figures 10 to 12.

Double reheat treatment of the carbonitrided steel specimens exhibited a longer fatigue life than conventional caburized steel and through hardened bearing steel under contaminated lubricant conditions as shown in figure 10. It is because of the a higher amount of retained austenite that an increase in fatigue life was observed.

Steel	SAE52100	SAE5120-Carbur.	S 3-Carbonitr.
$L_{10}(X10^6)$	1.0	4.0	5.7

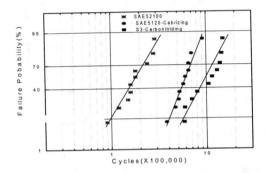

Figure10- *Results of rolling contact fatigue test under contaminated lubrication.*

However, as shown in figure 11, the double reheat treatment of the carbonitrided steel exhibits almost the same fatigue life as that of conventional caburizing steel under clean lubricant condition. This is probably because these two steels contain almost the same oxygen content as shown in Table 1.

Steel.	SAE5120-Carbur.	S 3-Carbonitr.
$L_{10}(X10^6)$	3.3	3.0

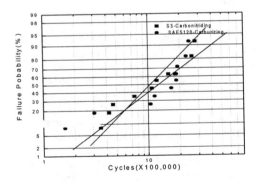

Figure.11 -*Results of rolling contact fatigue test under clean lubrication.*

As shown in figure 12, increase of double heating temperature from 860°C to 880°C reduced the fatigue life of the carbonitrided steel under contaminated lubricant condition.

Double Heat Treatment Temp.	880°C	860°C
$L_{10} (X10^6)$	4.1	5.7

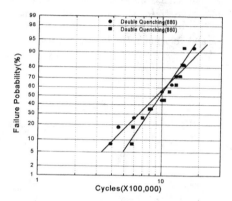

Figure.12 -*Fatigue life according to double heat treatment temperature (steel: S 3).*

Conclusion

The effect of micro-alloy and carbonitriding on the mechanical properties was investigated in the medium carbon steel based on SAE 5140H. The main conclusions were as follows.

1) Due to a larger number of fine V-carbonitried precipitated particles, the modified medium carbon steel with a high amount of retained austenite exhibited also relatively high hardness

2) To prevent the microcracking during oil quenching after carburizing (or carbonitriding), the austenite grain size should be below 45μm.

3) As the austenite grain size decreases, the amount of retained austenite increases. If the austenite grain size is below 25μm, the retained austenite level is typically amounts above 30% after a double reheat treatment.

4) Due to higher amount of retained austenite, modified and carbonitrided medium carbon steel specimens exhibit longer fatigue life under contaminate lubrication than conventional case carburizing steel.

References
[1] Brobst, R.P. and Krauss, G., "The Effect of Austenite Grain Size on Microcracking in Martensite of an Fe-1.22C Alloy," *Metallurgical Transactions*, Volume 5, February 1974, PP.457-462.
[2] Davies, R.G. and C Magee, C.L., "Microcracking in Ferrous Martensite," *Metallurgical Transactions*, Volume 3, January 1972. PP.307-313.
[3] Yoo, S.J., Han, S.K., Lee. J.S., Jung, B.J., Song, B.H.and Park, C.H., "Development of medium carbon carburized bearing steel for transmissions of vehicles." *Proceedings of the automotive technology innovation center workshop 2001*, PP.109-114.
[4] Muro, E., Sadaoka, Y., Ito, S. and Tsushima, N., *Proceedings 12th Japan Congress on Material Research Metallic Materials*, The Society of Materials Science, Japan, March, 969. P74.
[5] Yajima, E., Miyazaki, T., Sugiyama, T. and Terashima, H., *Journal of Institute of Metals*, Volume36, 1972, P.213.

Kenji Yamamura[1] and Manabu Oohori[1]

Development of a New Material for Guide Roll Bearings for Continuous Casting
Machine

Reference: Yamamura, K., and Oohori, M., "Development of a New Material for
Guide Roll Bearings for Continuous Casting Machine," *Bearing Steel Technology*,
ASTM STP 1419, J. M. Beswick, Ed., American Society for Testing and Materials
International, West Conshohocken, PA, 2002.

Abstract: The guide roll bearings for a continuous casting machine (CCM) are used
under extremely low rotation speed, high load, and debris-contaminated and water-
infiltrated lubrication. Therefore, raceway surfaces usually wear severely and outer
rings are sometimes fractured.

The purpose of this study is to prolong the CCM bearing life by material and heat-
treatment technologies. We investigated the fracture process of CCM bearings and
developed a new material, case hardened steel, that shows superior wear resistance to
SAE 52100 steel. Optimum control of retained austenite and hardness extends rolling
contact fatigue life under contaminated lubrication. In the simulation tests of a CCM
guide roll, superior wear resistance was confirmed under water-infiltrated lubrication
conditions.

Keywords: wear, spherical roller bearing, rolling contact fatigue life, retained
austenite, carbide, carbonitride, hardness

Introduction

Metal contact between the bearing ring and rolling elements of a rolling bearing
is prevented when an oil film is formed over the contact surface during ordinary

---

[1]Reserch Engineer and General Manager, respectively, NSK Ltd. Basic Technology
Research & Development Center, 1-5-50, Kugenuma Shinmei Fujisawa-shi,
Kanagawa 251-8501, Japan

operating conditions. However, when the bearing is operated at an extremely low speed, formation of the oil film lessens due to the difficulty of drawing lubricant over the contact surface. The resulting metal contact causes wear. A typical example is the spherical roller bearing used in the guide roll of a continuous casting machine (CCM).

The spherical roller bearings for CCM guide rolls are operated at extremely slow speed and suffer from insufficient lubrication further complicated by the entry of water and fine dust. Moreover, CCM bearings are used under high load. Therefore, raceway surfaces usually wear severely and outer rings are sometimes fractured. Due to these problems, it is necessary that the life of CCM bearings be prolonged.

The use of a cylindrical roller bearing with no differential slide would be effective for reduction of wear, but this bearing is applicable only to one side of the roll because it cannot carry the axial load. Improvement of the lubrication method is also effective for reducing wear, but there is a problem due to the cost of making modifications to existing equipment. With this in mind, we developed a bearing whose life has been extended by means of material and heat treatment technologies, which is also free of modifications to equipment, bearing type, or dimensions.

The purpose of this paper is to describe the effect of material and heat-treatment for wear resistance, and the characteristics of a new material for CCM guide roll bearings.

Development Concept

Understanding the damage mechanisms of a bearing is essential for extending bearing life. We have investigated the damage mechanism of spherical roller bearings for CCM [1]. Figure 1 shows the damage mechanism. Note that the raceway of a

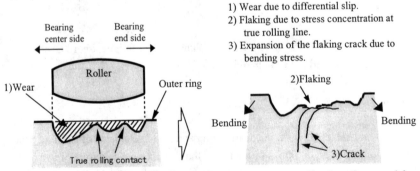

Figure 1-*Fracture mechanism of outer rings of self-aligning roller bearings used for CCMs.*

spherical roller bearing actually consists of two rows of raceways and that Figure 1 shows one of these raceways. The mechanism is as follows. First, wear occurs due to differential sliding and spin sliding. The hatched region in the figure shows the portion removed by wear. Two true rolling points with zero slip exist on the contact surface between the bearing ring and rolling element. Since wear at these points is small, these points appear to have two crest-like shapes. Next, stress concentration and flaking occur at the true rolling points, followed by crack propagation. Then, because of the bending stress acting on the outer ring, the crack is further propagated perpendicular to the raceway, eventually resulting in breakage.

In view of the challenges mentioned above, improving wear resistance is necessary to enhance the durability of CCM bearings. Accordingly, we studied about wear under low rotation speed in order to improve the wear resistance by material and heat-treatment technologies. Improving fatigue life property is also important. Due to the severe environment, flaking is considered a surface-originated type fatigue. Conversely, it is known that high hardness and optimization of retained austenite are effective against surface originated flaking [2]. Then, in addition to enhancing wear resistance, we accomplished optimum control of retained austenite and hardness, and developed a new material for CCM guide roll bearings. Furthermore, to prevent breaking finally, core toughness is improved by the use of case hardening steel as newly developed material instead of using through-hardening steel (SAE52100) commonly for conventional CCM bearing.

Wear Resistance

In order to improve wear resistance, it is considered that utilization of hard carbide is effective. The carbide in SAE 52100 is M_3C type, and $M_{23}C_6$, M_7C_3 and MC type carbide possess superior hardness to M_3C type carbide. It is known that increasing the number of hard carbides is effective in improving the wear resistance of tool steels for work rolls in rolling mills[3]. As for the rolling bearings, carbide, which has high hardness, is taken advantage of as a heat resistant steel used under high-temperature and high-speed conditions of jet engines, but, as far as a study regarding wear resistance of a pole with low speed rotation, it is not found. In addition, practical use of such high alloy heat resistant steel is difficult for CCM bearings due to costs. It is well known that vanadium is MC type carbide former. We then studied utilization of vanadium to improve the wear resistance.

Wear Test Procedure

Table 1 shows the principal chemical composition of test materials. We investigated the effect of vanadium by using samples containing 1.0% and 2.0% vanadium, and compared the results to conventional steel (SAE52100).

Table 1-*Chemical composition of test materials (wt%).*

Steel	C	Si	Mn	Cr	V
1V	0.40	0.36	0.80	1.48	1.02
2V	0.41	0.40	0.80	1.52	1.97
52100	0.99	0.27	0.45	1.52	—

Specimens were carburized or carbonitrided under several conditions for the purpose of testing different surface carbon content, nitrogen content, and hardness in the same material. As for the conventional SAE52100, through hardened sample was also tested. After specimens were quenched and tempered, they were ground to a final surface finish.

The two-ring type wear tester was used for evaluation of wear resistance. Figure 2 shows the outline of the wear tester. A pair of ring-shaped specimens (ø30 outside diameter × ø16 inside diameter × 7 mm width) was used in the test. The specified load was applied with peripheral surfaces in contact with the test pieces for the rotation test. The weight was measured before and after the test, and the loss of weight was assumed to be the amount of wear for evaluation. Test conditions included a rotation speed of 10 min^{-1}, a slip ratio of 30%, and contact pressure (P_{max}) of 880 MPa. The test was conducted for 20 hours while supplying lubricant at a rate of 2 cc/min. For the oil lubrication test, we used spindle oil. Water lubrication testing consisted of ion-exchanged water to check the effects of water on wear.

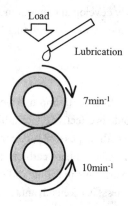

Figure 2-*Schematic of two-ring type wear tester.*

Result of the oil lubrication wear test

Figure 3 shows wear test results for specimens that have almost the same carbon and nitrogen concentration, and show wear resistance effect of vanadium. An addition of 1% vanadium improves wear resistance greatly. However, even if it is increased by more than 1%, no great change is seen in wear resistance. Figure 4 shows the influence of nitrogen concentration in wear resistance of 1% vanadium steels. In the case of nitrogen, over 0.2% is effective in improving wear resistance, but over 0.3%, the effect is nearly saturated. In addition, results of this examination show that for extremely low speed rotation, correlation between surface hardness and wear loss was not recognizable. In addition, no correlation between the amount of retained austenite and wear loss was found. From the above results, we selected carbonitrided 1% vanadium steel with a content of more than 0.2% nitrogen as newly developed material.

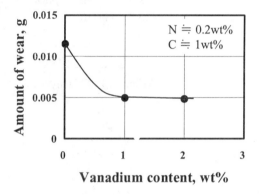

Figure 3-*Relationship between vanadium content and amount of wear.*

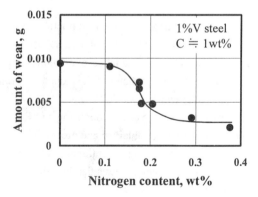

Figure 4-*Relationship between nitrogen content and amount of wear.*

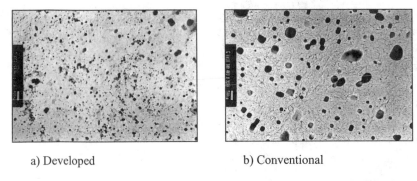

a) Developed   b) Conventional

Figure 5-*TEM photographs of precipitates by extraction replica method for the surface layer of developed and conventional materials.*

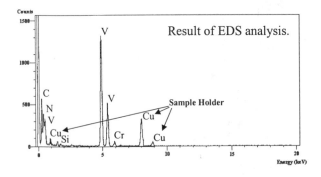

Figure 6-*EDS analysis result of extracted particle of developed material.*

Figure 5 shows observation results of precipitate by extraction replica method for the surface layer of developed material and conventional material. Compared with conventional steel, precipitates of developed material seem extremely fine. Figure 6 shows the EDS analysis results of extracted particles of developed material. From the element analysis, the precipitates are identified as VCN.

Observations of the worn surfaces were carried out using an SEM. As for newly developed material, many carbonitrides were obtained and protruding over the worn surfaces (Figure 7a). In contrast, surfaces of the conventional steels were worn smooth (Figure 7b). The observation of worn surfaces suggests that vanadium carbonitride, which has high hardness, inhibits wear.

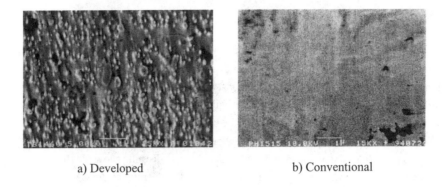

a) Developed   b) Conventional

Figure 7-*SEM images of worn surface.*

Considering manufacturing costs, and the fact that the other parts require no change, using the developed material for only the outer ring is suitable for a CCM bearing. In some cases, newly developed material, which possesses extremely high wear resistance, damages the material of the other components. Figure 8 shows that wear amount is not so different from test results of each mutual contact test when newly developed material and conventional steel are used in combination with each other. The newly developed material, which is superior in wear resistance, does not increase wear of the conventional steel. It is also evident that the wear resistance of the newly developed steel is not affected by conventional steel.

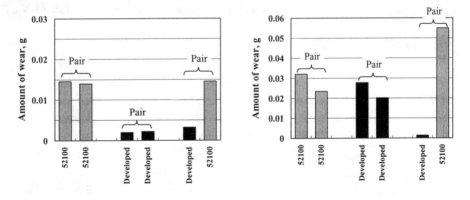

Figure 8-*Effect of material combination under oil lubrication test condions.*

Figure 9-*Effect of material combination under water lubrication test conditions.*

Result of the water lubrication wear test

Figure 9 shows the wear test results of using ion-exchanged water for the combination of conventional steels and that of the newly developed steels. The wear amount is almost equal for both combinations, but about two times more than for the combination of conventional steels in the oil lubrication wear test. Test results indicate that with entry of a large amount of water, the bearing may possibly fail in obtaining sufficient wear resistance of the newly developed steel. Accordingly, the test was made with a combination of developed and conventional steels. Results show that the wear of conventional steel was larger than a combination of conventional steels, but that the wear of the newly developed steel was much less. In addition, the worn surface was almost dark reddish-brown, and as a result of X-ray analysis, Fe_2O_3 and Fe_3O_4 were detected at the worn surface of development materials. As for the worn surface of conventional material, however, X-ray analysis detected no oxide. These observations suggest that wear resistance of the newly developed material was improved by protective action of the oxide film.

This result indicates that a material combination is of extreme importance when the entry of water is expected. As for the bearing of a continuous casting guide roll, we estimate that the bearing, as a whole, has superior wear resistance when the newly developed steel is used for the outer ring, and conventional steel is used for the rolling elements. When there is a significant amount of water contamination, wear of the rolling elements becomes a major concern. However, just as multiple elements share in the distribution of load, under heavy water contamination, multiple elements also share in the distribution of wear. Accordingly, a bearing is able to avoid substantial damage.

Result of Simulation Test of a CCM

A durability test was made under conditions of extremely low speed and water entry to simulate a CCM. A spherical roller bearing, 2210CD, with a bore of ø50, outside diameter of 90, and width of 23 mm, was used in the test. The experimental bearing used the newly developed material for the outer ring   in consideration of the result of our two-ring type wear test. All other part specifications were the same as for conventional bearings. The test was made under conditions of a rotation speed of 4 min^{-1} and a load of 25 kN. The durability test continued for 336 hours while circulating ion-exchanged water at 80   C within the housing and a steady supply of steam to the inside of the bearing (see Figure 10).

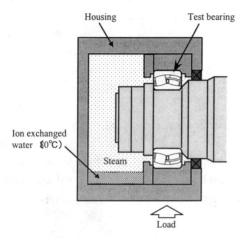

Figure 10-*Schematic of CCM simulation test apparatus.*

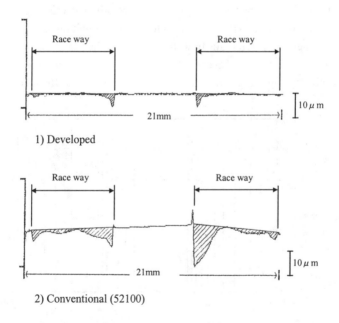

Figure 11-*Cross-section profile of outer ring.*

Figure 11 shows the surface profile of the outer ring raceway at the maximum loading position after the test. The hatched portion in the figure is a worn portion.

When compared in terms of the maximum wear depth, the wear amount of the experimental bearing is about one third of that of conventional bearings. Based on this test result, wear resistance of a newly developed material is about three times greater than conventional steel. When the wear amount is compared by means of the area of hatched portions, the wear amount of a newly developed material is about one seventh of that of conventional steel. After testing, a grease sample from inside the experimental bearing was analyzed, and showed extremely high water content of 12%, while that of conventional bearing was 2%. This fact means that the developed material demonstrates superior wear resistance regardless of severe lubrication conditions. Based on these results, it is considered that the effect of combining bearing materials seems to be the most effective for wear resistance under severe water contamination.

Surface Originated Flaking Life Characteristics

Figure 12 shows evaluation results of surface originated flaking life characteristics, under debris contaminated lubrication conditions using a thrust type life tester. When compared to the basis of the L_{10} life, the life of the newly developed material is about five times longer than that of conventional steel. Specimen surfaces of the newly developed material contained 32 vol% retained austenite on average, and

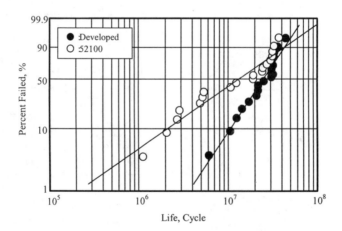

Figure 12-*Fatigue life characteristics under contaminated lubrication.*
Rotation speed: 1 000min^{-1}
Pmax: 4 900MPa
Lubrication oil: Turbine oil VG68

the hardness value was Hv758 on average. With such a combination of high-retained austenite and high hardness, the newly developed material showed superior life characteristics.

Conclusions

Developments were made to extend life through material and heat treatment technologies for rolling bearings, in which wear is a problem, specifically, the spherical roller bearing for CCM. The results obtained are as follows:
(1) The addition of Vanadium and Carbonitriding are very effective for wear resistance under extremely low rotation speed.
(2) Superior wear resistance of newly developed material was confirmed under water-infiltrated lubrication conditions by simulation testing of a CCM.
(3) Newly developed material proved to be superior not only in wear resistance, but also in surface-originated flaking life characteristics.
(4) In addition, because the newly developed material is case hardened, core toughness is also superior to conventional through-hardening steel (SAE52100).

References

[1] Yamamura, K., and Oohori, M., "The Damage Mechanism of Spherical Roller Bearing Using in a Continuous Casting Machine," *Proceedings of JAST Tribology Conference*, Nagoya, November, 1998, pp. 482-483.
[2] Furumura, K., Murakami, Y., and Abe, T., "Case-Hardening Medium Carbon Steel for Tough and Long Life Bearing under Sever Lubrication Conditions," *Bearing Steels: Into 21st century, ASTM STP 1327*, J. J. C. Hoo and W. B. Green, Eds., American Society for Testing and Materials, 1998.
[3] Koshizuka, N., Kimura, T., Oohori, M., Ueda, S., and Wanaka, H., "Influence of Microstructure on the Wear Resistance of High C-5Cr-V Steels for Work Rolls in Cold Rolling Mills," *TETU-TO-HAGANE*, Vol.75, No.3, 1989, pp. 132-138.

Pascal Daguier, [1] Gilles Baudry, [1] Jacques Bellus, [1(*)] Gilles Auclair, [1] Jaime Rofès-Vernis, [2] Gilles Dudragne, [3] Daniel Girodin, [3] and Gérard Jacob [4]

Improved Bearing Steel for Applications Involving Debris, Higher Loads and Temperatures

---

Reference: Daguier, P., Baudry, G., Bellus, J., Auclair, G., Rofès-Vernis, J., Dudragne, G., Girodin, D., and Jacob, G., **"Improved Bearing Steel for Applications Involving Debris, Higher Loads and Temperatures,"** *Bearing Steel Technology, ASTM STP 1419,* J. M. Beswick, Ed., American Society for Testing Materials International, West Conshohocken, PA, 2002.

Abstract: Due to the evolution of cleanness of bearing steels, the failures observed in service conditions move from deep initiated spalling on non-metallic inclusions to surface damage due to machining marks, lack or contaminated lubrication (dents).

To take into account, by the most economic way, these request for more demanding applications, ASCOMETAL, SNR et VALTI have developed a new steel grade [1,2] based on the classical analysis of 100Cr6 (SAE 52100), with higher characteristics in terms of in-service properties (sustaining high loading, high temperature and contaminated lubrication) without deteriorated steelmaking or forming process by an optimised composition of the steel.

Keywords: high temperature bearing steel, tempering stability, contaminated lubrication, retained austenite, high loading

Introduction

The operating conditions in certain bearing applications are tending to become increasingly severe. These more demanding applications include those for automotive components and systems, especially gearboxes and wheels. In such cases, and with

---

[1] Research engineer, manager, research engineer and manager, respectively, ASCOMETAL CREAS, B.P. 70045, 57301 Hagondange Cedex, (* now at TECPHY – Groupe HTM, Service Métallurgie, BP 141, 42704 FIRMINY Cedex).
[2] Marketing manager, GROUPE LUCCHINI, Immeuble Pacific, TSA 40004, 13 cours Valmy, La Défense 7, 92070 La Défense Cedex.
[3] Managers, SNR ROULEMENTS, 1, rue des Usines, B.P 2017. 74010 Annecy Cedex.
[4] R&D manager, VALTI, Route de Courtangis, 21500 Montbard.

320

present bearing steel cleanliness levels, spalling in bearing rings is caused principally by debris-induced surface damage and local loss of matrix strength at higher-than-usual loads and temperatures.

For gearbox applications, wear of the gear components produces debris that can cause indentation or wear of the bearing surface, depending mainly on debris size and hardness. In these conditions, the stresses and temperatures locally exceed the levels currently accepted for steel grades like 100Cr6.

For wheel applications, one of the main trends is the component weight reduction. However, the possibilities of downsizing are fairly limited with standard grades (through- and case-hardening alloy steels or induction hardened carbon grades). The main reasons for these limitations are the higher loads and temperatures induced by downsizing.

In order to maintain an acceptable life under these conditions, the bearings must have higher performance, particularly in the most heavily loaded regions beneath the rolling contact surface. In this context, ASCOMETAL, SNR and VALTI have developed an improved bearing steel, derived from 100Cr6 by additions of manganese and silicon, without deteriorated steelmaking or forming process by a optimised design of alloying elements.

State of the Art

The Need for a New Steel Grade for Actual In-Service Conditions

It is widely known that the fatigue life of bearing steel decreases under contaminated lubrication. This phenomenon is due to stress concentration at the edges of the indentation. Various type of debris can generate denting on the bearing raceway. Depending on the nature (hardness), the size of the debris, and the physical properties of the lubricant, various behaviours of debris and magnitude of damage are observed [3,4,5]

Chiu et al. [6] have computed the stress concentration due to the shoulder produced by the dent. They showed that the nominal Hertzian pressure increases when the ratio r /c decreases (where r is the radius of the shoulder and c is the semi dent width).

Furumura et al. [7] have noted that the level of retained austenite in steel influences the ratio r/c (r/c decreases when $\gamma_{rès}$ decreases).

For clean bearing steel under elasto-hydrodynamic working conditions, the spalling is due to local plasticity around the depth of maximum shearing stress. Numerous works have been performed in this field and the mechanism generally accepted is the diffusion of carbon atoms due to temperature and stress out of the martensite. This local softening of the martensite produces local plasticity, which is responsible for white band marks.

Nowadays, failure observed in service conditions are mainly due to those mechanisms than to spalling on non-metallic inclusions and, with actual grades like 100Cr6, fatigue lifes obtained for such conditions are not sufficient with respect to producer requirements.

Toward a New Steel Grade

The steel developed was designed to obtain a microstructure with high intrinsic resistance to denting, temperature, and overloads by optimised adjustment of alloying elements, which are mainly manganese and silicon.

The main interest of manganese is to increase the amount of retained austenite, according to the classical formula of Andrews on the evolution of Ms with alloying elements. Optimal composition is chosen between sufficient retained austenite and difficulties in producing clean steel.

Among the numerous effects of silicon, some are particularly interesting for manufacturing and in-service properties:

- an increase in hardness in the annealed condition, but also after other heat treatments, such as quenching and tempering;
- delaying of mechanical and thermal softening;
- more rapid strain hardening during cold forming operations, such as wire drawing, tube calibration, ring rolling, machining, etc...

These effects have been widely used in numerous special steel applications, such as springs, wear-resistant parts, high strength components (YS and UTS > 1500 and 2000 MPa respectively), etc. [8-10]. Works performed by different teams [11-14] suggest that:

- the silicon atom in substitutional solid solution in both α-Fe and γ-Fe causes a lattice contraction of about 3×10^{-4} per weight % addition;
- the existence of strong Fe-Si bonds reduces the amplitude of lattice vibrations and can slow down carbon diffusion;
- the lattice distortion around silicon atoms repulses carbon atoms in the immediate vicinity but the forces may become attractive at longer distances.

To look for an optimal composition of Si and Mn in a 100Cr6 based matrix, several experimental heats have been produced for a wide composition range of silicon and manganese.

Alloying Design and Metallurgical Characteristics

Properties for Forming Process

Considering the processes involved in the manufacturing of bearings, the main characteristics to be determined are the hardness in the annealed condition, the heat treatment response, particularly the quench hardenability, and the tempering behaviour. All of these properties can have a decisive influence on tube forming, machining and in-service performance. In the case of the modified 100Cr6 grade studied here, the influence of Si and Mn on these properties was determined first of all on laboratory heats before performing fatigue tests on industrial heats.

The presence of Mn and Si have a significant influence on the temperature of the transforming point. So, by adjusting the temperature of the annealing treatment, it is possible to obtain spheroidized microstructures similar to those in 100Cr6.

Figure 1 summarises the evolution of the hardness in the annealed condition, obtained on various products (bars, tubes, wires and forged components) and alloying content . It can be seen that there is a significant increase in the as-annealed hardness for silicon contents ranging from 1 to 1.5 %, and that there is little further increase beyond about 1.5% Si.

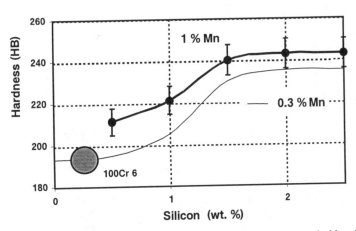

Figure 1 - *Influence of silicon and manganese content on annealed hardness.*

The alloying elements have a significant contribution to the forgeability curve of new grades. Depending on alloying content, the forging temperature range is reduced compared to 100Cr6. A good control of the rolling process is then important to prevent crack formation on bars or tubes.

Metallurgical Characteristics

With the addition of 1 to 1.5% Si and 1% Mn, the as-quenched microstructure contains about 15-25% of retained austenite, depending on the austenitizing and tempering temperature. This is mainly due to the decreasing of the Ms point induced by the manganese addition. Silicon acts only indirectly and has a smaller effect than manganese on both the Ms point and the amount of retained austenite. Figure 2 shows the variation of Ms with austenitizing temperature for 100Cr6 and two modified grades, with 1.5 and 2.5% Si respectively. The curves for the two silicon contents are virtually identical. Silicon affects the stability of the austenite and the kinetics of dissolution and precipitation of carbides, by slowing the diffusion of carbon [9].

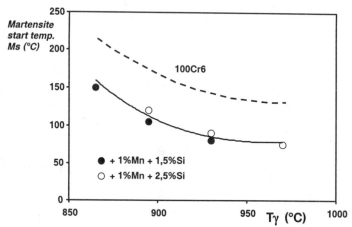

Figure 2 - *Influence of austenitizing temperature on the Ms point.*

Another important effect of silicon is to delay softening during tempering (Figure 3). After tempering at 300-350°C , the hardness remains at a level 15 to 25 % higher than that of 100Cr6.

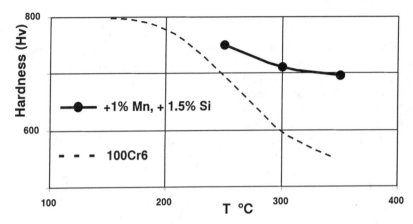

Figure 3 - *Evolution of hardness of the as-quenched structure with tempering temperature.*

For the compositions studied, both the martensite and the retained austenite show greater resistance to softening during subsequent tempering. Thus, with 1% Mn and a sufficiently high silicon content, the retained austenite does not begin to transform int martensite until about 300°C, or even 400°C (Figure 4).

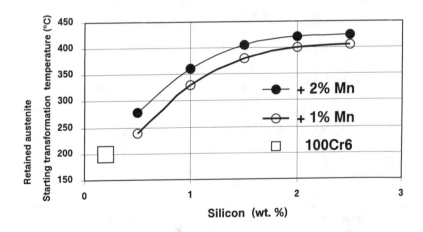

Figure 4 - *Evolution of the temperature of thermal decomposition of retained austenite with silicon and manganese content.*

Mechanical Properties for In-Service Applications

Classical fatigue tests and rolling fatigue tests on flat washer specimens or bearings performed on this new grade have demonstrated that the new steel enables the manufacture of bearings with significantly better properties than for 100Cr6 grade, particularly under severe operating conditions:
- higher resistance to indentation damage;
- longer lives under high loads and
- better fatigue resistance at high working temperatures.

Resistance to Indentation

The fatigue life of the modified 100Cr6, compared with classical grade in tapered roller bearing fatigue test in the presence of dents, is improved by at least a factor of four in the new grade. Table 1 summarises the results obtained.

Table 1 - *Comparison of fatigue life (L_{10}) between 100Cr6 and the new grade for clean and contaminated lubrication.*

grade	clean lubrication [1]	contaminated lubrication at 80°C [2]
100Cr6	218 h	12 h
modified 100Cr6	443 h	45 h

[1] Hertzian pressure of 3.3 GPa
[2] Hertzian pressure of 2.8 GPa

Higher Loads

Fatigue tests [15] (R=0.1, in compression) performed on the modified 100Cr6 shows that the fatigue limit increase of 400 MPa compared to the classical 100Cr6 (Figure 5).

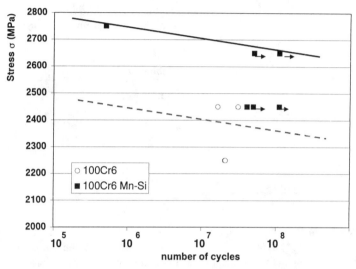

Figure 5 - *Comparison of the fatigue limit between 100Cr6 and the modified 100Cr6.*

These results are confirmed by tests performed on bearings under high loading (which correspond to Hertzian pressures of 3.4 and 3.8 GPa -see Table 2). Those tests show that the fatigue life (L_{10}) of bearings is also at least two or three times longer with the new steel.

Table 2 - *Comparison of fatigue life on real bearings between 100Cr6 and modified 100Cr6.*

type of bearing and test conditions	L_{10} (hours)	
	100Cr6	modified 100Cr6
Wheel bearing P_{Hertz}=3,4 GPa	20 to 50	150 to 200
Gearbox bearing P_{Hertz}=3,8 GPa	30 to 50	> 150

High Temperature

Torsion tests performed at room and at high temperature (170°C) showed that the fatigue limit of conventional 100Cr6 decreases of 15% whereas this new steel lost only 5% between these two temperatures (Table 3).

Table 3 - *Evolution of fatigue limit with temperature.*

grade	fatigue limit in torsion (MPa)		
	room temp.	160-170°C	Différence (%)
100Cr6	565	483	14,5
modified 100Cr6	580	550	5,2

These results on 100Cr6 are in agreement with previous results obtained by FAG on a rolling fatigue test [16] in the same range of temperature. Then, the decreasing of fatigue limit with temperature of the new steel is of the same order of magnitude as for M50 NiL for this temperature range.

Conclusions

A new steel for bearing applications dedicated to severe in-service conditions has been developed by ASCOMETAL / SNR and VALTI.

The overall results obtained show a significant increase of the characteristics of the modified 100Cr6 compared to the classical 100Cr6, due to an optimised design of alloying elements.

The microstructure of the modified 100Cr6 (martensite and austenite) is more stable during thermo-mechanical loading than the one of classical 100Cr6, which gives to this new steel a better resistance to dents, high loading (or overloading), and high temperature.

Moreover, as regards the potential applications, in addition to the uses envisaged here (gearbox and wheel bearings), the results already obtained, together with developments in progress, suggest that the new alloys could be successfully employed for other non-automotive purposes.

Acknowledgments : The authors acknowledge INSA of Lyon Laboratory (GEMPPM) for helpful contribution in the field of mechanisms of micro plasticity.

References

[1] Priority number – French patent reference 97-04092.

[2] Priority number – French patent reference 98-09740.

[3] Ville, F., « Pollution solide des lubrifiants, indentation et fatigue des surfaces », thèse INSA Lyon, France,1998.

[4] Nixon, H.P., Zantopulos, H., and Cogdell, J.D., "A Standardized method for evaluating debris resistance of rolling element bearings", SAE technical paper series, International Off-highway & Powerplant Congress & Exposition, Milwaukee, Wisconsin September 12-14, 1994.

[5] Lubrecht, A.A.,Dwyer-Joyce, R.S., and Ioannides, E., "Analysis of the influence of indentations on contact life", 18th Leeds-Lyon Symposium of Tribology, 3-6 September 1996.

[6] Chiu, Y.P., and Liu, J.Y., "An analytical study of the stress concentration around a furow shaped surface defect in rolling contact ", Journal of lubrication Technology, 1970, pp 258-263.

[7] Furumura, K., Murakami, Y., and Abe, T., " Developement of long life bearing steel for full film lubrication and for poor and contaminated lubrication ", Motion & control, no 1, 1996.

[8] Henry, G., Constant, A., and Charbonnier, J.C., Principes de base du traitement thermique, PYC Edition, Ivry-sur-Seine, 1992.

[9] Schaff, H., " Comparaison des traitements thermiques de trois aciers à hautes caractéristiques ", Internationaux de France du Traitement Thermique, Toulouse, 26-28 june 1991, pp. 29-35.

[10] Siekmann, G., and Berns, H., " Tieftemparaturverhalten von hochfesten vergütungsstählen ", Arch. Eisenhüttenwesen, 53(II), 1982, p. 451.

[11] Roy, S.K., " Diffusivity of carbon in austenitic Fe-Si-C alloys ",Arch. Eisenhüttenwesen, 51(3), 1980, pp.91-96.

[12] Kristhal, M.A., Fizika Metallov i Metallovedenie, 1960 9 pp. 317-319.

[13] Bannykh, O.A., Fizika Metallov i Metallovedenie, 1969 5 pp.837-841.

[14] Nicot, C., " Etude des mécanismes d'endommagement d'aciers à roulement sollicités en fatigue : Effet de défauts de surface simulant des conditions de lubrification polluée et rôle du traitement thermique ", Thèse INSA , Lyon (France), le 22 mars 1994.

[15] Sarete-Cerceuil, H., " Etude d'une nouvelle nuance d'acier a roulement pour conditions d'usage sévères et modélisation de son endommagement en présence d'une indentation ", thèse INSA, Lyon (France), 2000.

[16] Böhmer, H.J., Hirsch, T., and Streit, E., " Rolling contact fatigue behavior of heat resistant bearing steels at high operational temperatures ", Bearing steels : Into the 21st Century, ASTM STP 1327, J.J.C. Hoo and W.B. Green, Eds., American Society for Testing and Materials, 1998.

D. Carlson,[1] R. Pitsko,[1] A. J. Chidester,[2] and J. R. Imundo[3]

The Effect of Bearing Steel Composition and Microstructure on Debris Dented Rolling Element Bearing Performance

Reference: Carlson, D., Pitsko, R., Chidester, A. J., and Imundo, J. R., "The Effect of Bearing Steel Composition and Microstructure on Debris Dented Rolling Element Bearing Performance," *Bearing Steel Technology, ASTM STP 1419*, J. M. Beswick, Ed., American Society for Testing and Materials International, West Conshohocken, PA, 2002.

Abstract: Because of continuous improvements in bearing steel cleanliness, surface damage created by debris has become more influential in determining the life of rolling element bearings. The metallurgical structure of a bearing raceway can be modified to optimize strength and damage tolerance. The correct balance between raceway strength and damage tolerance can significantly improve bearing life in contaminated environments.

Retained austenite is known to add a degree of damage tolerance to hardened bearing steel. Samples made of ASTM A295 52100 steel were heat treated to obtain increasing amounts of retained austenite. Indentations were placed into the steel sample surfaces using a Rockwell 30N Superficial Hardness Tester. These indentations were examined and measured using light interferometry. The changes in the dent morphologies with increasing amounts of retained austenite will be discussed.

A test program has been developed to investigate the influence of microstructure on the life of debris dented rolling element bearings. Groups of 35 mm bore radial ball bearings were dented with either a Rockwell 30N Superficial Hardness Tester, or with hard powder metal particles. These bearings were then fatigue tested with uniform contact stress, speed and clean lubricant with a marginal lubrication film. The performance of different bearing steels and heat treatments were investigated, and test results from the two denting methodologies will be provided.

Keywords: anti-friction bearings, bearings, debris denting, retained austenite, ASTM A295 52100 steel, 3312 steel, heat treatment, carburizing, bearing testing, contamination testing, rolling contact fatigue testing

A Challenge for Bearing Manufactures: Damage Tolerant Bearing Steel

Customers are challenging bearing manufactures to provide bearings that can survive in debris-contaminated lubrication or endure debris damage without suffering serious life reduction. This challenge has led to a considerable amount of research into the most effective and economical methods to modify the raceway surfaces of bearings to make them damage tolerant. Most of the work has focused on using retained austenite to diminish the damage created by debris on rolling elements. However, relying on one metallurgical characteristic alone to achieve damage tolerance neglects the contribution that other properties like hardness, residual stress and dimensional stability make to the survival of a bearing in a demanding real world application. Another approach is to balance all of the important metallurgical properties to produce bearings optimized for specific harsh applications.

The Role of Austenite in a Damage Tolerant Bearing Steel

The cleanliness of modern bearing steels has caused the predominant failure mode for bearings to become surface initiated rolling contact fatigue. This surface initiated failure becomes especially more likely in applications where the bearing operates with a contaminated lubricant. Lorösch [1] first commented in 1981 that failure from debris damage was an increasingly important failure mode and would require new types of tests in order to keep life equation verification testing accurate.

The last 20 years has seen a large amount of work on the effect of debris denting in bearing steels [2-5] and has led to good understanding of the progression of surface fatigue failure from a debris dent. The debris particle damages the raceway surface when it is caught between the rolling elements and is pushed into the raceway surface. The debris particle will plastically deform the raceway, forming a depression. Due to the constancy of volume principle, much of the plastically deformed material will be displaced around the debris particle. This displacement of metal forms a "lip" or "halo" of raised metal around the perimeter of the depression. This lip of raised metal immediately becomes a "weak link" on the raceway surface. The EHD film thickness will likely be severely reduced over this raised metal lip resulting in a boundary lubrication condition. With the arrival of the next rolling element, the lip is subject to enormous contact stresses and lubrication film penetration. Repetition of this sequence eventually leads to a peeling failure mode on the raised metal lip crest and ultimately to a flaking and spalling failure at the trailing edge of the lip as shown in Figure 10 in reference [6].

The body of recent research work indicates that if the bearing raceway surface contains higher levels of retained austenite it will have a longer life in a contaminated environment. The reasons given for this improvement include:
1)   the inherent ductility of the soft austenite phase, which should work harden under the action of the high contact stresses found at the dent lip, thus strengthening it;

2)   the higher toughness inherent in austenite should impede fatigue crack propagation; and

3)   a surface topographic effect that results in a more rounded crest on the raised metal lip, which reduces the locally enormous contact stresses when struck by the rolling elements. Also, over time, the austenite in the lip will be deform again into a more smoothed surface with presumably a reduction of contact stress and increase in life [2, 3, 7].

This topographic effect described above in reason 3) has been defined as r/c, where r is the dent shoulder radius divided by c, which is equal to half of the dent width. As the austenite content of a bearing steel increases, the r/c ratio at a dent lip will increase and this has been shown [2,3,7] to correlate to increased life in laboratory dented bearings.

The measurement of r/c at a dent lip provides one measure of the severity of the raised metal lip that surrounds a debris dent. It has been established in the work cited that debris denting reduces bearing life by initiating early spalling at the trailing edge of the dent lip. This early spalling is due to the enormous contact stress generated between the rolling element and the top of the lip, which acts as a very severe asperity. Depending on the application conditions, the lip will alter the EHD film thickness in its local area. Over the lip, the film may be reduced to a boundary lubrication condition or worse. Due to EHD film thickness considerations, the actual magnitude of the lip height could provide useful information when specifying the lubrication for a given application. Knowledge of how lip height varies as a function of the amount of retained austenite in a microstructure would increase the understanding of the beneficial effect of austenite in bearing steels.

Dent Topography Measurement

New non-contact surface measurement devices are now available. One of these devices is a WYKO® optical interferometer that uses light rather than a physical stylus to measure surface roughness and surface features. Light interferometry is a powerful tool for measuring surface dents because it is able to measure the severe and abrupt elevation changes at a dent as well as accurately discriminate and measure very small features such as a dent lip. This device was used to measure the dent topography and lip heights on a number of samples heat treated to attain different austenite amounts.

Test Procedure

ASTM A295 52100 test slugs were divided into seven groups and austenitized at a given test temperature for 25 minutes at heat. The austenitizing temperatures used were: 816°C, 829°C, 843°C, 885°C, 900°C, 954°C and 982°C . After austenitizing the slugs were quenched in room temperature oil. One slug from each group was then refrigerated at -84°C. Each sample group was then tempered such that the final hardness of each group was in the range HRC 59-62. HR30N hardness strikes and retained austenite measurements were made on one of the flat surfaces. The retained austenite measurements were determined using X-ray diffraction. As expected, the percentage of retained austenite increased with austenitizing temperature.

Results

Each HR30N hardness indentation was then magnified and examined using light interferometry. A three-dimensional light interferometry image of an HR30N indentation is shown in Figure 1. The light area around the indentation is the raised metal lip. This sample was austenitized at 843°C and tempered to a hardness of HRC 60.5 with 22% retained austenite.

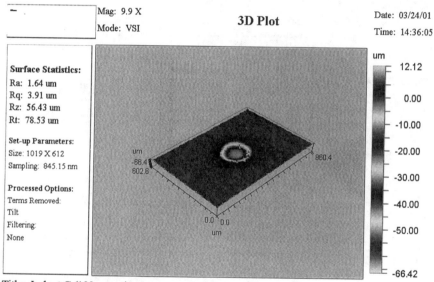

Title: Indent C (100x mag.)
Note: Sample #3 Austenitized 843C.

Figure 1 – *A three-dimensional view of a HR30N indentation at 100X using light interferometry. Note the white area of raised metal around the perimeter of the indentation. This sample material is ASTM A295 52100 austenitized at 843 °C and tempered to a hardness of HRC 60.5 with 22% retained austenite.*

In the study of debris denting, the most valuable representation of the hardness indentation is the two-dimensional profile. From this view information on the shape and depth of the indentation can be gathered (Figure 2). A set of cross hairs is positioned in the center of the indentation image at the extreme left. The profile measured along the horizontal cross hair is represented in the top image (labeled X profile). The profile measured along the vertical cross hair is represented in the bottom image (labeled Y profile). The height of the raised metal lip above the datum surface is given by the Rp value in the table at the far right (here about 2.88 microns). The width of the lip is measured manually to the point in which it blends into the datum surface (here 244.5 microns). Note the position of the two inverted triangles on the indentation image at the far left. These inverted triangles correspond to the triangles used to measure the raised metal lip width in the X profile view. This gives an appreciation for the size of the concentric ring of raised metal that surrounds the indentation. While a debris dent may be visible to the eye, this ring is invisible until after additional run time. This ring of raised metal is the effective area of damage caused by a debris dent. This entire ring of raised metal is operating under reduced EHD film thickness.

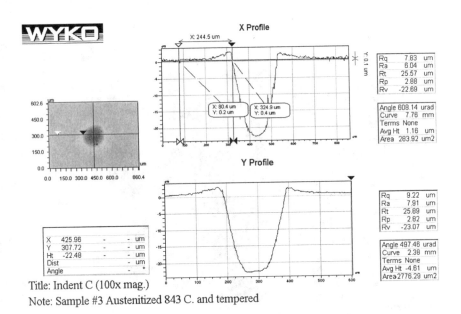

Title: Indent C (100x mag.)
Note: Sample #3 Austenitized 843 C. and tempered

Figure 2 - The HR30N indentation shown in Figure 1 is shown here in profile. The raised metal lip height and width can be measured. Also, a representation of the size of the ring of raised metal that surrounds the indentation is shown in the image at the far left. This sample was austenitized at 843 °C and tempered to a hardness of HRC 60.5 with 22% retained austenite.

Another sample that was austenitized at 843°C and quenched but then refrigerated and double tempered to reduce the retained austenite content was indented and examined using optical interferometry. The hardness of this sample was HRC 61 with 10% retained austenite. The profile across this indentation is shown in Figure 3. The reduced level of retained austenite was expected to change the shape of the raised metal lip around the indentation. The lip height was measured as 3.25 microns and the lip width as 237 microns. Thus, the refrigerated sample that has reduced austenite exhibits a lip that is 13% higher and 3% narrower than the sample than a similarly heat treated sample that was not refrigerated and has a higher austenite content.

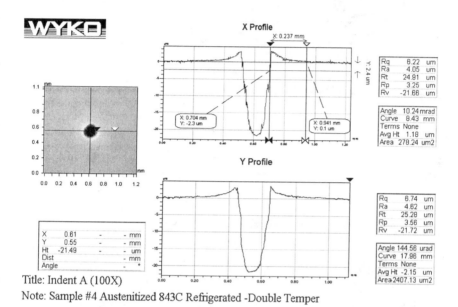

Title: Indent A (100X)

Note: Sample #4 Austenitized 843C Refrigerated -Double Temper

Figure 3 - *The HR30N indentation shown is from a ASTM A295 52100 sample that was austenitized at 843 °C and tempered to a hardness of HRC 61 with 10% retained austenite. Compare to the higher austenite content sample (Figure 2). Note That the reduced austenite content (and higher martensite content) of this sample has resulted in a greater lip height and a narrower lip.*

Lip height and retained austenite measurements were taken on the ASTM A295 52100 samples austenitized at the seven different austenitizing temperatures and then tempered to the HRC 59 – 62 hardness range. The height of the lip surrounding the HR30N dents as a function of the % retained austenite is shown in Figure 4. In Figure 4 it is interesting to note that lip height in hardened and tempered ASTM A295 52100 appears to be a linear function of the amount of retained austenite.

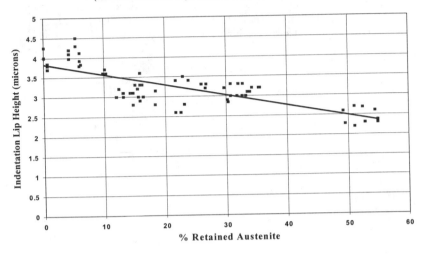

Figure 4 – *Lip height as a function of % retained austenite level.*

Discussion of Results

    The difference in lip size and shape shown in Figures 2 and 3 is due to the characteristics of the steel surrounding the indentation. A hardened bearing steel with a lower austenite content necessarily has a higher volume fraction of martensite. Martensite, being very hard with low ductility, will resist deformation. As the HR30N Brale penetrator (or a debris particle) deforms the steel, the surrounding martensitic structure will resist the lateral deformation. Consequently, the deformed metal that is constrained from flowing outward will flow upward resulting in a higher, narrower lip. As the raised metal lip height around a dent increases, the EHD film over the lip will get thinner. This reduced film thickness will promote shorter bearing life because the surface contact stress concentration at the lip will be elevated relative to the remainder of the raceway. The presence of retained austenite mitigates the damage caused by debris by reducing the lip height around the dent. The EHD film over this damaged area will be thicker and the surface contact stress concentrations less.

    Charts like Figure 4 could be determined for a given steel in a given application where the maximum debris size is known. The austenite content of the steel or the lubrication could be optimized to assure sufficient EHD film coverage over the maximum anticipated dent lip height. The result would be a reduction in the stress concentration at the lip and an increase in the bearing life.

The question then becomes – "How much austenite is enough?" Is it necessary to maximize the retained austenite content in a bearing that is running in a contaminated application?   A better approach is to look at the application and balance the metallurgical properties of microstructure, hardness, and residual stress profile in conjunction with the retained austenite content.   An optimized balance of these properties for a given application will truly maximize life in the bearing. To achieve this optimum balance of metallurgical properties will require a heat treatment that has also been optimized.

Optimized Heat Treatment

The benefits associated with the case carburizing of bearings are well understood in the bearing industry. Carbon and other alloying elements combine with heat-treating to produce the microstructure (tempered martensite, retained austenite and residual carbide). The microstructure determines the mechanical properties that govern how the metal behaves under rolling contact stressing. The high carbon tempered martensite provides the high hardness and strength, fatigue resistance and wear resistance characteristic of carburized steels [8]. The ductility of the carburized case comes from the retained austenite. Residual carbides also contribute to the wear resistance of the case.

A major advantage of the carburizing process is the introduction of compressive residual stresses in the case of carburized components. Increasing amounts of compressive residual stress on the surface and near surface of a bearing are known to increase life [9]. The effect of the compressive residual stress is most profound at the lower stress regime. At higher stresses, the typical residual stress in carburized bearings is overwhelmed by the applied stress and becomes less beneficial. Compressive residual stresses may also be beneficial when there are tensile stresses to be offset, either known as applied (interference fit, etc.) or unknown (micro-stresses) in the system.

One effective carburizing process used for roller bearing applications is the double-quench process. Rehardening provides a beneficial refinement of the grain structure. A finer grained austenite leads to a finer and consequently tougher quenched structure. The resulting microstructure consists of a uniform dispersion of residual carbides in a fined grained martensite. The third component of the microstructure is a level of retained austenite. The control of retained austenite is critical to development of the material's residual stress, hardness, wear resistance and stability characteristics [8]. The double quench process is followed with a refrigeration operation that transforms a portion of the retained austenite to martensite. This further transformation to martensite increases the surface hardness, wear resistance and the near surface residual compressive stress. After tempering, the volume of retained austenite is typically in the 10-20 % range. The surface hardness typically exceeds HRC 60. Near surface residual compressive stresses are in the 175-250 MPa range. This balance of high hardness and retained austenite has historically provided an optimal combination of properties for fatigue life, wear resistance and dimensional stability.

Literature has shown retained austenite levels far in excess of the levels found in the Torrington standard process are favorable for damage tolerant materials. Furumura et al, have shown that an increase in retained austenite content with accompanying reduction in hardness of a case hardened bearing increases the life in a contaminated lubricant [2]. It was also shown that maintaining a high surface hardness in combination with the increased retained austenite content could further increase bearing life. The volume of retained austenite reported was in the 30-35% range.

Heat treating trials were conducted to provide an optimal combination of retained austenite, surface hardness, and compressive residual stress to maximize the damage tolerance of the carburized surface. The goal was to increase the retained austenite content without compromising the surface hardness, wear resistance and near surface residual stress. To accomplish this goal, the standard double quench process was maintained. The retained austenite content was controlled by varying the refrigeration temperature and altering the duration of the final temper. Test coupons made of SAE 3312 material were carburized to an effective case depth of 3.0 mm (a typical case depth for the heavy-bearing product). The carbon profile for the coupons is shown in Figure 5.

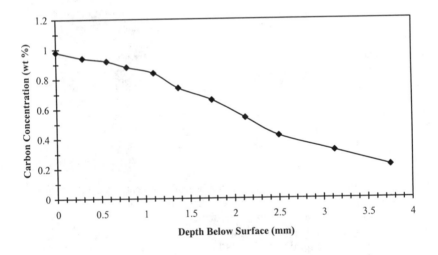

Figure 5 – *Carbon profile of carburized SAE 3312 coupons.*

At the refrigeration process step the coupons were divided into groups. One group did not receive any refrigeration. The remaining groups were refrigerated at -46°C, -60°C and -87°C, respectively. After refrigeration all of the coupons were tempered at the standard tempering temperature.

The case hardness, retained austenite content and residual stress profiles of the coupons refrigerated at the various temperatures are plotted (Figures 6, 7 and 8). The profiles reveal that the retained austenite content decreases as the refrigeration temperature is decreased (more negative). As the retained austenite content decreases, the near surface hardness and the magnitude of the near surface residual compressive stress increases. The microstructures consisted of a uniform dispersion of spheroidal carbides in a fine-grained tempered martensite with varying amounts of retained austenite.

The double-quench cycle with the refrigeration process at -46°C was selected for testing against the standard product. This heat treat cycle provided the optimal balance of retained austenite, near surface hardness and residual compressive stress.

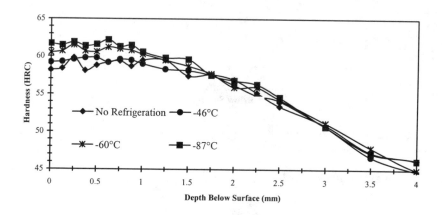

Figure 6 – *Hardness profiles of coupons refrigerated at various temperatures.*

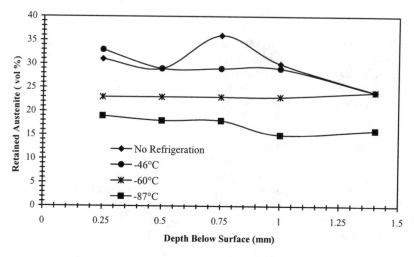

Figure 7 – *Retained austenite profile of coupons refrigerated at various temperatures.*

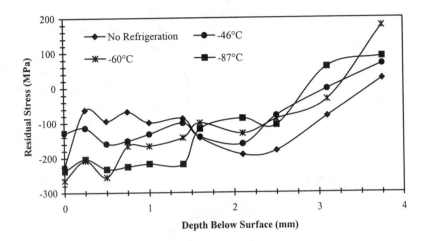

Figure 8 – *Residual stress profile of coupons refrigerated at various temperatures.*

Two Traditional Denting Methodologies

Bearing companies have published several technical papers to describe the test methodologies used to evaluate the damage tolerance of bearings. All test methodologies involve a denting sequence to simulate damage that would be caused by contamination. The denting procedures described can be classified as either a controlled or debris denting procedure.

In a controlled denting procedure, a standard load is applied to a hardened steel tool, such as a Rockwell Brale penetrator, to create a repeatable indentation. The controlled indentation provides a means to control not just size and shape, but also the number and position of the indentations created on the raceway surface. In this procedure, two bodies come in contact. One body retains its shape while the other body deforms plastically. While a controlled indentation is representative of handling damage that may occur prior to bearing installation, the raceway indentations in a typical bearing application are created by three-body contact.

Three-body contact is a feature of the second type of denting procedure, termed debris denting. When a bearing operates in contaminated conditions, foreign debris particles can infiltrate the bearing, working their way into the rolling element and contact ellipse. When a debris particle is trapped in this contact zone, the debris particle is severely deformed while both the rolling element and raceway undergoes mild plastic deformation. The properties of the material's microstructure, the debris particle's characteristics, and the localized contact stress determine the degree of plastic deformation.

A debris denting procedure utilizes three-body contact by introducing a controlled amount of a solid contaminant of a known size, shape and composition to the bearing during operation. A hard ductile particle will deform plastically and create in the raceway a distinct dent with a rounded bottom and a mild ridge of material about its perimeter. The rolling element is dented similarly. A hard brittle particle, such as a ceramic, will shatter in the contact region and embed shards of material into the raceway surface, leaving the raceway with a blasted appearance.

Correlating the Controlled and Debris Denting Methodologies

While technical papers describe the testing that has been performed using either controlled or debris denting techniques, there has been little work done to correlate the results of the two forms of testing. It is expected that a controlled indenting procedure would produce results with more repeatability than the debris denting method, due to the ability to control the size, shape, number, and position of the indentations created on the raceway surface. A debris denting procedure introduces variability into test data, because the size, shape, and number of dents produced in the raceway surface will vary from bearing to bearing. The position of the damage is a very important factor as well, since damage can only cause spalling if it is located under a contact ellipse caused by a loaded rolling element.

Although a controlled indentation procedure is more efficient than a debris denting procedure, a question lingers about the controlled indenting procedure's realism. To answer this question, testing on 35 mm bore radial ball bearings was performed on through hardened ASTM A295 52100 and standard case carburized 3312 steel bearings. The case carburized samples were not though carburized. The test was conducted using both the controlled and debris denting procedures.

First, a debris denting methodology was researched [10] and developed to test the life of radial ball bearings in a simulated debris contaminated environment. A known quantity of VimCru 20 powdered metal particles with size range of 90 – 105 µm and hardness of HRC 68 are mixed with a known quantity of filtered grease. The 35 mm bore ball bearings are packed with this contaminated grease mixture and assembled on a test rig. The bearing is loaded radially and hand rotated to dent the raceways. After the bearings are dented, they are cleaned, disassembled, and inspected. The inspection screens the dented bearing raceways to ensure that all the bearings put on test are dented comparably. While the inspection reduces some of the spread in life testing, it still does not produce the consistency of a controlled indentation procedure. After inspection, the bearings are reassembled and life tested (contact stress = 2.9 GPa, speed = 2500 rpm, lubrication = Mobil DTE Light, temperature = 79.4 °C, lambda = 0.8) in a clean lubricant with a marginal lube film. Failure is defined as the point at which a sizeable spall is created from one of the dents, causing the vibration sensors to shut down the test rig. Bearing life data is now generated for through hardened ASTM A295 52100 and standard case carburized 3312 with debris indentations.

Next, a controlled indenting methodology was developed. Ball bearings are disassembled and a Superficial Hardness Test Machine is used to dent the raceways with a HR30N indentation. The HR30N indentation was chosen in order to create damage large enough to quickly rate the damage tolerance of bearings while still allowing for differentiation between materials. After 16 HR30N indentations are placed in the axial center of the inner ring raceway, the bearing is reassembled. Life testing is conducted under the same load, speed, lubrication, and definition of failure as the debris dented bearings. New baseline bearing lives are generated for through hardened ASTM A295 52100 and standard case carburized 3312 with HR30N indentations. Because the degree of raceway damage for the debris-dented bearings is different than that for the damage created by the controlled indentations, these bearing lives should not be the same. However, both test methods should produce the same failure mechanism: a spall that has initiated from the trailing edge of a raceway dent. Thus, the relative lives of the standard case carburized 3312 as compared to the through-hardened ASTM A295 52100 should be similar for both debris and controlled test procedures.

Life Test Results

Figure 9 shows life test data comparing bearings constructed of through hardened ASTM A295 52100 and standard case carburized 3312. These bearings have been damaged with the debris denting methodology using VimCru20 particles mixed with filtered grease. The Eta, or characteristic life, which is the time at which 63.1% of the bearings will fail, of the standard case carburized 3312 is almost three times greater than that of the through hardened ASTM A295 52100. Standard case carburized 3312 is expected to outperform through hardened ASTM A295 52100 in a situation with a damaged raceway due to the inherent characteristics of a carburized case.

As expected, there is a large spread between each of the materials' data points in Figure 9. Again, this scatter is inherent in the randomness of the debris denting methodology.

Figure 10 shows life test data comparing the same bearings constructed with through hardened ASTM A295 52100 and standard case carburized 3312 steel. These bearings have been damaged with the controlled indenting methodology, using HR30N indentations. The Eta, or characteristic life, of the standard case carburized 3312 is about two times greater than that of the through hardened ASTM A295 52100.

The degree of variation between the controlled denting data points in Figure 10 is much less than that of the debris data shown in Figure 9. This is to be expected due to the consistent type of damage that a controlled indentation creates.

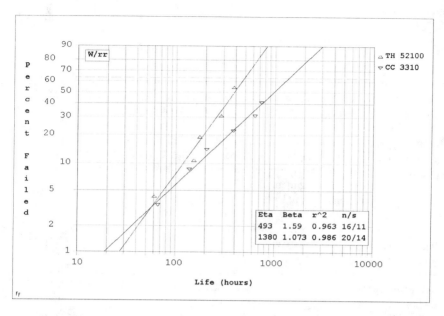

Figure 9 – *Life test of through hardened ASTM A295 52100 and standard case carburized 3312 samples with debris indentations.*

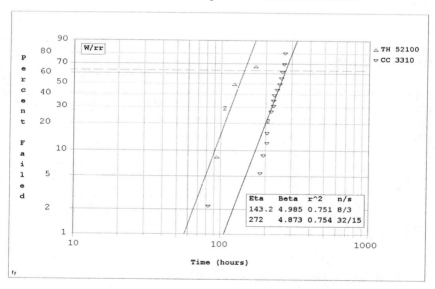

Figure 10 – *Life test of through hardened ASTM A295 52100 and standard case carburized 3312 samples with controlled indentations.*

Conclusions

1. The actual dent lip height can be measured using non-contact surface measuring equipment. This data shows that ASTM A295 52100 hardened and tempered bearing steel with low retained austenite will have higher dent lip heights than the same steel with high retained austenite which will have lower dent lip heights. For a given EHD film thickness higher lip heights will reduce the EHD film thickness over the damaged area.
2. Heat treatments can be successfully created and modified to optimize bearing performance for specific applications, such as damage tolerance or wear resistance.
3. A controlled indenting procedure produces results with more repeatability and less scatter than a debris denting method, due to the ability to control the size, shape, number, and position of the indentations created on the raceway surface.
4. The similarities in the relative lives of standard case carburized 3312 as compared to through-hardened ASTM A295 52100 samples as shown in the test results between the two different denting procedures prove the validity of the controlled denting procedure in determining the damage tolerance of bearings.
5. Standard case carburized 3312 outperformed through hardened ASTM A295 52100 in this test scenario with a damaged raceway, due to the inherent characteristics of a carburized case.

Acknowledgements

The authors wish to thank Mr. Ed Guydan and Dr. Joseph Braza of IR Torrington for permission to present this data. Our long-time mentor, teacher, colleague and friend Philip K. Pearson, FASM, contributed advice and seeded thoughts for this project. Numerous people at IR Torrington have given willingly of their talents and time to help advance this work, most notably Eleanor Arnold, Glenn DiCostanzo, Dave Monat, John Rhodes, Fred Suhy, Julio Susaya, and Harry Walton. Working with them on this project has been the most enjoyable part of the experience.

References:
[1] Lorösch, H-K., "Influence of Load on the Magnitude of the Life Exponent for Rolling Bearings," *Rolling Contact Fatigue Testing of Bearing Steels, ASTM STP 771*, J.J.C. Hoo, Ed., American Society of Testing and Materials, Philadelphia, PA, 1982, pp.275 – 292

[2] Furumura, K., Murakami, Y., and Abe, T., "The Development of Bearing Steels for Long Life Rolling Bearings Under Clean Lubrication and Contaminated Lubrication," *Creative Use of Bearing Steels, ASTM STP 1195*, J.J.C. Hoo, Ed. American Society for Testing and Materials, Philadelphia, PA., 1993 pp. 199 – 210.

[3] Beerbower, M., Shiratani, T., Murakami, Y., and Abe, K., "Fighting Debris: Increasing Life with HTF Bearings for Transmissions," *SAE 940728*, SAE International, Warrendale, PA, 1994.

[4] Nixon, H., Zantopulos, H., and Cogdell, J. D., "A Standardized Method for Evaluating Debris Resistance of Rolling Element Bearings," *SAE 941787*, SAE International, Warrendale, PA, 1994.

[5] Hengerer, F., Brockmüller, U., and Sörström, P.O., "Through-Hardening or Case-Hardening for Tapered Roller Bearings?", *Creative Use of Bearing Steels, ASTM STP 1195*, J. J. C. Hoo, Ed., American Society for Testing and Materials, Philadelphia, PA, 1993, pp. 21 – 33.

[6] Trojahn, W., Streit, E., Chin, H. and Ehlert, D., "Progress in Bearing Performance of Advanced Nitrogen Alloyed Stainless Steel, Cronidur 30," *Bearing Steels into the 21st Century, ASTM STP 1327*, J. J. C. Hoo and W. B. Green, Eds., American Society for Testing and Materials, West Conshohocken, PA, 1998.

[7] Furumura, K., Murakami, Y., and Abe, T., "Case Hardening Medium Carbon Steel for Tough and Long Life Bearing Under Severe Lubrication Conditions," *Bearing Steels into the 21st Century, ASTM STP 1327*, J. J. C. Hoo and W. B. Green, Eds., American Society for Testing and Materials, West Conshohocken, PA, 1998.

[8] Krauss, G. "Microstructure and Performance of Carburized Steel, Part II: Austenite," *Advanced Materials and Processes*, Vol. 7/95, pp 48u-48y.

[9] Schlicht, H., Schreiber, E. and Zwirlein, O., "Effects of Material Properties on Bearing Steel Fatigue Strength," *Effect of Steel Manufacturing Processes on the Quality of Bearing Steels, ASTM STP 987*, J.J.C. Hoo, Ed., American Society for Testing and Materials, Philadelphia, PA, 1988, pp. 81-101.

[10] Nixon, H., Zantopulos, H., and Cogdell, J. D., "Debris Resistance of Rolling-Element Bearings," *Automotive Engineering*, January 1995, pp. 35-40.

Developments in High Alloy Steel for Improved High Temperature and Enhanced Corrosion Resistance Properties

Alojz Kajinic,[1] Robert B. Dixon,[1] and Brian A. Hann[2]

Wear and Corrosion Resistant PM Tool Steels for Advanced Bearing Applications

Reference: Kajinic, A., Dixon, R. B., and Hann, B. A., "**Wear and Corrosion Resistant PM Tool Steels for Advanced Bearing Applications**," *Bearing Steel Technology, ASTM STP 1419*, J. M. Beswick, Ed., American Society for Testing and Materials International, West Conshohocken, PA, 2002.

Abstract: Candidate materials for the hardened steel raceways in ceramic-ball hybrid bearings, as well as steel components for other advanced bearing designs, are being increasingly specified to be capable of attaining combinations of material properties that have not previously been required of traditional bearing steels such as 52100, M50, and 440C. The desired properties may include one or more of the following: greater attainable hardness for higher static load capacity, good hot hardness and material stability at elevated operating temperatures, better adhesive and abrasive wear resistance to minimize galling or raceway damage under contaminated running conditions, good corrosion resistance for bearings which may be exposed to corrosive operating or storage environments, adequate shock loading survivability for potential satellite launching, and of course good fatigue life characteristics.

A number of recent bearing industry publications have discussed some of the properties and laboratory bearing test results for CPM® VIM CRU® 20™[3], which is a cobalt-free high-carbide-volume PM high speed steel with 66 HRC minimum attainable hardness capability and good hot hardness characteristics. Although this material remains one of the leading candidates for the hardened steel raceways in several of the hybrid bearing designs developed to date, it has low chromium content and therefore inadequate corrosion resistance for the operating conditions or storage environments anticipated for other bearing applications.

This paper discusses the potential application of more recently developed high-chromium and high-vanadium PM tool steels for advanced bearing designs where the alloying has been designed to achieve a unique combination of corrosion resistance, high attainable hardness, and exceptional wear resistance.

Keywords: PM, particle metallurgy, tool steel, bearing steel, corrosion resistance, wear resistance, impact toughness, bend fracture strength.

---

1 Research Engineer and President, respectively, Crucible Research Division, 6003 Campbells Run Road, Pittsburgh, PA 15205.
2 Process Engineer, Crucible Compaction Metals Division, 1001 Robb Hill Road, Oakdale, PA 15071.
3 CPM®, VIM CRU®, and 20™ are registered trademarks of the Crucible Materials Corp., Syracuse, NY.

Introduction

A high-carbide-volume bearing-quality particle metallurgy (PM) high speed steel, CPM® VIM CRU® 20™ – in this paper referred to as VIM CRU 20 – is currently the leading candidate for the steel raceways in several advanced hybrid bearing designs. These applications require a combination of high attainable hardness for increased static load capacity and resistance to brinelling, good hot hardness, and high wear resistance to minimize galling or abrasive surface damage due to breakdown of the bearing lubrication under extreme operating conditions [1-3].

VIM CRU 20 is a forged bar product that is produced from vacuum-induction-melted and gas-atomized pre-alloyed powder that has been consolidated by hot-isostatic-pressing (HIP). The material is fully dense and the microstructure consists of very fine and uniformly distributed primary alloy carbides and sulfides, which are characteristics of particle metallurgy (PM) tool steels that facilitate upgrading from conventionally ingot-cast alloy steels for improved performance [4]. Internal processing of VIM CRU 20 is further controlled to minimize the nonmetallic inclusion content for bearing applications, and the finished bar stock is subjected to stringent magnetic particle inspection (MPI) and immersion sonic inspection requirements.

Due to its alloy content, however, VIM CRU 20 does not have the corrosion resistance that may be required for bearing applications either where corrosive attack under severe operating conditions must be anticipated or where there is potential for atmospheric corrosion during extended inventory storage. Conventionally ingot-cast bearing steels such as 440C or BG-42®4 may provide adequate corrosion resistance, but they either have limited attainable hardness characteristics or are deficient in other properties for the intended applications.

Thus, bearing design engineers have expressed the need for the development of new corrosion resistant bearing quality steels that either approach the performance characteristics of VIM CRU 20 for the advanced hybrid bearing designs, or may offer improved performance over existing corrosion resistant bearing steels in other critical bearing applications.

Alloy Design Considerations

Designing through-hardening steels for both high attainable hardness capability and good corrosion resistance creates some unique and conflicting challenges.

The mechanisms by which high hardness is achieved during heat treatment in alloy steels are fairly well understood. Those steels which are capable of attaining the highest hardness (>65 HRC), and maintaining this hardness when exposed to moderate operating temperatures, are the high speed steels such as VIM CRU 20. These steels typically have high carbon content, may or may not contain cobalt for increased hot hardness, and are highly alloyed with strong carbide forming elements such as tungsten, molybdenum, and vanadium which combine stoichiometrically with the available carbon to form wear resistant primary carbides during solidification from the melt. During heat treatment,

---

4 BG-42® is a registered trademark of Timken Latrobe Steel Company, Latrobe, P.A.

these alloy carbides partially dissolve to provide a strong precipitation (or secondary) hardening contribution to the final hardness after multiple tempering at elevated temperatures, e.g., >1000°F (538°C). Standard bearing steels, such as 52100 and M50, are not sufficiently alloyed to develop as strong a secondary hardening response during heat treatment, and consequently their attainable hardness is limited to about 61-63 HRC and 62-64 HRC, respectively.

For good corrosion resistance, it is generally accepted that a through-hardening steel must contain at least 10-11 % "free" chromium in the martensitic matrix after heat treatment. To achieve this matrix chromium where high carbon must also be present for heat treat response, however, the steel must contain excess chromium due to the fact that chromium is a strong carbide former. Some chromium-containing carbides form at very high temperatures during solidification from the melt, and are relatively insoluble at the austenitizing temperatures used for heat treatment. Similar to the high speed steels discussed earlier, the main function of these "primary" carbides is to provide wear resistance. Other chromium-rich carbides form in the solid state at lower temperatures during process annealing, and are completely soluble during heat treatment. It is the latter carbides which mainly provide the matrix chromium necessary for corrosion resistance, as well as a significant percentage of the carbon required for hardening. This is the basis for the alloying found in martensitic stainless steels such as 440C bearing steel. It also explains why steels such as M50 and VIM CRU 20, which contain no more than about 4-5 % chromium for good air hardenability in large cross-sections, are not corrosion resistant.

Unfortunately, alloying with high chromium for corrosion resistance generally limits the attainable hardness capability and may cause other heat treating problems. As outlined in the previous section, there is a limit to how much carbon can be added to a high chromium steel for heat treat response without forming excess chromium-rich primary carbides that would reduce the matrix chromium available for corrosion resistance. There is also a limit to how much carbon and chromium can be dissolved at the austenitizing temperature during heat treatment without forming excessive amounts of retained austenite during hardening, which would lower the as-quenched hardness and may remain stable to relatively high tempering temperatures. Where low temperature tempering (<500°F or 260°C) must be employed for optimum corrosion resistance, the final hardness will be no higher than the as-quenched hardness, and usually slightly lower. Sub-zero freezing treatments may be employed to transform the softer austenite to the harder martensite structure. However, elevated temperature tempering (>950°F or 510°C) may still be required to develop additional precipitation (secondary) hardening response to meet the attainable hardness objectives. These are the main reasons why it is not possible to simply add high chromium to existing high alloy tool steel compositions such as VIM CRU 20. And in the case of high carbon steels that are alloyed primarily with chromium, elevated temperature tempering may also deplete the effective matrix chromium to unacceptable levels for adequate corrosion resistance due to sub-microscopic precipitation of chromium carbides.

An alternative approach is to use additional alloying with elements such as tungsten (W), molybdenum (Mo), and vanadium (V) not only to form wear-resistant primary carbides in the microstructure, but also to produce a stronger precipitation or secondary hardening response during heat treatment than can be achieved through alloying with chromium alone. If this alloying is controlled properly, it is possible to minimize both the formation of chromium-rich primary carbides during solidification from the melt as well as precipitation of chromium from the matrix during heat treatment. However, there is still a limit to how much additional hardening response can be realized in these high chromium compositions without jeopardizing the corrosion resistance objective, as will be discussed below.

Candidate Materials for Wear and Corrosion Resistant Bearing Applications

Composition, Primary Carbide Volumes, and Attainable Hardness Characteristics

Table 1 lists the nominal compositions, primary carbide volumes, and attainable hardness capabilities for conventional 440C and BG-42® bearing steels as well as for two high-vanadium PM tool steels, CPM® VIM CRU® 80™ and CPM® VIM CRU® 60™, which are considered to be prime candidates for high performance corrosion resistant bearing applications. The latter materials – in this paper referred to as VIM CRU 80 and VIM CRU 60, respectively – were initially developed by Crucible to address the abrasive and corrosive wear frequently encountered simultaneously in tooling applications such as the machine components used for the compounding (mixing) and injection molding of engineering plastics [4, 5].

Table 1 - *Wear and corrosion resistant steels for bearing applications.*

Material	C	Cr	Mo	V	Primary Carbide Vol (%)	Attainable Hardness (±1 HRC)
440C	1.05	17	0.5	---	13.5	59
BG-42	1.15	14.5	4	1.2	16	63
VIM CRU 80	2.35	14	1	9	23	62
VIM CRU 60	3.25	14	2.5	12	28	64

(composition in weight percent)

The relative compressive yield strength[5] capability or brinelling resistance of the steels listed can be predicted from the attainable hardness capabilities provided that excessive amounts of retained austenite are not present in the heat-treated microstructures. The hardness capability shown for 440C is that obtained when the material is given a standard heat treatment to optimize the hardness and corrosion resistance, i.e., 1900°F (1038°C) austenitizing, oil quenching, and 400°F (204°C)

---

5 Compressive yield strength is the stress which causes a material to exhibit a specified deformation. It is determined from the stress-strain diagram obtained in a compression test, and is expressed in force per unit area (for more details see ASTM E 9).

tempering. The hardness capabilities shown for the other three materials are for hardening in the range 2050-2150°F (1121-1177°C) and multiple tempering at about 975°F (524°C) to achieve the maximum secondary heat treat response afforded by the alloying. BG-42® has lower total chromium content than 440C, and derives its secondary hardening response primarily from the increased molybdenum content and to a lesser extent from the vanadium addition. The two PM steels contain nearly the same total chromium as BG-42®, molybdenum contents in between that of 440C and BG-42®, and vanadium contents substantially greater than either conventionally produced alloy. The relatively good attainable hardness numbers shown for the two PM alloys are due to a combination of the secondary hardening response provided by the vanadium and molybdenum additions and the substantially increased primary carbide volumes as will be illustrated below.

LOM and SEM Analysis of the Heat-Treated Microstructures

Figure 1 shows the primary carbide distributions that are observed in the heat-treated microstructures of these materials when viewed at approximately 500x magnification using light optical microscopy (LOM). These structures are representative of longitudinally oriented cross-sections of about 2 in (50 mm) diameter forged bar stock.

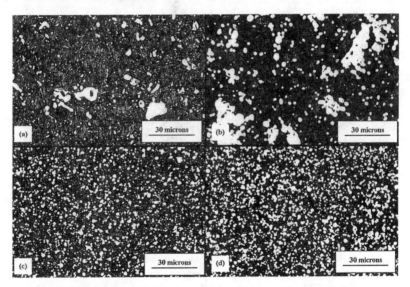

Figure 1 – *LOM photomicrographs of heat-treated microstructures:*
(a) 440C, (b) BG-42®, (c) VIM CRU 80, and (d) VIM CRU 60.

In the conventionally ingot-cast materials, the primary carbides (white particles) are typically non-uniformly distributed and vary in both size and morphology; these effects are a direct result of the slow solidification and alloy segregation (banding) that occur in the original ingot. In contrast, the primary carbides observed in the rapidly solidified and

HIP consolidated PM materials are uniformly distributed, much finer in size, and essentially spherical in shape. The significant increases in the total volume fraction of carbides in the two PM materials can be clearly seen in the photographs.

Figure 2 shows the primary carbide distributions observed in these same heat-treated samples when examined at higher magnifications in a scanning electron microscope (SEM). Using backscattered electron imaging and EDS chemical analysis of the individual carbides, it is possible to distinguish the primary carbide types by their relative gray shading and to determine their approximate stoichiometric compositions.

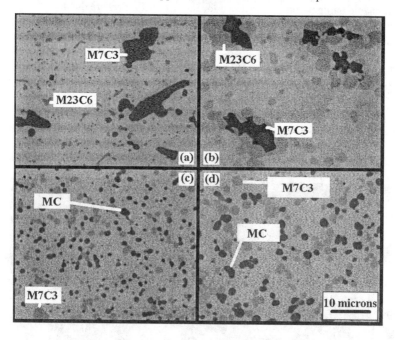

Figure 2 – *SEM backscattered electron images for: (a) 440C, (b) BG-42®, (c) VIM CRU 80, and (d) VIM CRU 60. The 10 μm scale bar applies to all the images.*

In the case of 440C and BG-42®, there are two types of primary carbides present – $M_{23}C_6$ (lighter gray) and M_7C_3 (darker gray). The approximate metallic contents of these two primary carbide types, based on EDS analysis, vary as shown in Table 2. The $M_{23}C_6$ and M_7C_3 carbides in 440C consist almost entirely of chromium and iron. In BG-42®, these same primary carbide types are not only high in chromium and iron, but also contain significant percentages of molybdenum and vanadium. Due to the banded (segregated) nature of the latter microstructures, it is difficult to make a precise determination of the relative amounts of each carbide present in the bulk material using the SEM due to the significant number of fields that would have to be analyzed at the magnifications required to distinguish between the carbide types. However, the majority of the carbides appear to be $M_{23}C_6$ for both steels, with the M_7C_3 carbides being more concentrated in the banded areas.

Table 2 – *Semi-quantitative EDS analysis of primary carbide types.*

Material	Carbide Type	Cr	Fe	Mo	V
440C	$M_{23}C_6$	49	50	<1	–
	M_7C_3	71	29	<1	–
BG-42	$M_{23}C_6$	43	43	10	4
	M_7C_3	54	29	8	9
VIM CRU 80	M_7C_3	50	29	2	19
	MC	10	12	3	75
VIM CRU 60	M_7C_3	48	28	5	19
	MC	9	8	10	73

(composition in weight percent)

There are also two primary carbide types present in the VIM CRU 80 and VIM CRU 60 materials - M_7C_3 (in this case, lighter gray) and MC (darker gray). The semi-quantitative EDS analyses of the metallic contents of these carbides are shown in Table 2. The M_7C_3 carbides in these high-vanadium steels are chromium-rich with high concentrations of iron and vanadium. The MC carbides are vanadium-rich with significantly lesser concentrations of chromium and iron. The MC carbides in VIM CRU 60 also contain a higher concentration of molybdenum, which is a direct reflection of the initial alloying. In contrast to the conventionally ingot-cast steels, the uniformity of the carbide distributions in the PM materials does permit the use of image analysis to estimate more precisely the relative amounts of each carbide type present. In both PM steels, approximately 45 % of the primary carbides are the MC type. The average size of the primary carbides in the higher alloyed VIM CRU 60 is somewhat larger than that of the lower alloyed VIM CRU 80, but both materials have considerably smaller carbide size than the conventionally ingot-cast bearing steels.

SEM-EDS analysis was also used to determine the approximate matrix composition for each material after heat treatment, which is an important indicator of the relative corrosion resistance that can be expected. This is done by selectively analyzing the areas in between the primary carbides, being careful to discard X-ray spectra with peaks for the individual elements that may indicate a primary carbide immediately below the surface being analyzed. These results are shown in Table 3, where it can be seen that all four steels have matrix chromiums of about 11-12 %, and similar silicon contents. There are significant differences in the matrix analyses for molybdenum and vanadium, which for the most part coincide with the differences in starting alloy content. It should be noted, however, that such an analysis cannot detect the matrix chromium (or other alloy) depletion that occurs during precipitation of sub-microscopic chromium-rich carbides when these materials are tempered at elevated temperatures. It was also not, of course, possible to determine the content of lighter elements such as carbon or nitrogen with the applied EDS method.

Table 3 – *Semi-quantitative EDS analysis of the matrix compositions.*

Material	Cr	Si	Mo	V
440C	12	0.4	0.1	–
BG-42	11	0.3	2.8	0.7
VIM CRU 80	12	0.4	0.8	2.6
VIM CRU 60	12	0.5	1.4	2.6

(composition in weight percent)

Corrosion Testing

The results of corrosion testing in dilute aqua regia and boiling acetic acid are shown in Table 4. The corrosion testing was conducted according to ASTM G 31.

Table 4 – *Corrosion resistance.*

Material	Austenitizing Temp °F (°C)	Tempering Temp °F (°C)	Hardness (HRC)	Dilute Aqua-Regia (mm/yr.)+	10% Boiling Acetic Acid (mm/yr.)++
440C	1900 (1040)	400 (204)	58	109	29
BG-42	2050 (1121)	975 (524)	63	733	290
VIM CRU 80	2050 (1121)	500 (260)	58	117	17
	2150 (1177)	500 (260)	59	102	9
	2150 (1177)	975 (524)	62	249	–
VIM CRU 60	2100 (1149)	500 (260)	61	111	57
	2100 (1149)	1000 (538)	62.5	355	141
	2150 (1177)	975 (524)	64	345	–
M50	2050 (1121)	1025 (552)	62	566	274
VIM CRU 20	2175 (1190)	1050 (566)	66	513	250

(+)   3 hours at 24°C in aqueous solution containing 5 vol. % HNO_3 and 1 vol. % HCl.
(++) 24 hours in a boiling aqueous solution containing 10 vol. % acetic acid.

When double tempered at 500°F (260°C), both VIM CRU 80 and VIM CRU 60 exhibit corrosion resistance characteristics comparable to that of 440C hardened from 1900°F (1038°C) and double tempered at 400°F (204°C). Tempering VIM CRU 60 at 1000°F (538°C) reduces the corrosion resistance compared to 500°F (260°C) tempering, but the corrosion rates are still significantly better than those obtained on M50 and VIM CRU 20.

The corrosion test results for BG-42® heat treated to obtain maximum secondary hardening response were surprisingly low compared to the results for VIM CRU 60 tempered at 1000°F (538°C), and at best comparable to the results obtained for non-corrosion resistant M50 and VIM CRU 20. We can only speculate that elevated temperature tempering may have depleted more matrix chromium in BG-42® than in VIM CRU 60, and that the slightly lower starting matrix chromium may have contributed to the problem. VIM CRU 80 is expected to exhibit corrosion test results comparable to those of VIM CRU 60 when heat treated to obtain maximum secondary hardening.

Wear Resistance

The relative wear resistance of high alloy martensitic steels under adhesive and mildly abrasive wear conditions is generally a function of the heat treated hardness, the total primary carbide volume, and the primary carbide type. Other factors that could influence wear resistance would include excessive retained austenite levels, which would lower the matrix hardness, and large carbide size, which could be beneficial for wear resistance under severely abrading conditions. More subtle factors, which may not be evident in simple laboratory wear testing, are the uniformity of the primary carbide distribution and the ability to achieve fine surface finishes. The latter are believed to be particularly important for quiet running bearings, and may also influence the service life in other critical bearing applications.

Comparing the two conventionally ingot-cast steels, BG-42® would be expected to exhibit better wear life characteristics than 440C because of the combined effects of its higher attainable hardness and somewhat greater total carbide volume. The increased molybdenum and vanadium contents of the M_7C_3 and $M_{23}C_6$ primary carbides in BG-42® may also increase their hardness and wear resistance.

VIM CRU 80 and VIM CRU 60 contain significantly greater total carbide volumes than either 440C or BG-42®. Furthermore, about half of the carbides that form in the two PM steels are vanadium-rich MC, which are significantly harder and therefore more wear-resistant than the chromium and iron-rich M_7C_3 or $M_{23}C_6$ types. However, these effects could be offset under abrasive wear conditions by the larger carbide size that is characteristic of the conventionally ingot-cast materials.

These wear resistance expectations are confirmed by the laboratory crossed-cylinder and pin-abrasion wear test data shown in Table 5. The crossed-cylinder wear test involves rotating a tungsten carbide rod against a hardened test piece and measuring the wear volume that develops on the contact surface of the test piece over time. A wear test number is calculated based on the load, sliding distance, and the measured wear volume; a larger number denotes better wear resistance. In the pin-abrasion wear test, a hardened test piece is traversed across an abrasive paper (in this case, 150 mesh Garnet paper), and the weight loss of the sample is recorded; a lower weight loss denotes better wear resistance. When tested at comparable hardness, VIM CRU 80 exhibits significantly better wear resistance than 440C in both tests, and somewhat better pin abrasion wear resistance than BG-42® at a slightly lower test hardness. The relatively good pin-abrasion test results for BG-42® can be attributed to its increased primary carbide volume compared to 440C, and its large carbide size compared to the PM materials. However, we would expect VIM CRU 80 to test significantly better than BG-42® under adhesive or less abrasive conditions, where the total and MC carbide volumes are expected to be much more influential. VIM CRU 60 exhibits better pin-abrasion wear test results than either VIM CRU 80 or BG-42® at comparable test hardness, and significantly better crossed-cylinder wear test results than VIM CRU 80. This is a direct result of the increased volume percent of primary carbides, including the vanadium-rich MC types. In all cases, test hardness affects the wear test results as would be expected.

Table 5 – *Wear resistance.*

Material	Austenitizing Temp °F (°C)	Tempering Temp °F (°C)	Hardness (HRC)	Crossed Cylind. Wear Test No*	Pin Abrasion Wt Loss (mg)**
440C	1900 (1040)	400 (204)	58	4	66
BG-42	2050 (1121)	975 (524)	63	–	41
VIM CRU 80	2050 (1121)	500 (260)	58	10	58
	2150 (1177)	500 (260)	59	12	51
	2150 (1177)	975 (524)	62	–	37
VIM CRU 60	2100 (1149)	500 (260)	61	39	31
	2100 (1149)	1000 (538)	62.5	51	27
	2150 (1177)	975 (524)	64	–	22

*High wear test number is better (for more details see ASTM G 83).
**Low weight loss is better (for more details see ASTM 132).

Impact Toughness and Bend Fracture Strength (BFS)[6]

Increasing the total alloy content and primary carbide volume generally decreases the impact toughness of martensitic steels, and may also negatively affect the bend fracture strength (BFS) properties. These effects can be offset by producing the materials in PM form, where the very uniform and fine carbide distributions enable significantly increased alloying with less detriment to the impact and strength characteristics, as illustrated in Table 6.

The C-notch impact and BFS values for BG-42® at 63 HRC are significantly lower than those for 440C at 58 HRC as might be expected due to differences in both the test hardness and the primary carbide volumes. However, the data available for VIM CRU 80 indicate that it has significantly better impact toughness and BFS properties than BG-42® at a comparable test hardness despite having about 50 % more primary carbide volume. Also note that the transverse BFS measured for a 6.5 in (165 mm) diameter bar of VIM CRU 80 is significantly greater than the transverse BFS measured for a 2 in (50 mm)

6 BFS tests are widely used as a method of determining the ultimate tensile strength of tool steels in the hardened condition.

diameter bar of BG-42®. The relatively high transverse test results are consistent with similar results previously obtained for VIM CRU 20 compared to M50 bearing steel, and can be directly attributed to the absence of alloy segregation (banding) in the forged PM microstructures. These results also suggest that the higher alloyed VIM CRU 80 may be safely considered as an upgrade for 440C in critical bearing applications.

Table 6 – *C-notch impact toughness and bend fracture strength (BFS).*

Material	Carbide Volume %	Hardness (HRC)	C-Notch - ft-lbs (J)		BFS ksi (MPa)	
			Long.	Trans.	Long.	Trans.
440C	13.5	58	33 (45)	–	580 (3999)	–
BG-42	16	63	11 (15)	–	507 (3496)	209 (1441)
VIM CRU 80	23	61	–	–	630 (4344)	627 (4323)
		62	19 (26)	–	630 (4344)	–

- 440C and BG-42 test samples cut from 1.25-2 in (32-50 mm) diameter bars
- VIM CRU 80 test samples cut from 6.5 in (165 mm) diameter bar

VIM CRU 60 is also expected to have reasonably good impact toughness and BFS values for its alloy content, but somewhat lower than those for VIM CRU 80 due to its significantly increased primary carbide volume. However, these properties are expected to be at least comparable to those of VIM CRU 20, which is typically applied at higher hardness.

Heat Treatment and Other Manufacturing Considerations

VIM CRU 80 and VIM CRU 60 are designed to have good heat treat response in cross-sections up to 2-4 in (50-100 mm) thickness. To achieve maximum secondary hardening, the materials should be hardened from 2100-2150°F (1149-1177°C) and multiple tempered in the range 975-1000°F (524-538°C). Rapid quenching from the selected austenitizing temperature is required to minimize re-precipitation of the dissolved alloy carbides and to prevent formation of non-martensitic transformation products. For vacuum heat treating, a minimum of 6-bar pressure should be specified for gas quenching to ensure that the effective cooling rate from the austenitizing temperature to below about 1000°F (538°C) is at least comparable to that achieved for forced air-cooling of 1-2 in (25-50 mm) diameter bars, i.e., a minimum of about 200°F (111°C) per minute. Sub-zero freezing or cryogenic treating may be incorporated into the heat treatment to reduce the retained austenite and improve the heat treat response when low temperature tempering is specified for optimum corrosion resistance. However, such treatments should not be necessary for the elevated temperature tempering that is required to develop maximum secondary hardening response.

VIM CRU 80 and VIM CRU 60 may be significantly more difficult to machine than either 440C or BG-42® due to their relatively high annealed hardness (about 28 HRC and 32 HRC, respectively) and their large primary carbide volumes (particularly the MC type). However, the grindability after heat treatment should be acceptable due to the inherently fine primary carbide size resulting from PM processing. VIM CRU 80 and VIM CRU 60 should also be capable of developing very fine surface finishes during polishing or when using other super-finishing techniques. However, due to the very high wear resistance of these materials, care must be exercised to obtain as fine a starting surface finish as possible during the preliminary machining or grinding operations. Both materials should also readily wire EDM[7], providing that they are adequately stress-relieved during heat treatment.

VIM CRU 80 can be readily produced in forged bar sizes down to about 0.500 in (12.5 mm) diameter. The higher alloyed VIM CRU 60 is more difficult to hot work, but has also been successfully produced in finished bar sizes down to about 2 in (50 mm) diameter.

Summary

Two high-vanadium and high-chromium PM tool steels – initially developed to address the abrasive and corrosive wear encountered in some tooling applications – are considered to be prime candidates for high performance corrosion resistant bearing applications. One of the materials, designated VIM CRU 80 in this paper, is capable of attaining 61-63 HRC where it should have significant corrosion resistance and mechanical property advantages over BG-42® heat treated to the same hardness level. It should also be considered as an upgrade for 440C in existing bearing applications, where it can either be tempered in the range 500-750°F (260-399°C) and applied at 58-60 HRC for comparable corrosion resistance, or tempered at 975-1000°F (524-538°C) to achieve maximum secondary hardening response with minimal sacrifice in the corrosion resistance. The second material, designated VIM CRU 60 in this paper, is capable of attaining 63-65 HRC and has significantly increased primary carbide volume for enhanced wear resistance. For these reasons, it should be considered for the advanced hybrid bearing designs where high attainable hardness is a prerequisite for load carrying capacity.

Both PM materials are produced using the same internal processing and final inspection criteria that are currently applied to bearing-quality VIM CRU 20, which is a leading candidate for the raceways in advanced hybrid bearing designs where corrosion is not an issue. However, fatigue and fracture toughness testing will be required to qualify these materials for advanced bearing designs.

Acknowledgments

The authors would like to recognize James E. McCalla, Maria K. Sawford, and William Stasko of the Crucible Research Division for their support in preparing this paper.

---

7 Wire EDM (Electrical Discharge Machining) is a method to cut conductive materials with a thin electrode. The method uses sparks of electrical energy to progressively erode the material, which is placed in a dielectric fluid to prevent premature spark discharge.

References

[1]   Pearson, P.K., Moll, J.H., Hannigan, C.J., and Atwell, D.R., "Evaluation of P/M Tool Steels for Bearing Applications," *Advances in Powder Metallurgy and Particulate Materials - 1994, Volume 5*, Metal Powder Industries Federation, Princeton, NJ, 1994, pp. 155-163.

[2]   Smith, D. W., Leveille, A.R., Hilton, M.R., and Ward, P.C., "Rex 20 / Si_3N_4 Control Moment Gyroscope Bearing Development," 32nd Aerospace Mechanisms Symposium, 13-15 May, 1998.

[3]   Hilton, M.R, Ward, P.C., Leveille, A.R., Park, W., McClintock, D.A., and Smith, D.W., "Rolling Contact Fatigue and Load Capacity Tests of M62 Bearing Steel," 32nd Aerospace Mechanisms Symposium, 13-15 May, 1998.

[4]   Dixon, R.B., Stasko, W., and Pinnow, K.E., "Particle Metallurgy Tool Steels," *ASM Handbook, Volume 7, Powder Metal Technologies and Applications*, ASM International, Materials Park, OH, 1998, pp. 786-802.

[5]   Stasko, W., Pinnow, K.E., and Eisen, W.B., "Development of Improved PM Wear and Corrosion Resistant Tool Steels," *4th International Tooling Conference*, Bochum, Germany, 1996.

Mark A. Ragen,[1] Donald L. Anthony,[1] and Ronald F. Spitzer[1]

A Comparison of the Mechanical and Physical Properties of Contemporary and New Alloys for Aerospace Bearing Applications

---

Reference: Ragen, M. A., Anthony, D. L., and Spitzer, R. F., "A Comparison of the Mechanical and Physical Properties of Contemporary and New Alloys for Aerospace Bearing Applications," *Bearing Steel Technology, ASTM STP 1419*, J. M. Beswick, Ed., American Society for Testing and Materials International, West Conshohocken, PA, 2002.

Abstract: This paper presents the results of several contributing sources in establishing the mechanical and physical properties of various new candidate alloys for aerospace bearing applications. The alloys evaluated included the high Nitrogen steels Cronidur 30 and XD15NW, the carburizing stainless steels Pyrowear 675 and CSS-42L, and the nitrided steel 32CDV13. The properties evaluated included hot hardness, recovery hardness, fracture toughness, corrosion resistance, abrasive wear resistance, and structural (rotating beam) fatigue strength. Elemental testing was performed independently of the material suppliers to evaluate these properties for the candidate alloys.

This paper is not intended to promote any one alloy as the best solution to all bearing needs, but rather to provide a data base to assist in the selection of the optimum solution to a specific bearing application. The test results obtained confirmed that each candidate material has unique strengths and weaknesses. For example, Cronidur 30 and XD15NW demonstrated very good corrosion resistance, but do not have good fracture toughness or wear resistance. Conversely, Pyrowear 675 and CSS-42L have very good fracture toughness, but are more susceptible to corrosion problems. The 32CDV13 nitrided steel also had very good fracture toughness and relatively good wear resistance, but demonstrated poor corrosion resistance.

Keywords: hot hardness, recovery hardness, fracture toughness, corrosion resistance, abrasive wear resistance, fatigue strength, Cronidur 30, XD15NW, Pyrowear 675, CSS-42L, 32CDV13

---

[1]Senior Engineering Scientist, Director of Engineering, and Manager of Product Development and Testing, respectively, MRC Bearings, A Unit of SKF USA, 402 Chandler Street, Jamestown, New York, 14701, USA.

Introduction

A variety of new alloys, which offer the potential to be used in aerospace bearing applications, have been introduced in recent years. Before these alloys can be properly utilized in bearing designs, it is essential that reliable mechanical and physical property data be obtained for them. An internally funded research program was undertaken at MRC Bearings starting in 1997 that was aimed at providing the required data by performing a variety of elemental and bearing rig tests. In this program, five (5) of the alloys considered the most promising were selected for evaluation. The alloys selected included CSS-42L (Latrobe Steel), Pyrowear 675 (Carpenter Technologies), 32CDV13 (Aubert & Duval), Cronidur 30 (VSG), and XD15NW (Aubert & Duval).

The properties evaluated for the selected alloys included hot hardness, recovery hardness, fracture toughness, corrosion resistance, abrasive wear resistance, and structural (rotating beam) fatigue strength. The elemental testing, which was used to establish these key mechanical / physical properties, was performed independently of the material suppliers. This paper presents the results obtained to date for the selected alloys. The RCF (rolling contact fatigue) performance testing of these alloys using 6309 test bearings is in progress and will be reported on at a later date.

Discussion of Alloys Evaluated

The alloys selected for evaluation in this program can be grouped into three (3) different categories. Pyrowear 675 [1, 2] and CSS-42L [3, 4] are carburizing grades of stainless steel. Cronidur 30 [5, 6, 7] and XD15NW [8] are high Nitrogen, through-hardened stainless steels. 32CDV13 [8] is a nitrided steel with relatively low (3.1%) Chromium content. Table 1 identifies the nominal chemical composition of the alloys tested. The chemical composition of the more traditional bearing alloys M50 and M50 NiL are included in Table 1 for reference. Also included in Table 1 is the melt method used to produce the alloys. VIMVAR indicates vacuum induction melting - vacuum arc remelting. PESR indicates pressurized electroslag remelting, and ESR indicates electroslag remelting.

Table 1 - *Chemical composition of alloys.*

Alloys	Melt Method	Elemental Composition (%)						
		C	N	Cr	Mo	V	Ni	Co
M50	VIMVAR	0.83	...	4.20	4.25	1.00	...	...
M50 NiL	VIMVAR	0.13	...	4.10	4.40	1.15	3.40	...
Cronidur 30	PESR	0.33	0.33	15.5	1.00	...	...	...
32CDV13	VIMVAR	0.33	...	3.10	1.00	0.25	0.30	...
Pyrowear 675	VIMVAR	0.07	...	13.0	2.00	0.60	2.50	5.50
CSS-42L	VIMVAR	0.15	...	14.0	4.75	0.60	2.00	12.5
XD15NW	ESR	0.38	0.20	15.0	1.60	0.30	...	...

Two variants of Pyrowear 675, reflecting different tempering temperatures, were evaluated throughout this program. The first variant, designated P1, was tempered at

315°C (600°F) for maximum corrosion resistance. The second variant, designated P2, was tempered at 496°C (925°F) to develop maximum hot hardness capability.

For the carburized materials (M50 NiL, CSS-42L, and Pyrowear 675) and the nitrided material (32CDV13), it is important to identify whether the specimens tested were representative of core or case properties. Of the tests reported in this paper, only the fracture toughness and structural fatigue tests were reflective of core properties. The remaining tests (hot hardness, recovery hardness, corrosion resistance, and abrasive wear) were reflective of case properties.

Hot Hardness Test Results

The hardness values for the candidate alloys were evaluated at Crucible Research in Pittsburgh, Pa., for temperatures ranging from room temperature to 371°C (700°F). The hardness values of all the alloys were evaluated at 149°C (300°F), 204°C (400°F), 260°C (500°F), 315°C (600°F), and 371°C (700°F). For CSS-42L, the hardness values were also measured at 52°C (125°F), and 93°C (200°F) to define better the shape of the hardness curve in the range from room temperature to149°C (300°F). Figure 1 displays the hardness values measured for the alloys as a function of temperature. For reference, HRC 58 is commonly accepted in the aerospace bearing community as the minimum threshold hardness considered necessary to provide resistance to plastic deformation and load carrying capacity.

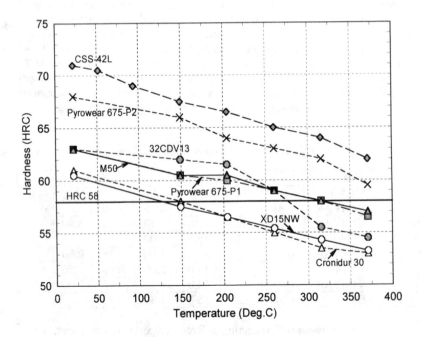

Figure 1 - *Hardness of alloys as a function of temperature.*

As shown in Figure 1, Cronidur 30 and XD15NW had the lowest hardness values of the alloys tested for the full temperature range examined. At approximately 150°C (300°F), the hardness of these alloys dropped to HRC 58. The highest hardness values were measured for CSS-42L, which had a hardness of HRC 71 at room temperature and HRC 62 at 371°C (700°F). The 496°C (925°F) temper (P2) version of Pyrowear 675 was the second hardest of the alloys tested, with a hardness of HRC 68 at room temperature and HRC 59.5 at 371°C (700°F). The hardness values of M50, the 315°C (600°F) temper (P1) version of Pyrowear 675, and 32CDV13 are similar up to 260°C (500°F). At temperatures above 260°C (500°F), the hardness of 32CDV13 drops off more quickly than the other two alloys.

Recovery Hardness Test Results

Recovery hardness is an attribute considered important for candidate bearing materials subjected to temperature excursions such as during soak back conditions. The objective of this test was to evaluate the ability of the alloys to retain their hardness during thermal cycling. The recovery hardness testing was performed at the MRC Bearings Jamestown plant for the candidate alloys and M50. The hardness of each alloy was measured after repeated exposure to three (3) different temperature levels: 204°C (400°F), 204°C (400°F), and 315°C (600°F). Two (2) specimens of each alloy were tested for each of the three (3) temperature levels.

The temperature cycle used consisted of heating the specimens from room temperature to the selected temperature level, holding there for one (1) hour, then cooling back to room temperature and holding there for one (1) hour. For each temperature level, the temperature cycle was repeated twenty-five (25) times. The hardness of each test specimen was measured at room temperature after the first, fifth, tenth, and twenty-fifth cycles. Table 2 summarizes the measurements recorded during the recovery hardness testing.

Table 2 - *Recovery hardness (HRC) measurements for alloys.*

Alloy	Pre-Test	204°C (400°F) Test				260°C (500°F) Test				315°C (600°F) Test			
		1 cyc.	5 cyc.	10 cyc.	25 cyc.	1 cyc.	5 cyc.	10 cyc.	25 cyc.	1 cyc.	5 cyc.	10 cyc.	25 cyc.
M50	60.0	60.5	60.5	61.5	61.0	60.5	60.0	60.5	61.0	60.0	60.0	60.0	60.0
Cronidur 30	60.5	61.0	61.0	61.5	60.0	60.5	61.0	60.0	60.0	61.0	61.0	60.5	60.0
XD15NW	60.5	60.5	60.5	61.5	61.0	60.5	60.5	61.0	61.0	61.0	60.5	61.0	61.5
Pyrowear 675 (315°C)	63.0	62.5	62.5	63.0	62.0	62.5	63.5	62.0	62.0	62.5	63.5	62.0	62.0
32CDV13	66.0	66.5	66.0	66.5	67.0	66.5	66.5	66.5	66.5	66.0	66.0	66.5	66.5
Pyrowear 675 (496°C)	67.0	66.0	66.0	67.0	65.5	67.0	67.0	65.5	65.5	67.0	67.0	65.5	65.5
CSS-42L	70.0	69.0	70.0	70.0	69.0	69.5	70.0	69.0	69.5	70.0	69.0	68.5	68.5

None of the alloys tested showed any appreciable loss of hardness, even after twenty-five (25) cycles at the highest temperature level. The small changes in measured hardness observed in Table 1 are considered to be within normal hardness measurement variability.

Fracture Toughness Test Results

Fracture toughness is the ability of a material to resist fracture in the presence of a crack or defect when subjected to a tensile stress field. It is a key property for the inner rings of high speed bearings because the tensile hoop stress due to rotational centrifugal force adds to the tensile hoop stress present due to the shaft press fit. Bearing ring fracture, which is a catastrophic failure mode, can then occur if the material has insufficient fracture toughness. The fracture toughness of a material is generally evaluated by determining the value of K_{1C}, the plane strain critical stress intensity factor. The value of K_{1C} is obtained by testing notched specimens that have been pre-cracked in fatigue by loading in tension or three-point bending.

The fracture toughness strength of the candidate alloys was evaluated by performing three (3) L-T and three (3) T-L fracture toughness tests for each. The fracture toughness testing was performed at Westmoreland Mechanical Testing and Research (WMTR) in Youngstown, Pa. The tests were performed at room temperature and conformed to the "Standard Test Method for Plane-Strain Fracture Toughness of Metallic Materials" (ASTM E399-90).

Table 3 summarizes the fracture toughness results obtained from the tests performed at WMTR. The values presented in Table 3 for the candidate alloys were obtained by averaging the L-T and T-L test readings. For the T-L test specimens, the crack is aligned along the direction of grain flow. For the L-T test specimens, the crack is oriented perpendicular to the grain flow direction. The fracture toughness values of M50 and M50 NiL were included in Table 3 for reference.

Table 3 - *Fracture toughness test results.*

Alloy	Fracture Toughness (MPa • √m)	Fracture Toughness (ksi • √in)
Cronidur 30	16	15
XD15NW (HRC 58)	18	16
M50	18	16
M50 NiL	60	55
Pyrowear 675 (496°C Temper)	60	55
XD15NW (HRC 35)	79	72
CSS-42L (496°C Temper)	109	99
32CDV13	180	164
Pyrowear 675 (315°C Temper)	183	167

Cronidur 30, which is a through-hardened material, had the lowest fracture toughness of the alloys tested. The fracture toughness of XD15NW (through-hardened to HRC 58) was slightly higher than Cronidur 30. Both of these materials were comparable in fracture toughness to M50. The rest of the alloys tested had fracture toughness values that were comparable to or better than M50 NiL. Pyrowear 675 tempered at 496°C (925°F) had a fracture toughness strength comparable to M50 NiL. For XD15NW hardened to HRC 35, which is representative of a "tough temper" core condition, the fracture toughness was about 30% higher than M50 NiL. The CSS-42L alloy, which was tempered at 496°C (925°F), had a fracture toughness strength almost twice that of M50 NiL. Pyrowear 675 tempered at 315°C (600°F) had the highest fracture toughness, approximately three times that of M50 NiL. The fracture toughness of 32CDV13 was very close to that of the 315°C (600°F) tempered Pyrowear 675.

Corrosion Resistance Test Results

The corrosion resistance of the candidate alloys was evaluated by performing temperature cycled NAVY corrosion tests. The corrosion testing was performed at MRC Bearings in accordance with the standard provisions of the NAVY corrosion test. Two (2) separate NAVY corrosion tests were performed because of the varying availability dates for the alloys. The first test was performed with eight (8) test specimens each of Cronidur 30, CSS-42L, Pyrowear 675 (315°C temper), and Pyrowear 675 (496°C temper). The second test was performed with eight (8) test specimens each of XD15NW, and 32CDV13. To establish a cross-reference to the first test, four (4) specimens each of Cronidur 30 and CSS-42L were also included in the second test.

Each corrosion test cell consisted of a one (1) liter glass bottle fitted with a rubber stopper, filled with 100 ± 1 mL of distilled water. The test specimens were installed in a nylon fixture and hung in the glass bottle using corrosion resistant (stainless steel) suspension wires. A photograph of one of the test cells with a hanging fixture in place is given in Figure 2.

Figure 2 - *Navy corrosion test apparatus.*

All the test specimens were cleaned prior to testing by successive washings in separate baths of toluene (twice), ethanol, naphtha, and acetone, in that respective order. The specimens were given sufficient time to drain between solvent baths, and, after the final bath, the specimens were air dried at 65°C (150°F) for a minimum of ten (10) minutes.

After the specimens were air dried, they were installed into the nylon test fixture, such that the cylindrical (side) surface of one (1) specimen was pressed against the flat (top) surface of the other.

Referencing ASTM D665, synthetic seawater of three (3) parts per million (ppm)—by weight of chlorides—was added to MIL-L-7808 oil. The water content of the lubricant was then adjusted to 600 ppm (by weight total) by the addition of distilled water. Each test fixture—with four (4) pairs of specimens—was immersed in this doped lubricant at room temperature, and was allowed to soak for one (1) hour (the doped lubricant was agitated periodically during this time). After soaking, the fixtures were removed from the doped lubricant, and allowed to drain for thirty (30) minutes, also at room temperature.

A rubber stopper closed each test cell loosely. The temperature of each test cell was cycled by heating to 65°C ± 1°C (150°F ± 2°F) for eight (8) hours and then cooling to 3°C ± 2°C (37°F ± 4°F) for sixteen (16) hours in temperature controlled equipment. Therefore, each cycle consumed one (1) day (twenty-four (24) hours), and the specimens were tested for a total of fourteen (14) consecutive cycles. After the fourteen (14) days of thermal cycling, the specimens were prepared for a post test evaluation by cleaning, again, in separate baths of toluene (twice), ethanol, naphtha and acetone.

After testing, the specimens were visually inspected and assigned a relative corrosion index based on their approximate corroded surface area. The values assigned for the relative corrosion index were 1 for slight, 2 for moderate, or 3 for severe. By consensus of three (3) inspectors, corrosion indices were assigned to each specimen tested. An overall rating for each alloy was established using the parameter, Total Corrosion Points, which was defined by the following equation:

Total Corrosion Points = (1 x No. of Slight + 2 x No. of Moderate + 3 x No. of Severe)

The Total Corrosion Points scores for the tested materials are listed in Table 4.

Table 4 - *Navy corrosion test results.*

Alloy	Total Corrosion Points Score
Cronidur 30	8
XD15NW	8
440C	8
Pyrowear 675 (315°C Temper)	16
CSS-42L (496°C Temper)	17
Pyrowear 675 (496°C Temper)	20
M50 NiL	20
32CDV13	24

Cronidur 30 and XD15NW clearly demonstrated the best corrosion resistance of the alloys tested. There were no corrosion pits of any size on any of the test specimens for either of these alloys. Both alloys received the best Total Corrosion Points score possible (8) for the NAVY corrosion test. In previous NAVY corrosion testing, 440C also achieved a Total Corrosion Points score of 8. However, some of the 440C test specimens had some very small corrosion pits on them. Therefore, Cronidur 30 and XD15NW demonstrated better corrosion resistance than 440C, even though they received the same score.

The other four (4) alloys tested exhibited considerably more corrosion than Cronidur 30 and XD15NW. The 315°C temper of Pyrowear 675 had the next best score of 16, narrowly beating out CSS-42L with a score of 17. The 496°C temper of Pyrowear 675 was next with a Total Corrosion Points score of 20. In previous NAVY corrosion testing, M50 NiL also had a Total Corrosion Points score of 20. The 32CDV13 alloy had the worst corrosion performance of the alloys tested with a score of 24.

Abrasive Wear Test Results

The frictional behavior and the abrasive wear resistance of the candidate alloys were determined using a Steyr RRVP wear test rig at SKF ERC (Engineering and Research Centre). Figure 3 is a schematic drawing of the Steyr wear test rig. In the fixed upper unit, three (3) silver-plated 4340 steel discs are mounted. The test disc, which is made from the candidate alloy, is clamped in a rotating mounting plate. The test disc rubs under load against the three (3) smaller silver-plated discs. This test configuration simulates the bearing cage-land contact.

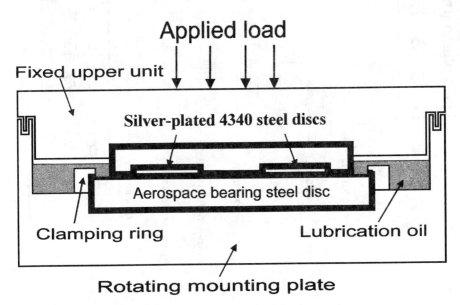

Figure 3 - *Steyr wear test rig schematic drawing.*

The standard abrasive test method developed in previous test programs was used to determine the relative wear resistance of the candidate alloys. Tests were conducted at temperatures in the range of 30 - 120°C (86 - 248°F), and at nominal contact stresses in the range of 0.038 - 0.47 MPa (5.5 - 68 psi).

The silver plating was applied to AISI 4340 substrates with a thickness of 0.035-0.039 mm (0.0014 - 0.0015 inch). Aluminum oxide powder with a particle size range of 60-90 μm and a concentration of 1 g/L was used as the abrasive. The lubricant was Mobil Jet Engine Oil II, a synthetic ester with anti-oxidant additives meeting the specifications of MIL-L-23699.

The friction coefficient was also measured between the three (3) silver-plated 4340 discs and the rotating alloy test disc at increasing loads and temperatures using clean (debris free) oil. Figure 4 presents the abrasive wear and friction coefficient measurements.

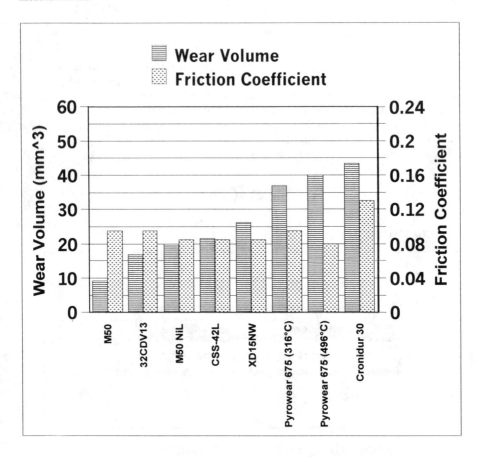

Figure 4 - *Abrasive wear test results.*

As shown in Figure 4, M50 had the lowest measured wear volume of the materials tested. M50 NiL had a wear volume approximately twice that of M50. Cronidur 30 had the highest measured wear volume, approximately twice that of M50 NiL. Both Pyrowear 675 variants tested also had high measured wear volumes, slightly less than Cronidur 30. 32CDV13 had the best wear resistance of the candidate alloys tested, with a wear volume slightly lower than M50 NiL. CSS-42L had the next best wear resistance of the candidate alloys, with a wear volume approximately the same as M50 NiL. XD15NW had a measured wear volume slightly higher than M50 NiL.

There was less variation in the measured friction coefficients, with all the values between 0.08 and 0.13. Cronidur 30 had the highest friction coefficient (0.13), and Pyrowear 675 with 496°C (925°F) temper had the lowest friction coefficient (0.08). The other alloys tested had measured friction coefficients between 0.08 and 0.10.

Structural Fatigue Strength Test Results

The structural fatigue endurance strength of the alloys was determined by rotating beam fatigue testing performed at SKF Ovako in Sweden. The testing was performed using completely reversed bending conditions (R=-1). The test specimens used were cylindrical rods 110 mm (4.33 inch) long with a maximum diameter of 16 mm (0.63 inch). The minimum diameter of the test rods in the central hourglass-shaped section was 10 mm (0.394 inch) and the radius of curvature was 50 mm (1.969 inch). A minimum of forty (40) test specimens was used for each material tested.

For the carburized materials (M50 NiL, Pyrowear 675, and CSS-42L), the test specimens were heat-treated to a condition representative of core material for a bearing ring (approximately HRC 40 - HRC 50). For the Cronidur 30 and XD15NW alloys, two (2) variants were tested, a through-hardened version (HRC 58) and a "tough temper" version with an approximate hardness of HRC 35.

The results of the rotating beam fatigue tests are summarized in Table 5. The fatigue limit values obtained for the various alloys tested are listed in descending order in Table 5. The 95% confidence limit values are also given in Table 5.

Through-hardened Cronidur 30 had the highest fatigue endurance strength of 1141 MPa (165 ksi), followed closely by through-hardened XD15NW at 1095 MPa (159 ksi). M50 and 52100, which are also through-hardened materials, had slightly lower fatigue endurance strengths of 1010 MPa (146 ksi) and 938 MPa (136 ksi), respectively. Among the carburized materials tested, CSS-42L had the highest fatigue strength of 863 MPa (125 ksi), with M50 NiL at 793 MPa (115 ksi) and the two Pyrowear 675 variants very close together at 698 MPa (101 ksi) and 683 MPa (99 ksi), respectively. The lowest measured fatigue strengths were for the "tough temper" versions of XD15NW and Cronidur 30 at 638 MPa (93 ksi) and 675 MPa (98 ksi) respectively, and for 440C at 666 MPa (97 ksi).

As can be observed in Figure 5, the fatigue endurance strength is, in most cases, approximately proportional to hardness. The biggest exception to this rule is exhibited by 440C, which has an endurance strength far below what would be expected based on its hardness. This is likely due to the large carbides present in 440C, which provide fatigue initiation sites. M50 and 52100 also exhibited slightly lower fatigue limits than would be expected based on their hardness. 32CVD13 had a slightly higher fatigue limit than would be predicted based on hardness.

Table 5 - *Rotating beam fatigue test results.*

Alloy	Fatigue Limit (MPa)	95% Confidence (MPa)	Hardness
Cronidur 30	1,141	+/- 17	HRC 58
XD15NW	1,095	+/- 9	HRC 58
M50	1,010	+/-29	HRC 60
52100	938	+/- 8	HRC 60
CSS-42L	863	+/- 12	Core
32CDV13	802	+/- 15	Core
M50 NiL	793	+/- 29	Core
Pyrowear 675 - P1 (315°C)	698	+/- 15	Core
Pyrowear 675 - P2 (496°C)	683	+/- 11	Core
Cronidur 30	675	+/- 14	HRC 35
440C	666	+/- 37	HRC 59
XD15NW	638	+/- 15	HRC 35

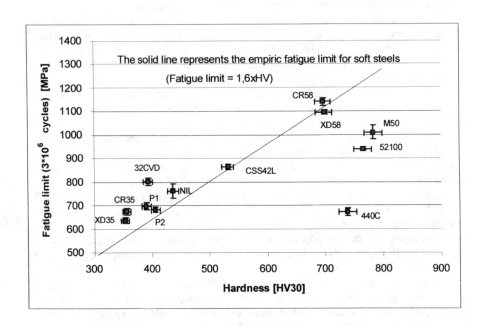

Figure 5 - *Alloy fatigue limits versus hardness.*

Summary Discussion

The test results obtained confirmed that each candidate material has unique strengths and weaknesses, and that no single alloy offers the best solution to all bearing needs. For example, Cronidur 30 and XD15NW demonstrated very good corrosion resistance, but do not have good fracture toughness or wear resistance. Conversely, Pyrowear 675 and CSS-42L have very good fracture toughness, but are more susceptible to corrosion problems. The 32CDV13 nitrided steel also exhibited very good fracture toughness and relatively good wear resistance, but demonstrated very poor corrosion resistance.

Acknowledgments

The authors would like to acknowledge the contributions of many individuals. Special recognition is given to the late Anthony T. Galbato of MRC Bearings who was instrumental in defining and launching the test program. Thore Lund and Patrik Olund of SKF Ovako Steel performed the rotating beam fatigue testing. Frank Fiddelaers of SKF ERC performed the abrasive wear testing. John Eckenrod and John Zurchin of Crucible Research performed the hot hardness testing. Westmoreland Mechanical Testing and Research performed the fracture toughness testing. The authors would also like to thank Aubert & Duval, Latrobe Steel, Carpenter Technologies, and VSG for supplying their materials.

References

[1]   McCaffrey, T. J., and Wert, D. E., **"Development of a Stainless Corrosion Resistant Carburizing Bearing Steel,"** *Creative Use of Bearing Steels, ASTM STP 1195*, J. J. C. Hoo, Ed., American Society for Testing and Materials, West Conshohocken, PA, 1993, pp. 137-148.

[2]   Grant, D. H., Chin, H. A., Klenke, C., Galbato, A. T., Ragen, M. A., and Spitzer, R. F., **"High Temperature Aircraft Turbine Engine Bearing and Lubrication System Development,"** *Bearing Steels: Into the 21st Century, ASTM STP 1327*, J. J. C. Hoo and W. B. Green, Eds., American Society for Testing and Materials, West Conshohocken, PA, 1998, pp. 409-434.

[3]   Burrier, H. I., Tomasello, C. M., Balliett, S. A., Maloney, J. L., Milam, D. L., and Ogden, W. P., **"Development of CSS-42L™, A High Performance Carburizing Stainless Steel for High Temperature Aerospace Applications,"** *Bearing Steels: Into the 21st Century, ASTM STP 1327*, J. J. C. Hoo and W. B. Green, Eds., American Society for Testing and Materials, West Conshohocken, PA, 1998, pp. 374-390.

[4]   Maloney, J. L., and Tomasello, C. M., **"Case Carburized Stainless Steel Alloy for High Temperature Applications,"** U.S. Patent No. 5,424,028, June 13, 1995.

[5]   Böhmer, H. J., Hirsch, T., and Streit, E., **"Rolling Contact Fatigue Behavior of Heat Resistant Bearing Steels at High Operational Temperatures,"** *Bearing Steels: Into the 21st Century, ASTM STP 1327*, J. J. C. Hoo and W. B. Green, Eds., American Society for Testing and Materials, West Conshohocken, PA, 1998, pp. 131-151.

[6]   Trojahn, W., Streit, E., Chin, H., and Ehlert, D., **"Progress in Bearing Performance of Advanced Nitrogen Alloyed Stainless Steel, Cronidur 30,"** *Bearing Steels: Into the 21st Century, ASTM STP 1327*, J. J. C. Hoo and W. B. Green, Eds., American Society for Testing and Materials, West Conshohocken, PA, 1998, pp. 447-459.

[7]   Berns, H., and Trojahn, W., **"High-Nitrogen Cr-Mo Steels for Corrosion Resistant Bearings,"** *Creative Use of Bearing Steels, ASTM STP 1195*, J. J. C. Hoo, Ed., American Society for Testing and Materials, West Conshohocken, PA, 1993, pp. 149-155.

[8]   Pichard, I., Girodin, D., Dudragne, G., and Moraux, J. Y., **"Metallurgical and Tribological Evaluation of 32CrMoV13 Deep Nitrided Steel and XD15N[TM] High Nitrogen Martensitic Steel for Aerospace Applications,"** *Bearing Steels: Into the 21st Century, ASTM STP 1327*, J. J. C. Hoo and W. B. Green, Eds., American Society for Testing and Materials, West Conshohocken, PA, 1998, pp. 391-405.

C. M. Tomasello,[1] H. I. Burrier,[2] R. A. Knepper,[3] Scott Balliett,[4] and J. L. Maloney[5]

Progress in the Evaluation of CSS-42L™: A High Performance Bearing Alloy

Reference: Tomasello, C. M., Burrier, H. I., Knepper, R. A., Balliett, S.A., Maloney, J. L., "Progress in the Evaluation of CSS-42L™: A High Performance Bearing Alloy," *Bearing Steel Technology, ASTM STP 1419*, Beswick, Ed., American Society for Testing and Materials International, West Conshohocken, PA, 2002

ABSTRACT: This paper presents a technical update on the on-going evaluation of CSS-42L™ (US Patent #5,424,028).[1] The alloy is a case carburizable, stainless steel alloy which has been demonstrated to have a key combination of properties suited for ideal bearing performance: High surface hardness, hot hardness for usage up to 427°C (800°F), high fracture toughness, and corrosion resistance. Initial rolling contact fatigue data suggested that the alloy should have superior bearing life. This paper concentrates on data generated since the last ASTM bearing symposium[2]. Both bearing life test data and wear resistance test data illustrate the alloy has excellent properties. Bearing life tests have been performed which illustrate superior life to both M50 and 52100. Wear resistance tests have also been performed. In a contaminated wear test environment of Al_2O_3, CSS-42L steel performs very well in comparison with M50 and Cronidur-30. Wedeven wear resistance tests on case components also show excellent behavior.

Background

The next generation of aircraft engine components requires high temperature bearing and gear alloys with high surface hardness for wear resistance while maintaining a core with good fracture toughness, ductility and impact toughness. In addition, corrosion resistance is a key alloy characteristic which is desired by most engine manufacturers. SAE Aerospace Material Specification AMS 6491 (M50) alloy provides good wear resistance but is deficient in both fracture toughness and corrosion resistance. AMS 6278 (M50-NiL) provides the excellent fracture toughness needed but fails to provide optimal wear resistance and is deficient in corrosion resistance for high temperature applications. AMS 5630 and 5618 (440C) have adequate corrosion resistance, but are deficient in wear, fracture toughness and the ability to maintain adequate hardness at elevated temperatures. There is an increasing demand for alloys combining all these characteristics for both present and future aerospace applications.

[1]Research Specialist, Timken Latrobe Steel, Latrobe, PA 15650
[2]Materials Technologist, The Timken Company, Canton, OH 44706
[3]Director of Technology, Timken Aerospace and Super Precision, Keene, NH 03431
[3]Director of Technology and Quality, Timken Latrobe Steel, Latrobe, PA 15650
[5]Manager – Advanced Materials, The Timken Company, Canton, OH 44706

provides the excellent fracture toughness needed but fails to provide optimal wear resistance and is deficient in corrosion resistance for high temperature applications. AMS 5630 and 5618 (440C) have adequate corrosion resistance, but are deficient in wear, fracture toughness and the ability to maintain adequate hardness at elevated temperatures. There is an increasing demand for alloys combining all these characteristics for both present and future aerospace applications.

CSS-42L was designed to combine high fracture toughness, hot hardness, wear resistance and corrosion resistance while retaining its core ductility and strength in order to meet the ever increasing need for high performance alloys. This alloy is able to achieve and maintain high surface hardness at temperatures up to 427°C (800°F) when carburized and heat treated. In addition to its superior hot hardness, the alloy has excellent fracture toughness and good metal to metal wear resistance.

CSS-42L

CSS-42L alloy is a double vacuum melted alloy that is nominally (in wt %) 0.12% carbon, 14.0% chromium, 2.0% nickel, 12.0% cobalt, 4.75% molybdenum, 0.6 % vanadium and 0.02% niobium. The alloy was developed by utilizing the current database on bearing alloy steels combined with the knowledge of stainless grade steels such as 440C, 422 and the more highly alloyed 12 - 15 wt% chromium steels such as BG-42 and AFC77. Refining the alloy content was based on the results of computer generated phase diagrams. The result was a stainless steel alloy that could provide these superior properties by the correct combination of the austenite stabilizing elements, primarily nickel and cobalt, with the correct combination of the most potent carbide forming elements: molybdenum, chromium, vanadium, and niobium. To date, four heats of CSS-42L have been made in production and subsequently tested and utilized in prototype bearings (Table 1). The alloy has been scaled up from a 305 mm (12 in) ingot as presented previously (2) to a 508 mm (20 in) diameter ingot. All ingots were stress relieved and homogenized to provide a uniform microstructure. The material was then forged to the desired size and furnace cooled. Final bar product was given a normalizing and tempering heat treatment to produce better microstructural uniformity.

Table 1 - *Composition (wt%) of CSS-42L heats.*

Heat	Ingot Size	C	Si	Mn	Cr	V	Ni	Mo	Co	Nb
99157	305 mm	0.13	0.15	0.16	13.84	0.60	2.11	4.67	12.48	0.04
G4096	406 mm	0.11	0.13	0.14	14.19	0.59	2.05	4.79	12.37	0.03
E4971	508 mm	0.14	0.15	0.17	14.12	0.57	2.01	4.74	12.47	0.02
E5140	508 mm	0.14	0.11	0.20	13.84	0.61	2.02	4.70	12.33	0.02

Mechanical property data from the various heats has been collected. Fracture toughness and tensile properties were evaluated on samples taken from billet and bar. Samples were austenitized at 1121°C (2050°F) and double tempered at 496°C (925°F). The fracture toughness of core material has been evaluated using both the standard ASTM Test Method for Plane-Strain Fracture Toughness (ASTM E399) and the ASTM

Test Method for Plane-Strain (Chevron-Notch) Fracture (ASTM E1304), sometimes known as the short-rod fracture toughness testing technique. Short rod fracture toughness has been chosen to represent heat data because of the alloy's high fracture toughness. The short rod fracture toughness data (ASTM E1304) from the production heats illustrate the alloy to have excellent fracture toughness (Table 2). The ASTM E399 fracture toughness of CSS-42L has also been compared to other alloys (Table 3). Even in its high strength, low toughness condition, CSS-42L exhibits high fracture toughness. The average tensile properties are also provided (Table 4).

Table 2 - *Short rod fracture toughness data.*

Heat	Loc.	Sample Orientation	K_{Ivj} Mpa$\sqrt{m}$ (Ksi$\sqrt{in}$)	K_{IVM} MPa$\sqrt{m}$ (Ksi$\sqrt{in}$)	K_Q MPa$\sqrt{m}$ (Ksi$\sqrt{in}$)
99157		RL		124.1 (113.0)	
		RL		129.6 (118.0)	
G4096	1-Bot.	LT	143.2 (130.5)		
	1-Top	LT	146.8 (133.7)		
E4971	1-Bot.	TL			146.2 (133.1)*
	1-Top	TL			153.5 (139.8)*
E5140	1-Bot.	TL			192.1 (174.9)**
	1-Top	TL	169.9 (154.7)		

* Invalid, p not in range
**Invalid, $B<1.25(K_q/YS)^2$

Table 3 - *ASTM E399 fracture toughness data.*

Alloy	Tempering Temp °C (°F)	K_{IC} MPa$\sqrt{m}$ (Ksi$\sqrt{in}$)
9310	149 (300)	98.9 (90)
Pyrowear 53	204 (400)	131.8 (120)
Pyrowear 675	316 (600)	164.8 (150)
CBS600	316 (600)	98.9 (90)
CSS42L	496 (925)	148.7 (135.3)*
CBS-50 NiL	524 (975)	57.1 (52)
M50	538 (1000)	19.7 (18)

* Invalid, $P_{max}/P_q > 1.10$

Table 4 - *Average tensile data.*

UTS, MPa (Ksi)	YS, MPa (Ksi)	El, % in 4D	RA, %	Young's Mod, GPa (x 10^6 Ksi)
1717 (249)	1192 (173)	17	47.0	207.9 (30.2)

The carburizing and heat treating procedures needed to achieve satisfactory properties in case-hardened CSS-42L include carburizing at 954°F (1750°F) by means of vacuum carburizing or gas carburizing for a time dependent on the case depth desired and subsequent heat treatment for final properties. Gas carburizing, however, requires special preoxidizing treatments to prepare the surface for carburizing. The subsequent hardening cycle includes austenitizing at 1093°C - 1121°C (2000°F - 2050°F) for 45 minutes, oil quenching to room temperature (or gas/fan quench), then subzero cooling to -79°C (-110°F) (or lower, whatever is convenient). The tempering cycle is a double tempering cycle with a cryogenic quench in between tempers. The temperature for tempering may be chosen based on the desired application. For instance, for the best hot hardness and wear resistance, a higher tempering temperature of 496°C (925°F) for two hours is desirable. For the optimum in corrosion resistance and fracture toughness, a lower tempering temperature such as 329°C (625°F) for two hours may be chosen. Most of the data presented in this report is obtained from material tempered at 496°C (925°F).

Case carburized samples austenitized then tempered at 496°C (925°F) were hardness tested at room and elevated temperatures. The surface hardness of CSS-42L was found to be superior to all known commercially available carburizable and through hardening bearing steels. The room temperature hardness of CSS-42L was measured at 68 HRC (a direct reading from HRC as opposed to a conversion) while the hot hardness only decreased to 62 HRC at temperatures up to 427°C (800°F). The case hardness for CSS-42L has been tested and compared to other alloys (Figure 1). It can be seen that the alloy still provides useful bearing properties at temperatures over 427°C (800°F) when measured against a typical bearing requirement of 58 HRC.

Experimental Results and Discussion

Wear Test Results

In a rolling contact bearing, wear can occur because of insufficient elastohydrodynamic (EHD) film thickness, relative to the height of asperities on the contacting surfaces. This type of wear is known as adhesive wear and is the result of the propagation of damage resulting from micro-welding events when surfaces come into contact. "Stainless" bearing materials can be particularly susceptible to adhesive wear if the lubricant additives are unable to react with the surfaces to form protective, separating films. A second type of wear, abrasive wear, is a result of contamination of the bearing environment by foreign particles which cause the removal of material from the mating surfaces through polishing, cutting and plowing actions. The geometry of the bearings and the dimensional accuracy of the entire mechanical system can be destroyed by excessive wear.

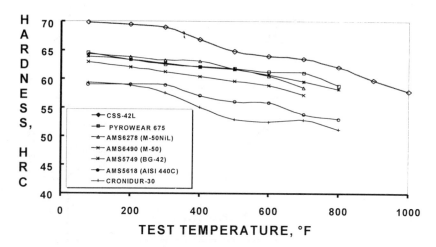

Figure 1 - *Hot hardness properties of various bearing steels.*

CSS-42L was tested in comparison to several other bearing materials by Wedeven Associates, Inc., in a test machine they had designed (WAM3). This machine applies a controllable combination of rolling and sliding contact forces to a ball and rotating disc. By varying the entrainment (rolling) speed, the thickness of the EHD film can be adjusted to provide a range of film thickness / surface finish (λ) ratios.

Under the common test conditions of 2.48 GPa (360 ksi) contact stress, slip ratios of 15%, 30% and –50%, and MIL-PRF-23699 (Mobil Jet II) lubricant at 200°C (392°F), M-50 balls were used to test discs of CSS-42L, M-50 and an unconventional stainless bearing steel for adhesive wear resistance. The form of the resulting data is illustrated (Figure 2). As the film thickness / surface roughness ratio is reduced by lowering the entraining velocity, the traction coefficient increases due to more asperity interactions. Here, the traction between the CSS-42L discs and M-50 balls is shown to be slightly higher than that of the comparison test of M-50 ball on M-50 disc.

A unique rating system has been devised by Wedeven Associates, which scores the materials on their avoidance of adhesive wear events, freedom from large increases in traction, and lack of catastrophic scuffing at the various levels of applied slip. The ranking is based on a maximum possible score of 50 when all of the conditions are combined. This score is used for the baseline which the M-50 / M-50 combination achieved in this test. All three of the test materials were ranked for their resistance to adhesive wear (Figure 3). CSS-42L, in comparison, scored about 20% lower, with 39.5 points. The M50 / stainless steel combination achieved 80% lower than baseline.

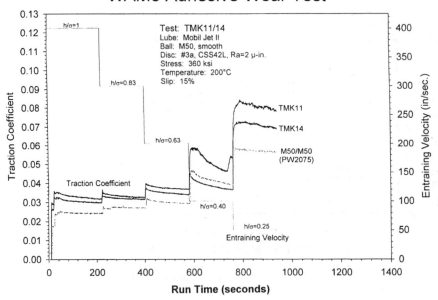

Figure 2 - *Comparison of wear results for CSS-42L with those of M-50 steel.*

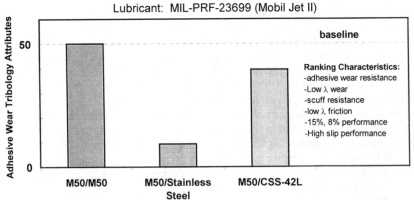

Figure 3 - *Comparison of Wedeven wear attributes for three steels.*

The second type of wear, abrasive wear, has been found to be particularly troublesome in a specific aerospace application. In turbine engine mainshaft bearings, excessive wear has been found to occur when the silver-plated ball retainer picks up hard debris particles in its surface and subsequently causes excessive amounts of wear to the inner ring land riding surface. That is, even though the race surface is much harder than the silver plate, the entrapped debris particles in the retainer surface cause large amounts of wear to the inner race. This has been a significant problem in the effort to replace M-50 as the inner race material with a tougher or more corrosion resistant material.

The abrasive wear resistance of CSS-42L was compared to that of the carburized bearing steel M-50NiL in a test performed by Wedeven Associates. In this test, the outer surface of a 34.92 mm (1.375 in) diameter cylinder of the test steel is rotated against a section cut from an actual silver – plated retainer to simulate the cage – land riding contact. Lubrication is by MIL-L-23699D (Mobil Jet II) to which abrasive material was added, in the form of "fine Arizona Road Dust." This abrasive contaminant consists primarily of 65-75% silica (SiO_2) and 11-17% alumina (Al_2O_3) particles with an average particle size of 8.5 microns (particle sizes range from 0.5 to 80 microns). The cylinder was rotated at 3.32 m/sec (131 in/sec) surface speed at an initial contact stress of ~ 50.3 MPa (7300 psi). The wear path was measured and the wear volume was calculated after each of 3 one-hour segments.

The progress of the wear which occurred to both the CSS-42L and the M-50NiL cylinders has been compared (Figure 4). While the M-50NiL suffered significant abrasive cutting and plowing from the fine Arizona Road Dust contaminant, the CSS-42L experienced only minor polishing wear of its surface features. Wear traces further demonstrate the superior wear resistance of CSS-42L relative to that of M-50NiL (Figures 5 and 6). This performance was judged to be at least equivalent to that of M-50 steel under these test conditions.

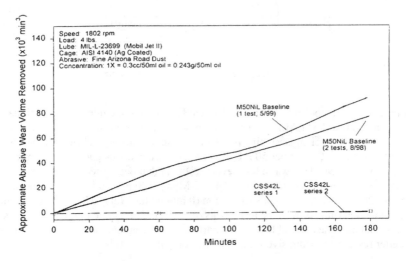

Figure 4 - *Comparison of abrasive wear of CSS-42L and M-50NiL.*

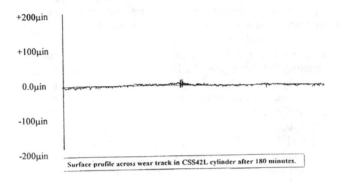

Figure 5 - *Wear scar on CSS-42L specimen.*

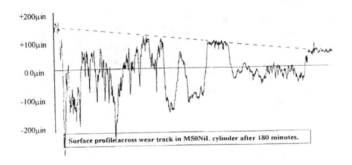

Figure 6 - *Wear scar on M-50NiL specimen.*

A test, similar in concept, was run at Timken Research to include some additional materials. In this test the "FALEX" cup – on – block wear test machine was used with silver – plated 4340 steel cups running on blocks of the test steels. Lubrication was with Mobil Jet II, to which 0.5 gm per 50 mL of alumina powder with a particle size from 30 – 45 microns was added. This was a less severe test than that performed at Wedeven Associates, with an initial contact stress of 48.95 Mpa (7100 psi) and a surface speed of 0.51 m/sec (20.3 in/sec.). The test was run for 10 minute intervals. The average amount of weight loss determined from the test blocks of each steel illustrate that CSS-42L lost much less than other steels (Table 5). This particular test demonstrates that CSS-42L has much better resistance to abrasive wear than the comparison steels.

Table 5 - *Results of contaminated wear tests on various steels advanced aerospace bearing steels.*

Block Material	No. Runs	Block Weight Loss (Avg.)
4620 STL., Carburized	2	175 micrograms
M-50 VIMVAR	4	240 micrograms
CRONIDUR-30	2	380 micrograms
CSS-42L	2	40 micrograms

CUP MATERIAL: 4340 STEEL – Silver Plated
LUBE: MOBILJET II @ 100 °C
DEBRIS: 0.5 gm / 50 ml AI_2O_3 (30-45 micron)
LOAD/SPEED: PV=720650
RUN TIME: 10 min.

Ball Bearing Fatigue Life Tests

The fatigue life of CSS-42L was compared to that of 52100 and M-50 steels through full – scale ballbearing tests. Inner races of 207 – sized angular contact bearings were tested in thrust loading at a maximum contact stress of approximately 2.758 GPa (400 ksi). The CSS-42L inner races were run with silicon nitride balls and M-50 outer races, while the 52100 and M-50 tests were run with balls and races of like materials. The loads were adjusted accordingly, to maintain the same level of contact stress. The tests were run with rotating inner rings, at a speed of 5400 RPM. Lubrication was with 0.946 l/min/brg (2 pt/min/brg) MIL-L-7808H synthetic lubricant at an inlet temperature of 71.1°C (160°F). The tests were performed as "first-in-four" tests, that is, when one of the inner races failed, all four bearings in the set were removed. The life, then, represented an estimate of the L-15.9 life of the sample.

None of the CSS-42L inner races failed in this test. The tests on the CSS-42L had to be suspended for other reasons. Even if there had been actual failures of the CSS-42L races at the time of suspension, the CSS-42L shows greatly superior rolling contact fatigue life to the 52100 and M-50 races (Figure 7). A Weibull slope of 1.5 was assumed to arrive at the 65% confidence bands for this plot. This data agrees with the fatigue data generated previously on CSS-42L using the ball-on-rod rolling contact fatigue life machine (Figure 8) [2]. The RCF ball-on-rod tests showed CSS-42L to have significantly superior fatigue life compared with other bearing materials.

LIFE, HRS

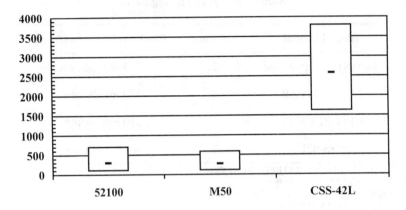

Figure 7 - *Life test of 207 ballbearing thrust inner races -
L15.9 life with 65% confidence bands.*

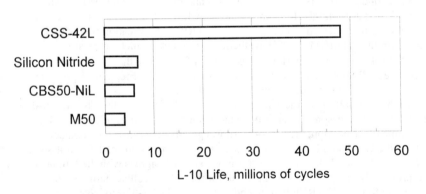

Figure 8 - *L-10 Life from Ball-on-Rod rolling contact fatigue test.*

Summary

The property goals of the original CSS-42L alloy development program were achieved and reported in a presentation and paper given at the last ASTM bearing symposium[2]. This paper has presented bearing life and wear data generated since that time.

The 207-sized angular contact ball bearing life data demonstrated that carburized CSS-42L had superior life when compared to both aerospace quality M50 and 52100 ball bearings in an accelerated test program. None of the CSS-42L inner races failed during the test program. However, all of the suspended CSS-42L tests were of a longer duration than any of the M50 or 52100 tests and exceeded even the predicted 65% confidence limits for these commonly used aerospace bearing alloys. This data further confirms the RCF ball on rod data generated earlier[2] .

Wear resistance is another critical property of any bearing or gear alloy. This attribute is even more difficult to achieve in stainless steel alloys as the propensity for galling and adhesive wear is a well known problem. Carburized CSS-42L alloy coupled with M50 balls performed at about 80% of the baseline M50-M50 couple and was far superior to another stainless steel bearing alloy coupled with M50 balls (less than 20% of the M50 couple).

CSS-42L also performed well in tests designed to measure the abrasive wear resistance in certain jet engine operating environments. In a test comparing the commonly used carburized M50NiL and carburized CSS-42L, negligible abrasive wear was observed in the CSS-42L samples but substantial wear of the M50NiL occurred. "FALEX" wear tests also confirmed this observation and ranked carburized CSS-42L as substantially more wear resistant than carburized AISI 4620, M50 or Cronidur-30.

From all the data generated to date, carburized CSS-42L steel is an excellent candidate for the most severe bearing and gear applications. It is expected that CSS-42L would have superior performance in any tribological applications requiring a balance of high surface hardness, hot hardness and rolling contact fatigue resistance coupled with good adhesive and abrasive wear resistance, fracture toughness and corrosion resistance.

References

[1] Maloney, J. L. and Tomasello, C. M., U.S. Patent No. 5,424,028, June 13, 1995, Trademark of Timken Latrobe Steel.

[2] H.I. Burrier et al, "Bearing Steels: Into the 21st Century," ASTM STP 1327, J.J.C. Hoo, Ed., American Society for Testing and Materials, West Conshohocken, PA, 1998, pp. 374-390.

Edgar Streit[1] and Werner Trojahn[2]

Duplex Hardening for Aerospace Bearing Steels

Reference: Streit, E. and Trojahn, W., **"Duplex Hardening for Aerospace Bearing Steels,"** *Bearing Steel Technology, ASTM STP 1419*, J. M. Beswick, Ed., American Society for Testing and Materials International, West Conshohocken, PA, 2002.

Abstract: A new process, duplex hardening, was developed, for two steels which are already widely used for aerospace applications, M50 and M50 NiL. The rolling contact fatigue and sliding wear performance of duplex hardened bearing components were evaluated on M50 and M50NiL steels. The rolling contact fatigue and sliding wear tests performed under the development program demonstrate superior performance of duplex hardened M50 and M50 NiL over conventional treated M50 and M50 NiL bearing components. The bearing rig tests performed in this study also demonstrate superior bearing performance of duplex hardened M50 and M50NiL steels over conventional heat treated M50 resp. M50NiL steels. Under boundary lubricating conditions, the duplex hardened M50 and M50NiL bearings did not even fail after 1500 hrs. In tests with predamaged races, duplex hardened M50 bearing races demonstrated more than ten times the calculated L_{10}-life. The tests on duplex hardened M50NiL bearings were interrupted after 1.500 hrs. runtime with no bearing failure.

Keywords: duplex hardening, aircraft bearings, bearing steel, wear resistance, rolling contact fatigue, rig testing, Weibull distributions, residual stress, surface hardness

Introduction

One of the main challenges currently facing the aerospace industry is cost, both in terms of purchasing the aircraft and - even more important - the cost of ownership. High performance bearings in modern aerospace engines and transmissions are required to operate most reliably at ever increasing operating speeds (rpm), temperatures and loads due to new designs and improvements to existing engines.

---

[1] Senior Manager, Product Development FAG Aircraft and Super Precision Bearings GmbH, Schweinfurt, Germany, Mailing address: Streit_E@fag.de

[2] Senior Manager, Materials Development FAG Industrial Bearings and Services AG, Schweinfurt, Germany, Mailing address: Trojahn_W@fag.de

Furthermore, the demands imposed by engine manufacturers associated with ETOPS certification and oil-off tolerance requirements make the use of advanced surface engineering techniques necessary. Duplex treatment (conventional hardening followed by nitriding) has the potential to meet all the perceived performance improvements necessary to provide the increased reliability and reduced cost of ownership desired.

The duplex hardening process was assessed by a number of European industrial companies and academic institutions in the Brite-Euram ASETT project (BE2077). The Brite-Euram project ASETT (The Development of Advanced Surface Engineering Techniques for Future Aerospace Transmissions) had the aim to develop and quantify the benefits of three advanced surface engineering techniques, namely:

(a) Duplex hardening,
(b) Solution nitriding of low nitrogen stabilised stainless steel, and
(c) Hard coatings by Physical Vapour Deposition (PVD) on a carburised substrate,

This paper will, however, concentrate on the results of the duplex hardening technology and the further work done beyond the scope of the Brite-Euram project [1].

The duplex hardening technology assessed in the ASETT project involves nitriding on top of a carburised surface. The work carried out on duplex treated M50NiL steel has demonstrated improvements in both axial and rolling contact fatigue [2].

The increased rolling contact fatigue life of duplex hardened bearing races the rolling elements made of conventional treated M50 became the life limiting component during the bearing rig tests. Therefore the development of the duplex hardening technology was extended to include also M50 steel.

Process Development

Steels

The two steels of highest interest in such applications as main shaft bearings for aircraft engines today are the through hardening grade M50 for rings and rolling elements, and the case hardening grade M50NiL, which is commonly used for rings only. The steels used in this program are VIM/VAR melted, the nominal chemical composition is given in Table 1. Both steels are finally hardened and tempered to a surface hardness of 60 – 64 HRC by tempering around 540°C (1005°F), the M50NiL being combined with an effective case with 58 HRC commonly of 0.75 mm minimum.

Table 1 - *Bearing steels, chemical composition (average) in wt.%.*

AMS/SAE	Name	C	Si	Cr	V	Mo	Ni
6491	M50	0,83	0,25	4,1	1,0	4,25	-
6278	M50NiL	0,13	0,18	4,1	1,2	4,25	3,4

Duplex Hardening

In a first attempt, both steels were nitrided by conventional salt bath and gas nitriding. A typical hardness profile as achieved by gas nitriding at 500°C (932°F) for 60 hrs on M50 (NH$_3$ content in nitriding gas 25%) is given in Figure 1. While the overall hardness of M50 was not affected by the nitriding process the surface hardness reached 1250 HV0.1, the total depth with a measurable hardness increase was approximately 0.25 mm.

Although the hardness profile is promising, heavy precipitation on grain boundaries occurred for both processes. This lead to the conclusion that both steels are very sensitive for precipitation and therefore need a very strict control of the nitrogen amount offered to the surface per time.

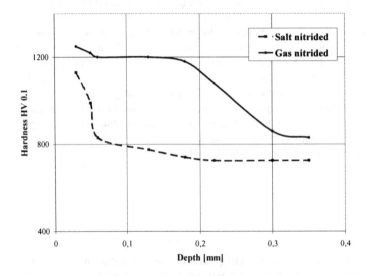

Figure #1 - *Hardness profiles for case hardened M50NiL after salt bath resp. gas nitriding.*

For the further process evaluation the plasma nitriding process was chosen due to the better control of nitrogen addition. After evaluation of various parameters the final process was established at a temperature of approximately 500°C (932°F) with a period of 40 to 70 hrs (depending on nitriding depth). The nitrogen content in the furnace atmosphere starts with 6 % decreasing with time to 4 %.

Material Characterisation

With the optimised process rings made of M50 and carburized M50NiL, as well as balls made of M50, were nitrided. Figure 2 shows as an example the hardness profiles of the nitrided M50 ball and an M50 Nil ring. Figure 3 shows the microstructure of the M50 ball. Nearly no precipitation is visible, but slight ones could not always be avoided. The M50NiL steel tends to build more precipitations than the M50 steel.

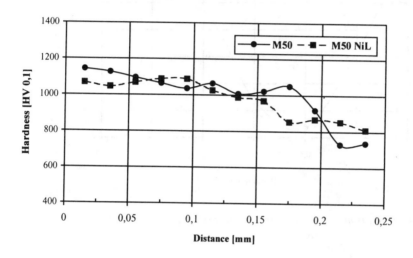

Figure #2 - *Hardness profiles of M50 ball and M50NiL ring.*

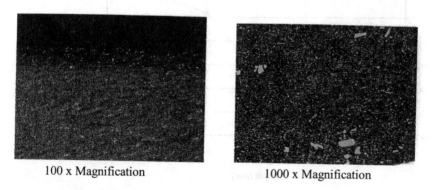

100 x Magnification   1000 x Magnification

Figure #3 - *Microstructure – M50 ball duplex hardened.*

Together with the hardness increase a significant build up of compressive residual stresses is to be expected. Figure 4 shows a typical residual stress profile for the M50 ball while Figure 5 shows a typical stress profile for the finished M50 ring.

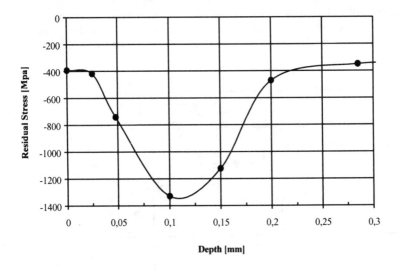

Figure #4 - *M50 (as nitrided) – duplex hardened residual stress profile.*

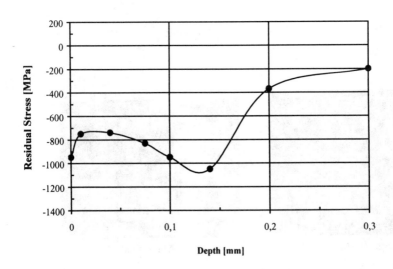

Figure #5 - *M50NiL (finish machined)- duplex hardened residual stress profile.*

The amount of compressive stresses is significant reaching values of − 800 to - 1000 MPa easily. The stress maximum occurs in a depth of approximately 0.15 mm, i.e. the depth where the maximum stress from the Hertzian contact can be expected. At the surface the grinding / honing processes still affect the stress profile although the hardness is in the range of the hardness typical for carbides. This change of residual at the surface and the near surface area caused by final machining indicates that despite the high hardness a certain amount of toughness must be still present.

The hardness increase due to duplex hardening is temperature stable. This has been demonstrated by hot hardness measurements as conducted by the University of Bochum, Figure 6. The difference between nitrided and unnitrided steels remains nearly constant over the whole temperature range and after returning to room temperature the same values are measured as before.

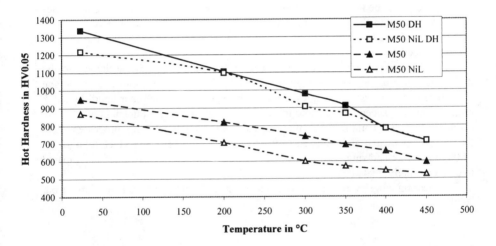

Figure #6 - *Hot hardness of M50, M50NiL and duplex hardened versions.*

Bearing Rig Testing

Preparation of Test Specimen and Manufacturing Experiences

The generic manufacturing steps for the duplex hardened M50 and M50NiL components is shown in Table 2.

Table 2 - *Generic manufacturing steps, duplex hardened bearing components.*

Manufacturing step	Description
1	Soft Machining
2	Case Hardening (M50NiL) by carburising
3	Heat Treatment (hardening and tempering)
4	Hard Machining
5	Inspection (destructive and non-destructive tests)
6	Duplex Hardening
7	Inspection (destructive and non-destructive tests)
8	Final machining operations
9	Final inspection

In the course of the development of the manufacturing process it turns out that special care has to be taken to avoid precipitation at corners. Here the nitrogen diffuses from two sides into the steel and adds up to an amount that automatically results in precipitation. To avoid nitriding of non-functional areas, a special masking process was developed.

Furthermore it is clear, that a slight attack of the grain boundaries at the surface by the plasma is present. As this may negatively influence the rolling contact fatigue strength a minimum grinding stock removal is required. On the other hand the stock removal cannot exceed a given amount to ensure a uniform layer thickness after finish machining of the complete functional areas. All final machining processes were therefore re-evaluated and adjusted to the new requirements. The surface topography of the duplex treated rings and rolling elements showed also improvements compared to conventionally treated parts.

The bearing rings were machined from 50 mm (2 inch) diameter hot forged bar stock.

Bearing Testing

The test were performed with angular contact ball bearings, type 7205B, with a 25 mm (1.016 inch) bore diameter, 50 mm (1.9685 inch) outer diameter, and 7.938 mm (0.3125 inch) balls, see Figure 7.

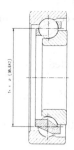

Inner ring curvature: 96 %
Outer ring curvature: 92 %
Ball diameter: 7.938 mm (0.3125 in)
Roughness Ra: $\ll 0.1\mu m$
P_{OIR} :   2 500 – 2 800 MPa
                      (360 – 406 Ksi)
Shaft rotation: 12 000 rpm
Lubrication: Mobil Jet II
                      Mobil Velocite 3

Figure #7 - *Test bearing configuration.*

The bearings were spring loaded resulting in a Hertzian contact stress of 2 800 MPa (406 ksi) resp. 2 500 MPa (360 ksi). The bearing test was conducted with an inner ring speed of 12 000 rpm. The test configuration is shown in Figure 8.

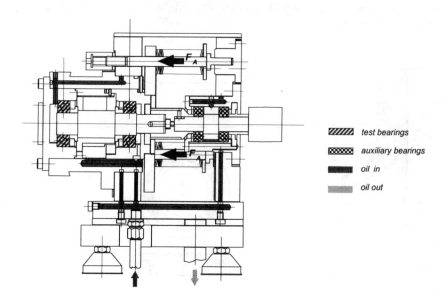

Figure #8 - *Bearing test rig , L17.*

For the bearing tests conducted under boundary lubrication conditions (intense metal to metal contact) the test conditions were as follows.

- Mobil Velocite 3 Oil. The oil film thickness was calculated to be <0.1 µm (<0.004 µin).
- Outer race operating temperature during testing reached 95 °C (205 °F).

For the bearing tests conducted with hardness indentations in the raceway the test conditions were as follows.

- Mobil Jet II Oil. The oil film thickness was calculated to be <0.5 µm (<0.02 µin).
- Outer race operating temperature during testing reached 95 °C (205 °F).

Testing was conducted on both pristine bearings and predamaged bearings. The predamaged bearings were prepared by Rockwell hardness indentations located in the load path of the race track. The indentation load was adjusted to produce round indentations of 0.18 mm (0.007 inch) diameter for conventional treated for M50 and M50NiL. With the load kept constant the indentation size for the duplex hardened versions of the two steels was 0.12 mm (0.0047 inch). The location of the indentations is shown in Figure 9.

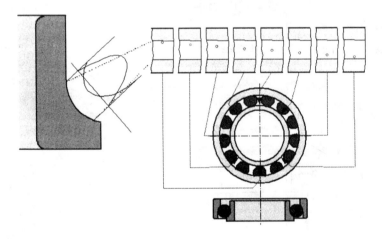

Figure #9 - *Location of the model-type indentations in the raceway.*

During the bearing rig testing the bearings were monitored by a vibration detector, which stopped the test when vibration caused by spalling was detected (normally < 1 mm^2).

Test Results

Previous RCF tests performed had already shown that under EHL conditions and applied loads of up to 4800 MPa (690 Ksi) the duplex hardened test specimen did not fail within 200 million load cycles before the test was suspended. Therefore the further bearing testing was concentrating on tests under boundary lubrication (severe metal to metal contact) and tests with hardness indentations to simulate operating under contamination (hard particle indentations).

Tests Under Boundary Lubrication - Tests were conducted under boundary lubricating conditions (severe metal to metal contact) at a Hertzian contact stress of 2500 MPa (360 ksi). The shortest life was experienced by the M50 races which reached just the calculated L_{10} life. The M50NiL races lasted approximately five times the calculated L_{10} life. Despite the intense metal to metal contact the duplex hardened M50 and M50NiL races demonstrated the longest life by reaching an operational lifetime of 1500 hrs before the tests were suspended, see Figure 10.

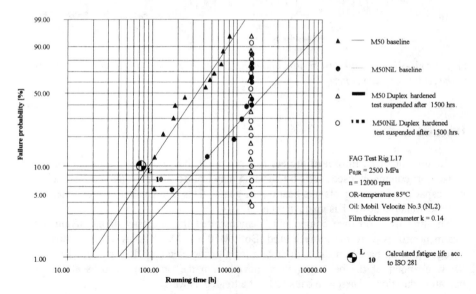

Figure #10 - *Bearing life test results under boundary lubrication.*

Tests Under EHL Conditions and Artificial Indentations in the Bearing Race - The test conditions for this test series were kept the same as described above, except that the test races were predamaged by Rockwell indentations in the load path of the inner race as described earlier.

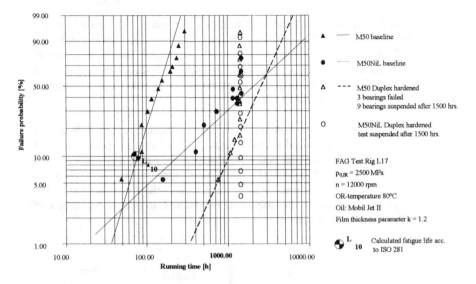

Figure #11 - *Bearing life test results under EHL conditions and artificial indentations in the rolling contact zone.*

Discussion

Results out of an European project had promised that additional hardening of the surface of commonly used steels by nitriding may lead to a longer life and / or higher load capacity of components like bearings or gears. This is in line with the experiences that the tooling industry has made in recent [3],[4].

The first trials on own components demonstrated the necessity of modifying the treatment processes to the furnace used. Both M50 and M50NiL are very sensitive to nitrogen pick-up based on the high amount of alloying elements. It was seen also that the week point of the bearing system moved from the rings to the balls at longer operation durations. Therefore balls had to be treated as well.

Furthermore it was found that not only functional areas have to be investigated. Corners especially may see an enrichment from two sides, leading to unfavourable structures with high brittleness.

At the end it was possible to modify the processes in a way to harden the surface far above the normal limits without destroying the surface by massive precipitations. It could be seen that the carburized structure of M50NiL is more sensitive than the through hardened M50. In combination of this sensitivity and the long process times, the surface region that can be nitrided is limited to a depth of approximately 250 μm max on plain surfaces. Geometry effects may lead to a decrease because the material volume increases with depth at a raceway radius.

Based on all restrictions the effective nitrided depth is approximately 130 to 150 μm. Within this area, despite the very high hardness, a microstructure is achieved that still has sufficient toughness and pronounced residual stresses.

The higher level of hardness /strength also at higher temperature that predicts the thermal stability of a nitrided surface is superior to a structure without the nitrogen addition. By this the stressed surface resists the bulk Hertzian pressure, preventing subsurface plastic deformation. In consequence the life capability under good and under marginal lubrication increases.

In contrast to this the danger is seen that the surface gets too brittle. A very high sensitivity to surface indentations by contaminations in the lubricant could be the consequence. Nevertheless, this was not seen in the tests on L17. It seems that the strength increase by nitriding, resulting in smaller indentations at constant load and the residual compressive stresses supersede the influence of toughness. At present it can't be separated which of both factors is dominating. Strength and residual compressive stresses are implemented by the duplex process at the same time and are linked to each other.

Based on these results bearings with larger dimensions went to a real test rig to absolve life tests under real turbine conditions. Though this program is not completed first results are promising.

Conclusions

1. The rolling contact fatigue performance of duplex hardened (plasma nitrided) M50 and M50NiL bearings was significantly better than that of conventional M50 and M50NiL bearings.

2. The duplex hardening of M50 and M50NiL bearing components did significantly increase the L_{10}–fatigue life under boundary lubrication conditions and under contaminated operating conditions.

3. The duplex hardening process has been shown to be a technology that has the potential to improve the performance of aerospace bearings under critical operating conditions and therefore provide cost of ownership savings.

4. The duplex hardening process of M50 and M50NiL has been optimised to achieve substantial improvements in rolling contact fatigue, bending fatigue and oil loss tolerance compared with conventional carburised gears.

Acknowledgments

The authors would like to thank FAG Aircraft and Super Precision Bearings GmbH for permission to publish this paper, the ASETT project partners for their support (GKN Westland Helicopters Ltd., Aerospatiale, Agusta, Aubert&Duval, Lucas Aerospace, Hispano Suiza, NSK, MIC, ZF Luftfahrttechnik, Birmingham University, Bochum University, Imperial College) and the European Commission for funding assistance via the Brite-Euram Programme.

REFERENCES

[1] Jenkins, S. L. and Davies, D. P., **"Duplex Hardening – An Advanced Surface Engineering Technique For Future Aerospace Transmissions,"** Publication GKN Westland Helicopters Ltd., Box 170 Yeovil, England BA20 2YB.

[2] Kleff, J. and Wiedmann, D., **"Neue Wege bei der Waermebehandlung und Oberflaechenbehandlung hochbelasteter Luftfahrt-Getriebebauteile,"** HTM 55, 2000, No. 1, Carl Hanser Verlag, Muenchen, Germany.

[3] Spies, H.-J., **"Erhoehung des Verschleißschutzes von Eisenwerkstoffen durch die Duplex – Randschichttechnik",** Stahl und Eisen 117, No. 6, 1997, pp. 45-52.

[4] Devi, M. U. and Mohanty, O. N., **"Plasma-nitriding of tool steels for combined percussive impact and rolling fatigue wear applications,"** Surface and Coatings Technology 107, 1998, pp. 55 – 64.

Dennis W. Hetzner [1]

Carburizable High Speed Steel Alloys

Reference: Hetzner, D. W., "**Carburizable High Speed Steel Alloys,**" *Bearing Steel Technology, ASTM STP 1419*, J. M. Beswick, Ed., American Society for Testing and Materials International, West Conshohocken, PA, 2002.

Abstract: A new family of patent pending high speed steel alloys has been developed. The compositions of the steels are related to the compositions of standard high speed steels (HSS) and die steels. However, the nominal carbon content of these alloys is approximately 0.20%. These are carburizable grades of HSS. The other major compositional differences between these alloys and conventional HSS are that the new alloys contain less than 1.50% chromium. Unlike alloy M50-Nil, these new steels do not have to be pre-oxidized prior to being carburized. The modified HSS alloys are carburized using standard processing identical to the procedures used with carburizable alloy steels such as 4320, 8620 or 8720. Once carburized, the alloys are then heat treated for maximum hardness using the time and temperature cycles employed for standard HSS. That is, the steels are preheated, austenitized, quenched, and double tempered.

To offset the effect of chromium on hardenability and secondary hardening, the molybdenum, tungsten, and vanadium contents of these alloys has been increased. Complete details of calculating the specific compositions of these types of alloys will be discussed.

Lab heats of modified alloys M1, M2 and M50 achieve surface hardnesses of 65 HRC. Residual compressive stresses in excess of –400 MPa 0.50 mm below the surface are obtained in cylindrical test specimens. Additionally, low levels of retained austenite are observed in these steels.

The ease of machining and heat treating these alloys in conjunction with their high hardness and excellent hot hardness make the steels ideal materials to be used for bearings in normal, debris, or high temperature applications.

Keywords: carburize, high speed steel, residual stress, retained austenite

---

[1] Research Specialist, The Timken Company, BOX 6930 Canton, Ohio 44706.

Introduction

It is well known that the stress state on or below a bearing race subjected to alternating contact loads can have a major influence on service life. Bearings made from carburized steels have compressive residual stresses on and near the surfaces. The origin of the stress state is directly related to the processing employed to heat treat these components. The absorption of carbon into a component during carburizing creates a carbon gradient. The carbon level is high near the surface and decreases as the distance away from the surface increases. When steel components are quenched from the austenitizing temperature, martensite is formed. The transformation of austenite to martensite is accompanied by a volume expansion that is directly proportional to the carbon content of the alloy. When quenched, the surface of a component cools more rapidly than the inner portion of a component. In addition, the Ms temperature (temperature at which austenite transforms to martensite) decreases with increasing carbon content. Thus for a carburized component, relative to the core, the case transforms to martensite at a lower temperature than would occur for a component of uniform composition. Consequently, these two effects operating in unison cause a relatively high compressive residual stress to be formed on surface layer [1].

This effect does not occur in components made from steels such as 52100 or forged P/M 46100 (C 1%, Mn 0.2%, Cr 1.8%, Mo 0.5%,) steel that has a uniform composition. Since most of the steel on and near the surface transforms to martensite at the same time and rate, the state of stress is essentially neutral. For comparative purposes, consider the differences in the state of stress on and below the surface of two LM12749 bearing cones manufactured from carburized 8119 tubing (C 0.19%, Cr 0.60%, Ni 0.30%, Mo 0.15%) steel and 46100 powder metal steel (Figure 1).

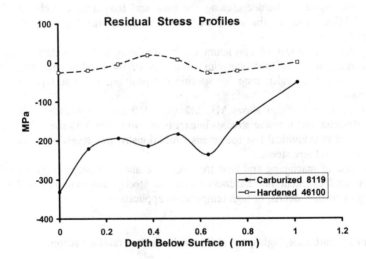

Figure 1 - *Residual stress profiles for carburized 8119 and through hardened 46100 steel bearing inner races.*

The compressive stresses in the carburized cone vary from −331.4 MPa on the surface to −155.7 MPa 0.75mm below the surface. While the highest compressive stress on the 46100 cone from the surface to 0.75mm below the surface was only −14.4 MPa.

Another factor where compressive residual surface stresses are beneficial involves the press fitting of bearing components on to shafts. It is well known that press fitting of bearings on shafts can create a tensile stress on the bearing. It has been demonstrated that the press fitting of through hardened 52100 steel definitely has an adverse effect on fatigue life [2]. However, similarly press fit bearings fabricated from carburized AISI 8620 were found to perform satisfactorily. It was concluded that under press-fitting conditions, carburized 8620 had superior fatigue characteristics compared to 52100.

To enhance performance of bearings made from these materials, carburizing types of heat treatments have been developed that created compressive surface residual stresses [3]. In this patent, high carbon steels such as 52100 and M50 were heat treated in carburizing atmospheres containing higher carbon potentials than used for standard carburizing steels. The carbon gradients produced lead to reasonable surface compressive residual stresses when these steels were quenched and tempered.

While carburized bearings fabricated from low carbon alloy steels have better properties than through hardened bearings fabricated from high carbon alloy steels, neither of these types of alloys performs well at continuous temperatures in excess of 200°C. Furthermore, brief exposures to temperatures of 250°C or greater can significantly soften components manufactured from most alloy steels. In demanding applications such as jet engine main bearings, high speed steels such as M50 are currently being used. High speed steels have higher tensile and compressive yield stresses than alloy steels. The high compressive yield stresses of these steels are a direct result of the high carbon content of the alloys and the presence of alloying elements such as chromium, molybdenum, vanadium and tungsten.

The heat treatments used for high speed steels are different from the heat treatments used for alloy steels. For example, a typical heat treating cycle for an alloy steel such as 4340, would be to austenitized the material at 840°C until the entire component was equilibrated for one hour at the austenitizing temperature. The material would then be rapidly removed from the furnace and quenched into oil. After the material cooled to approximately 75°C, it would be removed from the quench bath. The alloy would then be tempered for approximately two hours at a temperature of less than 715°C. For maximum hardness and strength, the alloy would be tempered at or below 175°C. However, if toughness was important, a tempering temperature of 620°C would be selected. For a bearing alloy such as 52100, the austenitizing may be 830°C. After quenching a tempering temperature of approximately 175°C would be used. Low temperature tempering would be used for any bearing fabricated from an alloy steel. This would ensure that the resulting component would be hard and have as high a compressive yield stress as possible. Tempering temperatures exceeding 175°C will lower the hardness, and consequently the compressive yield stress of bearings made from alloy steels.

For all alloy steels, after being austenitized and then oil quenched, increasing the tempering temperature is found to decrease the alloy's hardness. Steels having this type of tempering response, are referred to as Class 1 types of steels (Figure 2).

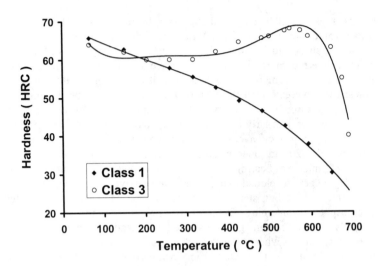

Figure 2 - *The tempering response of a Class 1 standard alloy steel and a high speed steel displaying secondary hardening, Class 3.*

The heat treating procedures used for high speed steels begin with a preheat of approximately 785°C to 840°C. Components fabricated from HSS are equilibrated at the preheating temperature for at least one hour. Following the preheat, high speed steel alloys are then quickly placed in an austenitizing furnace that is at a higher temperature. Depending on the alloy, the high austenitizing temperature may range from 1090°C to 1220°C. The components are only held at the austenitizing temperature for a brief amount of time - say 3 to 15 minutes. Following austenitization, the material is quenched into a salt bath at 540°C. After equilibrating in the salt bath, the components are allowed to air cool to at least 65°C. If an oil quench is employed, the material should be removed when it reaches 480°C; after which cooling to 65°C in still air is recommended. Today, vacuum furnaces rather than salt pots are often used for the austenitizing treatment.

Following quenching, high speed steel alloys contain untempered martensite, alloy carbides, and retained austenite. Tempering HSS must accomplish two things. The martensite needs to be tempered, and the retained austenite has to be transformed to martensite. The general procedure employed for tempering high speed steels is to heat the alloys to approximately 540°C for two hours and then air cool to room temperature. The cycle is then repeated one more time. Most high speed steels show Class 3 tempering response (Figure 2). When the appropriate tempering temperature is found, the hardness after the tempering cycles may actually be greater than the hardness immediately after quenching.

The material and chemical transformations occurring during the heat treating of high speed steels are much more complex than the transformations that occur in alloy steels. A typical high speed steel alloy contains from 0.80% to 1.40% carbon. In addition, up to 25% alloy elements may be present. The primary alloying elements are typically a combination of Cr, Mo, V, and W. Lesser amounts of Co, Nb, Si, Ti and Zr may occasionally be present. After these alloys are cast, hot rolled, and then annealed, the microstructure consists of low carbon iron, ferrite, and a large volume fraction of alloy carbides.

The alloy carbides in high speed steels are generally composed of a combination of alloy elements and carbon; hence the designation M_xC_y is used. M represents a metal atom and C designates carbon. X corresponds to the number of metal atoms in the carbide and Y is the number of carbon atoms respectively. Typical carbides in the annealed high speed steels would be MC, M_6C and $M_{23}C_6$.

When the annealed alloy is preheated to 840°C, the ferrite transforms to austenite, and some of alloy carbide may dissolve. When the steel is placed in the austenitizing furnace where the temperature is 1120°C or greater, all the $M_{23}C_6$ dissolves. As much as 50% of the M_6C and the MC may dissolve at the high austenitizing temperature. As the alloy carbides dissolve, the carbon is dispersed in the austenite matrix. When the alloy is quenched and then cooled to 65°C or less, most of the high carbon austenite transforms to martensite. Some of the austenite is retained, and the carbides that did not dissolve remain. The carbides present are types MC, and M_6C. At this stage in heat treating, the hardness of the alloy is high. Depending on the total alloy content, the hardness often exceeds 60 HRC (732 HK).

Tempering high speed steels to temperatures up to 425°C may slightly decrease the hardness of the alloy. However, tempering temperatures near 540°C increase the hardness of these steels (Figure 2). This phenomenon is referred to as secondary hardening. Two processes are occurring in this temperature range: first, retained austenite is transformed to martensite; second, very small alloy carbides such as Mo_2C, W_2C, and VC are formed. The high hardness of high speed steels as well as their resistance to softening at elevated temperatures is primarily due to the precipitation of these small carbides. The phenomenon is called secondary hardening. The small alloy carbides are primarily responsible for the excellent hot hardness these alloys exhibit.

As increased demands were placed upon bearings used in aircraft engines, M50 high speed steel was selected for applications requiring high temperature service. This alloy achieves its maximum hardness by the phenomena of secondary hardening. Hence, M50 has good strength at elevated temperatures. The nominal composition of M50 is 0.80% C, 4.10% Cr, 4.25% Mo and 1.00% V. Mo and V primarily cause secondary hardening in this alloy. The major disadvantage of M50, or other high speed steels, is that the high carbon and alloy content of the alloy greatly decreases its fracture resistance or toughness. Considering previous knowledge of the inherent benefits of using carburized components, a low carbon version of M50 was developed. The low carbon variety was named M50-Nil; its nominal composition is: 0.13% C, 4.20% Cr, 3.40% Ni, 4.25% Mo, and 1.2% V. The low carbon nickel added variant of M50 has excellent fracture toughness. Furthermore, since carbon is added to the case by a gas-metal reaction, the carbides formed during carburizing are smaller than the carbides in wrought M50. The absence of large carbides is beneficial to rolling contact fatigue life.

However, there is one major disadvantage associated with M50-Nil. Since the alloy contains 4.2% Cr, it is difficult to carburize. Components fabricated from M50-Nil must be pre-oxidized prior to being carburized. This step creates additional expenses and problems for bearing manufacturers using M50-Nil. Vacuum plasma carburizing can be used on non-oxidized M50-Nil, but this processing is very expensive when compared to standard gas carburizing.

There are several reasons why most of the high speed steels contain approximately 4% chromium. During the preliminary development of these alloys, it was observed that 4% chromium was the best compromise between hardness and toughness for high speed steels. It should be noted, however, that when compared to alloy steels, the toughness of any high speed steel is at best very poor. Chromium is mainly responsible for the great hardenability of these alloys; however, this property is only of importance in components having large cross-sectional areas. In machining tests, less than 4% Cr has shown to decrease cutting efficiency. However, the most important reason for having 4% chromium in these alloys was related to heat treating limitations that were common when these alloys were developed in the 1930s and 40s. Chromium was found to reduce the oxidation and scaling of these alloys during heat treatment. This was an important factor because economical, commercial vacuum furnaces were not available. While this factor was important in the 1940s, with today's modern furnaces and rectified salt baths, oxidation during heat treating can easily be prevented. It is of even greater interest to consider that the resistance to oxidation caused by chromium was considered beneficial, but this same property is what makes M50-Nil difficult to carburize.

A careful analysis of the benefits that have been achieved in using high speed steels in bearing applications as well as limitations experienced by these alloys and M50-Nil form the basis of the new alloys described in this paper. Ideally a bearing alloy for high temperature applications should possess the following properties: high compressive yield stress, high hardness, high hot hardness, excellent toughness, ease of manufacturing, and compressive residual stresses in the case

The new alloys described in this paper are low carbon high speed steels that can be easily carburized using conventional processes employed for standard alloy steels such as 8620, 8720, 4320 or 3311. These alloys contain less carbon than is in a standard grade of high speed steel. In addition the chromium content of the alloys is less than 4%. The low chromium content is a critical factor in enhancing the ease of carburizing these steels. The remainder of the alloy additions may include Mo, V, W, Co, Si, Nb, and other elements whose sum content is generally less than 25%. The selection of the alloy elements and their effect on properties will be described.

Experimental Procedures

The test specimens evaluated in this work all originated from either 22.5 or 45 kg vacuum induction melted laboratory heats that were teemed into graphite ingot molds. The ingots were annealed and rough machined to remove surface defects. The ingots were then heated to 1230°C and forged into 38 mm round corner square bars. Approximately one half of the bar was later hot rolled to 12 mm diameter bar. The test specimens were carburized at one of The Timken Company's production facilities. The test specimens were placed into a standard carburizing furnace and heated to approximately 960°C. They were given a standard case carburizing treatment using an endothermic gas having a natural gas enrichment. The gas is typically composed of 40% hydrogen, 40% nitrogen, and 20% carbon monoxide. The carbon potential of the gas in the furnace is approximately 1.40%. The total cycle time including heating was approximately 13 hours. After carburizing, the specimens were quenched in oil. Following the oil quench, the specimens were heated to 1220°C and held at temperature for 15 minutes. The specimens were then quenched in oil to approximately 75°C. The specimens were tempered for 2 hours at 550°C and cooled to room temperature two times.

Microstructural analysis was performed on the 12 mm diameter bars. The Knoop microindentation hardness traverses were performed with a load of 500gf. The X-ray retained austenite and residual stress measurements were performed on carburized cylindrical specimens machined from the 38 mm round corner square bars. The cylinders were 25 mm high and had inner and outer diameters of 22 mm and 35 mm respectively.

Results and Discussion

To evaluate experimentally the concept of a low chromium content, easily carburizable, high speed steel, a preliminary group of low carbon modified M2 steels were produced (Table 1).

Table 1 - *Experimental M2 Steels.*

| Heat | C | Composition (wt. %) | | | |
		Cr	Mo	V	W
HM2-a	0.17	.095	5.08	0.50	5.71
HM2-b	0.18	1.03	5.00	1.85	5.70
HM2-c	0.21	1.04	5.01	3.88	5.91
HM2-d	0.22	1.20	4.86	5.87	5.57
M2	0.83	3.75	5.0	2.0	6.0

Using the previously described processing, all four of these alloys were easily carburized, and had surface hardnesses exceeding 750 HK (Figure 3). The minimum distance below the surface where the hardness dropped below 60 HRC (720 HK) was approximately 0.75 mm. For specimens containing 2% or more vanadium, the case depth appeared to decrease as the vanadium content increased (Figure 3). It is important to note that no pre-oxidation or other type of processing was required prior to placing the test specimens in the carburizing furnace.

This group of alloys confirmed the theoretical concepts previously discussed. With this knowledge, several groups of modified M1 steels were melted and forged into 38 mm bars. For these heats, both a low carbon version and a higher carbon equivalent were produced (Table 2).

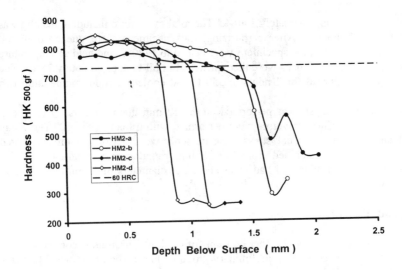

Figure 3 - *Hardness profiles of carburized modified M2 types of high speed steel.*

Table 2 – *Modified M1 steels.*

Heat	Composition (wt. %)				
	C	Cr	Mo	V	W
HM1-a	0.15	0.00	8.50	1.22	1.49
HM1-b	0.04	1.01	8.50	1.22	1.41
HM1-c	0.65	0.00	8.50	1.22	1.49
HM1-d	0.65	1.01	8.50	1.22	1.41
M1	0.83	3.75	8.7	1.2	1.75

Test specimens from the low carbon heats were carburized and heat treated. The modified M1 alloys were found to be very easy to carburize even though no pre-carburizing processing was employed (Figure 4). The positive effect of having some chromium in these steels is illustrated by comparing these two heats. Although the core hardness of both alloys is nearly identical, the surface and near surface hardness of the alloy containing 1% chromium is over 100 Knoop points harder than the alloy that does not contain any chromium (Figure 4). A similar effect is noted when the residual stress profiles of cylinders made from these steels are compared (Figure 5). A compressive residual stress is found up to depths of 1.5 mm in each specimen. However, the magnitude of the compressive stress from the surface to a depth of approximately 0.75 mm is larger in the specimen that contains 1% chromium.

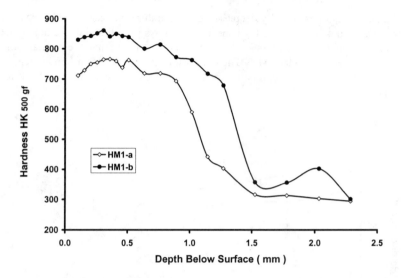

Figure 4 - *Hardness profiles of carburized modified M1 types of high speed steel.*

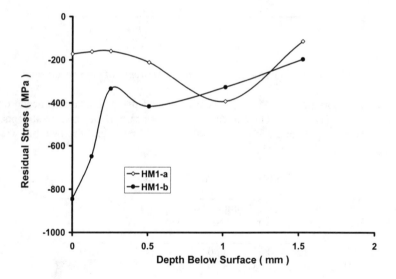

Figure 5 - *Residual stress profiles of carburized modified M1 types of high speed steel.*

Heats similar to HM1-a and HM1-b having a uniform carbon content of 0.65 were abricated into test specimens and used to evaluate the hot hardness properties of the new types of alloys (Figure 6). Both alloys had moderate decreases in hardness with ncreasing temperature up to approximately 500°C. At temperatures in excess of

500°C, the steel's hardness rapidly decreases as temperature increased. This behavior is similar to that reported for other high speed steel alloys [4]. It should be noted that the room temperature hardness of these alloys appears to be lower than the normal room temperature hardness of standard M1. The reason for this is that the carbon content of these alloys is only 0.65% as compared to a nominal carbon content of 0.82% for standard M1.

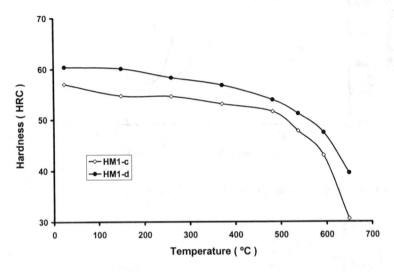

Figure 6 - *Hot hardness properties of two modified M1 types of high speed steel.*

Low chromium variations of M50-Nil were evaluated using the same procedures previously described (Table 3). Once again, with no pre-carburizing heat treatments, the specimens were found have a very uniform carburized case, and the material was easy to process (Figure 7).

Table 3 – *Modified M50 steels.*

Heat	Composition (wt. %)					
	C	Cr	Ni	Mo	V	W
HM50-a	0.20	0.61	3.50	6.55	1.00	0.03
HM50-b	0.22	1.08	3.59	6.63	1.34	0.06
HM50-c	0.75	0.55	3.39	6.49	1.47	0.56
HM50-d	0.83	0.95	3.37	6.49	1.07	0.08
M50 Nil	0.13	4.15	3.40	4.25	1.20	0

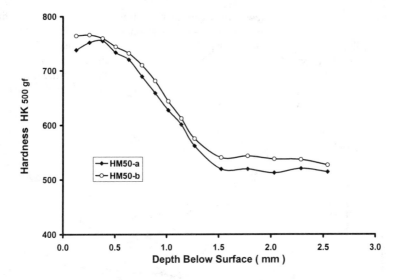

Figure 7 - *Hardness profiles of carburized modified M50 types of high speed steel.*

For the M50 types of alloys, the difference between 0.61% Cr and 1.08% Cr did not make a significant difference in case or core hardnesses. However, for the higher chromium alloy, the residual stress at depths below the surface up to approximately 0.5 mm was more compressive for the alloy containing the higher chromium content (Figure 8).

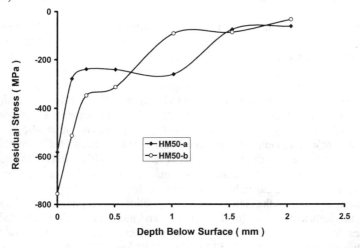

Figure 8 - *Residual stress profiles of carburized modified M50 types of high speed steel.*

The ease of carburizing the new alloys can be best illustrated by comparing the hardness profiles of the new alloys to 8119 steel, a standard carburizing grade, and 9310, a carburizing grade containing 1.20% Cr and 3.25% Ni. When subjected to the same carburizing cycle, and then given the appropriate heat treatment, at depths up to 1.2 mm, the modified M50 alloy was harder than either 8119 or 9310. Furthermore, the surface hardness of the modified M50 was significantly greater than the surface hardnesses of either 8119 or 9310 (Figure 9).

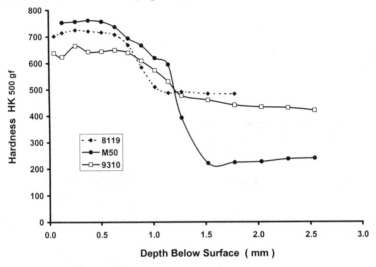

Figure 9 - *Hardness profiles from different carburized steels.*

There is another factor that should make these alloys very beneficial for bearing applications. The carbon content of most standard high speed steels is on the order of 0.80% C or more. Hence, there is a relatively large volume fraction of alloy carbides in these steels. Due to chemical segregation of these species during ingot solidification, carbide banding can develop and persist through further stages of processing. In some cases, the banding can be quite severe. ASTM Standard Practice for Assessing the Degree of Banding or Orientation of Microstructures (E 1268) presents a methodology for quantitatively assessing microstructural banding in these and other alloys. In E 1268, typical photomicrographs of banding in HSS alloys are illustrated. The nominal carbon content of the new carburizable alloys is less than 0.40%. Hence, the volume fraction of alloy carbides in these steels is much lower than that in their wrought counterparts. Furthermore, the carbides that form in the carburized case are created by the diffusion of carbon into the steel rather than by solidification phenomena. Thus the carbides in the surface of these alloys are smaller and more uniformly distributed than the carbides in the conventional alloys. This effect is clearly demonstrated by observing the microstructure of a 1350 kg VAR M50 low carbon alloy that has been forged and rolled into a 75 mm round bar (Figure 10).

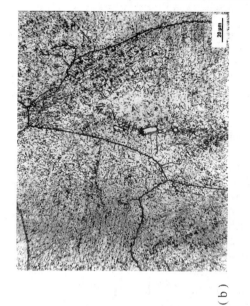

(b)

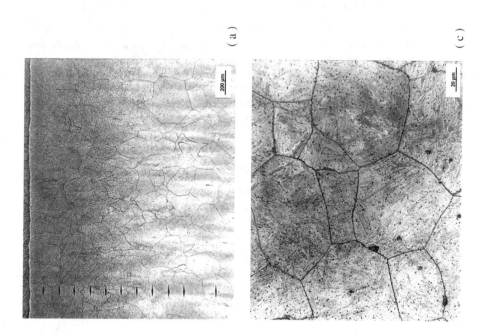

(a)

(c)

Figure 10. *Low carbon M50 carburized alloy;*

(a) *Carburized profile,*
(b) *Largest carbides in the case,*
(c) *Core structure, low carbon martensite.*

The carburized case depth for this particular specimen is approximately 1000 μm (Figure 10a). The carburized case microstructure consists of very fine carbides in a martensitic matrix (Figure 10b). When compared to conventional wrought M50 HSS, there are essentially no large, primary carbides in the case microstructure. Similarly, the core microstructure is a low carbon tempered martensite (Figure 10c); again, very few large primary carbides are found.

During the preliminary stages of developing these steels, to offset for the reduced levels of chromium, the molybdenum, vanadium, and tungsten contents of the experimental alloys were varied in a somewhat random manner to increase the degree of secondary hardening of the new alloys. A more detailed, less empirical approach originally reported by Crafts and Lemont in 1949 that considers the secondary hardening phenomena in these alloys was revisited [5]. Using their analysis, equations governing the effects of chromium, molybdenum, vanadium and tungsten of the secondary hardening response of high speed steels were developed. The changes in secondary hardening caused by the presence of alloy carbides can be expressed as

$$Vickers\ Increment\ (\ Cr\ ) = 550\ \left\{ \%C^{\ 0.87} \right\}\qquad(1)$$

$$Vickers\ Increment\ (\ Mo\ ) = 764\ \left\{ \%C^{\ 0.60} \right\}\qquad(2)$$

$$Vickers\ Increment\ (\ V\ \ ) = 678\ \left\{ \%C^{\ 0.60} \right\}\qquad(3)$$

$$Vickers\ Increment\ (\ W\ \ ) = 584\ \left\{ \%C^{\ 0.60} \right\}\qquad(4)$$

This analytical approach is now being used in developing newer chemistries to maximize the properties of these types of alloys. Some preliminary studies indicate that at chromium levels of only 1%, slightly more molybdenum and tungsten may be required to compensate for the reduction in secondary hardening. However, using the original ideas in conjunction the analytical models should result in a series of carburizable steels having maximum surface hardness and deep, highly compressive residual stresses in conjunction with a dimensionally stable material containing less than 5% retained austenite.

Conclusions

1. A new family of low carbon, carburizable high speed steels has been presented. These alloys can be carburized by using conventional processes at 940°C and then hardened in a salt bath or a vacuum furnace. No pre-carburizing processing is required for these alloys.

2. These steels are characterized by high surface hardness, high surface and near surface compressive residual stresses and retained austenite levels of less than 5%.

3. The hot hardness properties of the alloys are comparable to those of similar wrought high speed steels.

4. The carbides in these alloys are small and uniformly distributed. There is essentially no carbide banding in these alloys.

Acknowledgment

I would like to thank The Timken Company for allowing me to present this paper and for their continued support of my activities in ASTM. During the development of this project, the assistance provided by Dave Gang and Dave Wolfe in performing X-ray analysis of residual stress and retained austenite was invaluable. The excellent metallographic work and heat treating performed by Michelle Petraroli is gratefully appreciated. Finally I would like to thank George Waid for many helpful discussions and for supervising the melting of the experimental heats used in work.

References

[1]   *Carburizing and Carbonitriding*, Prepared Under The Direction of the ASM Committee on Gas Carburizing, American Society for Metals, Metals Park, Ohio, 1977.

[2]   Hustead, T. E., "Consideration of Cylindrical Roller Bearing Load Rating Formula," *SAE Reprint 569A*, 1962.

[3]   U.S. Patent 4,191,599; March 4, 1980

[4]   Bishop, E. C. and Cohen, M., "Hardness Testing of High Speed Steel at High Temperatures," *Metal Progress*, March, 1943, p, 413.

[5]   Crafts, W. and Lamont J. L., "Secondary Hardening of Tempered Martensitic Alloy Steel," TAIME, 1949, Vol. 180: pp, 471-512.

S.Tanaka,[1] K.Yamamura,[2] and M.Oohori [2]

The Development of Bearing Steels with Long Life and High Corrosion Resistance

---

Reference: Tanaka, S., Yamamura, K., and Oohori, M., **"The Development of Bearing Steels with Long Life and High Corrosion Resistance,"** *Bearing Steel Technology, ASTM STP 1419*, J. M. Beswick, Ed., American Society for Testing and Materials International, West Conshohocken, PA, 2002.

Abstract: The operating environments of rolling bearings are remarkably varied. With the use of bearings in various corrosive environments increasing, interest in stainless steel is growing. AISI 440C has been widely used in applications where corrosion resistance is of primary concern. However, its performance has not always been satisfactory because it contains coarse eutectic carbides that act as crack initiators under rolling contact stress and reduce Cr content in the martensitic matrix to the carbides. In response, we performed research to determine the most suitable bearing steel composition for both long fatigue life and noise performance and high corrosion resistance. Carbide size and hardness comparable to AISI 52100 steel were essential for the new stainless bearing steel(ES1), so we lowered the carbon and chromium contents and increased the nitrogen content of AISI440C. To control production costs, we applied conventional steelmaking processes for the nitrogen alloying. We evaluated the fatigue life and corrosion resistance of the new bearing steel(ES1). The new steel(ES1) outperformed conventional martensitic stainless steels in a tap water immersion test, a 5% aqueous sodium chloride immersion test, a saltwater spray test, noise level measuring test, water submerge life test, and oil lubrication life test.

Keywords: bearings, martensitic stainless steel, corrosion resistance, fatigue life, coarse eutectic carbides, nitrogen, carbon, chromium, production costs, conventional steelmaking processes

Introduction

Stainless steel used for making rolling bearings, like conventional bearing steel, must have high hardness. Martensitic AISI 440C steel is often used to meet such a requirement. AISI 440C, however, has high carbon and chromium content and therefore contains a large amount of chromium-concentrated coarse eutectic carbides. High contact pressure between the rolling elements and bearing rings causes stress concentrations in the coarse eutectic carbides, resulting in flaking. In addition, eutectic carbides reduce corrosion resistance due to loss of chromium in the martensitic matrix. Furthermore, the

---

[1]Research Engineer, [2]Research Engineer, [3]General Manager, respectively, NSK Ltd. Basic Technology Research & Development Center, 1-5-50, kugenuma shinmei, Fujisawa-shi, Kanagawa, 251-8501, Japan.

coarse eutectic carbides may reduce accuracy of the race surface finish or interfere with the bearing during operation resulting in excessive operating noise.

0.7C-13Cr martensitic stainless steel (hereinafter called 13Cr-SS), which had been developed to overcome the drawbacks of AISI 440C by suppressing the generation of eutectic carbides through the reduction of chromium and carbon contents, has been increasingly used particularly for hard disc drives (HDD) requiring quiet operation, as well as for rolling bearings having a relatively small diameter. 13Cr-SS shows an improvement in terms of eutectic carbides but shows little improvement with respect to corrosion resistance.

Alternatively, alloying a stainless steel with nitrogen is known to improve its corrosion resistance [1, 2, 3, 4].

We sought an optimum balance between carbon and chromium contents and to alloy stainless steel with nitrogen by a percentage suited for the material balance in the ordinary steel mass-producing process of 40- to 70-ton class. We have thus developed a martensitic stainless steel (ES1) for bearings, containing no eutectic carbides and having high corrosion resistance, low noise and vibration, and rolling fatigue life.

Experimental

In the first step, we melted eight steel pieces, A to H (Table 1), under 150 kgf of vacuum induction melting (VIM) and examined the effects of carbon and chromium contents upon the microstructure, hardening characteristics, and corrosion resistance of the steels. The melted steel pieces were elongated to a diameter of 23 mm, were then annealed for sphering, and $18\phi \times 10$mm test pieces were obtained. The obtained test pieces were heated to and held at 1 050°C for 30 minutes, then gas-cooled, subjected to sub-zero treatment at -80 °C for 1 hour, and then annealed at 160°C for 1.5 hours. For comparison, two conventional stainless steels, 13Cr-SS and AISI 440C, were also evaluated.

Table 1 *Chemical composition of steel specimens.*

Steel	C	Si	Mn	Cr	Mo	V	N	C+N
A	0.45	0.30	0.30	12.96	0.01	-	0.14	0.59
B	0.44	0.33	0.30	13.01	1.00	-	0.14	0.58
C	0.45	0.33	0.29	13.00	1.00	0.52	0.14	0.59
D	0.44	0.35	0.30	15.00	1.00	-	0.15	0.59
E	0.35	0.33	0.30	13.04	0.01	-	0.14	0.49
F	0.40	0.31	0.30	12.98	0.01	-	0.14	0.54
G	0.45	0.32	0.30	13.00	0.01	-	0.09	0.54
H	0.45	0.32	0.30	13.00	0.01	-	0.05	0.50
13Cr-SS	0.68	0.24	0.73	12.97	0.07	-	-	-
AISI440C	1.07	0.35	0.37	16.50	0.42	-	-	-

Table 2 shows the results of observation for coarse carbides in the hardened and annealed microstructure as well as the evaluation results of the hardening characteristics and corrosion resistivity of the microstructure. Under microscopic observation, an area of 0.08 mm^2 of the microstructure was observed for coarse carbides. For evaluating corrosion resistance, all surfaces of the test pieces were polished, one end of each test piece was finished with #800 emery paper and then passivation treatment was applied for one hour in a 30% nitric acid solution followed by immersion in a 3.5% NaCl aqueous solution for 15 hours.

Table 2 *Microstructure, hardness and corrosion resistance evaluation results of test pieces.*

Steel	Coarse carbides	Hardness (HV)	3.5%NaCl sol. immersion test
A	None	704	No rust
B	None	721	No rust
C	None	692	No rust
D	None	704	No rust
E	None	694	No rust
F	None	678	No rust
G	None	703	No rust
H	None	683	No rust
13Cr-SS	Max.7μm	703	rust
AISI440C	Max.30μm	690	rust

For test pieces A through H, coarse eutectic carbides were scarcely observed and hardness was equivalent to that of conventional steels. During immersion in the 3.5% NaCl aqueous solution, no noticeable rusting occurred on test pieces A through H, while it did develop on the conventional steel pieces in a short time. These evaluation results suggest that a nitrogen content even as low as 0.05 to 0.15 wt% may produce positive results by optimizing the balance between carbon and chromium content and by suppressing the generation of coarse eutectic carbides.

In consideration of cost, hardness, and corrosion resistance, we then melted the developed steel whose basic elements were that of test piece A (i.e. 0.45C-13Cr-0.14N), in a 70-ton argon oxygen decarburization (AOD) furnace. Table 3 shows the chemical composition of the newly developed steel, ES1, after being melted in the furnace.

The following description discusses the evaluation results of the microstructure, hardness, corrosion resistance, quietness, and fatigue life of ES1.

Table 3 *Chemical composition of ES1 melted in 70-ton AOD furnace.*

C	Si	Mn	Cr	Mo	N	C+N
0.46	0.25	0.36	12.98	0.04	0.14	0.60

Features of ES1 Steel - Results and Discussions

Microstructure and Hardness

Figure 1 shows the relation between the hardening temperature and hardness of ES1 and the conventional steels, 13Cr-SS and AISI 440C. Photo 1(a) shows a typical microstructure of ES1, and Figures 2(b) and 2(c) show microstructures of 13Cr-SS and AISI 440C. ES1 tends to be better hardened than the conventional stainless steels even when the hardening temperature is relatively low, and is also superior to the latter in heat treatment stability. It also shows a good microstructure in which fine carbides are evenly dispersed, having no coarse eutectic carbides unlike the conventional stainless steels as shown in Figures 1(b) and 1(c). For the following evaluations, we used test pieces or bearings that were heated to and maintained at 1 030°C for 30 minutes, then gas-cooled, sub-zero treated at –80 °C for 1 hour, and annealed at 160°C for 1.5 hours.

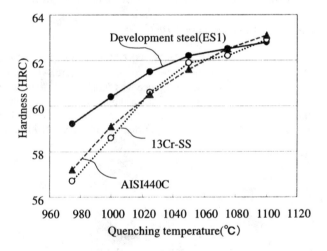

Figure 1 *Relation between hardening temperature and hardness of ES1 and conventional stainless.*

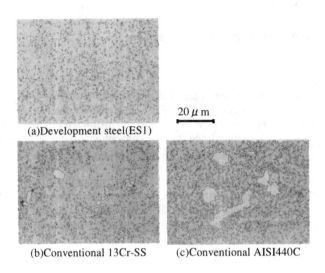

20μ m

(a)Development steel(ES1)

(b)Conventional 13Cr-SS   (c)Conventional AISI440C

Photo 1 *Microstructure of ES1 and conventional stainless steels.*

Corrosion Resistance – Tap Water Immersion Test

Photo 2 shows the appearance of ES1, 13Cr-SS, AISI 440C, and AISI 52100 immediately after a 72-hour immersion in tap water at room temperature. All surfaces of the test pieces were polished; one end of each test piece was finished with #800 emery paper, and subjected to the test. Passivation treatment was applied to all the test pieces, except for AISI 52100, for one hour in a 30% nitric acid solution. As a result, ES1 and AISI 440C showed no rusting, 13Cr-SS showed slight rusting, and AISI52100 showed extensive rusting.

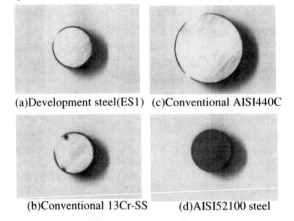

(a)Development steel(ES1) (c)Conventional AISI440C

(b)Conventional 13Cr-SS   (d)AISI52100 steel

Photo 2 *Appearance of ES1 and conventional stainless steel*
AISI52100 immediately after immersion in tap water (for 72 hrs.).

Aqueous Sodium Chloride Solution Immersion Test

Similarly to the tap water immersion test, all surfaces of the test pieces were polished; one end of each test piece was finished with #800 emery paper, and then passivation treatment was applied for one hour in a 30% nitric acid solution. Photo 3 shows the appearance of ES1, 13Cr-SS, and AISI 440C immediately after their 8-hour immersion in aqueous sodium chloride at room temperature. Conventional stainless steel rusted considerably while ES1 did not.

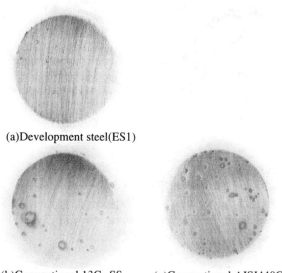

(a)Development steel(ES1)

(b)Conventional 13Cr-SS   (c)Conventional AISI440C

Photo 3 *Appearance of ES1 and conventional stainless steels immediately after immersion in aqueous 5% sodium chloride solution.*

Anodic Polarization Curve and Pitting Potential Measurement Test

The results of the aqueous sodium chloride solution immersion test showed that ES1 is superior in corrosion resistance to 13Cr-SS and AISI 440C in this test. To prove this electrochemically, anodic polarization curve measurements were taken per JIS G0579, and pitting potential measurements were taken per JIS G0577. In the anodic polarization curve measurement test, voltage was varied from natural electrode potential to 1200 mV at a rate of 20 mV/min. In the pitting potential measurement test, the voltage was varied from the natural electrode potential at a rate of 20 mV/min until the current density reached 1000 μA/cm^2. The anodic polarization curve and pitting potential measurements are shown in Figure 2 and Figure 3, respectively.

The measurement results are shown in Figure 2. ES1 has a wide passive state range and the current density to maintain the passive state in this range is approximately one-tenth smaller than those of conventional stainless steels. The conventional steels, 13Cr-SS and AISI 440C, showed very similar polarization curves, although the polarization curve of 13Cr-SS is on the higher current density side than that of AISI 440C. The pitting potential measurement results shown in Figure 3 indicate the exact same results. These measurement results clearly concur with the results of the tap water immersion test and the aqueous 5% sodium chloride solution immersion test.

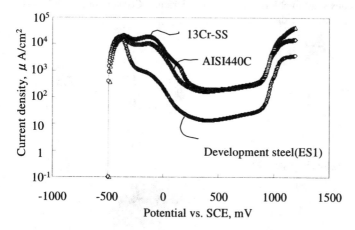

Figure 2 *Anodic polarization curve measurements of ES1 and conventional stainless steels.*

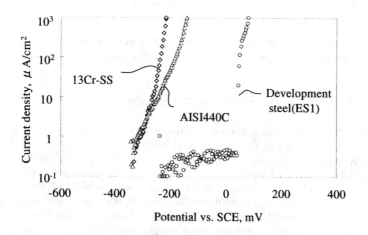

Figure 3 *Pitting potential measurements of ES1 and conventional stainless steels.*

Saltwater Spray Test

We conducted a saltwater spray test per JIS Z2371, on the outer and inner rings of bearings (6.35 I.D., 9.525 O.D, 3.175 wide) for HDDs. Aqueous 5% sodium chloride solution at 35°C was sprayed upon the outer and inner rings after ultrasonically cleaning them with an organic solvent. Photo 4 shows the bearing rings after the test. The 13Cr-SS bearing rings, a common HDD component, rusted considerably, while ES1 did not.

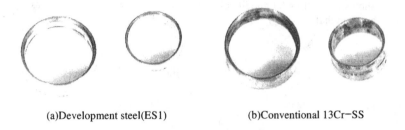

(a)Development steel(ES1)   (b)Conventional 13Cr−SS

Photo 4 *Appearance of ES1 and conventional stainless steels after saltwater spray test (for 2 hrs.).*

Noise Performance

We conducted a bearing noise performance test using the same HDD bearings (6.35 I.D., 9.525 O.D, 3.175 wide) previously mentioned. Low band, medium band, and high band noise levels were evaluated for 20 bearings made of ES1 and conventional 13Cr-SS. Measurements were taken under a preload of 0.5 kgf using an Anderon meter. Figure 4 shows that, overall, ES1 bearings are just as quiet, or quieter, than conventional stainless steel bearings.

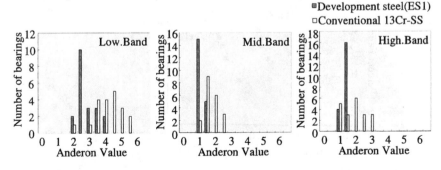

Figure 4 *Noise level measurements of ES1 and 13Cr–SS bearings.*

Rolling Fatigue Life and Water Submerge Test

Stainless steel bearings are used not only in precision equipment with little tolerance for corrosion, but also in vacuum or harsh environments where there is constant exposure to water. We evaluated bearing life with a water submerge test as shown in Figure 5. The test bearings used are thrust ball bearings 51305 (52mm O.D., 25mm I.D), with a machined fluororesin cage and silicon nitride ceramic rolling elements. Bearing life was deemed over when the bearing vibration level reached about five times its initial value. The bearings were tested under a load of 980N (maximum contact pressure 1470 MPa) at a running speed of 1 000 rpm.

Figure 6 shows that rolling fatigue life of ES1 with constant water exposure was five times longer than that of AISI 440C.

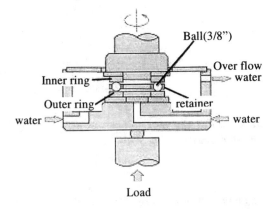

Figure 5 *Water submerge life testing apparatus.*

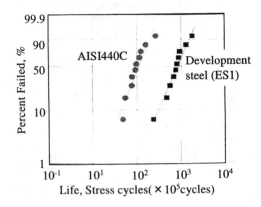

Figure 6 *Water submerge life test results of ES1 and*
conventional stainless steels.

Oil Lubrication Life Test

In this test, the life of deep groove ball bearings 6206 (62mm O.D., 30mm I.D.) was tested on a cantilever life tester with a lubrication system as shown in Figure 7. The test load P/C (P: dynamic equivalent load; C: basic rated dynamic load) of 0.71 and the running speed of 3,900 rpm were applied. The test was discontinued when the bearing vibration level reached about five times its initial value. The bearings were then checked for flaking.

AISI 440C balls have a tendency to begin flaking at an early stage. Therefore, silicon nitride ceramic rolling elements were used for this evaluation. Figure 8 shows the fatigue life test results. This figure clearly shows the superior rolling life of ES1 compared to AISI 440C. While the L10 life of AISI 440C was 5.3 hours, the L10 life of ES1 was 132.5 hours; almost 25 times longer.The calculation life corrected by the contact side pressure.

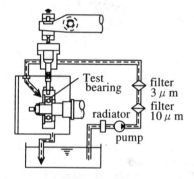

Figure 7 *Oil lubrication life testing apparatus.*

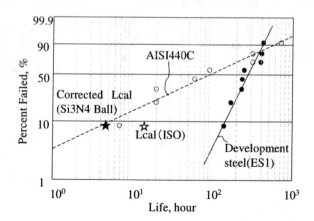

Figure 8 *Oil lubrication life test results of ES1 and conventional stainless steels.*

Conclusion

Our evaluation results of ES1 are summarized as follows:
(1) Hardness: Equal to AISI 440C and 13Cr-SS,
(2) Corrosion resistance: Higher than AISI 440C and 13Cr-SS,
(3) Quietness: Equal to or superior to 13Cr-SS, and
(4) Rolling life: Approximately five times longer under water lubrication, and
approximately 25 times longer under oil lubrication, as those of AISI 440C.

By reviewing the balance between carbon content and chromium content, suppressing the generation or coarse eutectic carbides, and by maintaining hardness in conventional stainless steels, we have developed a new type of 13Cr stainless steel, ES1. ES1 has a hardness comparable to, and corrosion resistance and rolling fatigue life higher than, those of AISI 440C. The ES1 steel we have successfully developed is also suited for mass production. Therefore in future, it is expected to be more commonly used as stainless steel for bearings.

Acknowledgment

We sincerly thank Daido Steel Co., Ltd. for their valuable assistance in the development of this steel.

References

[1]K. Osozawa, "The Effect of Nitrogen on the Corrosion Resistance of Stainless Steels," Heat Treatment, Vol. 36 No. 4, 1996, pp206-212.
[2]Hans Berns, Sabine Siebert," High Nitrogen Austenitic Cases in Stainless Steels," ISIJ International, Vol.36, No.7, 1996, pp927-931.
[3]Hans Berns, "Manufacture and Application of High Nitrogen Steels," Z.Metallkd86, Vol. 3, 1995, pp156-163
[4]Tomasello, C. M., Maloney, J.L., Ward, P.C., and Materkowski, J.P., "A New Corrosion Resistant, Martensitic Stainless Steel for Improved Performance in Miniature Bearing," Bearing Steels: Into the 21st Century, ASTM STP 1327, J. J. C. Hoo and W. B. Green, Eds., American Society for Testing and Materials, West Conshohocken, PA, 1998, pp437-446.

Microstructural Change and Its Relationship with Bearing Fatigue and Life Time Prediction

Alain Vincent,[1] H. Elghazal,[1] Gérard Lormand,[1] A. Hamel[1] and Daniel Girodin[2]

Local Elasto-Plastic Properties of Bearing Steels determined by Nano-Indentation Measurements

Reference: Vincent, A., Elghazal, H., Lormand, G., Hamel, A., and Girodin, D., **"Local Elasto-Plastic Properties of Bearing Steels determined by Nano-Indentation Measurements,"** *Bearing Steel Technology, ASTM STP 1419*, J. M. Beswick, Ed., American Society for Testing Materials International, West Conshohocken, PA, 2002.

Abstract: Methods for obtaining local elasto-plastic properties of bearing steels through nano-indentation measurements are described. The usual way to analyze the unloading part of a nano-indentation test in order to obtain the elastic modulus of nonmetallic inclusions or primary carbides in bearing steels is summarized. Then, emphasis is given to a new method that enables one to derive the profile of micro-plastic properties of a surface hardened bearing steel. Experimentally, it consists of measuring the residual displacement d_r of a spherical indenter, following loading-unloading cycles at increasing maximal force F_{max}. First, the direct problem, i.e., simulating by the finite element method the nano-indentation response, $d_r(F_{max})$, from the knowledge of the strain-hardening law, $\sigma(\varepsilon_p)$, is studied. It is validated on steel specimens that are carburised homogeneously with different carbon concentrations. Second, the inverse problem, i.e. obtaining the strain-hardening law from the nano-indentation response, is studied on carburised and nitrided layers.

Keywords: Nano-indentation, micro-plasticity, micro-yield stress, surface hardened steel, carburised layer, nitrided layer.

Introduction

In another paper presented at this symposium, a physically based endurance limit model is described for assessing the load rating of bearings with a view to ensuring an infinite life [1]. The proposed method consists in considering that, everywhere in the subsurface region, the local stress resulting from the contact loading must remain lower than the micro-yield stress of the martensitic matrix. Hence, several material properties to be introduced in the model must be measured. First, the Young moduli of the matrix and inhomogeneities, such as nonmetallic inclusions and carbides, are required to determine the local stress concentrations around these inhomogeneities that act as local

[1] Professor, research scientist and assistant professor, respectively, Groupe d'Etudes de Métallurgie Physique et de Physique des Matériaux (U.M.R. C.N.R.S. 5510) / I.N.S.A. / 69621 Villeurbanne Cedex /France.
[2] Research engineer, S.N.R. Roulements / B.P. 2017 / 74010 - Annecy Cedex / France.

stress raisers, thus being detrimental for the endurance limit. Then, the micro-yield stress of the matrix, which is considered as the threshold stress to be introduced in the fatigue stress criterion, must also be measured. In practical applications of this method, two types of bearing steels must be distinguished: through hardened steels and surface hardened steels, which are increasingly used in rolling bearing elements because they can offer both a high hardness to endure surface contact fatigue and a high toughness to ensure mechanical function.

In through hardened steels, the matrix properties can be determined easily from mechanical tests (uniaxial compression tests) performed on bulk specimens, since the volume fraction of material inhomogeneities is usually low enough to have a negligible influence on the macroscopic elasto-plastic behavior of the material. Concerning the inhomogeneities, the Young modulus can be deduced from classical nano-indentation tests performed directly on the small volume of the inhomogeneity [2]. This advanced technique allows one to measure, in an extremely sensitive way, both the force and the displacement of a small scale indenter during the indentation test [3,4].

In surface hardened steels, the matrix exhibits a profile of mechanical properties inherent to the treatment. Then, the knowledge of this complete profile is required when one wants to apply the aforementioned method. The matrix Young's modulus could be measured locally, by using the classical nano-indentation technique. However, generally this is not useful, because the matrix Young's modulus of the steel matrix is only weakly affected by the surface treatment. In contrast, the plasticity properties vary markedly as a function of the distance to the surface. These plasticity properties are usually characterized by hardness or micro-hardness measurements. Thus, for carburised steels, a conventional case-hardened depth is often defined as the surface distance beyond which the hardness becomes lower than a reference value (550 H_{v1kg} under 1 daN in norm ISO 281/1). Although the hardness is a good indicator for the mechanical behavior of steels, the plastic strain range involved in the indented area (typically 10 to 50% [5]) is far beyond that suitable for evaluating the micro-yield stress.

The aim of this presentation is to show how this problem can be solved by analysing the plastic part of the force-displacement response during a nano-indentation test. In this paper, first the experimental conditions are described. Then, it is shown how the elasto-plastic force-displacement response in a nano-indentation test can be computed from the knowledge of the stress-strain law of a material (direct problem). In the following part, the method to solve the inverse problem of practical interest, that is determining the stress-strain law of the material from the nano-indentation force-displacement response, $F(d)$, is described. The development of this method is illustrated for a carburising steel and a nitriding steel used by bearing makers.

Experimental Conditions

Materials

The specimens examined in this study were prepared from carburising and nitriding steels, 16NiCrMo13 (AISI 9310) and 32CrMoV13 (AMS 6481), respectively. Two types of specimens were prepared from both steels. First, special specimens were designed for validating the resolution of the direct problem. For that purpose, cylindrical tubes with a thin wall (external diameter 7 mm, wall thickness 2 or 1 mm, height 12 or 8 mm) were carburised or nitrided in order to obtain a quasi homogeneous carbon or nitrogen concentration throughout the wall thickness. Five carbon concentrations ranging from 0.35 wt% to 0.86 wt% were thus obtained by changing the carburising conditions. In contrast, it was possible to obtain only one nitrogen concentration (1.42 wt%). The level and homogeneity of the carbon and nitrogen concentrations throughout the specimen thickness were measured by a CAMEBAX SX microprobe. Second, thick specimens (40 mm x 40 mm x 13 mm) were carburised or nitrided in a classical way to produce a layer with a profile of properties. All carburised specimens were austenitised at 950°C for 20 minutes, quenched down to 220 °C in a salt bath, and then tempered for one hour at 220°C. Since nitriding is performed at 520°C, the 32CrMoV13 specimens were treated prior to nitriding, that is austenitised at 950°C for 20 minutes, oil quenched and then annealed at 630°C for three hours. For both the carburised and the nitrided steels, the microstructure resulting from these treatments consisted mainly of tempered martensite small plates, with different precipitates inside. The typical plate width was less than 1 µm in both cases. As it will be discussed later, in nano-indentation tests the tested volume must be suitable to this fineness of the microstructure. Some retained austenite was also present in the carburised steel (less than 5 vol.%). Besides, the thin compound layer, which formed at the surface of the nitrided specimens, was removed by grinding.

Uniaxial Compression Tests

The strain hardening laws of the carburised and the nitrided specimens were determined by means of uniaxial compression tests performed on the tube shape specimens. Strain was measured by means of strain gages glued to the external surface of the specimen. Owing to the non-linear elastic behavior of high strength steels [6], it is not possible to derive micro-plastic strains accurately from a single global stress–strain curve. Therefore, the specimens were successively loaded and unloaded at increasing maximal load, which allowed us to measure directly the subsequent increment of plastic strain after every unloading.

Nano-Indentation Tests

All nano-indentation measurements were performed using a Nano-Instruments Model II nano-indenter. With this instrument, loads ranging from 1 to 700 mN can be applied continuously to the indenter, while load and displacement are measured. The actual resolution of the displacement capacitor sensor is approximately 1nm for the strain range used in the present experiments. The surface to be indented has to be carefully polished in order to avoid any preparation artifact. As mentioned above, in the past this technique has been mostly used for measuring the local elastic properties of materials [2-4]. For such a purpose, this instrument is then equipped with a standard Berkovitch[3] indenter. A schematic load-displacement curve is shown in Figure 1. This curve can be divided in three parts: a loading part in the elastic range, a loading part in the plastic range, and the unloading part. Concerning the Young's modulus determination, first it should be mentioned that the loading part of the load-displacement curve cannot be exploited easily because, except for very hard materials, local plastic strain occurs even

---

[3] A Berkovitch indenter is a three-face pyramid, with an angle of 137° at each corner.

at low load, especially with a Berkovitch indenter which exhibits sharp edges. Therefore, only the unloading part, for which the material behavior is assumed to be purely elastic, is analyzed. The method for analyzing this part has been described by various authors [2,3]. It is derived from the classical description of the elastic contact between an indenter and a half space, which has been extensively studied since the early work of Boussinesq [7].

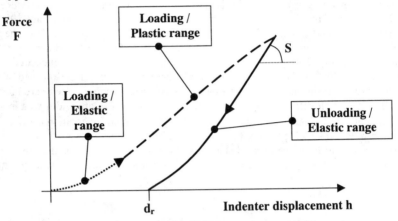

Figure 1 – *Schematic of the force – displacement response in a nano-indentation test.*

Thus the material modulus is deduced from the basic relationship:

$$S = \frac{dF}{dh} = \beta \frac{2}{\sqrt{\pi}} E_r \sqrt{A_r} \qquad (1)$$

where S is unloading slope, A_r is the projected area of the contact, E_r is a reduced modulus [3,8], and $\beta = 1.034$ for a Berkovitch indenter.

In Eq. (1), S is deduced straightforwardly from the $F(d)$ response. The A_r projected area is derived from the indentation depth, using the shape function of the indenter [3]. Finally, the material modulus can be deduced from E_r, knowing the modulus of the indenter material. Some previously published results [2] thus obtained for the Young modulus of nonmetallic inclusions found in bearing steels are collected in Table 1.

Table 1 - *Young's modulus, E, of typical nonmetallic inclusions found in 100Cr6 and 80MoCrV42 bearing steels, measured by means of the nano-indentation technique.*

Inclusion species	Alumina	Titanium nitride	Spinel[1]	Calcium Aluminate[2]	Calcium Aluminate[3]	Manganese Sulphide[4]
E (GPa)	375	380	279	126	195	103

[1] $(Al_2O_3)_3$, (MgO) ; [2] $(Al_2O_3)_2$, (CaO) ; [3] $(Al_2O_3)_6$, (CaO) ; [4] MnS .

For the purpose of exploiting the plastic response of the material, a pyramidal shape with sharp edges is no more suitable, since it produces wide stress and strain ranges near the pyramid edges, which renders very difficult the quantitative analysis of the contact by a finite element (FE) code. In contrast, with a spherical indenter the stress concentrations are minimised and the nano-indentation tests can be easily simulated by using the F.E. method in axisymmetric conditions. A micrograph of the indenter tip used in this work for such measurements is shown in Figure 2.

In order to separate the elastic and plastic contributions to the displacement, the specimens were successively loaded and unloaded, at increasing maximal loads. Then, the d_r residual displacement of the indenter after unloading (Figure 1) is a good parameter for characterizing this contact plasticity. However, due to the parabolic-like shape of the unloading curves, the measurement of this residual displacement at zero force is not very accurate. So, the difference between displacements at loading and unloading measured for a low load (10 mN), was chosen to characterize the plastic response of the contact. For each material, the procedure was repeated several times in different positions. The scatter on d_r values, presumably due to the heterogeneity of the microstructure, was generally less than +/- 3nm. A mean d_r value was calculated from these data.

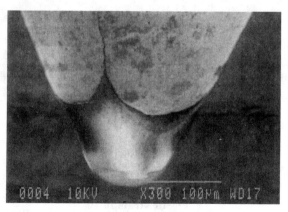

Figure 2 – *Scanning electron micrograph of the indenter tip. The effective radius of the tip is 105 μm.*

Experimental Results

Strain Hardening Laws

Figure 3 shows the strain hardening law obtained for the five carburised steels. The plastic strains, ranging from 10^{-5} to 10^{-2}, are plotted according to a logarithmic scale. Beyond the latter value the specimen deformation became inhomogeneous and led rapidly to fracture, especially for specimens with a high carbon concentration. As expected, the strength of these carburised steels increases with an increasing carbon concentration, whatever the considered proof strain may be. However, this trend tends to saturate for the higher concentration (0.86 wt % C). Furthermore, $\sigma(\varepsilon_p)$ data have been fitted with analytical strain hardening laws which are defined by only two or three parameters. Thus, a good fit can be obtained, for all the carbon concentrations, with the simple power law $\sigma = B \times (\varepsilon_p \times 10^6)^n$ (Figure 3). Only a small deviation can be noticed for the lower carbon concentration (0.35 wt % C) in the very low strain range ($\varepsilon_p < 80 \times 10^{-6}$). In addition, it should be mentioned that a single value of the exponent $n = 0.115$ is valid for all the specimens, which means that the shape of all the curves is the same. In contrast, the B factor varies from 715 to 1070 MPa for carbon concentrations ranging from 0.35% to 0.86%, respectively.

A similar procedure was used for the nitrided steel [9]. It should be noted that the steel behavior can no longer be well described with the previous power law. Thus, the Swift law, $\sigma = B \times (C + \varepsilon_p \times 10^6)^n$ with $B = 1450$ MPa, $C = 16$ and $n = 0.067$, had to be used. This means that, compared to the carburised steel, the nitrided steel exhibits a more marked stress threshold before a measurable micro-plastic strain can be detected.

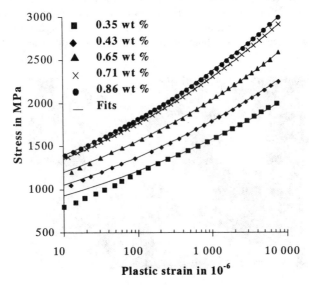

Figure 3 - *Strain-hardening curves of carburised steel obtained through compression tests on thin wall tubes. Individual marks = experimental data , continuous line = power law fit* $\sigma = B \times (\varepsilon_p \times 10^6)^n$ *with B ranging from 715 to 1070 MPa and n = 0.115.*

Nano-Indentation Response

Figure 4 shows, for the various carburised specimens, the evolution of the residual displacement deduced from each test as a function of the maximal load, $d_r(F_{max})$. As expected from the relationship between the strength and the carbon concentration in steel, the residual displacement for a given maximal force decreases as the carbon concentration increases. Furthermore, it should be noted that all the experimental data can be fitted with the power law $d_r = \alpha \cdot F_{max}^{\beta}$, with a single value of the exponent $\beta = 1.5$ for all the specimens.

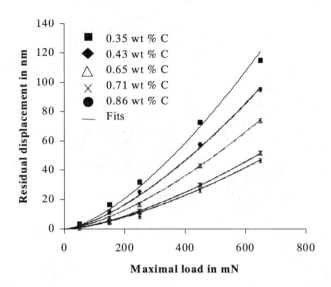

Figure 4 - *Indenter residual displacement vs maximal load, d_r (F_{max}), for homogeneous carburised tube like specimens ; individual marks = experimental data , continuous line = power law fit $d_r = \alpha \times F_{max}{}^{\beta}$ with α ranging from 47 to 121$\times 10^{-3}$ and β = 1.5.*

The same procedure was applied to the nitrided specimen [9]. It has been found that the above power law is also suitable to describe the experimental behavior, but with a β value (= 1.82) different from that obtained for the carburised steels.

Finite Element Simulation of the Nano-Indentation Test

Finite Element Modeling Conditions

The F.E. computations were carried out using the ABAQUS software. As the indenter was spherical, axi-symmetric conditions were used. A purely elastic isotropic constitutive law[4] was used for this diamond indenter. For the material to be indented, we used an elasto-plastic constitutive law with an isotropic hardening derived from the strain hardening law established in the previous section. In this law, the Tresca criterion was chosen as the plasticity criterion since plasticity mainly occurs in shear mode due to dislocation glide. Finally, it should be mentioned that, in this simulation, the material properties are assumed to be homogeneous at the scale of the indented region, which is justified by the fineness of the microstructure with respect to the scale of the stressed zone. The system "indenter/material" was meshed carefully, especially near the contact zone (Figure 5), with quadrilateral four node elements. The contact area was assumed to be frictionless but, for a selected case, it has been verified that this simplification does not introduce a significant deviation in the results.

---

[4] Young's modulus 1140 GPa, Poisson's ratio 0.07.

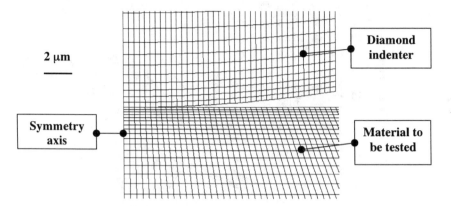

2 μm

Diamond indenter

Symmetry axis

Material to be tested

Figure 5 - *Finite element calculations : mesh details in the region of the contact.*

Validation of the FE Calculations

First, Figure 6 shows, for a series of successive loading-unloading tests carried out on the 0.43 wt% C carburised steel, a detailed comparison between the force computed using the F.E. method and the experimental load. It can be seen that the computed values correspond closely to the experimental data. This was true for all carburised and nitrided specimens.

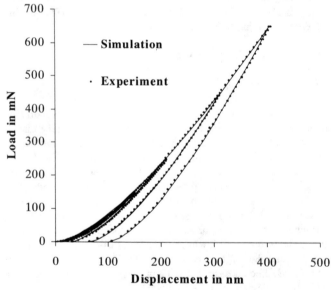

Figure 6 - *Load versus displacement, F(d), during successive loading-unloading sequences for 0.43 wt% C carburised steel; circle marks = experimental data; continuous lines = F.E. computations.*

To show this overall agreement, the experimental and computed values of the residual displacement d_r have been plotted as a function of the maximal force F_{max} in Figure 7 for all the carburised specimens and for the nitrided steel. All these successful comparisons prove the soundness of the assumptions and the validity of the method developed for solving the direct problem, i.e. predicting the nano-indentation response from the knowledge of the strain hardening law of the material. The resolution of the inverse problem in the case of the surface hardened parts with a strength profile is presented in the next section.

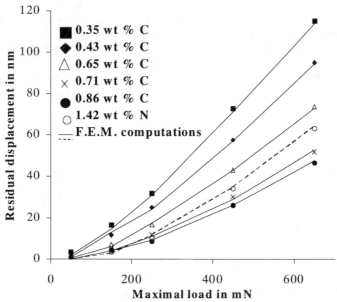

Figure 7 - *Residual displacement as a function of maximal load, d_r (F_{max}), for all the carburised steels and the nitrided one ; individual marks = experimental data ; continuous or dotted lines = F.E. computations.*

Application to Surface-Hardened Steels

A Method to Solve the Inverse Problem

The problem of practical interest consists in determining the local strain-hardening law from the $d_r(F_{max})$ nano-indentation response of the material. If the elasto-plastic law of the material was completely unknown, solving such an inverse problem would be quite difficult. However, the study presented above has proved that all homogeneously carburised steels exhibit strain hardening power laws which differ only in coefficient B. Hence, for the same steel prepared in the same conditions, but carburised with a carbon concentration profile (a real carburised layer in a thick specimen), it can be assumed that for a small volume, at any given depth, the strain hardening law would not deviate significantly from the general form found for the homogeneously carburised specimens. This assumption will be discussed later, but let it be mentioned that a good practical way to assess its validity consists in comparing the experimental data $d_r(F_{max})$ to the expected power law. As shown for homogeneously treated specimens, a good fit should be obtained by adjusting the B parameter only in the power law, otherwise it should be concluded that the assumptions on which the method is based are presumably no longer valid. This situation will be illustrated in the next section.

According to this approach, coefficient B remains to be determined as a function of depth when the carbon content profile is unknown. Then, one possible way for obtaining the microplasticity hardening law would consist in fitting the computed $d(F)$ law to the experimental data, with an adjustment of coefficient B in the strain hardening law introduced in the F.E. software. Such a method would be rather computer time consuming since it would have to be repeated for many depths. The method we use takes advantage of the fact that the strain hardening and nano-indentation laws both exhibit a power law shape with, for each law, only one parameter depending on the carbon concentration, B and α, respectively. Hence, from the previous results, a monotonic relationship $B(\alpha)$ can be established between these two parameters (Figure 8 - curve a).

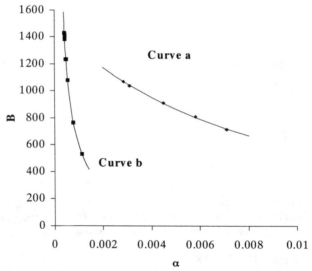

Figure 8 - *Relationship between the B and α parameters of the strain hardening and nano-indentation responses, respectively, for a) carburised specimens (experimental) ; b) nitrided specimens (F.E. simulations).*

For the nitrided steel, the relationship between B and α cannot be established in exactly the same way, since only one homogeneously nitrided specimen was available. However, it can be assumed that the constant shape property of the $\sigma(\varepsilon)$ law that was verified for the carburised steel also holds for the nitrided steel. That is to say a change in the nitrogen concentration can be described simply by changing B in the Swift law. Then, it has been verified from F.E. computations that with such an assumption, the nano-indentation response would also follow the power law $d_r = \alpha \cdot F_{max}{}^\beta$ with a single value of β. Hence, the aforementioned $B(\alpha)$ relationship can be derived from these F.E. computations of the $d_r(F_{max})$ nano-indentation response (Figure 8 - curve b).

To sum up, the method for obtaining the strain-hardening law comes down to :
- acquiring the nano-indentation $d_r(F_{max})$ response,
- adjusting the relevant power law with this response by means of the α parameter,
- deducing the B parameter, representative of the strain-hardening law, from α, by means of the $B(\alpha)$ relationship.

Results on carburised and nitrided steels

Acquisition of the nano-indentation data - One can think to two methods for acquiring the nano-indentation data throughout the treated depth of a carburised or a nitrided steel (Figure 9). First, the nano-indentation test can be performed from the surface. Then, by removing successively thin layers of the material and repeating the test after each layer removal, the complete depth range of interest can be tested. Second, a section perpendicular to the treated surface can be made. Then, from several tests performed at increasing distances from the surface corner, the complete depth range of interest can be tested. The former method is rather tedious. Therefore, in this work, the latter method was preferred, since it requires a single surface preparation.

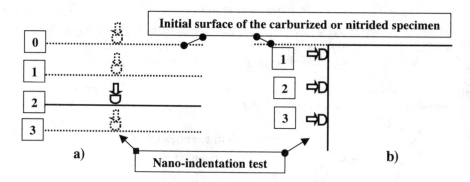

Figure 9 - *Schematic of possible nano-indentation procedures a) by successive removals of thin layers (1, 2, 3 ...) ; b) from a section perpendicular to the hardened surface.*

Results - The d_r (F_{max}) response was measured at various depths according to the method described above (Figure 9-b) . Then, these experimental data were fitted by the $d_r = \alpha \cdot F_{max}{}^{\beta}$ power law, with $\beta = 1.5$ and $\beta = 1.82$ for carburised and nitrided specimens, respectively. All the experimental d_r (F_{max}) data sets and corresponding best power law fits are presented in Figure 10 for the carburised specimens. Those obtained for nitrided specimens can be found in [9]. As expected, it appears that the residual displacement for a given maximal load increases as the depth at which the indentation is performed increases. Furthermore, it should be pointed out that a good agreement between the power law and the experimental data sets is observed for most of the cases. This testifies to the validity of the assumptions on which the method is based. However, for the greater depths below the surface (2500 μm), the agreement is not so perfect, which means that these assumptions are presumably no longer valid.

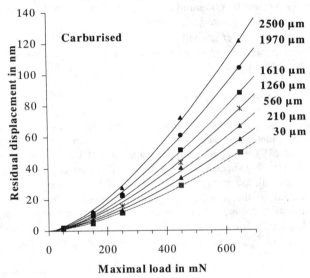

Figure 10 - *Comparison between experimental d_r (F_{max}) data and power laws ($d_r = \alpha \times F_{max}^{\beta}$ with $\beta = 1.5$) for various depths in the carburised layer (bulk specimen) ; individual marks = experimental data ; continuous lines = power laws*

Then, the strain hardening law at a given depth is deduced from the $B(\alpha)$ relationship. Finally, the micro-yield stress profile for any proof strain can be deduced

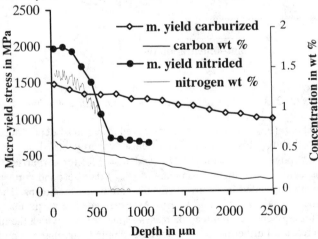

Figure 11 - *Micro-yield stress (proof strain of 20×10^{-6}), and carbon and nitrogen concentration profiles for the carburised and nitrided layers.*

from the knowledge of all the strain hardening laws. The micro-yield profiles relevant for the application to endurance limit model specified in the introduction, namely corresponding to a proof strain of 20×10^{-6}, have been plotted in Figure 11 for both types of surface hardening. These plots show that the micro-yield stress decreases gradually as the depth increases for the carburised layer, whereas it decreases much more steeply for the nitrided layer. In fact, it can be seen that these profiles are very closely related to those of the carbon and nitrogen concentrations, respectively (Figure 11). The level of micro-yield stress in the nitrided layer, within 250 μm depth, appears to be 33% higher than that of the carburised layer. It is worth noting that the difference is not so marked for the Vickers hardness, about 12%, which has been explained by a different hardening rate in the nitrided and carburised steels [9].

Discussion

In the method developed in the previous sections, the local strain-hardening law in a surface-hardened layer is determined from the local nano-indentation d_r (F_{max}) response of the material. At this step of the presentation, a few points should be discussed:
- the extension of the strained volume involved in the nano-indentation test, to know whether it is really suitable for characterizing the profile of mechanical properties in a surface-hardened layer;
- the strain range in this deformed volume, in order to verify that only micro-plastic strains are actually involved in such a test; and
- the role of first order internal stresses (often called residual stresses).

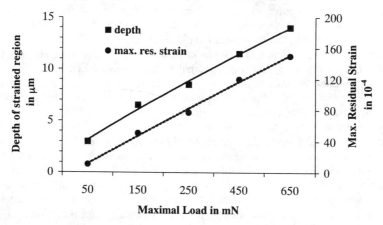

Figure 12 - *Total depth of the plastically strained region, P, and maximal residual strain, ε_{zz}, in this region versus the maximal applied load for the specimen carburised with 0.43 wt% C.*

The two first questions can be easily clarified by analyzing the data provided by F.E. computations, which allow one to obtain all the features of the strain field below the contact. For that purpose the following quantities have been derived from the FE results : the depth, P, of the plastically strained region where the micro-plastic strain exceeds 20×10^{-6} , the maximal residual strain ε_{zz} along the symmetry axis perpendicular to the contact.

In the case of the 0.43 wt% C carburised specimen (Figure 12), the results show that depth P of the plastically deformed region is of the order of a few micrometers for the lower maximal loads applied in the nano-indentation tests and that it extends up to 14 micrometers for the higher maximal loads. P values depend slightly on the material strength linked with the carbon or nitrogen concentration, but they do not deviate by more than 30% from those presented in Figure 12. The sizes of these volumes are quite satisfactory. On the one hand, these volumes are large enough as far as the scale of the various phases in the microstructure (tempered martensite plates, precipitates ..) to be homogenised over the measured volume is concerned for the individual properties. It should be mentioned that the prior austenite grain size (about a hundred micrometers) is much larger than the indented volume, but the initial crystalline anisotropy at this scale is smoothed out by the numerous martensite variants which are produced within such a grain. On the other hand, they are small enough regarding the scale of the hardened layer profile, i.e. the mechanical properties are quasi-uniform over the measured volume. In other words, the tested volume is well representative of the "macroscopic" properties at a given depth.

The data plotted in Figure 12 also show that the nano-indentation tests performed in this work are concerned only with small plastic strains whose maximal value increases with an increasing applied load, reaching about 1.5 % for the highest one. Thus, the plastic strain range involved in these nano-indentation tests is at least one order of magnitude below those involved in classical hardness tests for which plastic strains usually reach 10 to 50% [5]. This explains why the proposed method is a good way to identify the strain hardening law for very small plastic strains.

Concerning the third question, namely the possible influence of internal stresses, it is well known that compressive first order internal stresses are induced in the layer by carburising or nitriding treatments [10]. So, it might be feared that the superposition of the internal stress to the applied measurement stress would distort the nano-indentation results, that is to say that the (micro-) yield stress thus obtained would be an "apparent" (micro-) yield stress. In fact, in the case of our tube shape specimens, such first order internal stresses are not expected since the material expansion, which is at their origin in a thick specimen, occurs quasi-homogeneously within the thickness of the tube wall. In the case of the thick specimens, it should be noted that these first order internal stresses are, at least partly, relaxed by the cut inherent to the preparation of the surface to be indented (Figure 9). So, it is expected that the non-relaxed part of first order internal stresses does not introduce a large deviation in the results obtained for real layers [11].

Conclusion

The experiments and analyses performed in this work show that the nano-indentation technique is suitable to investigate the profile of microplasticity properties of surface hardened bearing steels. This method consists of two steps : first, solving the direct problem (simulation by F.E. computation of the nano-indention response from the knowledge of the microplasticity strain-hardening law of the material) ; then, identifying the unknown strain hardening law, but of pre-established form, from the nano-indentation $d_r(F_{max})$ response. The former step has been validated by comparing the experimental and simulated responses. The latter step has been applied successfully to the study of standard carburised and nitrided steels. Especially, their profiles of micro-yield stress with a proof strain of 20×10^{-6} has been obtained, which is quite useful for evaluating the endurance limit of bearings made of these materials [1].

Further improvement of the method would consist in accounting quantitatively for the non-relaxed part of first order internal stresses inherent to surface treatments. This complementary study is specially justified for nitrided layers because they exhibit a high level of residual stress [11].

References

[1] Vincent, A., Fougères, R., Lormand, G., Dudragne, G., and Girodin, D., "A Physically Based Endurance Limit Model for Through Hardened and Surface Hardened Bearing Steels," *Bearing Steel Technology, ASTM STP 1419*, J. M. Beswick, Ed. American Society for Testing Materials, West Conshohocken, PA, 2002.

[2] Lamagnère, P., Girodin, D., Meynaud, P., Vergne, F., and Vincent, A., "Study of elasto-plastic properties of Microheterogeneities by means of Nano-indentation Measurements : Application to Bearing Steels," *Materials Science and Engineering*, Vol. A215, 1996, pp. 134-142.

[3] Oliver, W.C. and Phar, G.M., " An Improved Technique for Determining Hardness and Elastic Modulus using Load and Displacement Sensing Indentation Experiments," *Journal of Materials Research*, Vol. 7, 1992, pp.1564-1583.

[4] Phar, G.M., Oliver, W.C., and Brotzen, F.R., "On the Generality of the Relationship among Contact Stiffness, Contact Area, and Elastic Modulus during Indentation," *Journal of Materials Research*, Vol. 7, 3, 1992, pp. 613-617.

[5] Milman, Y. V., Galanov, B.A., Chugunova, S.I., "Plasticity Characteristic Obtained Through Hardness Measurement," *Acta metallurgica et materialia,* Vol. 41, 1993, pp. 2523-2532.

[6] Sommer, C., Christ, H.J. and Mughrabi, H., "Non-Linear Elastic Behaviour of the Roller Bearing Steel SAE 52100 During Cyclic Loading," *Acta metallurgica et materialia*, Vol. 39, 1991, pp. 1177-1187.

[7] Sneddon, I. N., "The Relation between Load and Penetration in the Axisymmetric Boussinesq Problem for a Punch of Arbitrary Profile," *International Journal of Engineering Science*, Vol. 3, 1965, pp.47-57.

[8] Doerner, M. F. and Nix, W. D., "A Method for Interpreting the Data from Depth Sensing Indentation Instruments," *Journal of Materials Research*, Vol. 1, 1986, pp. 601-609.

[9] Elghazal, H., Lormand, G., Hamel, A., Girodin, D. and Vincent, A., "Microplasticity Characteristics obtained through Nano-indentation Measurements : Application to Surface Hardened Steels," *Materials Science and Engineering*, Vol. A303, 2001, pp.110-119.

[10] Eyzop, D., Viville, A., Robin, C., Chicot, D. and Lesage, J., "Extensometric determination and prediction of the residual stresses in carburized steels," *Proceedings of the Fourth European Conference on Residual Stresses* (Vol. 1), Cluny, France, june 4 - 6, 1996, S. Denis, J.L. Lebrun, B. Bourniquel, M. Barral, and J.F. Flavenot (Eds), SF2M and ENSAM publishers, 1996, pp. 417-425.

[11] Jacq, C., Lormand, G., Nelias, D., Girodin, D. and Vincent A., "On the Influence of Residual Stresses in Determining Micro-Plasticity Properties of Surface Hardened Steels through Nano-Indentation Measurements," to be published.

Aat P. Voskamp[1]

Microstructural Stability and Bearing Performance

Reference: Voskamp, A. P., **"Microstructural Stability and Bearing Performance,"** *Bearing Steel Technology, ASTM STP 1419*, J. M. Beswick, Ed., American Society for Testing and Materials International, West Conshohocken, PA, 2002.

Abstract: Predicting rolling performance and dimensional stability of rolling bearings under all combinations of load and temperature becomes a real challenge in the material science discipline, even knowing the differences in bearing performance for different steel alloys and applied heat treatments. The consistently maintained high level of steel cleanliness in present day bearing manufacturing, based on modern steel making technology, is not the only decisive parameter minimizing the probability for spalling fatigue. A second highly important factor is the micro-plastic behavior of the steel under conditions of repetitive cyclic stressing. The steel's elastic response, acquired during running-in, will deteriorate after some time, increasing the probability for crack initiation at and around weak points in the steel matrix and crack propagation away from there leading to fatigue failure. Aspects of shakedown and materials decay are thus related to the probability for bearing failure to occur in combination with steel cleanliness. The ability to maintain an elastic response during cyclic stressing is determined on one hand by the combined effects of applied stress level, running temperature and number of revolutions, and on the other by the selected steel alloy, the applied heat treatment and the work hardening response during running-in. Examples are discussed of observed microstructural stability and superb bearing performance under extreme conditions.

Keywords: material response, rolling contact fatigue, microstructural change, metal softening, X-ray diffraction analysis, high reliability in bearing performance.

Introduction

The superb reliability of ball and roller bearings, shown both in laboratory tests and in service, stimulates the engineer's wish either to increase allowable stress levels still

---

[1] Consultant, Voskamp XRD Consultancy, Mevrouw Leinweberlaan 32, 3971 KZ Driebergen, The Netherlands. Formerly with SKF Engineering & Research Centre B.V., 3430 DT Nieuwegein, The Netherlands.

further or to "down-size" the bearing product. Guidance is provided from a rather large database of laboratory bearing endurance tests, across a spectrum of load, speed, temperature and materials variants. Extrapolations however, have been found to be unreliable. Performance parameters, such as rolling track conformity, operating temperature and lubrication supply are just as important as the common factors of load and speed. And the robustness of the bearing in its application should be included with other factors influencing bearing failure, e.g., the dimensional instability of the bearing components or other phenomena such as surface distress due to insufficient lubrication. The concept used in rolling bearing design is based on the capacity to withstand rolling contact fatigue. In general, fatigue of metals is associated with the occurrence of crack initiated in regions in which micro-plastic deformation has accumulated. Typically this might be in the vicinity of stress raisers associated with discontinuities in the steel matrix, such as inclusions or carbide clusters, or with surface features in the contacting rolling bearing surfaces themselves. Micro-plastic deformation will always develop prior to crack initiation and will occur at all points in the steel matrix where the resultant stress level exceeds the local existing micro-yield limit. Particularly in the hardened microstructure of common rolling bearing steels, it is almost impossible to detect directly these localized regions in used bearings - only detailed TEM analysis provides direct evidence. This is for various reasons. One of them, most strikingly, is the inhomogeneous state of the steel's microstructure itself, which is in a quenched and partly tempered state, showing additional short-range variations due to carbide segregation as a result of "banding". This banding phenomenon is inherently related to the optimally efficient methods followed in producing commercial steel.

The direct detection of metal fatigue damage in these microstructures is therefore most difficult. Only by indirect measures is it possible to follow the damage process effectively. Evidence for the occurrence of micro-plastic deformation is the build up of residual stress, detectable by means of quantitative X-ray diffraction methods. This build up of residual stress is not the result of one localized event but rather the result of the accumulated effect of many small regions in which micro-plastic deformation is concentrated. The level of residual stress and the size of those regions in which residual stress is detected are thus volume-averaged measures of the severity of "the risk of fatigue damage initiation". Since these effects of accumulating plastic deformation may be detected prior to the actual development of crack initiation and propagation, an even higher reliability of bearing performance prediction is achievable, giving support to the new demands facing the bearing engineer.

Three Stages in Material Response

The analysis of residual stress concentrations in the highest loaded regions of bearings returned from service shows a partition of the microstructural changes during rolling contact loading into three stages [1]. These three stages are referred to as: (I) shakedown, (II) steady state (elastic response) and (III) instability, as discussed in detail in [1, 2]. This partition can be observed by plotting the recorded changes in the level of residual stress of bearings returned from service at different intervals with respect to the number of stress cycles experienced. The third stage of microstructural change is characterized by metal softening or a decrease of the micro-yield limit, as a result of which the material strength may fall below the elevated load-induced stresses associated with inclusions, always present in commercially produced steels. The probability of crack initiation at previously sub-critical size inclusions thus grows. This argument has been discussed in detail [3] with a number of examples involving many bearings on test.

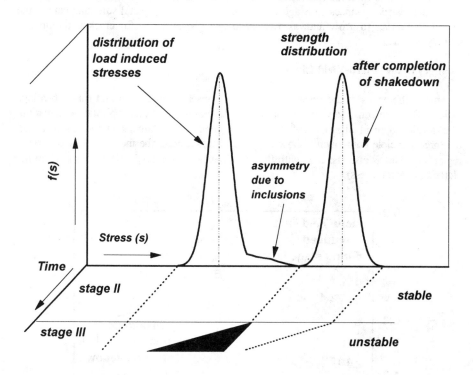

Figure 1- *Schematic illustration of a hypothetical strength distribution of the steel and a hypothetical asymmetric distribution of load induced stress, represented by density distribution functions f(s) of stress, both occurring in the highest loaded subsurface region. Metal softening in the third stage causes the strength distribution to shift to lower stress, consequently an ever-increasing amount of overlap will occur as the third stage progresses. Overlap of the distributions in the third stage of material response indicates an increasing probability of fatigue crack initiation.*

Figure 1 shows schematically the distributions of load-induced stresses and of material strength as a function of the number of stress cycles/time. Reflecting some degree of uncertainty, the strength density distribution $f(s)$ is given as a Gaussian. Similarly, the stress density distribution $f(s)$ is characterized by a Gaussian extended, however, by a high stress tail arising from stresses associated with inclusions in the steel matrix. Even if a cleanliness of one ppm of oxygen could be reached, this asymmetric feature would still persist. Such a tail should, therefore, always be added. Since crack initiation occurs preferentially where these two distributions overlap, it is clear that initiation is associated principally with inclusions. After shakedown, stage I not shown in Figure 1, with its attendant increase of the micro-yield limit as a result of work-hardening, the degree of overlap is negligible and the stable elastic material response Stage II is entered. No crack initiation is anticipated under such conditions. The degree of overlap, indicated in Figure 1 by the dotted lines in the time/stress plane, remains fixed and essentially zero. Once the local steel matrix advances to Stage III, however, progressive metal softening causes the region of overlap to grow and, as a consequence, the potential for crack initiation will steadily increase.

Changes in the Micro-Yield Limit

Small differences in the residual stress levels observed in un-run and run-in bearings indicate the high sensitivity of residual stress development to micro-plastic deformation. The developed residual stress σ_E^R state is a complex three-dimensional stress field and the three-principle components show depth gradients around the most severely deformed region [4]. This is also the case with the load-induced stress field (σ_E^L resulting from the Hertzian contact stress).

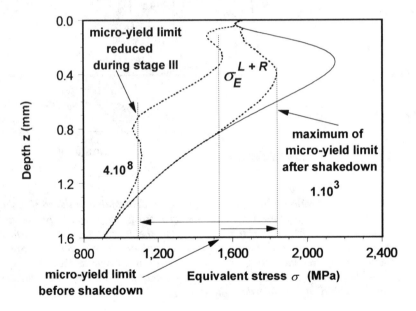

Figure 2- *Equivalent stress occurring in the subsurface region in the inner ring of a 6309 deep groove ball bearing at two stages of running under an imposed maximum Hertzian contact stress of 3.8 GPa. Three depth distributions are shown: one is the equivalent stress due to the Hertzian stress alone (σ_E^L, solid line) and the two dotted lines represent the equivalent stress, $\sigma_E^{(L+R)}$, resulting from superposition of the residual stress developed after completion of shakedown, the first stage, and after 4.10^8 inner ring rotations, deep into the third stage of material response.*

Consequently the effect of the residual stress can only be taken into consideration using the equivalent stress approach based on the distortion-energy hypothesis, according to von Mises. Accordingly, the equivalent stress $\sigma_E^{(L+R)}$ is calculated by superposition of both stress components in the three principal directions separately.

Figure 2 shows the depth distribution of this equivalent stress for a case where the maximum load-induced stress occurs at a depth of about 0.35 mm with amplitude of about 2200 MPa. This represents the stress depth distribution in a radially loaded (28 kN) type 6309 deep groove ball bearing inner ring. Due to the shakedown induced residual stress (not shown, reference is made to [5]), an **increase** of the micro-yield limit is predicted based on the above-mentioned method of superposition. By contrast superposition of the in Stage III developed residual stress on the load-induced subsurface stress results in a **decrease** in the maximum of the equivalent stress. After completion of the shakedown stage no further plastic micro-deformation will occur, giving direct evidence for the increased micro-yield limit as a result of work hardening during shakedown. This shift is indicated in the figure by a dotted line and an arrow at the lower part of the graph indicating a net increase of the micro-yield limit from an assumed level of 1520 MPa (a level three times the micro-yield limit in simple shear, as discussed in [2] based on the theoretical work of [6]) to a level of 1840 MPa. The graph also shows the subsequent decrease of the micro-yield limit once the third stage of material response is entered. Softening and the accumulation of residual stress with continuous cyclic stressing during this stage combine to shift this limit to a significantly lower level provided the load-induced stress is not modified by any substantial changes in the Hertzian contact ellipse due to uncontrolled groove formation. In the case shown, a reduction to about 1100 MPa is calculated. The depth distribution of the equivalent stress closer to the surface is peculiar. In the depth interval from 0.1 to 0.4 mm, only a relatively small reduction is observed, attributed to a secondary hardening phenomenon occurring in the steel in response to cyclic stressing at the particular operating temperature reached [5]. The continuous lowering of the micro-yield limit at larger depth indicates continuous micro-plastic occurrences in this region.

Stage III Threshold Prediction: Influence of Stress and Temperature

It has been shown in [3] how increasing levels of decay in the third stage of material response are associated with an increasing probability of bearing fatigue failure. It has also been shown how, by extrapolation of the trend in material response, the threshold to the third stage can be found, a point in time (expressed in number of revs.) before any bearing fatigue failures have actually been observed. The existence of such a point illustrates the most common rule that "fatigue is not caused by elastic stress cycling" (i.e. during Stage II). This extrapolation has been used and applied to predicting bearing performance from test results for all cases where material response was included in the database, yielding an exceptionally high degree of reliability for this "zero failures" time. Such success is in striking contrast to the classical extrapolation of failure occurrences by means of a Weibull distribution, which assigns the value zero to the "zero failures" point [7]. Especially with present day high levels of cleanliness of common bearing steels resulting in very long endurance test times, such an alternative method for life prediction based on current understanding of materials behavior, as discussed in [3], is most valuable. As shown in [1] the length of the second stage is determined not only by the maximum occurring load-induced stress and the materials characteristics. There are other parameters that might also contribute to the length of the second stage. The operating bearing temperature is one most significant parameter, whose effect is more critical then might be expected, its magnitude depending on which bearing component is of greatest importance to the bearing life expectation. Major differences in fatigue occurrence might even develop due to temperature differences within the bearing (inner ring, rolling element, or outer ring) caused by the operational conditions. Table 1 shows the time to Stage III threshold (expressed in number of inner ring rotations) of radially loaded 6309 type deep groove ball bearings for five combinations of applied radial bearing load, velocity (inner ring rotations per minute), and maintained outer ring operating temperature.

Table 1- Results from material response analysis showing the Stage III threshold values, expressed in number of inner ring rotations, obtained from quantitative X-ray diffraction measurement of residual stress for the given bearing running conditions. These, standard type 6309 deep groove ball bearings, were made of quenched and tempered SAE 52100 steel. Heat treatment and lubrication conditions are shown below the table.

Radial bearing load (kN)	C/P	P_{max} Hertz (GPa)	Outer ring temp (°C)	Velocity (rpm)	Stage III Threshold (revs)
13.2	4.0	2.9	55	6000	1.5×10^{9}
13.2	4.0	2.9	83	1500	5.0×10^{7}
18.8	2.9	3.3	45	6000	1.5×10^{9}
18.8	2.9	3.3	83	1500	1.0×10^{7}
28.0	1.9	3.8	55	6000	5.0×10^{7}

austenitized 840 °C/15' ; quenched 60°C/15' ; tempered 150°C/60'
lubricant Vitrea 33 oil ; viscosity 3.44 $10^{-5} m^2 s^{-1}$ at 50°C

For the lower applied load, comparison of the first two combinations shows that the time to threshold is reduced by a factor of 30 when the operating temperature is increased by as little as 28°C, from 55°C to 83°C! Similarly, the first and third combinations show that when the applied load is increased from 13.2 kN to 18.8 kN, the same time to threshold may still be obtained just by reducing the temperature by 10°C, from 55°C to 45°C! The classical Lunderg and Palmgren [7] approach to bearing life expectation using the phenomenological formula, which reads: $L_{10}=10^6 \cdot (C/P)^3$, is not easily able to cope with these observations. Furthermore, it is not clear whether the material response should be linked to the C/P approach or to the Hertzian contact stress approach. This dilemma is highlighted in Figure 3. In this figure four solid lines are shown in a diagram of applied bearing load P (kN) versus the ratio of C/P. The lines represent the capacities of four type 6309 deep groove ball bearings modified by applying different inner ring groove radii of, respectively 9.05 mm, 9.34 mm, 10.38 mm and infinity (a cylindrical inner ring), resulting in different ellipticities of the Hertzian contact at the inner ring. Vertical lines of constant C/P clearly do not coincide with lines of constant Hertzian contact stress, also drawn in this diagram. This difficulty is highlighted in Figures 4 and 5, which are details taken from Figure 3.

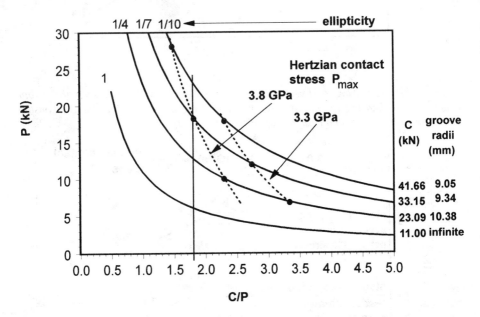

Figure 3- *Radial bearing load versus C/P ratio for modified 6309 type deep groove ball bearings. Lines of constant C/P ratio do not coincide with lines of constant Hertzian contact stress.*

In the first detailed diagram of Figure 4, the bearing life results for two sets of tested bearings are given. These modified bearings were tested under different loads, respectively 18 kN and 27 kN, chosen to give approximately the same C/P ratio of 1.2 shown by the vertical line. Two lines of constant Hertzian contact stress and two lines of constant bearing capacity are also shown. Clearly the line of constant C/P intersects the lines of different capacity at different loads for which, according to the classical approach, the two lives should be equal.

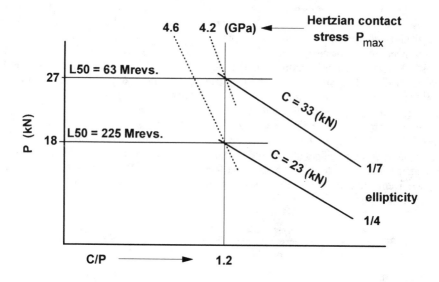

Figure 4- Radial bearing load versus C/P ratio for modified 6309 type deep groove ball bearings. Two bearing life results are shown with the corresponding lines of constant Hertzian contact stress and bearing capacity.

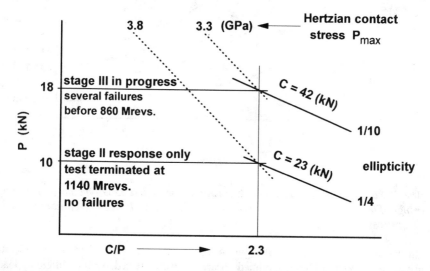

Figure 5- Radial bearing load versus C/P ratio for modified 6309 type deep groove ball bearings. Information about material response is provided for the two sets of bearings on test together with the corresponding lines of constant Hertzian contact stress and bearing capacity.

However, longer lives were observed for bearings with the lower capacity operating at the lower load, although these bearings were operating under a considerably higher Hertzian contact stress. A similar result has been observed at a different location in Figure 3 at a higher C/P level, in this case 2.3, as shown in Figure 5. In this case of relatively high C/P, complete bearing life estimation was not possible due to the low number of failures observed. For the bearings with the higher capacity (42 kN) operating under the higher load but at a lower Hertzian contact stress (3.3 GPa) several failures were observed before the test was terminated at 860 Mrevs., while the test of the bearings with the lower capacity operating under the lower load but at a higher contact stress (3.8 GPa) was terminated after 1140 Mrevs. and showed no failures at all. Additional information obtained from material response analysis is given in Figure 5. The bearings tested at the higher maximum Hertzian contact stress (3.8 GPa) were investigated after termination of the test and showed no further development of subsurface residual stress concentrations following those installed during shakedown. The bearings with the higher capacity and operating at the lower maximum Hertzian contact stress (3.3 GPa) showed Stage III development.

Stage III Threshold Prediction: Influence of Microstructural Stability

The results of material response analysis and bearing performance shown so far involve the 52100 bearing steel, which had been martensitically hardened (840°C/15') and tempered (150°/1h) according to standards used in practice. These bearings operate very satisfactorily for most normal applications. The constituents in the steel microstructure are however thermodynamically unstable and can potentially cause problems when the bearing is used at higher temperatures. Minor volume changes might occur upon transformation of one of the constituents. Bearings operating under more critical conditions, for example at higher temperatures, or involving maintenance of extreme stability or under very high demands of operational reliability, will thus require alternative heat treatments or even higher alloyed steels. In such cases a more stable microstructure than the normal tempered steel must be introduced. In case of operating bearing temperatures above 100°C the steel can still be used but should be tempered to higher temperatures (240°C) to remove most of the austenite from the steel matrix. Such higher tempering results in a small loss of hardness and a little gain in toughness. The size and dispersion of carbide precipitates in the martensite matrix will also change. This change has a significant impact on the micro-yield behavior of the steel under cyclic stressing conditions. Consequently, it will affect the length of the second stage of material response. Understanding the mechanism of stability of Stage II can thus lead to major improvement in bearing operational reliability in more critical bearing applications. In [1] the effect of applied bearing load on the length of Stage II was presented, while in [2] the effect of temperature on Stage III threshold was given. These two effects can be combined in a more complex temperature-stress-log.revs.-diagram as shown in Figure 6. In addition to some of the most important results from past-published data, two new experimental data points are included from high speed bearing applications run at significantly higher temperatures in the range from 150°C to 190°C involving higher tempered steel. At high stress, Figure 6 shows the significant temperature effect on the length of Stage II described earlier in [1] and [2]. However, the time to threshold at lower stress is less affected by temperature. The higher tempered steel maintains its stability,

Stage II response, at operating temperatures as high as 190°C while operating under a Hertzian contact stress of 1.8 GPa at least up to 1.10^{10} inner ring rotations! And under a maximal occurring Hertzian contact stress of 1.6 GPa and an operational bearing temperature of 150°C the stability is proven for at least 1.5×10^{10} inner ring rotations.

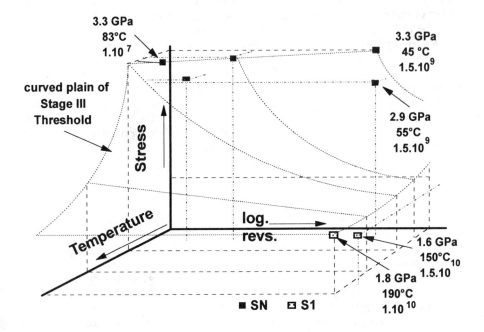

Figure 6- *Material response records of stage III threshold values, represented in a temperature-stress-log.revs.-diagram. Two different tempering temperatures have been used, designated by SN = 150°C for 1 hour (applied for the type 6309 deep groove ball bearing) and S1 = 240°C for 4 hours (applied for the type BA2-9005 angular contact ball bearing used at high operating temperature in a high speed application).*

Although the number of data points is sparse, a curved surface can be sketched in the temperature-stress-log.revs.-diagram to represents the behavior of the Stage III threshold. Such a surface is indicated by the dotted lines in the figure. The remarkable performance of S1 at lower stress is interpreted as the positive effect of the changes occurring in and around the small precipitates in the martensitic matrix formed during the higher initial tempering.

Stage III Threshold Prediction: Influence of Surface Features

After termination of a long exposure test at high speed and high temperature, several angular contact ball bearings, manufactured from SAE 52100 steel, containing 10 ppm Oxygen and 0.017 wt.-% Sulphur, showed material damages in the rolling track of the outer ring, which in the first-instance were ascribed to classical sub-surface initiated rolling contact fatigue. These damages (not noticed during running) occurred in the upper part of the rolling track of the rings and were randomly positioned around the whole circumference, at sometimes more the 10 locations within one ring, as illustrated in the schematic of Figure 7. X-ray diffraction investigation revealed a stable subsurface microstructure in these rings, so that clearly the material microstructure remained as it was entering Stage II after shakedown. The near surface region, at the outer edge location of the contact ellipse, showed however a change in the residual stress pattern, which indicates near surface plastic deformation, a phenomenon usually associated with, and leading to, surface distress. All the damaged regions were located at the outer edge of the contact ellipse where the Hertzian contact stress is significantly lower than its maximum value at the centre. In fact, the damage appears at y_{max} where the sliding velocity rather than the contact stress is a maximum [8]. The implication is that the hydrodynamically generated (viscous) shear stress on the surface, which is maximum there, makes plastic deformation in a thin surface layer more likely to occur.

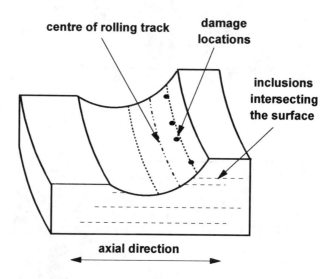

Figure 7- *Schematic highlighting the location of fatigue failures in the upper part of the contact path in the angular contact ball bearing outer ring. These damaged regions occurred randomly over the whole ring circumference.*

SEM analysis then revealed that the damage originated at the surface at locations where inclusions were intersecting the rolling track. Furthermore, the main crack propagation direction was axial, not circumferential, as shown in the SEM pictures of Figures 8 and 9. It is clear, then, that discontinuities in the steel surface are the trigger points for damage initiation. The subsequent crack propagation then followed the weakest direction from the initiation point, namely the direction in which the stringers occurred in the steel matrix. Bearings with conforming flow lines, i.e., parallel to the rolling track surface, on test in the same application were free of these damages. They performed as well as other bearings, as predicted from the bearing performance analysis high lighted in [9].

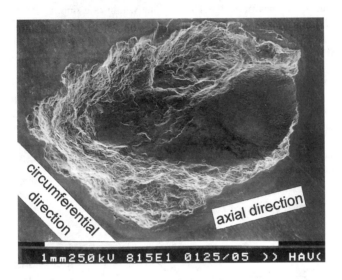

Figure 8- *SEM picture of the localized fatigue damage in the upper part of the rolling track in a type BA2-9005 angular contact ball bearing outer ring.*

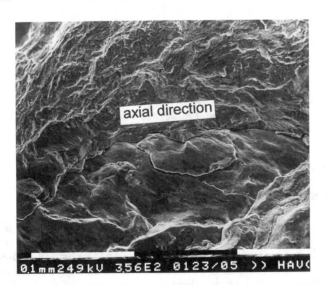

Figure 9- *SEM picture of the localized fatigue damage in the upper part of the rolling track in a type BA2-9005 angular contact ball bearing outer ring. This picture shows clear evidence for crack development in axial direction.*

Conclusions

Contrary to the commonly held opinions, contact fatigue in rolling bearings, manufactured from clean steels run with clean lubrication conditions, has been shown to be initiated by microstructural micro-plastic decay.

Maintaining a Stage II elastic response under cyclic stressing for as long as possible is key to extending bearing life. This is determined by the stability of the finely dispersed carbides in the tempered martensite.

An understanding of the three stages of material response allows optimization both of microstructural stability and of the technological parameters like steel cleanliness, conforming flow lines and surface integrity. By providing in addition fully flooded and clean lubrication conditions, superb bearing performance will be achieved.

Acknowledgment

The author would like to thank Dr. J.H. Tripp for critical reading the manuscript and is indebted to Dr. H.H. Wittmeyer, Group Technical Director of SKF, for permission to publish this paper.

References

[1] Voskamp, A. P., "Material Response to Rolling Contact Loading," *ASME Journal of Tribology*, Vol. 107, 1985, pp. 359-366.

[2] Voskamp, A. P., "Microstructural Changes During Rolling Contact Fatigue," *Ph D Thesis*, Delft University of Technology, Delft, The Netherlands, 1997, ISBN: 90-9010187-x.

[3] Voskamp, A. P., "Fatigue and Material Response in Rolling Contact," *Bearing Steels Into the 21st Century, ASTM STP 1327*, J.J.C. Hoo, Ed., American Society for Testing and Materials, West Conshohocken, PA, 1998, pp. 152-166.

[4] Voskamp, A. P. and Mittemeijer, E. J., "Residual Stress Development and Texture Formation During Rolling Contact Loading," *Industrial Applications of X-Ray Diffraction*, F. H. Chung and D. K. Smith, Eds., Marcel Dekker Inc., New York, 2000, ISBN: 0-8247-1992-1, pp. 813-846.

[5] Voskamp, A. P., "Subsurface Residual stress Concentrations during Rolling Contact Fatigue," *Materials Science Forum*, Vols. 347-349, 2000, pp. 346-351.

[6] Merwin, J. E., and Johnson, K. L., "An Analysis of Plastic Deformation in Rolling Conact," *Proceedings of the Institution of Mechanical Engineers*, Vol. 177, 1963, pp. 676-690.

[7] Lundberg, G. and Palmgren, A., "Dynamic Capacity of Rolling Bearings," *Acta Polytechnica, Mechanical Engineering Series,* Vol. 1, 1947, pp. 1-50.

[8] Tzenov P. I. and Sankar, T. S., "An Improved Model for Nonplanar Contact Sliding in Ball Bearings," *ASME Journal of Tribology,* Vol. 116, 1994, pp. 219-224.

[9] Voskamp, A. P., Nierlich, W., and Hengerer, F., "X-ray Diffraction Provides Answers to Bearing Failures," *SKF Evolution,* Vol. 4, 1997, pp. 25-31.

Material Factors in Bearing Life Calculations

Alain Vincent,[1] Roger Fougères,[1] Gérard Lormand,[1] Gilles Dudragne[2] and Daniel Girodin[2]

A Physically Based Endurance Limit Model for Through Hardened and Surface Hardened Bearing Steels

Reference: Vincent, A., Fougères, R., Lormand, G., Dudragne, G., and Girodin, D., " A Physically Based Endurance Limit Model for Through Hardened and Surface Hardened Bearing Steels," *Bearing Steel Technology, ASTM STP 1419*, J. M. Beswick, Ed., American Society for Testing and Materials International, West Conshohocken, PA, 2002.

Abstract: A physically based model for calculating the load rating of rolling bearings for an infinite life is presented. The proposed model is based on the fact that, for bearings operating under EHD conditions, material fatigue can not occur as long as the maximal local shear stress built up in the subsurface region does not exceed the micro-yield shear stress of the steel matrix. The calculation of the local shear stress can account for the presence of, on the one hand, hoop stresses or residual stresses and, on the other hand, on the steel inhomogeneities (nonmetallic inclusions, carbides) that act as stress raisers. The model is applied to investigate the influence of material parameters and operating conditions for various through hardened steels and surface hardened steels (carburized or nitrided).

Keywords: bearing steel, endurance limit, rolling contact fatigue, inclusion, inhomogeneity, through hardened steel, surface hardened steel.

Introduction

The concept of infinite life of bearings has grown during the last 20 years, thanks to the improvement of bearing steel manufacturing processes. However, available methods for calculating load rating of bearings are not suitable when an infinite life is required. As mentioned in many papers devoted to bearing life, bearing failure may occur in several ways, in relation with operating conditions and material properties [1,2,3]. So any concept of infinite life can become relevant only once these characteristics are well defined. Then, bearing life is determined by that damage mechanism that exhibits the greatest risk, in relation with the considered operating conditions and material properties.

---

[1] Professor, Groupe d'Etudes de Métallurgie Physique et de Physique des Matériaux (U.M.R. C.N.R.S. 5510) / I.N.S.A. / 69621 - Villeurbanne Cedex / France.
[2] Research manager and research scientist, respectively, at S.N.R. Roulements / B.P. 2017 / 74010 - Annecy Cedex / France.

This paper is concerned with the material point of view. For that purpose, the bearings are here considered to operate under elasto-hydrodynamic (E.H.D.) pure rolling conditions, with perfectly smooth contact surfaces. Under such conditions, the infinite life concept is actually related to the endurance limit of bearing steels. This idea of a stress threshold below which a material would not be damaged was first introduced by Weibull to fit statistical rupture data obtained from tensile tests. Since then, the concept of endurance limit has been introduced by various authors as a material constant in bearing fatigue models [4,5,6]. However, this material constant has to be determined from numerous endurance tests [7], which precludes any prediction for materials produced through a new process or with a new composition. Then, this paper aims at presenting a physically based approach of the endurance limit of bearing steels in the context of rolling contact fatigue. A specific character of such a fatigue problem is the very nonuniform stress field to which the material is subjected in the subsurface region. Two kinds of materials will be distinguished : through hardened steels and surface hardened steels. In the former case, the mechanical properties of the material can reasonably[3] be considered as uniform at the scale of the loaded volume. In contrast, for surface hardened steels the situation is more complicated because the mechanical properties can no longer be considered as uniform at the scale of the loaded volume : the profile of property has to be accounted for in relation with the nonuniform contact stress field. In the next section, the physical bases and the general conditions used for calculating the endurance limit are presented. Then, the method is applied to through hardened steels, for which the role of nonmetallic inclusions and carbides is emphasized. In the last section, the method is extended to surface hardened steels, for which the profile of mechanical property is accounted for.

Principles and General Conditions for Calculating the Endurance Limit on Physical Grounds

Physical Grounds of the Method

According to the scope of this work defined in the previous section, the greatest risk of failure is assumed to be the material fatigue. Then, generally speaking, the fatigue of metallic materials can be broadly classified according to the following stages :
1) The stage of microstructure changes, which are associated with cyclic (micro-) plasticity mechanisms, and
2) The damage stage.
The latter stage generally includes several sub-stages :
a) the creation of micro-cracks (crack nucleation),
b) the growth and, eventually, the coalescence of the micro-cracks,
c) the stable propagation of one or several major cracks, and
d) the catastrophic rupture, which may follow either the percolation of micro-cracks or the unstable growth of a major crack.
Moreover, it should be emphasized that metallic materials contain inhomogeneities, which exhibit an elastic or plastic behavior different from that of the matrix. Typically, in

---

[3] Except for the very thin surface layer that is affected by the final grinding process.

the case of bearing steels, these inhomogeneities are nonmetallic inclusions or carbides. They act as stress raisers when the material is loaded mechanically. Therefore, the aforementioned mechanisms occur preferentially in or around these inhomogeneities. For instance, in 100Cr6 and 80MoCrV42 steels, stage "1" is often evidenced by the appearance of white etching areas (WEA) around alumina inclusions or primary carbides [8]. Then, micro-cracks are often detected in these WEA [9].

In the context of rolling contact fatigue, various criteria have been proposed for assessing the endurance limit, which is convenient to define as the loading conditions under which the bearing life would be infinite [10]. As will be justified in the next section, these loading conditions will be hereafter expressed in terms of Hertzian pressure. Hence, a lower bound of the endurance limit, H_1, can be assessed as the maximum Hertzian pressure that does not engage stage "1". Then, for Hertzian pressures higher than H_1, cyclic micro-plasticity occurs. So, the maximum Hertzian pressure for which stage "2" would not be engaged, i.e., crack nucleation does not occur, could be considered as an alternative criterion (hereafter noted H_2). Finally, the maximum Hertzian pressure for which a crack is nucleated, but does not propagate to the surface [9], and hence spalling does not occur, could be also taken as a third possible criterion (hereafter noted H_3). It should be mentioned that, when an infinite number of cycles is considered, H_2 is expected to tend towards H_1. Moreover, it is rather difficult to calculate H_3 because crack propagation is strongly dependant both on the material microstructure and the contact geometry. In view of these elements, it appears that the lower bound H_1 can be calculated using the elasticity theory. Defining the endurance limit of the bearing in that way considers the local shear stress, τ_d, corresponding to the driving force acting on dislocations, as a fatigue criterion, and the critical shear stress to move dislocations in the martensitic matrix, i.e., the shear elastic limit, τ_f, as the threshold value of the criterion.

It should be mentioned that, on the one hand, the driving force in the material must be calculated locally, accounting for both the Hertzian stress field and the material inhomogeneities. On the other hand, the shear elastic limit also has to be considered locally, which is of fundamental importance for surface hardened steels exhibiting an elastic limit varying as a function of depth. In that way, an infinite life can be assessed for the whole bearing population provided the criterion is fulfilled everywhere in the subsurface stress field in the material, whatever the position of the most harmful inhomogeneity in this stress field:

$$\tau_d(x,y,z) \leq \tau_f(x,y,z) \qquad (1)$$

where x, y, z are the coordinates in the stress field due to the contact.

Conditions for Calculating the Lower Bound of the Maximal Hertzian Pressure for an Infinite Life

The Macroscopic Stress Field - As mentioned previously, we look for the lower bound H_1 of the maximal contact pressure for an infinite life of a bearing submitted to E.H.D. pure rolling conditions. However, for a sake of simplicity, we take benefit of the studies reported by Dowson and Higginson [11], which show that the Hertz contact theory gives a good approximation to the sub-surface stress field, except for high rolling speeds. So, in this work, Hertzian contact pressure distributions with zero tangential traction acting on the surface have been used for calculating the macroscopic sub-surface stress field. Additionally, the influence of hoop stresses, which may be caused either by a very high rotational speed or a shrink fit of the ring over the shaft, has been studied by superposing both stress fields.

The Local Stress Field - When elastic inhomogeneities are present in the bearing steel, the stress concentration has to be calculated. For that purpose, the Eshelby's method [12,13] has been preferred to the finite element method that requires longer computation times. Thus, Eshelby has solved the problem of the local stress field around inhomogeneities with spherical and ellipsoidal shapes, in an infinitely extended matrix submitted to a uniform strain field under the condition that the system behaves elastically. For isolated inclusions, whose sizes are small with respect to the characteristic sizes of the stressed zone, it has been shown elsewhere that the local stress field is thus obtained with a very good approximation [14]. Moreover, the extension of the Eshelby's method proposed by Moschovidis [15] enables one to treat more difficult situations with two or more interacting inclusions located in a non-uniform stress field.

Furthermore, in order to introduce realistic material parameters in this calculation, the Young's modulus of inhomogeneities such as nonmetallic inclusions and primary carbides have been measured by means of the nano-indentation technique [16]. These data are presented in Table 1. Regarding the elastic mismatch between inclusions and the martensitic matrix, whose Young's modulus is in the range 200-210 GPa for bearing steels, alumina and titanium nitride appear to be the most harmful species, with almost the same modulus values. However, alumina inclusions are more frequently met than titanium nitride ones in bearing steels. Hence, unless specified, alumina inclusions will be considered as the most harmful inhomogeneities leading to the greatest failure risk.

Table 1 - *Young's modulus, E, of typical inhomogeneities found in 100Cr6 and 80MoCrV42 bearing steels, measured by means of the nano-indentation technique.*

	Alumina	Titanium nitride	Spinel	Calcium Aluminate[1]	Primary carbide[2]	Primary carbide [3]
E (GPa)	375	380	279	126	302	320

[1] $(Al_2O_3)_2$, (CaO) ; [2] type M_2C , molybdenum rich ; [3] type MC , vanadium rich .

Thus, two examples of the shear stress distribution calculated using the methods mentioned above have been mapped for alumina inclusions of spherical shape, with 5 μm in radius, situated below the contact at the depth where the shear stress of the Hertzian stress field is maximum. In Figure 1 the inclusion is isolated, whereas in Figure 2, it is interacting with another inclusion whose center is 15 μm apart. From these maps it appears that the local shear stress around the inhomogeneity is rather unequal, exhibiting marked maxima and minima. The former are located either at the matrix/inclusion interface (Figure 1) or at mid-distance between the two inclusions (Figure 2).

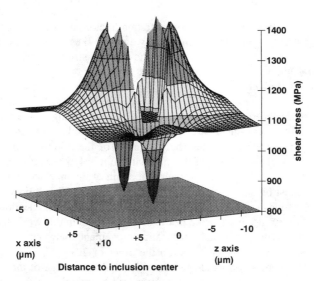

Figure 1 - *Local shear stress distribution around an alumina inclusion in 80MoCrV42, 5 μm in radius (for a sake of clarity, the stress within the inclusion is not represented). The inclusion is located 450 μm below the circular contact (between two spherical bodies 40 mm in radius) with a Hertzian pressure of 3.5 GPa. Axes x and z are parallel and perpendicular to the contact, respectively.*

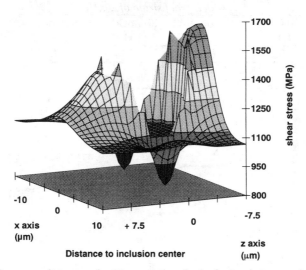

Figure 2 - *Same conditions as for Figure 1, but the inclusion is interacting with a twin inclusion whose center is 15 μm apart (not represented). The pair axis is oriented parallel to the z axis and the pair center(x = 0 ; z = - 7.5μm) is located 450 μm below the circular contact.*

Furthermore, the elastic stress concentration factor, defined as the ratio of the maximal shear stress around the inhomogeneity over the shear stress at the same position but without inclusion, can be derived from the stress distribution : in the situation of Figures 1 and 2, the values 1.38 and 1.47 were found for the isolated inclusion and the inclusion pair, respectively.

The Threshold Stress of the Fatigue Criterion - According to the fatigue criterion defined above, the local shear stress has to be compared to the local elastic limit everywhere in the material. The threshold value τ_f of the criterion cannot be deduced from the conventional yield stress of the material, but it has to be chosen according to the physical bases of the method. That is, the proof strain of the mechanical test selected for determining τ_f must be such that irreversible movements of dislocations, which are the source of dislocation accumulation finally leading to damage nucleation under cyclic loading, do not occur. For martensitic bearing steels studied in this work, the proof strain, which would induce only reversible dislocation movements between obstacles opposing these movements, was estimated to be on the order of 20×10^{-6} [14]. A more accurate evaluation of the proof strain would require a detailed knowledge of the distributions of the microstructure features. Nevertheless, it should be mentioned that the micro-yield stress values deduced from the micro-plastic behavior of bearing steels are not dramatically influenced by the choice of the proof strain value [10].

Table 2 - *Micro-yield shear stress for 100Cr6 and 80MoCrV42 prepared with the standard treatment for aircraft applications ; deduced from uniaxial compression tests with a proof strain of 20×10^{-6}.*

	100 Cr 6 (R.T.)	80MoCrV42 (at R.T.)	80MoCrV42 (100 °C)	80MoCrV42 (230 °C)	80MoCrV42 (280 °C)
τ_f (GPa)	0.92	0.86	0.74	0.57	0.51

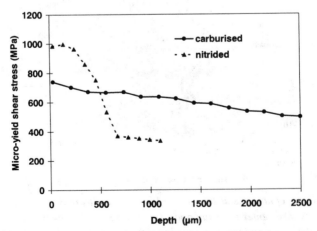

Figure 3 : *Micro-yield shear stress profile deduced from nano-indentation tests for the 16NiCrMo13 carburised steel and the 32CrMoV13 nitrided steel (from reference [17]).*

Concerning the experimental test that has to be used for the determination of τ_f, one has to distinguish through hardened steels and surface hardened steels. In the former case, τ_f can be considered as uniform in the bulk of the material. Hence, it can be determined by uniaxial compression tests. Some data thus obtained for through hardened steels are given in Table 2 for 100Cr6 and 80MoCrV42 bearing steels, including the influence of temperature for the latter steel. In the latter case, τ_f is decreasing with increasing depth from the surface, which renders any bulk mechanical test inoperative. Moreover, classical hardness tests usually used for characterizing the mechanical property profile of such treated layers are not relevant since the plastic strains involved in the test are of order of few 10%. Therefore, a specific method based on nano-indentation measurements has been developed recently for measuring locally, over a volume of order 10 μm^3, the micro-plastic properties of high strength steels. This method is presented in this conference [17], and two examples of micro-yield shear stress profiles thus obtained on a carburized and a nitrided steel are reported in Figure 3.

Application to Through Hardened Steels

Example of Calculation of the Endurance Limit

A first example of calculation of the endurance limit performed as described above for a through hardened steel is illustrated in Figure 4. For the presented example, namely 80MoCrV42 steel operating at 100°C, the calculation of the maximal local shear stress has been carried out by considering the alumina inclusions (assumed to be of spherical shape in this calculation) as the most harmful inhomogeneities. Figure 4 shows the relationship between the maximum local shear stress in the matrix at the inclusion-matrix interface and the applied Hertz pressure, in the case of a circular contact. The lower bound of the endurance limit H_1 is easily deduced from this relationship by setting the appropriate value of the threshold stress τ_f taken in Table 2. At 100°C, a lower bound of 1.72 GPa was thus found for the endurance limit [10].

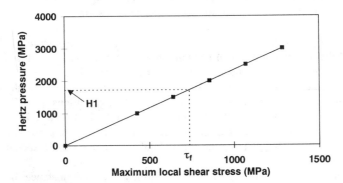

Figure 4 - *Relationship between the Hertz pressure and the maximum local shear stress, for a circular contact. 80MoCrV42 steel, τ_f = 736 MPa at 100°C : corresponding lower bound of the endurance limit H_1 = 1720 MPa.*

Influence of Microstructure Parameters

Influence of the Inhomogeneity Size - Under the assumptions of the proposed approach, the lower bound of the endurance limit H_1, is not dependent on the size of the inhomogeneity. Indeed, as predicted by elastic theories, the stress concentration around an inhomogeneity is independent of its size, as far as considering the applied stress field as uniform in the area occupied by the inhomogeneity remains a reasonable approximation.

Influence of Inhomogeneity Species - According to our approach, the inhomogeneity species is expected to influence the endurance limit through its Young's modulus. Then, the endurance limit H_1 has been calculated for two inhomogeneity species which in 80MoCrV42 steel, exhibit large elastic mismatch with respect to the matrix, namely alumina inclusions and primary carbides, as well as for the matrix free of any inhomogeneity. Assuming that the friction stress τ_f of the steel matrix remains independent of the inhomogeneity species, H_1 is found to be 2.37 GPa, 1.9 GPa and 1.72 GPa for a matrix without inclusions, with primary carbides, and alumina inclusions, respectively. This means that the endurance limit H_1 is strongly reduced by about 30% and 20% by the presence of alumina and primary carbides, respectively, with respect to what would be obtained for a material free of any inhomogeneity.

Influence of the Shape and Orientation of Inhomogeneities - For inhomogeneities of ellipsoidal shape, two parameters must be considered : the orientation and the aspect ratio. For investigating the influence of the orientation, prolate ellipsoids with a typical aspect ratio of 2 have been considered. It has been found that, for the same operating conditions as those used in Figure 4, H_1 is 1.78 GPa and 1.48 GPa when the ellipsoid long axis is oriented parallel and perpendicular to the contact surface, respectively. Comparing the former result with that obtained in the previous section enables one to conclude that the ellipsoidal shape is not more harmful than a spherical one when the ellipsoid long axis is parallel to the surface. In contrast, H_1 appears to be markedly lower when the ellipsoid long axis is perpendicular to the contact surface.

Influence of the Interaction between Neighboring Inhomogeneities - First, the influence of the orientation of a pair of twin inhomogeneities has been investigated. For that purpose, the analysis considered two alumina spherical inclusions distant by one radius from each other, and located in the region where the applied shear stress without any inhomogeneity is maximum. For the same operating conditions as in Figure 4 (for which H_1 was found to be 1.72 GPa), H_1 is now found to be 1.71 GPa, 1.70 GPa and 1.6 GPa, as the axis of the inclusion pair is oriented parallel, at 45° and perpendicular to the contact surface, respectively. Thus, the perpendicular orientation again appears to be the most harmful.

For this most harmful orientation, the influence of the distance between the inhomogeneites has been reported in Figure 5. It appears that H_1 is markedly reduced as the distance between inclusions is decreased. However, the evolution is not perfectly continuous. The detailed analysis of the local stress field shows that, as suggested by the observation of Figures 1 and 2, the position where τ_d is maximum can be located either at the matrix-inhomogeneity interface for long (>15 μm) or short (<11 μm) distances, as for an isolated inclusion (Figure 1), or at the middle point between the inhomogeneities for intermediate distances (11 < distance < 15 μm) (Figure 2). These position changes do coincide with the slope changes observed in Figure 5.

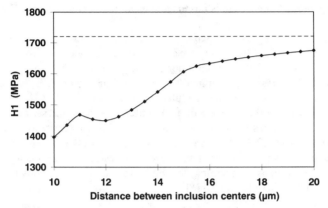

Figure 5 – *Influence of distance between spherical inclusions on endurance limit H_1. Twin inclusions, with 5 μm radius aligned perpendicularly to the contact surface. Circular contact. 80MoCrV42 steel. T = 100°C. The dashed line indicates the H_1 level for an isolated inclusion.*

Influence of Contact Geometry - In order to investigate the influence of contact geometry, the calculation of H_1 presented above for a circular contact (Figure 4) was repeated using the same conditions, but for a linear contact. The value of H_1 was then found to be 1.77 GPa, which is very close to the value found for the circular contact, namely 1.72 GPa. So, the contact geometry does not appear to be a strongly influential parameter, as long as bearings are only subjected to Hertzian stresses.

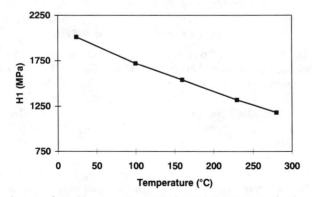

Figure 6 - *Endurance limit H_1 vs. temperature for 80MoCrV42 steel. Alumina inclusions are assumed to be the harmful inhomogeneities.*

Influence of Operating Temperature - When the slight changes of elastic moduli of inhomogeneties and matrix as a function of temperature are disregarded, the main influence of this operating parameter is expected to occur through the micro-yield stress of the matrix. Such an influence is best illustrated in Figure 6 in the case of 80MoCrV42. Thus, it is shown that the lower bound of the endurance limit H_1 is reduced in the ratio 1/1.7 as the operating temperature is raised from room temperature to 280°C.

Influence of a Hoop Stress - As explained previously, when residual or hoop stresses are present in the bearing, they must be added to the contact stress field. In order to illustrate the influence of such additional stress fields, the case of a simple circumferential hoop stress has been investigated. Thus, in Figure 7, H_1 has been plotted vs. the hoop stress level for linear and circular contacts. It appears that H_1 is influenced in a rather complex way by the presence of a circumferential hoop stress. Thus, in the case of a linear contact, H_1 goes through a maximum for a small compressive hoop stress in the range -100 MPa to - 200 MPa, whereas this beneficial effect does not occur in the case of a circular contact. It is worth noting that these results are in good agreement with experimental observations concerning the beneficial effect of a small compressive residual stress on the life of bearings [*18*].

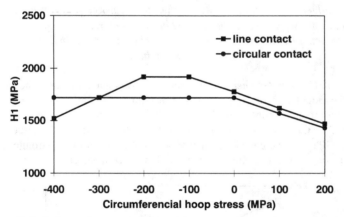

Figure 7- *Influence of a circumferential hoop stress on endurance limit H_1 for a 80MoCrV42 bearing steel submitted to circular (●) and linear (■) contact loadings (T = 100 °C). Alumina inclusions are assumed to be the harmful inhomogeneities.*

Application to Surface Hardened Steels

Implementing the Method

In surface hardened steels, the method for calculating H_1 cannot be applied in the same way as that shown in Figure 4 for through hardened steels. First, residual stresses that are inherent to carburizing or nitriding processes in surface hardened materials, must be accounted for. This means that the residual stress field has to be superimposed to the stress field resulting from the contact. Second, the micro-yield shear stress τ_f in the material is no longer a single material parameter, but a function of depth beneath the surface. First, one has now to consider the maximum local shear stress at any depth d and compare this maximum value to the corresponding $\tau_f(d)$ value, while for through hardened steels, it is adequate to consider the overall maximal shear stress and compare it to the τ_f value of the material. Implementing in such a way the method for surface hardened steels is illustrated in Figure 8 for the 16NiCrMo13 carburised steel prepared in standard conditions as reported in reference [17]. Since this material was produced using the vacuum remelting process, it has been considered that the potential sites for damage (stress raisers) are the carbides (Young's modulus E = 310 GPa), which may be formed during the carburising process. A series of profiles of local shear stress corresponding to increasing values of the Hertzian pressure between a ball with a 5 mm radius and a flat surface has thus been calculated (Figure 8). The micro-yield shear stress profile (Figure 3) is also plotted in Figure 8. It appears that a Hertzian pressure of about 2.2 GPa is the maximum contact pressure beyond which the corresponding stress profile exceeds the $\tau_f(d)$ profile. Hence, H_1 is equal to 2.2 GPa. It should be mentioned that similar calculations have been carried out by omitting the residual stress field. In that case the maximal Hertzian pressure was found to be equal to 2 GPa. This shows the beneficial influence of the residual stresses[4], which lead to an increase of about 10% of the endurance limit in this material.

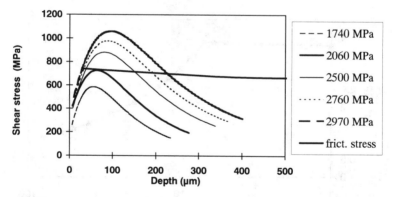

Figure 8 – *Shear stress profile for various Hertzian pressures (including residual stress and local stress concentration) compared with the micro-yield shear stress. 16NiCrMo13 carburised steel. Circular contact (ball 5 mm in radius /flat surface).*

Influence of the Material

For the sake of comparison, the 32CrMoV13 nitrided steel has been studied using the same approach as that used for the 16NiCrMo13 carburised steel. Thus, by

---

[4] The residual stress level is about - 110 MPa in the region where the shear stress of the Hertzian stress field is maximum.

considering the same operating conditions (same radius of the contacting bodies) the H_1 endurance limit was found to be 3.7 GPa for the 32CrMoV13 nitrided steel. This high value, compared to that one found for the 16NiCrMo13 steel, can be explained as resulting from the addition of three favorable characteristics of the material : a high value of the matrix micro-yield shear stress, the absence of harmful inhomogeneities in the material and the high level of residual stresses in the material (about - 450 MPa in the Hertzian zone of the circular contact studied in this work : ball 5 mm in radius /flat surface).

Influence of the Contact Size

In through hardened materials the contact size has no influence on the endurance limit, at least within the limits of the assumptions and the conditions under which the calculations have been carried out (specifically, perfectly smooth contact surface, constant τ_f value, inhomogeneity size << characteristic sizes of the Hertzian stress field). In contrast, the influence of the contact size, which is linked to the radius of the contacting bodies, may become predominant for surface hardened materials. This is illustrated in Figure 9, which shows the variation of H_1 versus the radius R of the rolling balls, for the 16NiCrMo13 carburised steel. A marked decrease of H_1 thus appears as R is increased. This decrease of H_1 is obviously due to the fact that the most stressed region is shifted towards increasing depth with increasing the radius of the contacting bodies, where the material micro-yield stress is lower.

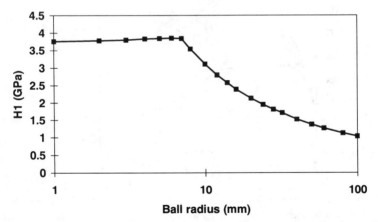

Figure 9 – *Endurance limit H_1 vs. the radius of a ball in contact with a flat surface. 32CrMoV13 nitrided steel.*

Conclusions

In this paper, a physically based method of calculating load rating of rolling bearings for an infinite life has been presented. This method is based on the comparison between the local elastic shear stress built up in the subsurface region and the micro-yield shear stress of the martensitic matrix. The calculation of the local stress can account for the presence of, on the one hand, hoop stresses or residual stresses and, on the other hand, of the steel inhomogeneities that act as stress raisers. It is difficult to validate all the values of H_l predicted by this method, due to the great number of long fatigue tests that would be required. However, it has been verified in some particular situations that the predicted values are in good agreement with those reported in the literature, which were deduced from the analysis of numerous fatigue tests [7,19]. Moreover, these predictions appear to be sound and compatible with most trends observed by bearing designers.

The main advantages of our approach are its predictive potential and its ability to account explicitly for material properties, as well as for operating conditions. Although the potential of the method has been illustrated by considering pure rolling for the operating conditions and using the Hertz theory to calculate the sub-surface stress field, other operating conditions as well as more refined theories of the contact have to be used, in order to account more precisely for the actual operating conditions linked with lubrication, sliding, spinning and surface roughness or indentation. Furthermore, the theory should be extended to study the surface initiated fatigue failure problem. For that purpose, the local stress field should account for both material inhomogeneities and surface asperities which act together as stress raisers, as it is outlined in Reference [20].

Acknowledgments

Some parts of this work were supported by the European Economic Community (Brite Euram Contract Elabomm BR2.CT92.0209) or Ascometal Company, which are gratefully acknowledged.

References

[1] Littman, W.E., and Widner, R.L., " Propagation of Contact Fatigue from Surface and Subsurface Origin, " *ASME Journal of Basic Engineering*, 1966, pp. 624-636.

[2] Furumura, K., Shirota, S., and Hirakawa, K., "The Sub-surface-initiated and the Surface-initiated Rolling Fatigue Life of Bearing Steels, " *Proceedings of the JSLE-ASLE International Conference on Lubrication*, Tokyo, 1975, pp. 475-483.

[3] Nelias, D., Dumont, M.L., Champiot, F., Vincent, A., Girodin, D., Fougeres, R., and Flamand, L., "Role of Inclusions, Surface Roughness, and Operating Conditions on Rolling Contact Fatigue, " *ASME Journal of Tribology*, Vol. 121, 1999, pp. 240-251.

[4] Ioannides, E., and Harris, T.A., "A New Fatigue Life Model for Rolling Bearings, " *ASME Journal of Tribology*, Vol. 107, 1985, pp. 367-378.

[5] Lösche, T., "New Aspects in the Realistic Prediction of the Fatigue Life of Rolling Bearings, " *Wear*, Vol. 134, 1989, pp. 357-375.

[6] Ioannides, E., Harris, T.A., and Ragen, M., "Endurance of Aircraft Gas Turbine Mainshaft Ball Bearings- Analysis Using Improved Fatigue Life Theory : Part 1 -

Application to a Long-life Bearing, " *ASME Journal of Tribology*, Vol. 112, 1990, pp. 304-308.

[7] Harris, T.A., Ioannides, E., Ragen, M., and Tam H., "Endurance of Aircraft Gas Turbine Mainshaft Ball Bearings- Analysis Using Improved Fatigue Life Theory : Part 2 - Application to a Bearing Operating Under Difficult Lubrication Conditions, " *ASME Journal of Tribology*, Vol. 112, 1990, pp. 309-316.

[8] Schlicht, H., " Über die Entstehung von White Etching Areas (WEA) in Wälzelementen, " *Härterei-Tech. Mitt.*, HTM 28, Heft 2, 1973, pp. 112-123.

[9] Guy, P., Meynaud, P., Vincent, A., Dudragne, G., and Baudry, G., "Subsurface Damage Investigation by High Frequency Ultrasonic Echography on 100Cr6 Bearing Steel, " *Tribology International*, Vol. 30, N°. 4, 1996, pp.247-259.

[10] Lamagnere, P., Fougeres, R., Lormand, G., Girodin, D., Dudragne, G., Vergne, F., and Vincent, A., " A Physically Based Model for Endurance Limit of Bearing Steels, " *ASME J. of Tribology*, Vol. 120, 1998, pp.421-426.

[11] Dowson, D., and Higginson, "Elasto-Hydrodynamic Lubrication , " *International Series in Materials Science and Technology*, Vol. 23, Pergamon Press, Oxford, 1977.

[12] Eshelby, J. D., "Elastic Inclusions and Inhomogeneities, " *Progress in Solid Mechanics*, Vol. 2, Snedon, I.N., and Hill, R., Eds., North-Holland, Amsterdam, 1961, pp. 87-140.

[13] Mura, T., "Micromechanics of Defects in Solids, " Martinus Nijhoff Publishers, Dordrecht, 1987.

[14] Lamagnere, P., "Etude et Modelisation de L'amorçage des Fissures de Fatigue de Roulement au Voisinage des Microhétérogénéités dans l'Acier 80MoCrV42," *Ph.D. INSA, Lyon, (France)* 1996.

[15] Moschovidis, Z.A., "Two Ellipsoidal Inhomogeneities And Related Problems Treated By The Equivalent Inclusion Method, " *Ph. D. Northwestern University, Evanston, Illinois (U.S.A.)*, 1975.

[16] Lamagnère, P., Girodin, D., Meynaud, P., Vergne, F., and Vincent, A., "Study of Elasto-Plastic Properties of Microheterogeneities by Means of Nano-indentation Measurements : Application to Bearing Steels," *Materials Science and Engineering A*, Vol. 215, 1996, pp.134-142.

[17] Vincent, A., Elghazal, H., Lormand, G., Hamel, H., and Girodin, D., "Local Elasto-plastic Properties of Bearing Steels from Nano-indentation Measurements," *Bearing Steel Technology, ASTM STP 1419*, J. M. Beswick, Ed. American Society for Testing Materials, West Conshohocken, PA, 2002.

[*18*] Maeda, K., Kashimura, H., and Tsumshima, N., "Investigation on the Fatigue Fracture of Core in Carburized Rollers of Bearings," *ASLE Transactions*, Vol. 29, N°.1, 1984, pp. 85-90.

[*19*] Zaretsky, E.V., Poplawski, J. V., and Peters, S.M., "Comparison of Life Theories for Rolling-Element Bearings," *STLE Preprint* N° 95-AM-3F-3, 1995.

[*20*] Fougeres, R., Lormand, G., Vincent, A., Nelias, D., Dudragne, G., Girodin, D., Baudry, G., and Daguier, P., "A New Physically Based Model for Predicting the Fatigue Life Distribution of Rolling Bearings," *Bearing Steel Technology, ASTM STP 1419*, J. M. Beswick, Ed., American Society for Testing Materials, West Conshohocken, PA, 2002.

Tedric A. Harris[1]

Fatigue Limit Stress - A New and Superior Criterion for Life Rating of Rolling Bearing Materials

Reference: Harris, T. A., **"Fatigue Limit Stress - A New and Superior Criterion for Life Rating of Rolling Bearing Materials,"** *Bearing Steel Technology, ASTM STP 1419*, J. M. Beswick, Ed., American Society for Testing and Materials International, West Conshohocken, PA, 2002.

Abstract: Rolling bearings are rated for their capabilities to withstand rolling contact fatigue. All other means of bearing failure are considered preventable through proper attention to bearing manufacture, mounting, lubrication, and minimization of contaminant ingress. The standard methods for calculation of rolling bearing capacities and fatigue lives are based on the 1947 and 1952 publications of Lundberg and Palmgren. They defined separate material factors for ball bearings and roller bearings fabricated from 52100 steel, through-hardened to at least 58 Rockwell C; the fatigue life predictions, were strongly influenced by these capacity-multiplying factors. The standard was in use for less than five years, when it became apparent bearings fabricated from ever-cleaner materials; for example vacuum degassed and vacuum melted steels, were out-performing standard life predictions. Moreover, tapered and cylindrical roller bearings routinely fabricated from carburizing steels such as SAE 4118, 4320, 8620, etc. were not directly covered by the standards. This deficiency is accommodated by the use of material-life factors applied to the Lundberg-Palmgren life equations. The Society of Tribologists and Lubrication Engineers (STLE) recommends the use of separate material-life factors to cover basic steel metallurgy, heat treatment, and metal shaping. It has been demonstrated that, together with other life factors for lubrication effectiveness and contamination, this cascading of life factors is insufficiently accurate to predict life because in most cases, these effects on bearing endurance are interdependent.

In 1985, Ioannides and Harris published a rolling bearing life prediction method based on applied and induced contact stresses and body stresses. The resultant material stresses could be combined by classical strength of materials methods of superimposition; these resultant stresses could then be compared against fatigue limit stress as the material strength criterion to determine resistance to fatigue. From 1992 through 2000, the United States Navy funded a research project to establish appropriate fatigue limit stress values for common and special rolling bearing materials and to employ such values in computerized calculation tools to effectively apply this technology to modern bearing applications. This paper presents these developments.

Keywords: Ball bearings, roller bearings, rolling bearings, fatigue life, fatigue limit stress, stress-life method

[1]Professor of Mechanical Engineering, Pennsylvania State University, 320 Leonhard Building, University Park, PA 16802

Background

Lundberg and Palmgren (LP)

Ball and roller bearings, i.e., rolling bearings, have historically been, and currently are rated according to their capabilities to withstand rolling contact fatigue, all other means of bearing failure in a given application being considered preventable through proper attention to bearing manufacture, bearing mounting, lubrication, and minimization of contaminant ingress. The standard methods for the calculation of bearing capacities and fatigue lives are based primarily on the published works of LP [1, 2]. Considering the developments by Weibull [3, 4], which provided statistical means to represent fatigue failure of engineering solids, LP established bearing capacity and life rating methods based on the following relationship

$$\ln \frac{1}{S} \propto \frac{N^e \tau_0^c V}{z_0^h} \tag{1}$$

where $S =$ probability of survival,
$N =$ number of stress cycles endured,
$\tau_0 =$ maximum orthogonal shear stress under the contact
surface,
$z_0 =$ depth from the surface to the location of τ_0 , and
$V =$ volume of material stressed.

The singular mode of bearing failure considered by LP was spalling of the inner or outer raceway (Figure 1). Failure of rolling elements was not included.

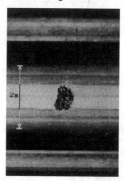

Figure 1 - *Rolling contact fatigue spall in a ball bearing raceway.*

In Eq. 1 the exponent e is called the Weibull slope or shape parameter. In (Figure 2) e is the slope of the distribution of bearing lives (failures) plotted on a Weibull coordinate graph. LP [1] determined that e = 10/9 for point contact bearings (ball bearings and lightly loaded spherical roller bearings) and 9/8 for line contact bearings (cylindrical, tapered and heavily loaded spherical roller bearings).

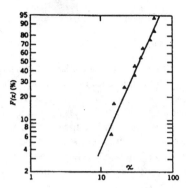

Figure 2 - *Bearing fatigue lives plotted on Weibull coordinates.*

LP further attributed the spalling to originate with a crack occurring in the bearing ring steel beneath the raceway; the crack propagating to the surface to cause the spall. According to Weibull, the crack was associated with a "weak" point in the material; LP concluded that the weak points occurred in the vicinities of material voids or non-metallic inclusions, e.g., oxides, sulfides, and such. LP further assumed that the crack was initiated by cyclic maximum orthogonal shear stresses τ_0 occurring in the subsurface due to the repeated application of concentrated contact stresses (Hertz stresses) on the raceway surface. Although, for any Hertz contact, the magnitude of the maximum subsurface shear stress $\tau_{yz,max} > \tau_0$, LP concluded that the range of the maximum orthogonal shear stress, i.e., $2\tau_0$, was the crack-initiator. For typical bearings, τ_0 occurs at a depth below the contact surface $z_0 \approx 0.5b$; b being the half-width of the contact area in the direction of rolling motion.

As a result of their efforts LP developed the following equation to predict fatigue life of bearings

$$L = \left(\frac{C}{P}\right)^p \qquad (2)$$

where L = 90% reliability bearing fatigue life in 10^6 rev; e.g., L_{10} ,
     C = basic dynamic capacity,
     P = equivalent applied load, and
     p = the load-life exponent

From their endurance test results, LP [1] concluded that exponent p = 3 for ball bearings, and p = 4 for line contact roller bearings. Subsequently, recognizing that most modern cylindrical and tapered roller bearings operate with crowned rollers or/and raceways, and that spherical roller bearings most likely operate with combinations of point and line contacts, LP [4] proposed the exponent p = 10/3 for roller bearings. (For discussions of ball-raceway and roller-raceway contacts, and bearing performance in general, the text by Harris [5] may be consulted.)

Commencing with the individual rolling element-raceway contacts and utilizing simple internal distributions of load among the rolling elements, LP established C, the basic dynamic capacity (also basic load rating) as a function of bearing internal geometry and the properties of the bearing steel. In Eq. 2, the basic dynamic capacity C represents that fictitious load that 90% of the bearings will survive with a fatigue life of 10^6 rev. LP developed the following equations defining C for radial and angular-contact ball bearings

$$C = f_c (i \cos \alpha)^{0.7} Z^{2/3} D^{1.8} \tag{3}$$

$$f_c = 39.9 \left\{ 1 + \left[1.04 \left(\frac{1-\gamma}{1+\gamma} \right)^{1.72} \left(\frac{f_2}{f_1} \cdot \frac{2f_1 - 1}{2f_2 - 1} \right)^{0.41} \right]^{10/3} \right\}^{-0.3} \frac{\gamma^{0.3} (1-\gamma)^{1.39}}{(1+\gamma)^{1/3}} \left(\frac{2f_2}{2f_{2-1}} \right)^{0.41} \tag{4}$$

where C = bearing basic dynamic capacity,
i = number of rows of rolling elements (balls),
   = contact angle,
Z = number of rolling elements (balls) per row,
D = rolling element (ball) diameter,
d_m = pitch diameter,
$\smile = (D \cos \quad) \div d_m$, and
f = raceway groove radius $\div D$.

In Eq. 4, subscripts 1 and 2 refer to the outer and inner raceways respectively. The constant 39.9 (metric units) is a maximum value for ball bearings accurately manufactured from good-quality, through-hardened, 52100 steel of the LP era. The exponents in Eq. 3 and (4) are derived from the exponents c, h, and e in Eq. 1 and the exponent p in Eq. 2. These exponents c and h were established empirically by LP as c = 31/3 and h = 7/3.

For radial roller bearings, LP developed the following equations

$$C = f_c (i l_{eff} \cos \alpha)^{7/9} Z^{3/4} D^{29/27} \tag{5}$$

$$f_c = 207 \Lambda \left\{ 1 + \left[1.04 \left(\frac{1-\gamma}{1+\gamma} \right)^{143/108} \right]^{9/2} \right\}^{-2/9} \frac{\gamma^{2/9} (1-\gamma)^{29/27}}{(1+\gamma)^{1/4}} \tag{6}$$

where l_{eff} = roller-raceway contact effective length, and
   ┐ = factor to accommodate degree of crowning.

LP developed similar equations for thrust ball and thrust roller bearings.

Load and Life Rating Standards

In simplified, user-friendly format, the LP load and rating method was adopted as a standard in the United States [6]. Within a few years after issuance, the standard [6] proved ineffective. Bearings fabricated from improved versions of 52100 steels were enduring much longer than predicted. Bearings fabricated from vacuum-melted steels for aircraft gas turbine mainshaft and power transmission applications achieved even longer fatigue lives; many experienced no fatigue failures. Roller bearings manufactured from case-carburized steels could not be properly rated by the standard.

In the early 1960s, it was determined that the thickness of lubricant films in the rolling element-raceway contacts has a substantial influence on bearing endurance. It was found possible for lubricant films to achieve sufficient thickness to completely separate the rolling elements from the raceways; under such condition, bearing failure was highly improbable. A parameter Λ (ratio of the minimum lubricant film thickness to the composite rms *roughness* of the rolling surfaces) was established to quantify the effectiveness of lubrication. For $\Lambda \geq 3$, bearing life was considered to be approximately three (3) times rating life calculated using Eq. 2.

Owing to the above life-multiplying effects, it became practical to consider bearing lives at higher reliabilities; hence, a life adjustment for reliability of performance ensued. The LP equation with life adjustment factors resulted

$$ L_{na} = a_1 a_2 a_3 \left(\frac{C}{P} \right)^P \tag{7} $$

where a_1 = life adjustment factor for the selected reliability level,
a_2 = life adjustment factor for material,
a_3 = life adjustment factor for operating conditions, and
L_{na} = adjusted bearing fatigue life in 10^6 rev.

In Eq. 7, subscript "a" refers to reliability (probability of failure) level; e.g., L_1 in lieu of L_{10}. Based on a Weibull slope of 10/9 and the data of Tallian [7] and Harris [8], values of a_1 are given (Table 1) for various probabilities of failure.

Table 1 - *Values of a_1*

Failure Probability (%)	a_1
10	1.00
5	0.62
4	0.53
3	0.44
2	0.33
1	0.21

Based on Eq. 7, the standard was revised; standards [9, 10] resulted. Eq. 7 was also adopted for the international standard [11].

In 1970, ASME Lubrication Division convened the Rolling-Elements Committee to quantify values of the life-adjustment factors; this resulted in the *ASME Engineering Design Guide* by Zaretsky et al. [*12*]. The *Design Guide* further split the materials-life factor into two parts, i.e., a metallurgy factor and a material processing factor, and added individual life factors for speed and misalignment effects. STLE [*13*] continued this cascading of life-adjustment factors; additionally, a life adjustment factor for contamination was inserted.

SKF [*14*] and other bearing manufacturers considered that the life adjustment factors for material and lubrication, e.g., a_2 and a_3 , were interdependent and established an a_{23} factor which could be obtained from the chart below (Figure 3).

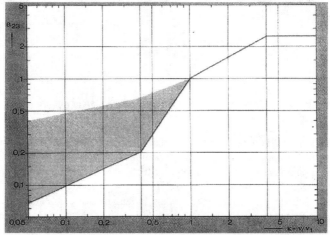

Figure 3 - a_{23} *life adjustment factor vs lubricant adequacy parameter* κ *(from [15]).*

In (Figure 3) $\kappa = \nu/\nu_1$, where ν is lubricant kinematic viscosity at operating temperature and ν_1 is the lubricant kinematic viscosity, which assures adequate separation of the rolling surfaces. It can be shown that $\kappa \approx \Lambda^{1.4}$. The major implication of life adjustment factor a_{23} is that a deficiency in lubrication cannot be overcome by using a superior steel. Moreover, when lubricant film thicknesses only marginally separate the rolling surfaces, additives in the lubricant may significantly influence bearing endurance; this is indicated by the shaded area in (Figure 3).

Design of Engineering Structures to Withstand Fatigue

In the design of engineering structures, the adequacy of design is determined by comparing the stresses at critical locations in the structure with the material strength at those locations. If after reducing the material strength by a design factor of safety, the strength exceeds the stress, the design of the structure is presumed safe. The stress at each critical location is generally determined by superposition of stresses due to the various applied and induced loads. This is an integration of the stresses. Moreover, it is possible to include stresses built into the material due to heat processing and manufacturing.

Considering design for the prevention of fatigue, the concept of an endurance limit S_e is employed, particularly for structures fabricated from steel. When the application stresses in the structure do not exceed the endurance limit, fatigue is considered to be obviated. A typical S (stress) - N (stress cycles) plot for a structural steel component is illustrated (Figure 4).

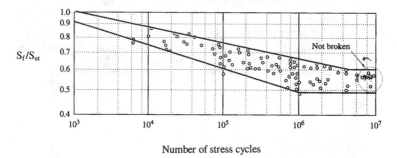

Figure 4 - *Typical S-N plot for a structural steel component.*

In (Figure 4) S_f is the stress at which fatigue failure occurred, and S_{ut} is the ultimate strength in tension of the material. The upper and lower horizontal lines bounding the data points on the right represent the maximum and minimum values of the endurance limit S_e. This engineering concept had not been applied to bearings.

Notwithstanding the lengthened bearing fatigue lives predicted using Eq. 7, in many applications, bearings achieved yet much longer lives. Also, in many applications; e.g., electric motors, bearing fatigue failures do not occur when the bearing is properly selected, mounted, and lubricated. Moreover, ball bearings under extremely high radial loads giving maximum Hertz stresses of 3300 MPa were endurance tested consistently without fatigue failure for several hundred million revolutions [15]. Nevertheless, even for extremely light loads, Eq. 7 still predicts the occurrence of fatigue failure.

Ioannides and Harris (IH)

Because of modern bearing application and testing experiences as indicated above, IH [16], included the effects of a fatigue limit stress in a basic equation defining fatigue endurance

$$\ln \frac{1}{\Delta S_i} \propto \frac{N^e (\sigma_i - \sigma_u)^c \Delta V_i}{z_i^h} \tag{8}$$

Compared to LP Eq. 7, the IH Eq. 8 has the following differences:

1. A generalized stress criterion σ was used for the failure-initiating stress in lieu of the maximum orthogonal shear stress τ_0. This implies that another failure-stress criterion may be more appropriate for bearings.

2. Eq. 8 contains a fatigue limit stress σ_u, similar to fatigue life equations describing structural fatigue. Thus, at a given location "i" in the material, unless $\sigma_i > \sigma_u$, fatigue failure of the volume element ΔV_i will not occur; and the probability of survival ΔS_i of ΔV_i under stress σ_i is 100%.

3. When τ_0 is selected as the failure-initiating stress, and $\sigma_u = 0$, Eq. 8 is identical to Eq. 7. Therefore, the LP equation is a special case of the more general IH equation.

It is of interest that Palmgren [17] initially considered the use of a fatigue limit stress, but he apparently discarded the concept since the endurance-tested bearings of that era all tended to experience fatigue failure when operated under heavy load. It is also of interest that IH [16] successfully demonstrated the application of Eq. 8 to fatigue-tested engineering elements such as rotating beams, torsionally cycled rods, and rods subjected to tension-compression cycles.

Stress-Based Rating Life Calculation

Application Stresses

The LP load and life rating method is based solely on the maximum orthogonal shear stress τ_0 occurring in the sub-surfaces of the bearing raceways due to the applied loads and resulting Hertz stresses. It does not include the effects of:

1. Contact surface shear stresses due to sliding friction.
2. Raceway hoop stresses due to ring rotation and/or press-fitting of the inner ring on the shaft or the outer ring in the housing,
3. Contact surface stress concentrations caused by hard particle contaminant denting of the rolling surfaces, and
4. Bending stresses.

Since fatigue life varies inversely with stress raised to the 9.3 power (See Harris and Yu [18]), the foregoing applied stress augmentations can have considerable influence on bearing life. As apparent from Eq. 7 and references 12 and 13, common practice has been to cascade inclusion of these effects through the use of individual life adjustment factors. Not only does this practice lack scientific elegance, it is incorrect. To approach the bearing life prediction accuracy required by modern applications, an integration of all of the applicable stresses is necessary.

Material Residual Stresses

Many roller bearings, particularly tapered roller bearings, are manufactured from surface-hardened, mostly case-carburized, steels. The base or core steels contain only a fraction of 1% carbon. Heat processing commences in a carbonaceous environment wherefrom carbon is absorbed in the surface of the steel component; the completed process leaves the component surface with up to approximately 1% carbon. After quenching, the component surface volume is left with compressive residual stress; typically -170 MPa (approximately). At a distance below the surface; i.e., in the *core* material under the *case*, tensile stress occurs. This tensile stress is necessary to maintain equilibrium in the component; however, the *case* is generally sufficiently deep such that the tensile stress of the *core* does not negatively influence fatigue endurance.

Residual stresses are also introduced into the surfaces of rolling components by material finishing processes; e.g., grinding and honing. These residual stresses, sometimes beneficial and sometimes detrimental, need to be integrated into the life calculations.

Failure-Initiating Stress Criterion

An investigation by Harris and Yu [18] demonstrated that the range of the maximum orthogonal shear stress, $2\tau_0$, is unaltered by the magnitude of surface shear stress. This is illustrated below (Figure 5).

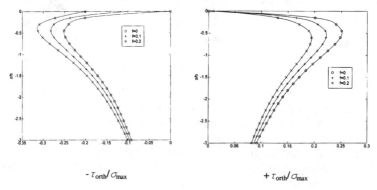

$- \tau_{orth}/\sigma_{max}$ $+ \tau_{orth}/\sigma_{max}$

Figure 5 - τ_{orth}/σ_{max} *at x/a = 0 vs depth z/b for a ball-raceway contact.*

In Figure 5, f is the coefficient of friction on the contact surface, σ_{max} is the Hertz stress magnitude occurring in the center of contact, and a is the half-length of the contact surface in the direction transverse to rolling motion. The minimum value $- \tau_{orth}/\sigma_{max}$ occurs near the leading edge of the contact and the maximum value $+ \tau_{orth}/\sigma_{max}$ near the trailing edge.

Because $2\tau_0$ is not influenced by surface shear stress, and because in many applications surface shear stress due to friction is significant; e.g., in angular-contact ball bearings and spherical roller bearings, it was necessary to consider an alternate failure stress criterion. In 1995 ASME Tribology Division created a Technical Committee to establish an improved method to calculate life ratings of modern rolling bearings. Among their deliberations, the Technical Committee [19] agreed on the efficacy of use of the von Mises stress σ_{VM} as the failure stress criterion

$$\sigma_{VM} = \frac{\sqrt{2}}{2}\left[\left(\sigma_x - \sigma_y\right)^2 + \left(\sigma_y - \sigma_z\right)^2 + \left(\sigma_z - \sigma_x\right)^2 + 6\left(\tau_{xy}^2 + \tau_{yz}^2 + \tau_{zx}^2 +\right)\right]^{1/2} \qquad (9)$$

In Eq. 9, σ_x, σ_y, and σ_z are the normal stresses acting on the material element dx, dy, dz located in the material at point (x, y, z); τ_{xy}, τ_{yz}, and τ_{xz} are the shear stresses acting in the planes of the element faces. All of these stresses can be determined from the applied, induced, and residual stresses of the application. Thus, σ_{VM} can properly integrate all stresses of the application.

The Life Equation

The load and life rating standards based on the LP theory and methods have been in worldwide use for more than 40 years. Although it is scientifically appealing to develop a completely new rating method based only on comparison of application integrated stress to component material strength, an interim evolutionary method has been proposed in the format of Eq. 10.

$$L_a = a_1 a_{SL}\left(\frac{C}{P}\right)^P \tag{10}$$

where a_1 = life adjustment factor for the selected reliability level,
a_{SL} = integrated life adjustment factor inclusive of all stress effects, and
L_a = adjusted bearing fatigue life in 10^6 rev.

The calculation of a_{SL} for a bearing application is complex and requires a digital computer program. Such a program has been developed through the efforts of the ASME Tribology Division Technical Committee and will be made available worldwide. To determine a_{SL} for the application, it is necessary to estimate the bearing internal load distribution and all resulting material stresses. Thereafter, for each rolling element-raceway contact, a surface extending from the contact surface into the rolling component and containing the maximum von Mises stresses, both on the contact surface and in the sub-surface, is defined. (Figure 6) from [18] shows such two such surfaces, one for simple Hertz (normal) stress loading and the other for combined normal and shear stress loading. Harris [19] - [21] demonstrated the development of a "life integral" associated with the surface of maximum stresses.

Fatigue life for an individual rolling element-raceway contact may be calculated as follows:

$$L_{mj} = a_1 a_{SLmj}\left(\frac{Q_{cmj}}{Q_{mj}}\right)^P \tag{11}$$

where Q_{cmj} = the basic dynamic capacity of the contact, and
Q_{mj} = the contact load.

In Eq. 11, subscript m refers to the raceway and j refers to the contact azimuth location.

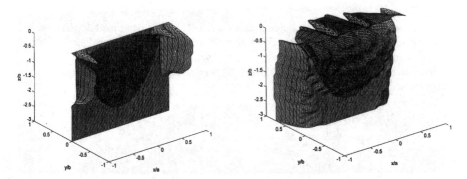

(a) Normal stress loading   (b) Normal and shear stress loading

Figure 6 - *Surfaces of* $\sigma_{VM,max}$:

For ball bearings Q_{cmj} is given by

$$Q_{cmj} = 98.1 \left(\frac{2f_m}{2f_m - 1} \right)^{0.41} \frac{(1 - c_m \gamma_{mj})^{1.39}}{(1 + c_m \gamma_{mj})^{1/3}} \left(\frac{\gamma_{mj}}{\cos \alpha_{mj}} \right)^{0.3} D^{1.8} Z^{-1/3} \tag{12}$$

In Eq. 12 coefficent $c_m = +1$ for the outer raceway; $c_m = -1$ for the inner raceway. For roller bearings,

$$Q_{cmj} = 552 \frac{(1 - c_m \gamma_{mj})^{29/27}}{(1 + c_m \gamma_{mj})^{1/4}} \left(\frac{\gamma_m}{\cos \alpha_m} \right)^{2/9} D^{29/27} l^{7/9} Z^{-1/4} \tag{13}$$

Raceway and bearing lives are calculated using Eq. 14 and 15 respectively.

$$L_m = \left(\sum_{j=1}^{j=Z} L_{mj}^{-e} \right)^{-1/e} \tag{14}$$

$$L = \left(L_1^{-e} + L_2^{-e} \right)^{-1/e} = \left(\sum_{m=1}^{m=2} L_m^{-e} \right)^{-1/e} \tag{15}$$

Based on LP theory, it was shown in [19] – [21], that a_{SLmj} can be determined for each contact using Eq. 16.

$$a_{SLmj} = \frac{L_{actual,mj}}{L_{LP,mj}} = \frac{\left\{ \sum_{l=1}^{l=n} c_l \sum_{k=1}^{k=n} c_k \left[\frac{\left(\sigma_{VM,kl} - \sigma_{VM,\lim it}\right)^c}{r_k^h} \right] \right\}^{1/e}_{actual,mj}}{\left\{ \sum_{l=1}^{l=n} c_l \sum_{k=1}^{k=n} c_k \left[\frac{\left(\sigma_{VM,kl}\right)^c_{LP}}{r_k^h} \right] \right\}^{1/e}_{LP,mj}}$$

(16)

where c_l and c_k are coefficients used in a Simpson's rule numerical integration, and r_k is dimensionless depth, i.e., $r_k = z_k/b$.

LP [1] stated that the stressed volume V of Eq. 1 was proportional to $az_0\pi d$, d being the diameter of the raceway track. The depth z_0 was defined by the location of τ_0, z_0 being approximately equal to $0.5b$. Thus, LP did not define the actual depth below the surface in which material was vulnerable to fatigue. Using the life integral concept, Harris and Yu [18] showed that for all $\sigma_{VM,kl} < 0.6\ \sigma_{VM,max}$, the life integral is affected by less than 0.2%. This is illustrated by (Figure 7), from which it can be seen that life is influenced by stresses to a depth of approximately $1.6b$, substantially in excess of the $0.5b$ depth implied by LP.

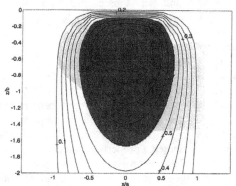

Figure 7 - σ_{VM} vs depth z/b and transverse distance $x/a = 0$ for simple Hertz stress loading.

In Eq. 16, the numerator is the life integral associated with the totality of stresses acting on the contact material; the denominator is the life integral associated with simple Hertz stress loading. The overall value a_{SL} is the ratio of the life calculated according to Eq. 11 – 15 with that calculated using Eq. 2.

Hard Particle Contaminants

Sayles and MacPherson [22] were the first to quantify the effect of hard particle contaminants on bearing life. Webster et al. [23] demonstrated that the dents produced by these contaminants caused stress concentrations that could significantly shorten life.

Ioannides et al. [24] developed equations and a series of charts to define a contamination factor that is a function of ISO 4406 contamination level, bearing size (d_m) and adequacy of lubrication κ. An example of such a chart is shown below (Figure 8).

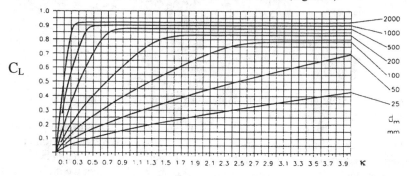

Figure 8 - C_L vs κ and d_m for filtered circulating oil - ISO 15/12 - $\beta_{12} = 200$ (from [24]).

C_L (Figure 8) is a contamination-life factor. In [19], it is shown that the stress concentration factors $C_L^{-1/3}$ for ball bearings and $C_L^{-1/4}$ for roller bearings can be used to augment the contact surface normal and shear stresses, thereby accounting for the effect of hard particle contamination on life.

Material Strength Ratings

Fatigue Strength Testing

The stress-based bearing life calculation method described above requires quantification of fatigue limit stress $\sigma_{VM,limit}$ for each rolling component material. While the designated fatigue limit stress, $\sigma_{VM,limit}$ may also be considered the material strength in fatigue. Strength is generally considered a property of material chemistry and metallurgy after heat treatment and material processing. This is the case with endurance limit S_e for structural steels. The rings and rolling elements of the majority of rolling bearings used worldwide are manufactured from 52100 steel, heat treated to a specified standard minimum of 58 Rockwell C scale hardness throughout. Thus, $\sigma_{VM,limit}$ may be considered the *strength* of that material. For bearings having surface-hardened rolling components achieved by heat processing; e.g., carburizing, induction-hardening, nitriding, etc., it is necessary to establish component residual stress levels separately. Otherwise, these residual stresses would be improperly included in the material strength, $\sigma_{VM,limit}$, determined via endurance testing. As mentioned above, residual stresses may also be introduced during the raceway and rolling element surface finishing processes. These stresses are usually confined to the surface and a very thin layer of material below the surface. They tend to be altered during initial bearing operation under load. It would be also proper to consider these residual stresses separately from the strength.

In structural materials, the endurance limit S_e is determined by endurance testing rod specimens using cyclic push-pull, cyclic torsion, and/or rotating beam equipment.

For rolling bearings, endurance testing of complete bearing assemblies has historically been employed; it had not been possible to correlate results of tests conducted with elements such as balls or rollers with those of bearing tests. Recently however, because of the development of stress-based life prediction methods, it has been feasible to use element testing in lieu of the more expensive bearing testing. See Harris [25]. To minimize testing duration, element tests are generally conducted at approximately 4100 MPa applied Hertz stress; some testing is conducted at 5500MPa. Endurance testing of bearings has generally been limited by 3300 MPa maximum applied Hertz stress; this compares to continuous application of 2100 MPa maximum Hertz stresses in heavy-duty machinery. To correlate bearing and element endurance testing results therefore, care must exercised to recognize the increased plastic deformations incurred by testing at elevated stresses.

Bearing and Rolling Element Performance Computer Programs

In the LP method development, only relatively simple bearing geometries and applied loading and the resulting Hertz stresses were considered. For example, ball bearing geometry was defined by ball diameter D, pitch diameter d_m, dimensionless raceway groove radii f_i and f_o, and constant contact angle α. For radial bearings only line-to-line fit conditions were included; e.g., zero internal radial clearance. All bearing performance calculations were performed using slide rule and/or mechanical computation devices. To employ the stress-based, life calculation methods properly many more geometry and operating parameters must be included; e.g., bearing ring geometries, roller and raceway crowning profiles, surface topographies of raceways and rolling elements, bearing mounting fits, bearing ring, rolling element, shaft, and housing material mechanical properties, lubricant rheological properties, material thermal properties, contaminant type, particle size, and amount, etc. Harris [5] discusses the methods to calculate all of the associated stresses. To perform the calculations for ball and roller applications requires the use of digital computer programs.

Computer programs TH-BBEAN and TH-CYBEAN are cited in [20, 21] for analysis of the performance of ball and cylindrical roller bearings respectively. Under Phase II of the U. S. Navy-sponsored project reported by Harris [20], these programs which perform all of the required calculations for stress-based bearing life prediction, were made more user-friendly, augmented with improved bearing internal temperature and lubricant film calculation procedures, and include the stress-life method calculation procedures cited in this discussion. In their present format the programs are designated TH-BBAN and TH-RBAN. The latter program now covers tapered roller bearings and spherical roller bearings as well as cylindrical roller bearings.

As indicated above, element tests may be also be used in the determination of material fatigue strength. One such test method uses the ball/v-ring rig. This test rig is illustrated schematically (Figure 9).

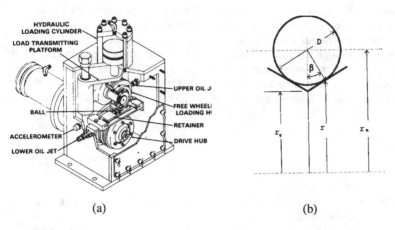

(a)   (b)

Figure 9 - (a) *Schematic diagram of ball/v-ring test rig developed by Pratt and Whitney, United Technologies Corp.*, (b) *Schematic diagram of ball in v-ring.*

A mathematical model for the performance of the test balls within this rig was developed; the resulting computer program is designated TH-BTAN.

Fatigue Limit Stresses

For a given material, the fatigue limit stress may be determined as follows:

1. A number of endurance tests must be run on bearings or test elements. Alternatively, field data may be accumulated on a bearing in an application. For each of the endurance data sets, bearing or element L_{10} life and Weibull shape parameter (slope) e is determined by statistical analysis.
2. The bearing or element test rig geometries are input to programs such as TH-BBAN, TH-RBAN, or TH-BTAN. Also input is an assumed value of fatigue limit stress $\sigma_{VM,limit}$. If the calculated L_{10} life is different than the measured L_{10} life, a new value of $\sigma_{VM,limit}$ is input, and the computer program is re-run. This trial-and-error procedure is continued until calculated L_{10} = measured L_{10}.
3. The above calculation procedure is repeated for each data set corresponding to the component material being investigated. Thus, for each material a set of values of $\sigma_{VM,limit}$ is generated. These values are then statistically evaluated to determine a common value of $\sigma_{VM,limit}$ for the material.

The form of the data input is given in Appendix 1 of [20]. The statistical methods of analysis used to obtain overall values of the fatigue limit stress are described in Appendix 7 of [20] and in the Appendix of [21].

The U. S. Navy Phase I project [20] included 62 bearing endurance data sets obtained from 12 different sources. The database included deep-groove and angular-contact ball bearings and cylindrical roller bearings. Under the Phase II project, this database was expanded to 126 bearing application data sets, which include deep-groove and angular-contact ball bearings and cylindrical, tapered, and spherical roller bearings. The breakdown of the bearing types is given below (Table 2).

Table 2 - *Bearing types in investigation.*

Bearing Type	Total Number Data Sets Supplied	Number Data Sets Used in $\sigma_{VM,limit}$ Calculations
Radial Deep-Groove Ball Bearings	43	32
Angular-Contact Ball Bearings	33	27
Cylindrical Roller Bearings	30	18
Tapered Roller Bearings	18	17
Spherical Roller Bearings	2	2
All	126	96

Only 96 of the 126 data sets were able to be used in the development of $\sigma_{VM,limit}$ values. The remaining 30 data sets contained 0 or only 1 failure; therefore, an accurate L_{10} life value could not be determined for each of these data sets. Thus, values of $\sigma_{VM,limit}$ estimated from this analysis will tend to be somewhat conservative.

The bearings in these data sets were fabricated from five (5) different basic rolling bearing quality steels; the breakdown of data sets by bearing steel is given below (Table 3).

Table 3 - *Bearing steels in investigation*

Bearing Steel Type	Number of Data Sets
52100 (carbon vacuum degassed)	53
M50 (Vacuum Induction Melted, Vacuum Arc Remelted)	35
M50NiL (VIMVAR)	5
Carburizing (SAE 4118, 4340, and 8620)	31
Induction-Hardening	2

In addition to the bearing endurance data sets, $\sigma_{VM,limit}$ data were obtained using ball/v-ring tests for the following materials: 52100, VIMVAR M50. 12 balls of each material were endurance tested under the conditions listed below (Table 4).

Table 4 - *Ball/v-ring rig endurance test parameters.*

Parameter	Value
D (mm)	28.575
d_v (mm)	159.41
$Ra_{v\text{-surface}}$ (μm)	0.05
$Ra_{ball\text{-surface}}$ (μm)	0.0125
Ring Speed (rpm)	7800
Lubricant	Mil-L-23699
Lubricant Supply Temperature (°C)	93.3
Lubricant Supply Rate (liter/sec)	0.063
V-Ring Material	VIMVAR M50 steel

Based on the overall bearing and ball endurance test results, the fatigue limit stresses $\sigma_{VM,limit}$ determined are listed below (Table 5).

Table 5 - $\sigma_{VM,limit}$ *per bearing steel*

Steel Type	Mean $\sigma_{VM,limit}$ (MPa)
CVD 52100	684
VIMVAR M50	717
M50NiL	579
Carburizing	590
Induction-Hardening	460

In comparing the fatigue performance of bearings manufactured from the carburizing, induction-hardening, and M50NiL steels against those of CVD 52100 and VIMVAR M50 steels, it must be considered that the proper level of compressive residual stress occurring in the rolling components fabricated from the surface-hardening steels augments fatigue endurance. Thus, the endurance of the surface-hardened steel bearings may equal or exceed that of through-hardened steel bearings.

In the Weibull statistics evaluation of bearing lives, the Weibull shape parameters e determined for the various steels are given below (Table 6).

Table 6 - *Weibull shape parameter by type of bearing steel.*

Steel Type	Mean Value e
CVD52100	1.51
M50	1.73
M50NiL	1.10
Carburizing	1.32
Induction-Hardening	1.24

It was concluded that there is no significant difference in Weibull shape parameter among the steels represented in the table. Hence, the value of 10/9 for 52100 steel and 1.5 for M50 steel were used in the fatigue life analyses.

ASME Life

The $\sigma_{VM,limit}$ values (Table 5) have been built into the computer programs TH-BBAN and TH-RBAN so that these programs may be used to estimate bearing fatigue lives according the results of the investigation. These programs tend to be used by relatively sophisticated engineers, often engaged in the design of high precision bearings for demanding operating environment applications. For most bearing applications, however, bearing users select bearings from manufacturers' catalogs. For each bearing, the catalogs provide data on basic load rating C, basic static capacity C_0, radial load factor X, axial load factor Y, speed limit, etc. As a result of the efforts of the ASME Tribology Division Technical Committee "Life Ratings for Modern Rolling Bearings," a computer program ASME LIFE has been developed. ASME LIFE performs bearing life calculations using the same methods as TH-BBAN and TH-RBAN; however, it is only concerned with those relatively simpler catalog-type applications.

Conclusion

A new stress-based method for the calculation of fatigue lives for ball and roller bearing applications has been developed to replace the standard factor-based method. The latter method has been in general use for approximately 25 years, and, in at least the last 10 years, it has proved to be ineffective in predicting the bearing lives in many applications. This is especially so in bearing applications involving relatively light loading. In many size and weight-sensitive applications. e.g., aircraft power transmissions, the standard method fails to take advantage of the performance of modern steels and modern manufacturing techniques resulting in excessively robust bearings and increased mechanism size and weight. In 2000, ISO included the concept of a stress-based rating method in their bearing load and life rating standard [11]. The method discussed herein enables the use of the new ISO standard [11]. Moreover, the proposed method is consistent with standard engineering means for the design and evaluation of engineering structures with regard to mechanical fatigue. Finally, a computer program ASME LIFE has been developed and is available for engineers to use in the application of the new stress-based, life rating method.

References

[1]   Lundberg, G. and Palmgren, A., "Dynamic Capacity of Rolling Bearings", *Acta Polytechnica Mechanical Engineering Series*. **1**, No. 3, **7**, Royal Swedish Academy of Engineering Sciences (1947).

[2]   Lundberg, G. and Palmgren, A., "Dynamic Capacity of Roller Bearings", *Acta Polytechnica Mechanical Engineering Series*. **2**, No. 4, **96**, Royal Swedish Academy of Engineering Sciences, (1952).

[3]   Weibull, W., "A Statistical Theory of the Strength of Materials", *Proceedings of Royal Swedish Institute for Engineering Research*, No. 151, Stockholm (1939).

[4]   Weibull, W.,"A Statistical Representation of Fatigue Failure in Solids", *Acta Polytech. Mech. Eng. Ser.* **1**, No. 9, **49**, Royal Swedish Academy of Engineering Sciences, (1949).

[5]   Harris, T., *Rolling Bearing Analysis, 4th Ed.*, Wiley (2001).

[6]   American Standards Association, "Load Ratings for Ball and Roller Bearings", *ASA   Standard B3.11-1959* (1959).

[7]   T. Tallian, "Weibull Distribution of Rolling Contact Fatigue Life and Deviations Therefrom", *ASLE Transactions*, 5 (1) (April 1962).

[8]   Harris, T., "Predicting Bearing Reliability", Machine Design, pp129-132, (January 3, 1963).

[9]   American National Standards Institute, American National Standard (ANSI/ABMA) Std. 9-1990 ("Load Ratings and Fatigue Life for Ball Bearings" (July 17, 1990).

[10]   American National Standards Institute, American National Standard (ANSI/ABMA) Std. 11-1990 ("Load Ratings and Fatigue Life for Roller Bearings" (July 17, 1990).

[11]   International Organization for Standards, *International Standard ISO 281/1*, "Rolling
Bearings-Dynamic Load Ratings and Rating Life (2000).

[12]   Zaretsky, E., Bamberger, E., Harris, T., Kacmarsky, W., Moyer, C., Parker, R., and
Sherlock, J., *Life Adjustment Factors for Ball and Roller Bearings, ASME Engineering Design Guide* (1971).

[13]   Society of Tribologists and Lubrication Engineers, *STLE Life Factors for Rolling Bearings*, E. Zaretsky Ed., STLE Publication SP-34 (1992).

[14]   SKF, *General Catalog*, Catalog 4000 US, 2nd Ed. (1997).

[15]   Åkesson, J., and Lund, T., "SKF Rolling Bearing Steels-Properties and Processes", *Ball Bearing Journal*, No. 217, pp32-44 (1983).

[16]   Ioannides, E., and Harris, T., "A New Fatigue Life model for Rolling Bearings", *ASME Trans, J. Tribology*, Vol 118, 297-310 (1985).

[17]   Palmgren, A., "The Service Life of Ball Bearings", *Zeitschrift des Vereines Deutscher Ingenieure*, **68**, No. 14, pp339-341 (1924).

[18]   Harris. T. and Yu, W.-K., "Lundberg-Palmgren Theory: Considerations of Failure Stress and Stressed Volume", *ASME Trans, J. Tribology*, Vol 121, 85-89 (January 1999).

[19]   Barnsby, R., Harris, T., Ioannides, E., Littmann, W., Lösche, T., Murakami, Y., Needelman, W., Nixon, H., and Webster, M., "Life Ratings for Modern Rolling Bearings", ASME Paper 98-TRIB-57, presented at the 1998 ASME/STLE Tribology Conference, Toronto, Canada (October 26, 1998).

[20]   Harris, T., "Establishment of a New Rolling Contact Bearing Life Calculation Method", Final Report, U. S. Navy Contract N68335-93-C-0111 (January 15, 1994).

[21]   Harris, T., and McCool, J., "On the Accuracy of Rolling Bearing Fatigue Life Prediction", *ASME Transactions, Journal of Tribology*, Vol 118, pp 297-310 (April 1996).

[22]   Sayles, R., and MacPherson, P., "Influence of Wear Debris on Rolling Contact Fatigue", ASTM STP 771, J. Hoo, Ed., pp 255-274 (1982).

[23]   Webster, M., Ioannides, E., and Sayles, R., "The Effect of Topographical Defects on the Contact Stress and Fatigue Life in Rolling Element Bearings", Proceedings 12th Leeds-Lyon Symposium on Tribology, pp 207-226 (1986).

[24]   Ioannides, E., Bergling, G., and Gabelli, A., "An Analytical Formulation for the Life of Rolling Bearings", *Acta Polytechnica Scandinavica, Me137*(1999).

[25]   Harris, T., "Prediction of Ball Fatigue Life in a Ball/V-Ring Test Rig", *ASME Transactions, Journal of Tribology*, Vol 119, pp 365-374 (July 1997).

Acknowledgement

The author is grateful to the United States Navy, Naval Air Warfare Center-Aircraft Division, Patuxent River, Maryland for their support in the development of the stress-life method and for permission to publish this paper.

Gérard Lormand,[1] David Piot,[1,2] Alain Vincent,[1] Gilles Baudry,[2] Pascal Daguier,[2] Daniel Girodin,[3] and Gilles Dudragne[3]

Application of a New Physically Based Model to Determine the Influence of Inclusion Population and Loading Conditions on the Distribution of Bearing Lives

Reference: Lormand, G., Piot, D.,Vincent, A., Baudry, G., Daguier, P., Girodin, D., and Dudragne, G., "Application of a New Physically Based Model to Determine the Influence of Inclusion Population and Loading Conditions on the Distribution of Bearing Lives," *Bearing Steel Technology, ASTM STP 1419*, J. M. Beswick, Ed., American Society for Testing and Materials International, West Conshohocken, PA, 2002.

Abstract: The principal cause of failure in bearings under E.H.D. conditions is deep spalling initiated beneath the surface. The corresponding damage mechanisms have been clearly identified (fatigue "butterflies," crack nucleation and propagation to the surface). In this context, a statistical model, based on a mixed approach combining micromechanics and physical metallurgy, has been developed for predicting the distribution of bearing lives from the inclusion population in the steel. The model has been validated by comparing its predictions with experimental failure probability curves determined from flat washer fatigue tests performed on a steel whose inclusion distribution had been accurately established. The existence of non zero survival rates for very long lives indicates that Weibull distribution [1] is not suitable to represent the complete life distribution for modern bearings. The predictive capabilities of the model have been used to study the influence of parameters, such as the applied load, the specimen size, etc.

Keywords: bearing steel, rolling contact, inclusion, crack nucleation, crack propagation, statistic, fatigue life

[1] Assistant Professor, Doctor and Professor, respectively, at Groupe d'Etude de Métallurgie Physique et de Physique des Matériaux (U.M.R. C.N.R.S. 5510) / I.N.S.A. / 69621 Villeurbanne Cedex / France.

[2] Senior Engineer and Manager, at CREAS ASCOMETAL / BP 140 / 57360 Amnéville / France.

[3] Senior Engineer and Manager, respectively, at Département Laboratoire, Analyse et Mesures, SNR Roulements/ 74010 Annecy / France.

Introduction

Due to various in service conditions, the damage phenomena that determine the life of bearings are complex and are affected by numerous factors related to both the conditions prevailing in the contact during service and the fatigue behavior of the material. When abundant lubrication ensures an elasto-hydrodynamic (E.H.D.) regime, the principal cause of bearing failure is material fatigue, which is revealed as deep spalling initiated at microstructural heterogeneities beneath the surface.

In spite of the fact that the mechanisms responsible for this type of spalling in martensitic steels are well-known (formation of fatigue "butterflies" around inclusions due to local stress concentration, leading to crack initiation in the butterflies and propagation to the surface), the durability of bearing steels can only be determined by long-term fatigue tests on large numbers of specimens.

Bearing design codes thus usually refer to Weibull's statistical approach [1], as improved by Lundberg and Palmgren [2] using the life rating equation

$$L = a_1\, a_2\, a_3\, (C/P)^n$$

where L represents the fatigue life, a_1 is the reliability-life factor (equal to 1 for a reliability of 90%), a_2 takes into account the quality of the steel, a_3 is related to the lubrication conditions, C is the basic dynamic load, P is the equivalent applied dynamic load and the exponent n is equal to 3 for ball bearings and 3.33 for roller bearings.

With the improvement in the endurance of bearing steels, several modifications have been proposed. In particular, Ioannides and Harris [3] suggested the relation

$$Ln\left(\frac{1}{S(N)}\right) = AN^e \int_V \frac{(\tau - \tau_u)^c}{z'^h} dV$$

where S is the survival rate, N is the number of cycles, A is a coefficient that normalizes the survival probability, τ_u is the endurance limit of the steel, τ is the shear stress in the plane normal to the rolling direction, V is the critical volume beneath the contact where $\tau > \tau_u$, z' is the stress-weighted mean depth, and finally, e, c, and h are parameters that must be adjusted for each type of bearing and each steel, based on a large number of fatigue tests.

In order to limit the need for such tests, a new method has been developed for quantitatively determining the fatigue life of bearing steels, based on their elasto-plastic characteristics and their inclusion populations [4].

The present paper briefly describes the principle of this statistical model, indicating the experimental measurements that must be made on the material. In particular, the distribution of inclusions is evaluated by the analysis of a significant volume of metal, giving a more quantitative description than the characterization obtained using the ASTM Standard Test Methods for Determining the Inclusion Content of Steel (E45-97e2). The simulations are then compared with the experimental data, and finally, applications of the model are described.

Life Distribution Model

The overall model includes :
- a crack initiation model based on physical metallurgy and related to the cyclic plastic strain in the fatigue butterfly, proposed by Champaud [5], and developed by Sanchette [6] and Lamagnère [7];
- a crack propagation model, also based on physical metallurgy and resulting from the work of Rocher [8] and Champiot-Bayard [9]; and
- a statistical use (Monte-Carlo method) of these physical models, proposed by Meynaud [10] and based on a random distribution of inclusions into the bearings according to the inclusion population measured experimentally.

Crack Initiation Model

The crack initiation model employed can be summarized as follows. The contact pressure generates a stress field that can be approximated under EHD conditions to a Hertzian field. An inclusion situated in this field induces a stress concentration due to the differences between its elastic constants and those of the matrix. The resulting strain incompatibilities are calculated using the Eshelby method [11]. When the loading level is sufficient, this stress concentration causes local plastic strain during the first load cycle. Dislocations are emitted and the region swept out by these dislocations defines the volume of the future butterfly. Under the action of the cyclic stresses, the dislocations move to and from this volume. However, due to the partial irreversibility of the dislocation movements, the dislocation density gradually increases, cycle after cycle, up to a critical level that is related in Friedel's double pile-up model to a critical climb stress [12]. When this threshold is reached, a crack is formed, whose initial length is close to the size of the fatigue butterfly. In fact, not all the mobile dislocations in the butterfly accumulate. The proportion of them that do so is defined by a damage accumulation factor f* whose value is determined by comparing the lifetime to crack initiation life predicted by the model with experimental measurements of crack initiation times using ultrasonic echography during interrupted fatigue tests [13]. The quality of the interfaces between the inclusions and the matrix is described by a parameter that reflects the efficiency of load transfer between the matrix and the inclusions. In physical terms, it can be interpreted as the thickness of an infinitely plastic uniform interface layer.

The model determines N_a, the number of cycles to crack initiation, from the elastic properties of the inclusions and the elasto-plastic properties of the steel.

Crack Propagation Model

The crack propagation model associates the increase in length of a crack loaded in Mode II to the net balance between the emissions and absorptions of dislocations at the crack tip, during the loading and unloading parts of the cycle, respectively [8, 9]. This model leads to the prediction of a threshold stress intensity factor below which propagation cannot occur. It has been applied to cracks loaded in rolling fatigue, considering an effective shear stress that accounts for friction between the crack lips due to the component of compression normal to the plane of the crack. Beyond the threshold stress intensity factor, the propagation rate is described by two successive Paris laws, whose integration enables one to calculate the number of cycles necessary for each crack to reach the surface. Due to the shape of the cracks, whose length increases much more rapidly than their width, the geometrical contribution to the stress intensity factor can decrease more rapidly than the square root of the length, so that for some cracks the stress intensity falls below the threshold level, and propagation stops before they reach the surface [9].

Statistical Implementation

The statistical implementation of the model, based on the Monte-Carlo method, involves :
- successive random generating of :
    * the number of inclusions of each species in the specimen, based on the experimental inclusion characterization (uniform distribution for the species and binomial distribution for the number);
    * the position of each inclusion (uniform distribution of the positions);
    * the diameter of each inclusion, assimilated to spheres (according to the experimentally observed size distribution);
- application of the crack initiation model and calculation of the cycle number to crack initiation for every inclusions;
- application of the crack propagation model and calculation of the number of cycles required for every initiated cracks to reach the surface;
- calculation of the total life for every inclusions, defined as the sum of the initiation and propagation cycle numbers;
- determination of the specimen cycle number, defined as the minimum of the potential cycle numbers calculated in the previous step;
- repetition of the above procedure for all the specimens, to obtain the distribution of lives for the overall population of bearings studied.

Material Characterization

The present study was performed on a 52100 steel in the martensitic condition. However, the procedure adopted can be used for other steels [7, 9]. The material studied was from a fairly old melt, which no longer meets today's quality requirements. It was deliberately chosen to obtain a relatively large number of failures in FB2 washer fatigue tests [14], and also to facilitate measurement of the inclusion population.

The required mechanical parameters were determined by appropriate mechanical tests (nano-indentation for the elastic moduli of inclusions, microplasticity tests in compression and cyclic compression tests to measure the elasto-plastic properties of the matrix).

A detailed characterization of the inclusion population in a significant volume of steel was made by combining several techniques [15] and assuming a uniform spatial distribution of the inclusions.

Thus, the size distribution is determined on metallographic sections of large area (320 mm^2). The inclusion morphology provides information on their chemical nature, while image analysis techniques were used to measure the number of inclusions and the distribution of their apparent size. This metallographic part of our oxide inclusion characterization agrees with the recommendations of the ASTM (E45-97^{e}2) method. These two-dimensional data obtained on planar sections are converted to three-dimensional data, assuming that the inclusions are spherical and using the relations of Saltykov [16] and Scheil [17]. These data are obtained on a very small volume of few cubic millimeters and they are complemented then by high frequency ultrasonic measurements (50 MHz) carried out on few cubic centimeters to characterize the rare exogenous inclusions. The apparent ultrasonic sizes are converted in real diameters, still assuming that the inclusions are spherical. The conversion factor is determined by comparing the ultrasonic data with metallographic examinations carried out on some large inclusions after their ultrasonic detection.

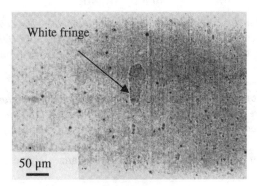

Figure 1 - *High resolution X-ray microradiography obtained on 52100 steel sample. A white Fresnel fringe around the inclusion increases the inclusion detectability.*

The whole of this data are used to determine the shape and the parameters of the distribution law of the real diameter. Practically the best agreement is obtained for the log-normal distribution. These data are also qualitatively completed by high resolution X-ray micro-radiography carried out on flat samples (20 mm by 20 mm by 1) submitted to a X-ray beam with a very high lateral coherence of the waves (synchrotron radiation). In these conditions Fresnel fringes appear at interface between inclusion and matrix allowing a more easy detection of inclusions (see Figure 1) [18]. The information obtained by this technique only gives an upper bound of the distribution of the real diameter because the morphology of detected inclusion is not used to select metal oxide inclusions.

Figure 2 illustrates the consistency of the results obtained using these different techniques for the steel studied. The log-normal law used was based on a population of 2140 inclusions / mm^3 (1/3 alumina and 2/3 spinel), with a mean diameter of 1.1 µm and a standard deviation of 0.76.

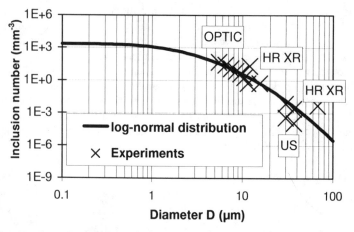

Figure 2 - *Number of inclusions which exceed a given diameter - The crosses show the positions of the experimental data obtained by optical micrography (OPTIC), high frequency ultrasonic echography (US) and high resolution X-ray microradiography (HR XR) (old steel data).*

Table 1 – *Comparison of the number of inclusions larger than a given diameter which cut a 320 mm^2 area and are in the stressed volume of a FB2 washer (150 mm^3) according to the distribution of the real diameter previously determined (old steel data).*

Diameter larger than (in µm)	Number on a 320 mm^2 area	Number in 150 mm^3
10	8.9	197
15	1.9	31.4
20	0.54	7.25
25	0.17	2.12

From the distribution law for the real diameter it is easy to compute the average number of inclusions larger than a given diameter which cut a 320 mm² area and the stressed volume of one FB2 washer submitted to an Hertzian pressure of 4.2 GPa (150 mm³). The results are given in Table 1. These data outline the difficulty to detect large inclusion by metallographic examination and the great utility of complementary techniques to contribute to the quantification of the tail of the inclusion size distribution.

Experimental fatigue lives were measured from FB2 washer tests (15 ball / plane contacts using 9.922 mm diameter balls) with a contact pressure of 4.2 GPa. Most of the undamaged specimens were tested for at least 1000 h (675 Mcycles). For the few tests interrupted prematurely (due to the procedure), two life estimations are performed. First, the bearing life is set equal to the time of interruption of the test, second, it is set equal to infinity, thus leading to "by default" and "by excess" estimations of the life distribution, respectively. The results of these tests are shown in Figure 3, where the uncertainty bars correspond to a confidence level of 80 %.

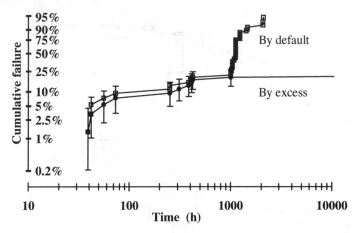

Figure 3 - *Results of life tests on a batch of 50 FB2 washers subjected to a contact pressure of 4.2 GPa (old steel data ; 1000 h=675 Mcycles).*

Simulation and Validation Results

The results of four life distribution simulations, performed using the inclusion distribution shown in Figure 2, are reported in Figure 4, which also includes the limits of the 80% confidence region determined in the fatigue tests of Figure 3. Three simulations were carried out with different batches of 50 washers selected at random (curves with different symbols), while the fourth was performed with a batch of 5 000 washers (continuous curve).

All these simulations are situated essentially within the experimental 80% confidence level and the cumulative failure probability does not exceed 25 %. It should be noted in particular that the latter observation is incompatible with a description of the life distribution based on a Weibull law.

For the 50 washer batches, the scatter in life is fairly large, about a factor of ten. This scatter decreases with batch size and is practically negligible for the batch of 5 000 in the range of cumulative failures visible in Figure 4. From this simulation, precise estimations of L_1, L_2 and L_{10} are possible, namely 29, 42 and 154 h respectively. It can be seen that the ratio L_1/L_{10} (0.19) is, in this case, not very different from that recommended in bearing design rules for the coefficients a_1 associated with these two probability levels (0.21).

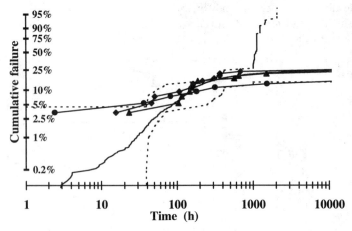

Figure 4 - *Results of simulations of life tests on 3 batches of 50 washers and one batch of 5000 washers – the dotted curves are the limits of the 80 % confidence region obtained in the experimental tests (old steel data ; 1000 h=675 Mcycles).*

Based on the lives obtained using the model, it is possible to simulate sudden death tests [*12*], by distributing the results into series of five batches of ten washers and determining for each series the parameters L_2, L_{10} and β, according to the usual procedure involving a life distribution described by a Weibull law [*1*]. Such an analysis was performed on 500 sudden death tests. The median values and the first and last deciles for every of the parameters are given in Table 2.

The disagreement between these median values obtained from sudden death tests ($L2 = 35$ h; $L10 = 218$ h) and those determined directly from the total population ($L2 = 42$ h ; $L10 = 154$ h) is a consequence of the inadequacy of the Weibull law for describing the life distribution. In addition, it should be noted that this inadequacy also contributes to the very large scatter in the estimation of $L2$ and $L10$ from the sudden death tests. This inadequacy had already been reported for the compilation of a large number of life tests performed on washers produced from a series of very old melts [*15*] with very poor internal cleanliness compared to today's standards.

Table 2 - *Statistics for a series of 500 sudden death tests. Values of L2 and L10 are given in h (old steel data).*

Parameter	First decile	Median	Last decile
β	0.56	0.88	1.77
L2	11	35	76
L10	104	218	460

Effect of Scatter in Inclusion Distribution Measurements

All the above simulations were carried out using exactly the same inclusion distribution. Since the determination of this inclusion distribution is a complex process, it seems useful to analyze the effect of scatter on the results of life simulations. For this purpose, based on the inclusion distribution law already presented, 50 micrographic cross sections with an area of 320 mm^2 were simulated. From these 50 recomposed sections 50 apparent size distributions were determined using the techniques already mentioned. The populations of each size class (width 1μm) effectively analyzed (between 5 and 15 μm) were small and widely scattered. These results were used to determine 50 real size distributions and from each size distribution the corresponding life distributions were calculated using our modeling. The results are indicated in Figure 5, which shows the median values and the width of the scatter bars for typical failure probability levels.

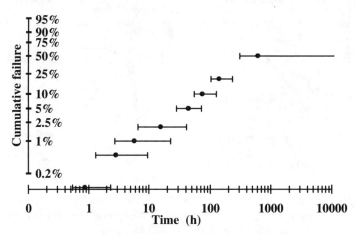

Figure 5 - *Scatter in simulation results for batches of more than 50 000 specimens due to uncertainty in the measured inclusion distribution (1000 h=675 Mcycles).*

Relative Contributions of Initiation and Propagation Times

The simulation results can be analyzed to study the respective contributions of crack initiation and propagation on the total life. Rather than to perform a statistical analysis on a large number of simulations, initiation, propagation and life time values were determined for an alumina inclusion situated at different depths along the contact point symmetry axis for various particle diameters. The corresponding results are summarized in Figures 6a (for initiation life), 6b (for propagation life), 6c (for total life) and 6d (for the ratio between the initiation life and the total life). The inclusion diameter varied regularly between 23 μm (short curves) and 40 μm (long curves).

The initiation time is minimum at the maximum value of the Tresca equivalent shear stress (at a depth of 135 μm for the contact considered). It decreases when the diameter increases, this effect being due principally to the interface layer effect (cf. Figure 6a). The propagation time is minimum for a greater depth than the initiation time, due to the retarding effect of friction between the crack lips, which tends to decrease with increasing depth (cf. Figure 6b).

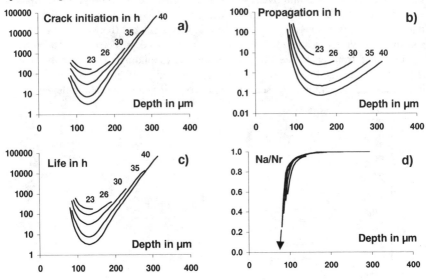

Figure 6 - *Effect of position and inclusion diameter on the initiation, propagation, and total lives and on the ratio N_a/N_r for spherical alumina inclusions with diameters expressed in μm (1000 h=675 Mcycles).*

Although, the parameters of the crack propagation law are taken to be independent of the inclusion content of the matrix, as observed by Beswick [19], the time of propagation to the surface decreases with increasing the inclusion size (cf. Figure 6b). Indeed, the initial size of a nucleated crack varies as the inclusion diameter. Hence, the initial stress intensity factor and the initial propagation rate increase when the inclusion diameter increases. The total life varies in practically the same way as the initiation time, due to the relatively small contribution of propagation (cf. Figure 6c). However, this similarity in the shape of the curves does not imply the existence of a constant ratio between the initiation and propagation times. For inclusions close to the surface, the initiation time is relatively short and propagation time is very long because of the high normal stress acting on the crack lips. In contrast, for relatively deep inclusions, initiation time can be very long with a short propagation time. In fact, the ratio between the initiation and propagation lives is found to vary between 0 and 1.

Application of the Model

The validation of the model previously described justifies its use for a systematic study of the influence of the parameters governing bearing fatigue life.

Effect of Scale

First of all the influence of bearing size on life distribution was studied. This was done by varying the diameter of the raceway (washer) used with the ball elements in the fatigue tests. Figure 7 illustrates the results of the simulations for different diameters. The reference diameter is the diameter actually used in the experimental tests (54 mm).

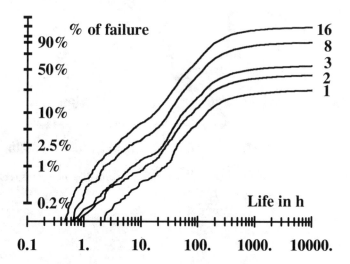

Figure 7 - *Influence of raceway relative diameter(1000 h=675 Mcycles).*

It can be seen that an increase in specimen size decreases the survival rate for an infinite life. This is explained by the increased number of harmful inclusions that are present in the larger volume of metal subjected to loading, and the consequent greater probability of encountering a very large inclusion, leading to a shorter life for a given level of reliability.

Influence of Inclusion Concentration

The variation of fatigue life distribution has been studied when an increasing concentration (from 0 to 0.5 inclusion per mm^3) of 30 μm diameter inclusions is added to the existing population (cf. Figure 8). The observed decrease in survival rate is again explained by the increase in the number of harmful inclusions. The failure probabilities rise abruptly at a life value corresponding to that for initiation at 30 μm inclusions (cf. Figure 6a). These simulations quantify the practically observed high sensitivity of bearing life to abnormal large inclusions caused by incidents during melting and refining (degradation of refractories, reoxidation, etc.) and outline the utility to characterize the inclusion distribution in the high diameter range to predict the behavior for high reliability.

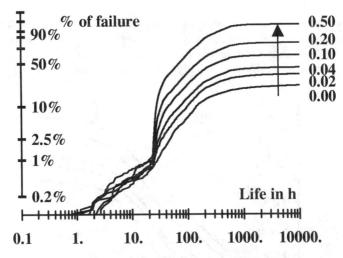

Figure 8 - *Influence of an addition of 30 μm diameter alumina inclusions (concentration in number of inclusions per mm^3 ; 1000 h=675 Mcycles).*

Influence of the Applied Pressure

Similarly, simulations have been performed to determine the effect of loading magnitude on the life distribution, assuming that the damage mechanisms remain unchanged. An increase in pressure at the center of the contact corresponds not only to higher stresses, and therefore to an acceleration of the crack initiation and propagation rates, but also to a larger stressed volume. These three effects induce a decrease of the survival rate at infinite life (cf. Figure 9).

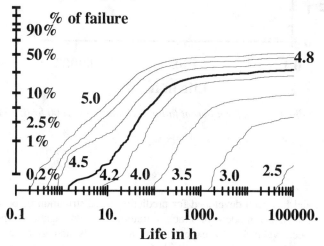

Figure 9 - *Variation of failure probability with contact pressure, expressed in GPa (1000 h = 675 Mcycles).*

From the data shown in Figure 9 and for each failure probability, α, the variation of the corresponding life, L_α, versus the Hertzian pressure can be determined to obtain the Wöhler curves of Figure 10. Each Wöhler curve seems to present a horizontal asymptote which defines a limit pressure. It should be noted that, even for a very high survival rate of 99.95 % ($L_{0.05}$), this limit pressure is significantly higher than the upper bound of the endurance limit, H1, defined by Lamagnère's model [20]. This value is about 1.6 GPa for 52100 steel for the spherical inclusions considered in this paper.

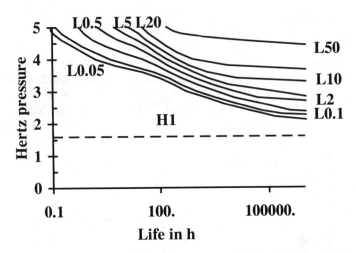

Figure 10 - *Wöhler curves for different failure probabilities (1000 h=675 Mcycles).*

Conclusions

A statistical model has been developed for predicting the distribution of bearing fatigue lives, based on physical models of crack initiation and propagation. The approach employed has been validated by experimental test results and gives a quantitative evaluation of the fatigue life of bearing steels from representative measurements of their inclusion populations. Moreover, the new procedure will enable a more reliable and more reactive control of melting and refining practices, compared to standard methods involving conventional inclusion rating and fatigue testing.

The inadequacy of Weibull statistics [1] for describing the complete distribution of bearing lives has also been demonstrated. In particular, in agreement with experiments performed on modern high cleanliness steels, the model predicts the existence of an infinite survival level corresponding to the probability of not encountering sufficiently large inclusions, i.e. harmful, in the volume submitted to loading.

Furthermore, the predictive nature of the method can be used for more thorough optimization of manufacturing processes (melting, refining, heat treatment), and provides a basis for improving bearing design to enhance fatigue life.

References

[1]   Weibull W., "A statistical Representation of Fatigue Failure in Solids," *Acta Polytechnica – Mechanical Engineering Series*, Vol. 1, No 9, 1949, pp. 1-50.

[2]   Lundberg G. and Palmgren A., "Dynamic Capacity of Rolling Bearings," *Acta Polytechnica - Mechanical Engineering Series*, Vol. 1, No 3, 1947, pp. 1-50.

[3]   Ioannides E. and Harris T. A., "A new Fatigue Life Model for Rolling Bearings," *Journal of Tribology*, Vol. 107, 1985, pp. 367-378.

[4]   Fougères R., Lormand G., Vincent A., Nélias D., Dudragne G., Girodin D. Baudry G. and Daguier P., "A New Physically Based Model for Predicting the Fatigue Life Distribution of Rolling Bearings" *Bearing Steel Technology, ASTM STP 1419*, J. M. Beswick, Ed., American Society for Testing and Materials, West Conshohocken, PA, 2002.

[5]   Champaud P., *Contribution à l'étude de la fatigue d'un alliage Fe-C-Cr (100 C 6) soumis à un champ de contraintes de Hertz – Proposition d'un critère d'amorçage*, Thesis, Génie des Matériaux, INSA Lyon, 1988, 215 p.

[6]   Sanchette L., *Contribution à l'analyse et à la modélisation de l'amorçage des fissures dans l'acier 100 Cr 6 soumis à la fatigue de roulement*, Thesis, Génie des Matériaux, INSA Lyon, 1993, 203 p.

[7]   Lamagnère P., *Étude et modélisation de l'amorçage des fissures de fatigue de roulement au voisinage des microhétérogénéités dans l'acier M50 (80 Mo Cr V 42)*, Thesis, Génie des Matériaux, INSA Lyon, 1996, 172 p.

[8]   Rocher S., *Contribution à l'analyse et à la modélisation de la propagation des fissures courtes dans l'acier 100 Cr 6 soumis à la fatigue de roulement*, Thesis, Génie des Matériaux, INSA Lyon, 1994, 290 p.

[9]   *Champiot-Bayard F., Étude et modélisation de la propagation des fissures de fatigue de roulement amorcées en sous-couche dans l'acier M50 (80 Mo Cr V 42)*, Thesis, Génie des Matériaux, INSA Lyon, 1997, 252 p.

[10]   Meynaud P. *Prévision de la durée de vie en fatigue de roulement d'un acier à partir de ses caractéristiques élastoplastiques et de celles de ses inclusions*, Thesis, Génie des Matériaux, INSA Lyon, 1995, 201 p.

[11]   Murat T. *Micromechanics of Defects in Solids*, Martinus Nijhoff Pub., Dordrecht, 1987, 587 p.

[12]   Friedel J., *Dislocations*, Pergamon Press, London, 1964, p. 320-347.

[13] Guy P., Meynaud P., Vincent A., Dudragne G. and Baudry G. "Subsurface Damage Investigation by High Frequency Ultrasonic Echography on 100Cr6 Bearing Steel," *Tribology Internatinal*, Vol. 30, 1996, pp. 247-259.

[14] Lormand G., Meynaud P., Vincent A., Baudry G., Girodin D. and Dudragne G. "From Cleanliness to Rolling Fatigue Life of Bearings – A new Approach," *Bearing Steels : Into the 21st Century, ASTM STP 1327*, J.J.C. Hoo, Ed., 1997, pp. 55-69.

[15] Auclair G., Ruby-Meyer F., Meilland R. *et al.,* "Caractérisation des aciers à haute propreté – Application aux aciers à roulements," *La Revue de Métallurgie - Cahiers d'Informations Techniques*, special issue SF2M Journées d'Automne, 1997, p. 74.

[16] Saltykov S. A., *Stereometric Metallography*, Metallurgizdat, Moscow, 2nd Ed., 1958, p. 446

[17] Scheil E., "Statistische Gefügeuntersuchungen," *Zeitschrift für Metallkunde*, No 27, 1935, pp. 199-209.

[18] Cloetens P., Pateyron-Salomé M., Buffière J.-Y." Observation of microstructure and damage in materials by phase sensitive radiography and tomography," *Journal of Applied Physics*, Vol. 1201, 1997, pp. 5878-5886.

[19] Beswick J. M. "Fracture and Fatigue Crack Propagation Properties of Hardened 52100 Steel," *Metallurgical Transactions A*, Vol. 20A, 1989, pp. 1961-1973.

[20] Lamagnère P., Fougères R., Vincent A., Lormand G., Girodin D., Dudragne G. and Vergne F. "A Physically based Model for infinite Life of Rolling Bearings," *ASME Journal of Tribology*, Vol. 120, 1998, pp. 1-6.

Antonio Gabelli,[1] Stathis Ioannides,[2] John Beswick,[3] Gunnar de Wit,[4] Hans Krock,[4] Bram Korenhof,[5] and Aidan Kerrigan[6]

Rolling Bearing Material Quality Fatigue Testing - Material Quality Life Factors

---

Reference: Gabelli, A., Ioannides, S., Beswick, J., de Wit, G., Krock, H., Korenhof, B., and Kerrigan, A., **"Rolling Bearing Material Quality Fatigue Testing - Material Quality Life Factors,"** *Bearing Steel Technology, ASTM STP 1419*, J. M. Beswick, Ed., American Society for Testing and Materials International, West Conshohocken, PA, 2002.

Abstract: The rolling contact fatigue testing of low oxygen, high quality, rolling bearing steels is a major challenge to steel makers, bearing producers and end users. Material specimen based rolling contact fatigue tests were used for a number of years, mainly as acceptance tests. Often in this type of test, the applied contact stress exceeds the stress normally found in rolling bearing applications and also exceeds the limit stress for rapid cyclic micro-plastic groove formation in the rolling contact. For these reasons the established methods have limited ability to discriminate material quality effects in modern high cleanliness rolling bearing materials. Furthermore, the results of tests based on a material specimen are difficult to translate into life calculation factors for the bearings. In this paper a novel test method is presented and used to determine the effect of steel internal cleanliness on the performance of rolling bearings. To achieve this result considerable care is required in the preparation of the test elements, the selection of the specific test conditions and in the analysis of the results. This work also led to an ability to determine the dependence of steel quality on the steel making processes. Material cleanliness is characterized using the statistics of extreme values of the micro-inclusion size population allowing the steel cleanliness quality rating to be related directly to the fatigue performance of rolling bearings through the introduction of a material cleanliness factor η. The expected bearing life performance for materials with different inclusion size ratings can thus be calculated. Results correlate well with measurements demonstrating that the quality rating of the material can now be reliably included in standard bearing life calculations.

Keywords: Steel quality, material cleanliness, bearing test methods, bearing fatigue life models, micro inclusions, bearing life factors, statistics of extremes

---

[1] Senior Engineer, SKF Engineering & Research Centre, P.O. Box 2350, Nieuwegein, The Netherlands
[2] Group Technical Director, SKF Group Technology Dev., P.O. Box 2350, Nieuwegein, The Netherlands
[3] Manager Steel Technology, SKF Group Purchasing, P.O. Box 2350, Nieuwegein, The Netherlands
[4] Engineer, SKF Engineering & Research Centre, P.O. Box 2350, Nieuwegein, The Netherlands
[5] Test Centre Head, SKF Engineering & Research Centre, P.O. Box 2350, Nieuwegein, The Netherlands
[6] Portfolio Manager Materials, SKF Engineering & Research Centre, Nieuwegein, The Netherlands

Nomenclature

A_{SLF}	Stress Life Factor for fatigue load limit and added stress
a	Contact semi-axis in transverse direction, [m]
A	Constant of proportionality in life equation
c	Exponent in the stress-life equation
C	Basic dynamic load ratings, [N]
e	Weibull exponent
h	Exponent in the stress-life equation
l	Length of raceway contact, [m]
L	Life, [Mrevs]
L_{10}	Basic rating life, (10% failure life), [Mrevs]
N	Number of load cycles
p	Exponent in life equation,
P	Equivalent dynamic bearing load, [N]
P_u	Fatigue load limit, [N]
S	Survival probability, %
V_0	Lundberg-Palmgren fatigue stress volume of the contact
w	Exponent in the load-stress relationship
z_i	Stress-weighted average depth of ΔV_i, [m]
z_0	Depth of max. orthogonal shear stress of Hertzian contact, [m]
η, η'	Material quality factors for stress concentrations
τ_i	Fatigue Stress Criterion at the volume element i, [Pa]
τ_0	Maximum orthogonal shear stress amplitude in the contact, [Pa]
τ_R	Effective real weighted shear stress in bearing contacts, [Pa]
τ_u	Fatigue limit shear stress, [Pa]
$\delta\tau$	Local stress concentration at inclusions or stress raisers, [Pa]
$\langle ..... \rangle$	Macauley bracket, the value is set to zero if the argument is < 0

Introduction

It is well-known that material quality has a profound influence on rolling bearing contact fatigue life. The steel quality is of course dependent upon the applied steel-making process as regards the quantity and distribution of the internal stress raisers such as non-metallic inclusions. The literature contains numerous references to methods of testing the rolling contact fatigue strength of bearing steels. The 2nd International ASTM Bearing Steel Symposium, Phoenix, 1981 [1], was devoted to the subject of bearing life testing and the symposium proceedings contain several papers on the subject of bearing steel rolling contact fatigue testing and related technologies. Much of the literature on bearing steel life testing for metallurgical quality assessment describes the so-called test element, specimen or coupon test methods. These typically select Hertzian contact stresses high enough to produce failure in conveniently short testing times. A number of the reported rolling contact fatigue, or material quality fatigue strength, test methods are summarized in Table 1.

Table 1 - *Summary of reported element test methods for steel quality rolling contact fatigue strength testing, [1].*

Description:	Typical Hertzian Contact Stress (GPa):	Reference:
Polymet	5.5	2
"V" Groove	2.8	2
Ring to Ring	2.293	3
Radial Cylinder	4.41	4
Ball on Rod	5.42	5
Unisteel	4.17 to 4.65	6
Mori Thrust Washer	4.9	7
"Caterpillar"	3.102	8
A0	5.0	9
U6309	5.03	9
FB2	4.2	10
"S" Machine	3.75	10
NASA Five Ball	5.52	11

Some bearing producers use high stress level rolling contact fatigue tests, as part of their steel supplier approval procedures [5,10]. By performing these fatigue tests over many years, suppliers providing poor bearing steel, (giving drastically shorter bearing lives), may be discriminated from state-of-the-art suppliers. However, for a number of reasons these "standard" high stress level tests have poor discrimination capabilities for the modern low oxygen, low sulphur, high quality steels that can be supplied by top level rolling bearing steel producers. The papers by Johnstone et al. [9] and Lorösch [12], for example discuss the limitations of high stress testing for the characterization of contact fatigue strength and the derivation of metallurgical quality parameters. They also describe rolling contact plastification effects observed in high stress testing.

Methods of producing steels, rolling bearing rings and rolling elements are changing, together with rolling bearing functional requirements. With the market pressure for cost reduction, metalworking and forming reductions are decreasing while, due to bearing downsizing, the inner ring thickness and related hoop stress, are typically increasing. Downsizing also produces higher bearing temperatures as a result of the higher power density, higher rotary speeds and somewhat higher loads. With these changing requirements in mind a modified approach to material quality characterization was taken. Specifically, a new test method was developed for the quantitative investigation of the effect of material internal cleanliness on rolling bearing fatigue performance.

Rolling Contact Fatigue Test Method

The rolling bearing industry has used deep groove ball bearings for many years to test bearing functional performance. The current ISO life models were developed and principally based on results from such tests. Using "standard conditions" and current industry quality standard martensitic hardened steel, (ASTM A 295-98 52100) "Standard Specification for High-Carbon Anti Friction Bearing Steel," the life now often exceeds 1000 million revolutions, which requires ½ to ¾ year testing time at 6000 rpm. However, due to the high cost of testing, 500 million revolutions is the maximum commonly set in life test programmes. In practice, than, the life may not be measurable ("infinite"). Obviously finite lives are required to determine steel quality parameters and major changes in the test conditions are needed to reach this objective: these are described in Table 2

Table 2 - Changed parameters in new material quality life test method

Parameter:	Method:
Low reduction ratio and turned test rings	The inner rings are turned out of 100 mm Ø bar material.
Increased running temperature, 83 °C instead of 53 °C	Full film lubrication conditions are maintained by the use of thicker oil, Turbo T100.
Additional hoop stress, 170 MPa, applied	Tighter interference fit between bore and shaft for the inner ring.

6309 deep groove ball bearings were used and the endurance tests were performed on 30 inner rings from each steel quality variant, according to standard procedures for the endurance testing R2 machines with a constant radial load. Details of the test conditions are shown in Table 3.

Table 3 - Bearing test conditions

Parameter:	Value:
Load	25000 N
Maximum contact stress	3317 N/mm^2
Speed	6000 rpm
Lubrication	Shell Turbo T 100 oil
Lubricant film parameter (λ)	11.9 (kappa > 4)

Based on initial life estimates made in setting up the test program, an L_{10} life below 300 million revolutions was anticipated for bearings produced from state-of-the-art quality rolling bearing steels. The resulting time needed to complete a test series, was therefore well within the economical requirements. In practice, between two weeks and two months testing time per test variant was required depending, of course, on the quality of the particular bearing material variant.

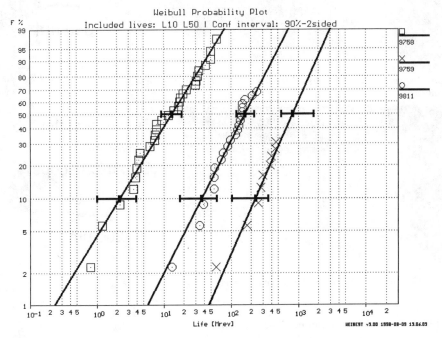

Figure 1 - Weibull failure distributions. Test Series: 9758, 9759 and 9811 (Weibest v.3)

The test method produced the typical failure distributions shown in Figure 1. For clarity in Figure 1, only three, of the five variants that were life tested, are plotted. The large majority of failures were inner rings with more than 20 failures per test variant. An example of a typical spalling failure is shown in Figure 2. The spalls were sub-surface initiated with a rather straight leading edge as a consequence of the applied hoop stresses. Also shown is the crack propagation of the spall cross-section, see Figure 3. It can be seen that the spalls propagate to a depth close to the maximum shear stresses. Sometimes a crack may also develop in the direction towards the bore as a consequence of the hoop stresses. The limited depths of these latter cracks show that the hoop stresses were not so high as to lead to through cracking of the inner rings.

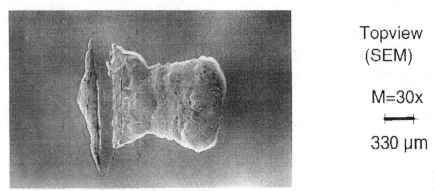

Topview
(SEM)

M=30x

330 µm

Figure 2 -Typical spall and related failure mode resulting from the use of the described test conditions.

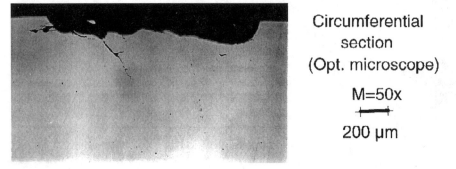

Circumferential
section
(Opt. microscope)

M=50x

200 µm

Figure 3 - Metallographic section through typical inner ring spall.

Material Quality Metallographic Characterization

The method of extreme value statistics was applied [*13*] in order to characterize the material metallurgical quality. The extreme value method of micro inclusion rating was used, based upon traditional metallographic sectioning and recording of the largest inclusion area per field until a sample of a specific number of fields has been accumulated. The following procedure was applied to obtain the necessary extreme value statistics information on the micro inclusion distributions.

*   The samples were metallographically prepared such that the section plane was approximately at the maximum Hertzian shear stress depth for the 6309 life test conditions.
*   A Leco image analyser was used, connected to a Zeiss light optical microscope and a purpose-built image analysis software routine.
*   The analysed area was 65 mm^2 at a magnification of 100X.

- In total 108 fields from each metallographic sample were measured. The fields were analysed stepwise adjacent to each other with the operator verifying that no artifacts were present in the measurement field prior to determination of the largest inclusion equivalent area.
- Fields with and without inclusions were used for the analysis.
- The square root area that is proportional to the equivalent diameter of the largest inclusion in each field was calculated.

Subsequently a cumulative percentage size distribution, F_j , is obtained as a function of the square-root area, defined by

(1) $$F_j = j \cdot \frac{100}{(n+1)}$$

The reduced variate y_j is as follows

(2) $$y_j = -\ln\left\{-\ln\left(\frac{j}{n+1}\right)\right\}$$

$n =$ Total number of examined fields,
$j =$ Number of fields with a particular square root projected area size interval.

The square root extreme size cumulative distribution functions for 6309 deep groove ball bearings inner ring test samples that were endurance tested are shown in Figure 4.

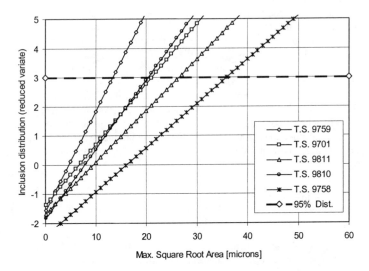

Figure 4 - Cumulative distribution of the square root inclusion area measured on five test series of 6309 deep groove ball bearings inner rings used in the endurance life test program.

Bearing Life Models

The Ioannides and Harris [14] bearing life model can, in brief, be summarized as a generalization of the Lundberg and Palmgren [15,16] fatigue life theory. The Ioannides and Harris life equation for rolling contact fatigue reads

$$(3) \qquad \ln\frac{1}{S} = \sum_{1}^{n} \ln\frac{1}{\Delta S_i} \approx N^e \sum_{i}^{n} \left(\frac{\langle \tau_i - \tau_u \rangle^c \, \Delta V_i}{z_i^h} \right)$$

S	Survival probability %,
τ_I	Fatigue stress criterion for the discrete fatigue stress volume ΔV_i [Pa],
z_i	Stress-weighted averaged depth [m],
c	Lundberg – Palmgren stress exponent (31/3),
e	Weibull exponent ,
h	Lundberg - Palmgren depth weighting exponent,
V	Volume at risk, and
N	Number of revolutions.

In Equation (3) a fatigue limit stress, τ_u, is introduced which, when subtracted from the local equivalent stress criterion, τ_i, defines the effective stress inducing fatigue damage in the related stress volume. This rolling bearing specific fatigue life expression includes the full subsurface shear stress history of each volume element, the hydrostatic pressure components, and a threshold shear stress, enabling the model to include local stress effects, as well as residual compressive or tensile hydrostatic stresses.
The probability of failure is therefore calculated as the cumulative contribution from differential volume elements of the discrete stress field of the material. This in turn requires extensive numerical integration using specialized software and, preferably, fast workstations. Clearly, this approach is only suitable for research purposes [17] and may discourage the use of the Ioannides and Harris method for standard application engineering work. Therefore a simple formulation of the Ioannides and Harris model, to produce analytical equations suitable for catalogue application, was developed [18,19]. To accomplish this, it may be noted that Equation (3) can be written using the maximum alternating shear stress amplitude in each volume element as the fatigue stress criterion, then a Lundberg and Palmgren type of life formula, including the fatigue limit stress, may be derived

$$(4) \qquad \ln\frac{1}{S} \approx N^e \left(\frac{\langle \tau_0 - \tau_u \rangle^c \, a \, z_0 \, l}{z_0^h} \right)$$

τ_o	Maximum orthogonal shear stress amplitude in Hertzian contacts [Pa],
z_o	Depth of maximum orthogonal shear stress in Hertzian contacts [m],
a	Contact width in transverse direction [m], and
l	Length of raceway contact [m].

In Equation (4), τ_0 becomes the effective average maximum alternating shear stress amplitude in the risk volume i.e., the volume in which the Macauley bracket is non-zero. In this formulation the effect of inclusions in bearing steels can be modelled as a random presence of local stress raisers in the material matrix subjected to Hertzian stresses. To model the internal stress concentration effect in the calculation, a measure of the real dominating alternating shear stress is introduced. This quantity considers local effects resulting from the presence of inclusions, voids or other local stress raisers

(5) $$\tau_R = \tau_0 + \delta\tau$$

In practice this is achieved by substituting τ_R in place of τ_0 in Equation (5). In other words τ_R, represents the effective real weighted stress present in the contact, averaged throughout the Hertzian volume at risk. The additional stress $\delta\tau$ is a global representation of localized stress concentrations, which in this instance, are material or geometrical imperfections related mainly to the presence of a given inclusion population distribution. When this measure of the real dominating alternating shear stress τ_R, is used in Equation (5) the Macauley bracket becomes

(6) $$\langle \tau_R - \tau_u \rangle^c = \langle (\tau_0 + \delta\tau) - \tau_u \rangle^c = \langle \tau_0 - (\tau_u - \delta\tau) \rangle^c = \langle \tau_0 - (\eta' \cdot \tau_u) \rangle^c$$

where the factor η' is just $1 - \delta\tau / \tau_u$ In this reformulation, then, the effect of stress concentrations induced by localized stress raisers, e.g. inclusions, is taken into account by introducing a modification factor of the fatigue limit τ_u. Using Equation (6) in Equation (4), the following model is obtained

(7) $$\ln\frac{1}{S} \approx N^e \left(\frac{\langle \tau_0 - \eta' \cdot \tau_u \rangle^c a z_0 l}{z_0^h} \right) = \left\langle 1 - \eta' \cdot \frac{\tau_u}{\tau_0} \right\rangle^c \left(\frac{N^e \tau_0^c a l}{z_0^{h-1}} \right)$$

Applying the well-known relationships between induced stresses and applied loads for Hertzian contacts, either point or line, as done by Lundberg and Palmgren [15], an equation corresponding to Equation (7) but written in terms of the equivalent bearing load and the basic load ratings, is obtained. For full film clean lubrication and 10% failure probability, the above equation can be written in the following way [18]

(8) $$L_{10aa} = \left[A \left\langle 1 - \left(\eta \frac{P_u}{P} \right)^w \right\rangle^{-\frac{c}{e}} \right] \left(\frac{C}{P} \right)^p = A_{SLF}(\eta) \left(\frac{C}{P} \right)^p$$

Where A_{SLF} is known as the "stress life factor". Here the η parameter applies to the fatigue load limit, P_u, of the bearing, in contrast to the fatigue stress limit, and is thus given by: $\eta=\eta'^{1/w}$. Equation (8) shows that the effect of inclusions can be incorporated into the life prediction equation simply by applying the factor, η, dependent on the inclusion rating of the material, to the fatigue load limit of the bearing. [Note that for constant loading conditions, P, as used in the present life test program, the stress life factor of Equation (8) is a function only of the η factor of the different steel variants used in the test program.] It is important to remember that the value of P_u appearing in Equation (8) has been obtained using the fatigue stress limit applicable to a nominal value of steel cleanliness (inclusion size), for which η and η' are both unity.

In 1994, Murakami [13] developed an inclusion rating method based on the statistics of extreme values which has since been extended for use in SKF rolling bearing life prediction models [20]. Changes in the effective fatigue strength of the material can be estimated by this method. In [20] the effective fatigue limit in the Ioannides and Harris model was determined by application of the Murakami methodology [13], with the following assumptions:

✓ The fatigue strength is proportional to the square root of the projected area of the non-metallic inclusions and the hardness of the steel.

✓ The morphology and composition of the internal inclusions do not directly influence the fatigue strength.

✓ The lower scatter bound of the fatigue strength can be determined by the maximum size square root area of inclusions.

✓ The statistics of extremes are relevant for the prediction of maximum square root area of inclusions.

As the definition of η shows, the influence of the stress concentrations on life depends upon the steel matrix tolerance to the stress concentrations. The Murakami model has proved to be suitable for treatment of the inclusion as a stress concentration as follows

$$(9) \qquad \sigma_{u\,Murakami} = \frac{C\cdot(HV+120)}{(\sqrt{Area\_Inclusion})^{1/6}}\left(\frac{1-R}{2}\right)^{\alpha}$$

$\sigma_{u,Murakami}$	=	Murakami fatigue limit [Mpa],
$area$	=	Square root area of inclusions [micrometres],
HV	=	Vickers hardness [kgf/mm^2],
C	=	Surface inclusions =1.59,
R	=	$\sigma_{min}/\sigma_{max}$, and
α	=	$0.226 + HV\ 10^{-4}$.

In [20] the Murakami methodology was adapted for rolling bearing life prediction to be used in relation to bearing steel cleanliness quality. The τ_u value in the Ioannides-Harris equation is influenced by the stress concentration induced by material inclusions. Following this methodology the fatigue limit used in the calculations is effectively changed to account for the presence of stress concentrations in the vicinity of inclusions of different sizes. Assuming for rolling contact that $\tau_u \sim \sigma_{u,incl}$ a stress fatigue limit determined by the material cleanliness, to be used in the Ioannides–Harris rolling contact fatigue model was derived as follows

(10)
$$\sigma_{u,incl} = \frac{a \cdot (HV + b)}{\left(\sqrt{Area\_Inclusion}\right)^{1/6}}$$

τ_u	=	Fatigue limit shear stress [MPa],
$\sigma_{u,incl}$	=	Stress fatigue limit - inclusions [MPa],
HV	=	Matrix Vickers hardness, and
a, b	=	Constants from Murakami (matrix).

From Equation (10) the fatigue risk ΔR_{incl}, of an elementary volume element can thus be written as

(11)
$$\Delta R_{incl} = (\sigma_{matrix} - \sigma_{u,incl})^c \cdot V_{incl}$$

σ_{matrix}	=	Matrix fatigue criterion [MPa], and
V_{incl}	=	Volume at risk [m^3] .

Material Quality Life Factors

Material cleanliness factors to be used in standard life prediction equations, i.e. Equation (8), may easily be derived directly from bearing endurance testing data, for example from the results of the 6309 bearings test program.

To accomplish this, bearings were specifically manufactured from various steel qualities ranging from poorly de-oxidised materials, to VIM-VAR re-melt quality and state-of-the-art clean air melt and vacuum degassed 1C-1.5Cr rolling bearing steels. The life test elements were the inner rings, yielding the relevant endurance life of the bearing. The applied through hardening heat treatment of the test elements is shown in Table 4.

Table 4 - 6309 deep groove ball bearing inner ring test element heat treatment

Heat Treatment Parameter:	Value:
Salt bath austenitization	850 °C, 20 min.
Oil quench	50 °C
Temper	240 °C, 4 hours

The 6309 deep groove ball bearings were tested according to the test methodology described in Tables 1 and 2. The resulting bearing lives for the five steel quality variants are shown in Table 5.

Table 5 - Summary of life test results of the five bearing material variants.

Code	L_{10} [Million revs.]	Lower and Upper 90% Confidence Intervals of L_{10} [Mrev]	ß Slope
9759	229.7	103 to 357	1.47
9701	74.4	47.4 to 101.1	2.1
9811	36.7	17.3 to 61.3	1.27
9810	14.99	7.7 to 23.9	1.38
9758	2.6	1.2 to 4.6	1.1

All of the variants produced finite lives with numerous, > 20, failures, see Figure 1. The inner ring test elements were also used to perform measurements of extreme value statistics of the micro-inclusion size distribution as shown in Figure 4. The measurements were used to characterize the material cleanliness. Figure 5 shows the results of the extreme value inclusion size for the different steel grades plotted against the measured L_{10} life. Curve fitting of these results provides a correlation coefficient of 0.82 see Figure 5.

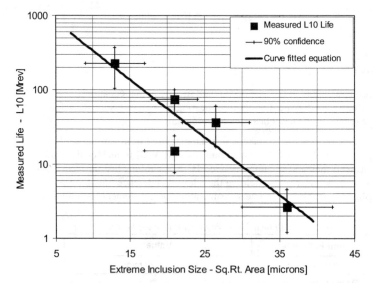

Figure 5 - Relation between the extreme value of the micro-inclusion size statistics (at 95% of the distribution) and measured L10 life for the five 6309 material quality variants.

The strong influence that material cleanliness has on the bearing life is clearly displayed in Figure 5. The observed variation of the L_{10} life is a factor of 100 for the range of the material cleanliness used in the test program. This striking effect on endurance life indicates the need for a material cleanliness factor that can link the steel quality rating to the expected performance of bearings. In Figure 6 (left) the curve fitting of the experimental data in Figure 5 is repeated using weighting factors for the data points in order to improve the treatment of two less reliable points of the set. This method provides somewhat better results, with a 0.96 correlation for the new fitted equation shown in Figure 6 (left).

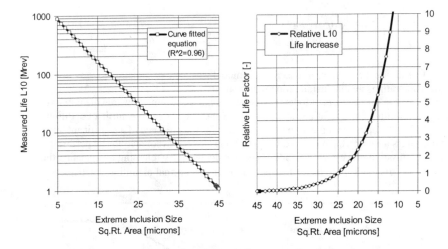

Figure 6 (Left) measured effect of the extreme value inclusion size, i.e. material cleanliness rating, on the rolling bearing life. (Right) relative bearing life vs. material cleanliness

This relationship between material internal cleanliness and the measured bearing life is re-plotted on a linear scale, using life relative to its value for a nominal 25 micron inclusion size in Figure 6 (right). In this way a measure of the relative life change due to variations of the material cleanliness rating is made easily visible.

Material Cleanliness Quality Factor η

In the following analysis the experimental results presented in Figures 5 and 6 are translated into a life factor η to account for material cleanliness in bearing life calculations. The method is designed for the analytical life model of Equation (8), which is used in rolling bearing catalogues and engineering handbooks. The aim is to fit the life factor η, as a simple function of the material inclusion rating so that it can be introduced in Equation (8) in a straightforward manner. The value for P_u appearing in this formula is the Catalogue value based on the fatigue stress limit for nominal steel cleanliness.

To achieve this, the material cleanliness factor η is introduced using a simple exponential function, of the square root area of material inclusions i.e., the quality rating factor of the material

(12)
$$\eta\left(\sqrt{Area\_inclusion}\right) = \exp\left[m - n\left(\sqrt{Area\_inclusion}\right)^q\right]$$

This model implies an upper and lower asymptotic limit towards the maximum and minimum fatigue strength of the material. In Equation (12) m, n and q are the material factor η constants. These constants are determined by minimizing the error, between the η values calculated from Equation (12) and from Equation (8), using the measured relative lives, Figure 6 (right), as fitted by the following expression

(13)
$$\left[\frac{A_{SLF}\left[\eta\left(\sqrt{Area\_inclusion}\right)\right]}{A_{SLF}\left[\eta = 1\right]} = 65 \cdot \exp\left(-\frac{\sqrt{Area\_inclusion}}{6}\right)\right]_{error \to 0}$$

An additional constraint imposed in the model was the extrapolation to very low inclusion ratings i.e., inclusion rating with a square root area < 10 microns. As mentioned in this range the model behaviour is made asymptotic towards the maximum expected rolling contact fatigue strength for the specific material. A further condition applied in the optimisation is to make allowance for the presence of a significant level of hoop stress affecting the measured life. The hoop stress is accounted for by performing the optimisation process with an additional penalty term. By releasing this penalty, the model reverts to an η life factor for applications using normal mounting practices.

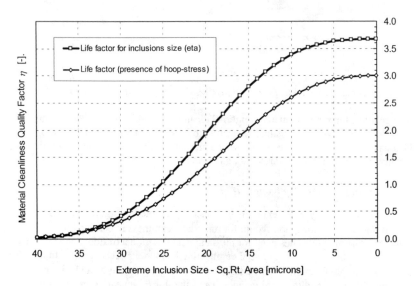

Figure 7 - Material cleanliness quality factor η function of the extreme value (95% of the distribution) of the micro inclusions size, i.e. square root area.

The results of the derived quality factor η for material cleanliness are shown in Figure 7. In the graph the factor for material cleanliness is plotted vs. the inclusion size rating for both standard press fitting and for the mounting conditions used in the test program. Finally the performance of the η model, Figure 7, is compared with available experimental data. The aim is to show the ability of the model to predict lives of bearings manufactured with different levels of material cleanliness and to provide practical examples of the use of this calculation method. The results of this exercise are summarized in Figure 8. It is found that the predicted bearing lives correlate well with the observed L_{10} lives for all four cleanliness quality levels that were examined. On the other hand, life calculation based on the present standard equation using $\eta = 1$ (thus without the effect of material cleanliness quality and hoop stress) clearly will either underestimate the bearing life, in cases of very clean steel, or provide large overestimation of the life for materials that are below the nominal (standard) cleanliness specifications, see Figure 8.

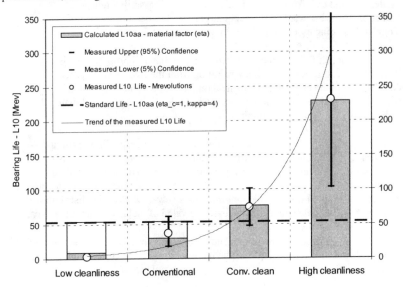

Figure 8 - Comparison between measured and calculated lives using the material factor η to describe the different levels of internal cleanliness of the steel used in the manufacturing of the test samples.

Figure 8 shows also an exponential growth of the bearing life moving from conventional levels to high cleanliness levels. This indicates that increased cleanliness provides a rising premium for the performance of rolling bearings that can be now quantified and used in bearing design optimisation and value engineering. Furthermore, the above results show that the effect of different kinds of inclusion populations (stress raisers) in the bearing material can be given a general or global representation in the life equation by means of single stress concentration factor η applied to the fatigue load limit of the bearing.

This factor can now be derived from accurate measurements of the material internal cleanliness, based on the statistics of extreme values. A factor η higher than one, indicates a cleanliness level above the standard, while, correspondingly, η factors lower than one apply to material quality below standard. The general Murakami approach is to relate material cleanliness quality to fatigue properties by the use of extreme value statistics characterizing the micro-inclusion size distribution. These material quality characteristics, combined with the use of a comprehensive endurance test program, have proved successful for introducing material related quality characteristics into standard analytical equations for bearing life prediction, Ioannides et al. [18].

Conclusions

- In order to avoid over-specification, and related unnecessarily high steel production costs, knowledge of steel quality related to bearing service life is recognized as being essential in the rolling bearing industry.

- The rolling contact fatigue endurance strength is a material property that is affected by metallurgical cleanliness resulting from the steel making process. With the much increased life, due to steel quality improvements, endurance testing of a large number of modern bearings, made of a specific steel material, can be enormously time consuming.

- The basic quality of the steel has a direct effect on the intrinsic fatigue strength of the bearing, compared to the extrinsic nature of the other factors such as lubrication. One objective of the current work was thus to develop a method of relating this fatigue strength to some reliable material cleanliness measurements. The measure adopted was the maximum inclusion size, (95% of the distribution) based on the observed statistics of the extreme value of inclusion equivalent area.

- This will enable the development of standard methods for cleanliness assessment and related specifications and allows the incorporation of the corresponding material fatigue strength property in bearing life calculations.

- The methodology for calculation of the bearing life related to the stress concentration effects i.e., the Ioannides-Harris life model, represents a significant progress in rolling bearing engineering design and related steel quality specifications. The application of this methodology has resulted in the material quality factor η shown in this paper.

Acknowledgments

The authors wish to express their thanks to Dr. H. H. Wittmeyer, SKF Group Senior Vice President, for his kind permission to publish this paper.

References

[1]   *Rolling Contact Fatigue Testing of Bearing Steels*, Hoo, J.J.K., Ed., *ASTM STP 771*, American Society for Testing and Materials, Philadelphia, PA, 1981.

[2]   Galbato, A., "The Methods of Testing for Rolling Contact Fatigue of Bearing Steels", *Rolling Contact Fatigue Testing of Bearing Steels*, Hoo, J.J.K., Ed., *ASTM STP 771*, American Society for Testing and Materials, Philadelphia, PA, 1981, pp 169-189.

[3]   Tokuda, M., Nagafuhi, M., Tsushima, N. and Muro, H., "Observations of Peeling Mode of failure and Surface-Originated Flaking from a Ring-to-Ring Rolling Contact Fatigue Test Rig", *Rolling Contact Fatigue Testing of Bearing Steels*, Hoo, J.J.K., Ed., *ASTM STP 771*, American Society for Testing and Materials, Philadelphia, PA, 1981, pp 150-165.

[4]   Sugiura, I., Ito, S., Tsushima, N. and Muro, H., "Investigation of Opimum Crowning in a line Contact Cylinder-to--Cylinder Rolling Contcsr Fatgue Test Rig", *Rolling Contact Fatigue Testing of Bearing Steels*, Hoo, J.J.K., Ed., *ASTM STP 771*, American Society for Testing and Materials, Philadelphia, PA, 1981, pp 136-149.

[5]   Pearson, P.K., "Rolling Contact Behaviour of High Hardness Surfaces", Proceedings of Ascometal 2nd International Bearing Steel Symposium, Arles June 6-8, 1995.

[6]   Day, K.L., "Unisteel Testing of Aircraft Engine Bearing Steels", *Rolling Contact Fatigue Testing of Bearing Steels*, Hoo, J.J.K., Ed., *ASTM STP 771*, American Society for Testing and Materials, Philadelphia, PA, 1981, pp 67-84.

[7]   Tsubota, K. and Fukumoto, I., "Production and Quality of High Cleanliness Bearing Steel" Proceedings of 6th International Iron and Steels Congress, Nagoya, 1990, ISIJ, pp. 637-643.

[8]   Lamothe, R.M., Zagaeski, T.F., Cellitti, R. and Carter, C., "Efferct of test Variables on the Rolling Contact Fatigue of AISA 9310 and VASCO X-2 Steels", *Rolling Contact Fatigue Testing of Bearing Steels*, Hoo, J.J.K., Ed., *ASTM STP 771*, American Society for Testing and Materials, Philadelphia, PA, 1981, pp 392-405.

[9]   Johnstone, G.B., Andersson, T., V.Amerongen, E. and Voskamp, A., "Experience of Element and Full-Bearing Testing of Materials over Several Years", *Rolling Contact Fatigue Testing of Bearing Steels*, Hoo, J.J.K., Ed., *ASTM STP 771*, American Society for Testing and Materials, Philadelphia, PA, 1981, pp 190-205.

[10]   Girodin, D. and Dudragne, G., "Methods of Qualification of Bearings and the Quality Specification of Steel", Proceedings of Ascometal 2nd International Bearing Steel Symposium, Arles June 6-8, 1995.

[11]   Zaretsky, E.V., Parker, R.J. and Anderson, W.J., "NASA Five Ball fatigue Tester - Over 20 Years of Resarch", *Rolling Contact Fatigue Testing of Bearing Steels*, Hoo, J.J.K., Ed., *ASTM STP 771*, American Society for Testing and Materials, Philadelphia, PA, 1981, pp 5-45.

[12]   Lorösch, H-K., "Influence of Load on the Magnitude of the Life Exponent for Rolling Bearings", *Rolling Contact Fatigue Testing of Bearing Steels*, Hoo, J.J.K., Ed., *ASTM STP 771*, American Society for Testing and Materials, Philadelphia, PA, 1981, pp 275-292.

[13]   Murakami, Y., "Inclusion rating by statistics of extreme values and its application to fatigue strength prediction and quality control of materials" *J. Res. Natl. Inst. Stand. Technol*, Vol. 99, 1994, pp. 345-351.

[14]   Ioannides, E., "Component Reliability Analysis - A Fatigue Life Model Common to Rolling Bearings and Structural Components", SEECO J. of the Society of Environmental Engineers, June 1985, pp.3-7(23).

[15]   Lundberg, G. and Palmgren, A., "Dynamic capacity of rolling bearings", Acta Polytechnica Mechanical Engineering Series, Royal Swedish Academy of Engineering Sciences, Vol. 1, No. 3, 7, 1947.

[16]   Lundberg, G. and Palmgren, A., "Dynamic capacity of roller bearings:, Acta Polytechnica, Mechanical Engineering Series, Royal Swedish Academy of Engineering Sciences, Vol. 2, No. 4, 96, 1952.

[17]   Gabelli, A., Voskamp, A.P., Shearer S. and Ioannides, E., "The Service Life of Rolling Elements Bearings - Stress Field and Material Response Analysis" VDI Berichte Nr. 1380 / Gleit und Walzlagerungen, March 1998.

[18]   Ioannides, E., Bergling, G. and Gabelli A., "An Analytical Formulation for the Life of Rolling Bearings". Acta Polytecnica Scandinavica, Mechanical Engineering Series, No.137, Espoo, 1999.

[19]   SKF Publication 4000 "General Catalogue", AB SKF, Gothenburg, Sweden - 1989.

[20]   Beswick, J., Gabelli, A., Ioannides, E., Tripp, J. H. and Voskamp, A.P. "Rolling Bearing Life Models and Steels Internal Cleanliness", *Advances in the Production and Use of Steel with Improved Cleanliness, ASTM STP 1361*, Philadelphia, PA, 1999.

Author Index

Subject Index